Resettling America

Resettling America
Energy, Ecology & Community

EDITED BY
Gary J. Coates
FOREWORD BY
Amory Lovins

♭

BRICK HOUSE PUBLISHING COMPANY
ANDOVER, MASSACHUSETTS

Published by Brick House Publishing Co., Inc.
34 Essex Street
Andover, Massachusetts 01810

Production Credits:

Editors: Jack D. Howell and James Bright
Copy Editors: Carol Higgins, Dianne Pitochelli and Joyce Thompson
Designed and Produced by Mike Fender

Library of Congress Cataloging in Publication Data

Main entry under title:
Resettling America.

   1. Cities and towns—United States—Addresses, essays,
lectures. 2. City planning—United States—Addresses,
essays, lectures. 3. Environmental policy—United
States—Addresses, essays, lectures. 4. Energy policy—
United States—Addresses, essays, lectures. 5. Self-
reliance—Addresses, essays, lectures. I. Coates,
Gary, 1947–
HT123.R45   307.7′6′0973   81-2878
ISBN 0-931790-52-2   AACR2
ISBN 0-931790-06-9 (pbk.)

This book was set in Bembo and Caslon 540 by
Progressive Typographers of York, Pennsylvania;
and printed on 60 pound Decision Opaque by
Halliday Lithograph of West Hanover, Massachusetts.

Printed in the United States of America

Contents

Acknowledgments

THIS BOOK WAS CONCEIVED nearly five years ago in the aftermath of a joint Canadian-American symposium that Jack Smith, a Canadian graduate student, and I organized at the College of Human Ecology on the campus of Cornell University. Titled, "In Search of Symbiotic Community," this meeting brought together policy planners, academics in a variety of disciplines, architects and designers, neighborhood activists, and members of intentional communities and alternative businesses to examine the ethical, social, political, and environmental issues raised by emerging energy and resource scarcities.

Given the extraordinary diversity of interests, life-styles, and values represented at this symposium, there was a remarkable degree of consensus that the crisis of industrialism would not be resolved without a major cultural transformation based on a movement toward greater local self-reliance in the areas of energy, food, shelter, and other basic necessities. There was also shared recognition of the need for a recovery of a genuine sense of community and the restoration of spiritual values and practices rooted in a sense of the sacredness of the earth and the sanctity of the person.

Beyond these rather general areas of agreement, however, the diversity of the group reflected itself in the emergence of serious disagreement about how to create a social order that would express such values. The dualistic modes of thinking which have plagued western civilization over the past 2,000 years seemed to erupt as a reminder of the difficulties the end of the days of "having and getting" will pose for us all. Intellectuals and social theorists, concerned primarily with the historical and cultural roots of the present crisis, were pitted against pragmatists and activists, who were mainly concerned with the actual mechanics of cultural and institutional change, in a modern variant of the false dichotomy between theory and action. The historical schism between fact and value, between science and religion, found new expression in the arguments that developed between politically inclined activists and spiritually based communitarians. At times it seemed that the search for an alternative to industrial society would itself founder on the same divisions of self and society that made the changes necessary in the first place.

As organizers of this often stormy but always revealing event, we felt that the issues that divided us could, with a shift in perspective, be seen as a source of unity and strength rather than as a cause of conflict and separation. We felt that political activism need not be divorced from the search for a whole and integrated self, and that the hands-on construction of renewable energy systems should be the outcome of, rather than an alternative to, the critical analysis of the existing socio-technical order. In short, we felt that what the movement for personal, social, and environmental change needed was a comprehensive vision of possibilities rooted in a thorough understanding of the nature and meaning of the crisis of urban-industrial society. While the form of this book has changed considerably over the course of its development, this purpose has remained constant.

The scope of this collection encompasses, therefore, the political as well as the spiritual, the practical as well as the theoretical, and the personal as well as the social. It is both a critical analysis of where we have been and an imaginative vision of where we could be headed. While much of the content deals with the development and application of solar energy and other non-violent, environmentally benign, and humanly scaled technologies, the intent is to present a much broader historical, cultural, and metaphysical framework for theory and action related to community building in an era of energy and resource scarcity. There is a growing tendency for people in the "appropriate technology movement" to become too narrowly technical and individualistic in their concerns. The autonomous house, self-sufficient homestead, and solar suburb themes which characterized much of the first generation of literature in this area, while valuable as explorations of new technologies and paradigms, often betray a "me first" attitude, a kind of new age, neighbor-be-damned ethos. If we are to overcome the legacy of competitiveness and narcissism we have inherited from our industrial past, we must begin to talk about strategies aimed at self-transcendence through community action. Issues of equity and energy, and the political and spiritual implications of the shift to a sustainable culture must become more prominent in the second generation literature related to appropriate technology and the use of solar energy. If this book contributes to the elevation of such concerns to a more central place in our efforts to reshape the mindscape and landscape of industrialism, then it will have succeeded in its main purpose.

In many respects this book can be seen as a running dialogue with the many other authors who have thought and written about the wide range of issues covered in this volume. While it is impossible to express the full extent of my indebtedness to all those who have helped to shape and inform my thinking, it is possible to at least mention those authors who have had the most obvious and significant impact on the central ideas of this book: E. F. Schumacher, Ivan Illich, Erich Fromm, Theodore Roszak, William Irwin Thompson, Gregory Bateson, Roy Rappaport, Murray Bookchin, Wendell Berry, and of course, Lewis Mumford. Readers who are familiar with the work of those mentioned will find in the following pages many direct and indirect reminders of their influence. Without claiming to do justice to the many subtle and complex ideas they have so eloquently presented, I express my deep appreciation for all I have learned from them.

However, in editing this book, for which nearly every article has been specially written, I have spent much of my time corresponding with, telephoning, and visiting contributors all around the country. In a very real sense the image of the future embodied in this book is the result of this extended dialogue with the people who are already personally involved in the long, hard process of resettling America. From them I have learned faith in the possibility of positive change as well as a host of specific policies and actions which can help us create a more equitable and just society out of the chaos which is accompanying the end of the fossil fuel age. Because of their example and their willingness to describe here what they are doing, it is now possible for many others to share these lessons.

This book has taken many forms over the course of its evolution. The present edition does not include many of the fine papers that were submitted for earlier versions. The decisions about what to include reflect a range of criteria, from issues of representativeness and editorial focus to problems related to deadlines and the final size of the manuscript. In no way do they imply a lesser value to those projects and papers which were not finally included. To those authors whose material does not appear, I extend my gratitude for their invaluable contributions to the development of this book.

At one point, after my move from Cornell to Kansas State University, this book sat in limbo. Without the timely and enthusiastic encouragement of Professor Jeffrey Cook in the Department of Architecture at Arizona State University, there is a good chance it would have remained there. I thank Jeffrey for reminding me of my obligations and convincing me that such a book was needed now more than ever.

The desire to follow through on a project is one thing. Finding the time to do so is another. For anyone who has not tried to put together a book such as this, it is impossible to imagine how much time is involved. Without the generous administrative support of the College of Architecture and Design at Kansas State University this manuscript would still be in draft form. In particular I thank Eugene Kremer, the Chairman of the Department of Architecture, for providing release time from part of my teaching duties for a semester so that I could work on this book and related community design and solar demonstration projects. I am also deeply grateful to Bernd Foerster, Dean of the College of Architecture and Design, whose own commitment to the principles of human scale, ecological balance, and architectural excellence in the design of the built environment has created the kind of intellectual climate necessary for the nurture and development of the ideas embodied in this book.

Without the constant questioning, intellectual stimulation, and moral support provided by my students, both at Cornell and Kansas State, many of the central ideas in this book would have been much less clear and developed. I would especially like to thank Gary Klein, Alan Wyatt, Allison Bryant, Anne Cicero, Michael Shepard, David Wilson, Bruce Snead, Phil Korchek, Sy Zacher, Doug Walter, Doug Selby, Rahim Borhani, and Alan Edgar for their help in focussing issues and providing a forum for the elaboration of ideas and possibilities.

Many colleagues have also provided assistance. In particular I thank David Howard Bell for the many hours spent discussing the ideas contained in my own essays and introductions.

I am grateful to Jack Howell and the others at Brick House Publishing Company for their cheerful willingness to adapt to my numerous failures to meet deadlines, and for their help in all aspects of manuscript preparation.

I owe a special note of thanks to Jack Smith, without whose initiative the book would never have been started. Had Jack not returned to Canada as I was leaving for Kansas, we would have remained together as co-editors.

My gratitude to my wife Julie cannot be adequately conveyed. Not only did she gracefully accept my absence night after night and weekend after weekend on a project that seemed like it would never end, but she remained, as always, my best and most trusted critic, advisor, and friend. Without her patience, encouragement, understanding, editorial assistance, and sacrifice this book would never have been completed.

Finally, I owe our son, Jason Christopher, a special kind of thanks. It was his birth during the final months of work on this manuscript that convinced me that the great cultural transformation called for and prefigured in the following pages is indeed possible because it is necessary. If future generations are to have an opportunity for a life of peace, dignity, and joy, then we must succeed in the great task before us.

It is my hope that this book, by presenting a comprehensive vision of the kind of world it is in our power to create, will stimulate others to take an active part in the resettling of America. While it often seems that such a vision of possibilities must forever remain a naive and unrealized utopian dream, the incredible number, range, and variety of projects I have discovered over the last four years have convinced me that a better world is indeed possible. The same laws of exponential growth which underly the demise of industrial civilization seem to apply as well to the movement for its transformation. As the ever-expanding base of grass-roots change continues to build, it soon reaches such a large size that each future doubling represents an unimaginable increase in the total. I am firmly convinced that we will soon achieve the critical mass necessary to transform our finest hopes for the future into our everyday experience of the present.

Thus, I fully expect that within several years another book will be needed to describe the many new projects which will have emerged to carry forward the themes and tasks identified in this collection. In the interests of continuing to serve as a midwife in this process of giving birth to a new society, I invite those of you who are similarly involved to send me information describing what you are doing so that others might learn from your example. My forwarding address for this purpose is 315 North 15th Street, Manhattan, Kansas 66502.

Gary Coates
Manhattan, Kansas

Foreword

Amory Lovins

ON AN EVENING long ago, the great Persian humorist Nasruddin came before the villagers he was to entertain and asked them, "People, do you know what I'm going to talk about?" They answered with a bewildered "No." He replied, "If you don't even know what I'm going to talk about, there's no point, is there?" and went away. The villagers brought him back, and again he asked, "People, do you know what I'm going to talk about?" This time, being smarter, they all exclaimed, "Yes!" To which he answered, "If you already know what I'm going to talk about, there's no point, is there?" and went away again. So they brought him back a third time, and he asked, "People, do you know what I'm going to talk about?" By now, thoroughly confused, half said "Yes!" and half said "No!" So Nasruddin said, "Those of you who know, tell the ones who don't know," and went away.

Sometimes the diverse people whose fusion of philosophy and practice, grace and works, makes this book so exciting, must feel a bit like Nasruddin.

It is bewildering to be living in the middle of a great cultural transformation such as hasn't occurred for centuries. Today we may meet: someone who knows, and cares, that a dumptruck of topsoil floats by New Orleans every second as the soil mines of agribusiness approach depletion; someone who knows the vital work of the New Alchemy Institute and the Land Institute, the reforestation projects in Los Angeles and the South Bronx, the greenhouses in the Rockies and the aquaculture in West Overshoe; someone who worries about the way the chemical companies are buying up the seed banks. Yet tomorrow we may meet: someone else who hasn't heard and couldn't care; someone who, admonished by Welsh development economist Alwyn Rees that "When you have come to the edge of an abyss, the only progressive move you can make is to step backwards," only shouts, "Forward, lemmings!" It is almost as if, in Professor Mark Christensen's metaphor, we live in a society of Joneses who are busy keeping up with each other, and Greens who aren't, with the ratio of Joneses to Greens gradually declining—so bleeding off more steam from the high-pressure engines of acquisitive expansionism that the Joneses seek—and thus, perhaps incubating still more social tensions.

Our society seems to futurist Willis Harman rather like a psychoanalytic patient approaching a crisis—one that can eventually be resolved from within, and far less painfully if the patient realizes what is happening, and that it is a common experience to which there are many known answers. I hope this book will help provide that guidance in resolution and will serve as a catalyst that can make our cultural rigidities more elastic, less brittle, in preparation for the next few decades' nasty shocks.

This book spans a vast range of concerns—politics, how people can live together, food, energy, land use, and more. My main professional concern, energy policy, is necessarily somewhat more focused. But I share Gary Coates's sense of being surrounded not only by what Pogo called "insurmountable opportunities" but also by real achievements. I see a "soft" energy future, based on the very efficient use of energy from appropriate renewable sources, already starting to implement itself at a grassroots level with a speed I would not have thought possible when I proposed such a future only three years ago. Such a policy is being planned and put into practice today in many hundreds of American towns, cities, and counties. In late 1979 we approached our two hundred thousandth solar building in the United States. Roughly half of these are passively solar heated (capturing and storing solar heat in the fabric of the building itself) and half were made by modifying existing buildings, mainly with attached greenhouses. In our most solar-conscious communities, anywhere from a quarter to all of the new houses started in 1978 were passively solar heated. Stimulated by modest, no-red-tape government grants, the people of Nova Scotia weatherstripped and insulated half their entire housing stock in one year. In the whole United States, as systems analyst Vince Taylor has beautifully shown, improvements in the efficient use of energy contributed over two and a half times as much new U.S. energy supply from 1974 to 1978 as did all conventional supply expansions combined, including nuclear power, Alaskan oil, and increased oil imports. In other words, from 1974 through 1979, even before the 1978 National Energy Act could show its effects, higher energy productivity, won through millions of individual small gains, had already given us twice the new energy-supplying capacity than advocates of synthetic fuels claim they can build over the next ten years.

Why and how has this impressive and all-but-unnoticed energy revolution happened? Surely it is in part the working of traditional market forces. Though we still subsidize conventional U.S. fuels and power by more than $100 billion per year to make them look cheaper than they really are, and though countless silly rules and customs still prevent people from using energy in ways that save money, chilly market signals are, nevertheless, beginning to penetrate the barriers. Even the Harvard Business School's 1974–1979 faculty study, *Energy Future,* found that conventional supply expansion—more oil, gas, coal, nuclear power, and oil shale—doesn't really work. It yields too little, too late, and at too high a cost. In traditional economic terms, the study found, the real payoffs are in more efficient energy use and in the benign renewable sources. And Roger Sant, former head of Federal energy conservation programs, has calculated that if over the past ten years we had simply bought the cheapest energy systems available, in the knowledge of today's energy prices, we would today be using some 28 percent less oil (cutting oil imports by one half) and over a third fewer central power stations than we are actually using—thus, cutting our energy bills by 17 percent. Nearly all the difference would be made up by using technical ways to wring more work from our energy.

Fashionable (and tactically convenient) though it is, however, to suppose that people's behavior is guided only by economic rationality, I suspect more subtle forces are at work too. I cannot find in U.S. history a major public-policy decision about energy that our government has in fact based on economics. We have instead based such decisions on political expedience and then juggled the subsidies to make the economics come out to justify them. The real springs of action in energy policy, then, are probably the political gut issues that people really worry about—problems like centrism, vulnerability, inequity, technocracy, and dependence (the East Eleventh Street Project described by Freedberg in this book has more similarities to a developing country facing the multinationals than we like to think). In some cases these concerns are clearly a major force not only in legislatures' but in individuals' energy decisions. It is not only because heating oil is becoming expensive that over 40 percent of northern New England householders now heat mainly with wood, or that there are now over 150 wood-fired factories in New England; no, it is because people are afraid they may not be able to get oil at any price. That perceived vulnerability focuses the mind wonderfully.

It is not only savings in money that lead people to build houses so heat-tight that they need little or no heating or cooling energy even in our worst climates. Other motives matter too, such as greater comfort and beauty, independence from distrusted institutions, better rapport with natural rhythms, more scope for sitting in the sunspace in February munching fresh tomatoes, and greater resilience (in such a house, failure of the heating system may go unnoticed for days or weeks, whereas if you lived in a sieve, you would freeze promptly). It is not only improved economics from higher densities that is making solar energy sprout in our cities; it is also the driving forces of basic human needs, local control, and economic regeneration that are seizing on energy as a key organizing principle to arrest urban rot. In short, our technical innovations are teaching us anew that walls, whether of concrete or adobe, are not as important as how people live and feel inside them, and that more technological gadgetry is no substitute for intelligent social choice—though it can, if appropriate, greatly stimulate such choice.

The very accessibility of small, simple, technical innovations to lots of ingenious tinkerers is itself a liberating force, and the main source of the good news about energy supply in recent years. I have seen a letter from an Alaskan bush homesteader of little education but high intelligence, describing various energy devices he had developed. In one, a solar-tempered biogas digester, he wanted to digest diverse wastes, including paper, but his bacteria balked at the paper; so he looked around his biome, noticed a moose eating a willow tree, seeded his digester with moose gut, and found that the richer mix of bacteria would happily chew up paper and even significant pieces of wood. He has apparently discovered something important—thanks to the absence of what Herman Kahn, perhaps the best living example of it, calls "educated incapacity."

What is it that sparks such innovation, whether technical or social? In my energy experience, sometimes the spark is struck directly from a specific local decision. When giant utilities propose to sell a small Midwestern town a piece of their next coal-fired power station, at a capital cost of nearly $2000 for every man, woman, and child in town, or to build a new submarine cable to Vancouver Island at a capital cost of about $10,000 per household, that is enough to make ordinary people say, "Wait a minute! That's so much money that with it we could instead fix up every building in town so it would never need heating or cooling again, and we'd have money left over. Doesn't that make more sense?"

Sometimes, though, the process is less specific in starting point, more spontaneously welling up out of the ground. Thus the remarkable Franklin County (Massachusetts) Energy Study sketched in this book—showing that future energy needs, even when projected far too high, can be met with local renewable resources at about the present price, and with great local economic benefits—arose from a few people's vision and hard work, and from a general feeling in this poor, oil-dependent county that something was terribly wrong with current policy. At the Franklin County "town meeting," held in Autumn 1978 to discuss the study's striking results, people for the first time were able to see the energy problem as their problem, something concrete and fine-grained that they could address with their own resources in ways they already knew a lot about. The problem, so seen, isn't meaningless statistics that bureaucrats in Boston or Washington should worry about, but rather the cracks around my window, something I have to fix. As the realization dawns in hundreds—by now perhaps thousands—of communities, we are rediscovering that people are pretty smart, and, given incentive and opportunity, can go a very long way in solving their own energy problems.

The lessons we are learning the hard way in energy can be applied elsewhere: not only in, say, water (where we are making exactly the same conceptual mistakes all over again), but also in developing ways and places to live. This is not a book about soft energy paths—least of all the "pure technical fix" approach I assume, with no significant changes in where or how we live—but it does offer living examples of innovation in energy-efficient human settlements and patterns of living, valuable both in their own right and as a parable for ecologically conscious communities. Conversely, energy use is not only important in our buildings, but offers us policy lessons, for example, cases where societies have smoothly and quickly modified major capital stocks, as in the British shift to smokeless fuels and North Sea gas, the Dutch shift to Groningen gas, the Swedish shift to district heating, and the postwar conversion of metropolitan Toronto and Montreal from 25- to 60-Hertz electricity (using fleets of specially equipped vans to modify all the motors and controls). These accomplishments help us learn how to fix up our communities on a truly large scale, as neatly as the Swedes switched to right-hand driving or the British to decimal coinage. Energy people and settlements people have much to learn from each others' experience.

I have always emphasized that a soft energy path offers an opportunity for, but does not require, a more Jeffersonian, humane, and ecologically balanced society. I have been content to rest my analysis on the tacit ideology of market economics rather than on the explicit ideology of the fundamental value changes which I believe are already occurring (though often for other reasons). But in practice, it is becoming clear that the wider social and mental modifications that will make the technical ones much easier than I assumed are already well under way, profiting from the immense vitality and fertility of our social ferment. For example, after attending an April 1979 New Alchemy Institute meeting on "The Village As Solar Ecology,"* I supposed I was already acquainted with the major U.S. projects seeking to build or rebuild communities that would be largely self-reliant in energy and food and that would be ecologically and (most difficult of all) socially sustainable. But reading this book has revealed several projects quite new to me. And only last week I heard that there is a network of dozens of such communities already operating in the mountains of central Ecotopia—northern California and south and central Oregon—and accessible only if one knows the right people, for they have felt it more important to do their work than to tell the world about it or to live on display.

No doubt many such pioneering efforts remain to be discovered and—so far as this does not inhibit their success—reported to others seeking to

---

* See John and Nancy Todd, (eds.), *The Village as Solar Ecology,* Proceedings of the New Alchemy/Threshold Generic Design Conference, April 16–21, 1979. Available (in limited quantity) from The New Alchemy Institute, P.O. Box 47, Woods Hole, Massachusetts, 02543. See also, Van der Ryn/Calthorpe (eds.), *Proceedings of the Westerbeck Conference on Solar Cities,* (Golden, Colo.: Solar Energy Research Institute, 1980).

learn from their experience. Perhaps this book will stimulate its own supplements and successors as well as expand our space for inward exploration. More accounts of what people have actually done are needed to lend vividness and concreteness to our dreams. What John Steinhart calls the "gap between the unavoidable and the miraculous"—is still, for many, too great a strain on the imagination without the support of explicit descriptions and visual images of real accomplishments. There are certainly many success stories not reported here, ranging from Valerie Pope's major solar manufacturing and installing program in the Black community of San Bernadino (California) to the greenhouses in the San Luis Valley (Colorado). But at least as exciting, because of their open-ended potential, are the nascent projects sprouting from Arkansas to Montana, Wisconsin to Maine, and in a cathedral close in Manhattan, that are now receiving their share of inspiration and that should soon bear fruits we can taste, plant, and compost.

This book offers a rich base for that compost, and at a critical time in the germination of our awareness. Lao Tzu said, "Leaders are best when people barely know they exist, not so good when people obey and acclaim them, worst when people despise them. Fail to honor people, they fail to honor you. But of good leaders who talk little, when their work is done, their job fulfilled, the people will all say, 'We did this ourselves.'" Gary Coates and his collected authors are providing us with that sort of leadership. Their timely ideas can practice the politics of water, ". . . of all things most yielding, penetrating that which is most hard. . . . Being substanceless, it can enter in even where there are no cracks."

Bill McLarney, co-founder of the New Alchemy Institute, was once berated by a critic who couldn't understand why he was messing around with fish and algae and green goo when the really important thing in the world was love. Bill responded: "There's theoretical love; and then there's applied love." This anthology offers us both in full measure; and love, just as much as truth, shall make us free.

Amory B. Lovins
Pinkham Notch, New Hampshire

General Introduction

THERE IS A GROWING SENSE that something has gone wrong in the world, that the road toward a future of unlimited wealth and happiness through science, technology, and the American Way of Life may, in fact, be a dead end. Indeed, it seems that Western culture has reached the limits of its material strength and spiritual vigor just at the point of its greatest power. The symptoms of this decline are everywhere. When we look outward toward the world that we have created, we encounter a proliferation of intractable and interrelated crises: exponential population growth; nonrenewable resource and energy depletion; rampant and uncontrolled pollution and environmental degradation; cancerous urban growth and suburban sprawl; chronic food shortages and massive levels of malnutrition and starvation; global inflation in a world economy completely out of control; constantly diminishing levels of basic services delivered by constantly growing, ponderous, and impersonal bureaucratic machines; widespread, often violent, authoritarian forms of social control. But, as Theodore Roszak has observed, these crises are but the "outward mirror of our inner condition, the first discernible symptoms of advanced disease within."[1] And when we look within we increasingly find a void, an emptiness that can no longer be filled with the distractions and compulsive busyness of the consumer society.

Growing numbers of people, especially in the affluent, overdeveloped parts of the world, are beginning to realize that the unrestricted satisfaction of all desires does not necessarily lead to well-being nor does the pursuit of happiness, in the form of material wealth, necessarily lead to security and self-fulfillment. It is increasingly evident that a society that must cultivate selfishness, egotism, envy, and greed to sustain its economy does not, through some magical and omnipotent "invisible hand," become a great society based on cooperation, community, and generosity. While we

A sort of freedom comes from recognizing what is necessarily so. After that is recognized, comes a knowledge of how to act. You can ride a bicycle only after your partly unconscious reflexes acknowledge the laws of its moving equilibrium.

Gregory Bateson,
*Mind and Nature:
A Necessary
Unity*

1

once believed that we were escaping the limits to our freedom set by the small town and village, we are now learning in our increasingly unmanageable cities that the mechanistic order of the systems manager cannot adequately replace the organic order of the community of shared responsibility and mutual obligation.

Rather than producing an egalitarian society in which everyone is supplied with the material necessities of life, the urban-industrial experiment has produced a world in which unconscionable wealth for the few is achieved at the expense of unspeakable poverty and deprivation for the many. And the gap between the rich and poor grows wider with every well-intentioned effort to overcome it. Our hoped-for salvation, technological progress, has not only failed to solve the problem of production but has instead produced the basis for much of our current despair, in the form of ecological degradation and the ever-present dangers of nuclear war and global destruction. With the growth of an "objective" science, uncontaminated by purpose or value, we thought that we had finally demystified nature and society, only to find that science itself has become an ideology that mystifies the nature of self and society and is in the process of generating a new priesthood of power, a "value-free," white-collared, technocratic elite.

Through crisis and contradiction, paradox and confusion, we are experiencing the end of an illusion, the failure of the "Great Promise of Unlimited Progress—the promise of the domination of nature, of material abundance, of the greatest happiness for the greatest number, and of unimpeded personal freedom—[which] has sustained the hopes and faith of generations since the beginning of the industrial age."[2] Whether viewed collectively in its outward effects or experienced personally in its inward reality, the crisis of our time can be seen as the inevitable outcome of a world view and a way of life that is inherently violent and ultimately self destructive. It is the thesis of this book that what we are experiencing at this moment in history is not just another series of crises *within* industrial civilization, but rather, the final crisis *of* that civilization.

The "limits to growth" debate is no longer about whether it is possible (or desirable) for infinite material growth to continue in a finite world. Rather, it is about *when,* and *how* a transition can be made to a sustainable and, it is hoped, a just society. Expressing a view which is rapidly becoming the conventional wisdom of our day, the editors of *The Ecologist* have summarized the overriding issue that now confronts us:

> The principal defect of the industrial way of life with its ethos of expansion is that it is not sustainable. Its termination within the lifetime of someone born today is inevitable—unless it continues to be sustained for a while longer by an entrenched minority at the cost of imposing great suffering on the rest of mankind. We can be certain, however, that sooner or later it will end (only the precise time and circumstances are in doubt) and that it will do so in one of two ways: either against our will, in a succession of famines, epidemics, social crises

and wars; or because we want it to—because we wish to create a society which will not impose hardship and cruelty upon our children—in a succession of thoughtful, humane and measured changes.[3]

The fundamental premise of the present volume is that the accelerating depletion of nonrenewable energy and natural resources, and escalating levels of environmental degradation have already set in motion changes that will force a transition to an entirely new form of human culture. Whether these changes represent an improvement in the human condition depends largely on this generation's ability to accept the inevitability of this great transformation and to work creatively to guide the direction of change. In the next quarter century, through conscious choice and default, we will decide what kind of people we want to be, what our relationship should be to the environmental systems that sustain us, and what kind of technological systems, social structures, and patterns of settlement we shall live within. Whatever we decide, we shall bear the consequences for the forseeable future on this planet.

These decisions, if left to the momentum of present conditions or the discretion of existing institutions and cultural managers, are likely to result in a frantic effort to sustain our environmentally destructive way of life until it collapses through the sheer weight of its life-denying tendencies. Consequently, this book is addressed to those who feel that it is time to take responsibility for reshaping their own lives, neighborhoods, and cities. It is addressed to those who feel that our built environment, if still a mirror of who we are, is no longer a reflection of who we want to be. It is a call, therefore, for a grass-roots movement for personal, social, and environmental change—a call for the resettling of America.

The purpose of this introduction is twofold: (1) to summarize the factual basis for the thesis that the inevitable end of industrial civilization is clearly in sight, and (2) to outline the implications of that thesis and describe how the contents of this book delineate the emerging alternative to industrialism, an alternative that is not a regression to the preindustrial past but an historically unique synthesis of the past and present in an emergent future.

To achieve these aims it is first necessary to define the nature of the crisis of industrial civilization. This can be done with a single word—scarcity. The idea of scarcity does not imply that the earth cannot provide in perpetuity for the needs of a prudent population. But, as we shall see, industrial peoples are far from prudent. All the values, philosophies, technologies, and institutions of the modern world have been formed during an historically unique and materially unreplicable era of apparently endless abundance. Thus, the assertion that we are experiencing a return to scarcity is met, quite understandably, with incredulity, ridicule, and often, anger. Yet, not only is scarcity returning, but it is doing so in a particularly disturbing form. The political scientist William Ophuls has referred to this new condition as "ecological scarcity," which is ". . . an ensemble of separate but interacting limits and constraints on human action."[4] This form of scarcity "includes not only Malthusian scarcity of food but also impending shortages of mineral and energy resources, biospheric or eco-systemic limitations on human activity, and limits to the human capacity to use technology to expand resources ahead of exponentially increasing demands (or to bear the costs of doing so)."[5]

As we examine the evidence for this return to the habitual condition of humankind it should also become clear that ecological scarcity poses problems far more serious and intractable than those presented to previous forms of human culture, problems that will exist regardless of the persistence of belief to the contrary.

The end of the fossil fuel age

The United States, on a per capita basis, consumes more natural resources than any other nation on earth. With only 6 percent of the world's population, we consume 33 percent of the petroleum and 36 percent of the metals and non-metal natural resources. This means that each American directly or indirectly uses (in 1972) almost 20 metric tons of resources annually, half of which end up as solid waste, eventually to become a source of pollution.[6] This extraordinary level of consumption is sustained only by the constant flow of rapidly diminishing fossil fuels.

The obvious question is, How much longer will world supplies of conventional fossil fuels be able to meet such enormous (and ever-increasing) requirements? The answer depends on a number of variables, from the estimated reserves and the potential for new discoveries, to the rate of use and the model used to make the estimates. While there is considerable disagreement about each of these variables, and considerable room for error, the emerging consensus is that world demand will outstrip supply between 1995 and 2015.[7]

The figures seem to indicate that the earth is in the last decades of the fossil fuel age. Since energy is so crucial to everything from food supply to transportation to thermal control of buildings, let us look more closely at the basis for this assertion.

Several types of indices are used to estimate the depletion of a finite resource. The *static reserve index* is the number of years a known reserve will last at a constant rate of use. Use of this index has led many people to suppose that we have enough fossil fuels to last several centuries or more. For example, the static reserve index estimates that world supplies of coal would last from 3100 to 5100 years.[8]

However, the static reserve depletion model does not take into account the central fact of industrial society, that all resources are being consumed at an exponential rate. The *exponential reserve index* is the number of years a known reserve will last if consumed at a constant growth rate per year. Thus, in the case of coal, which has a growth rate of 4.1 percent per year, the exponential reserve is estimated to be only 118 to 132 years.[9]

The important thing to notice about the effect of exponential growth is that depletion times are relatively unaffected by errors in estimated reserves. For example, world reserves of coal are estimated at 7.6 trillion metric tons. If we assume these reserves are consumed at a growth rate of 3.5 percent, they will be exhausted in 120 years. If it was then found that reserves are twice those initially estimated, coal use would be extended only another 20 years. However, if the rate of use increased to 5 percent, based on the initial reserve figure, the coal supply would last only 84 years.[10] So the key variable is the estimated rate of growth.

While those estimates are instructive, they do not provide an accurate means of predicting resource depletion. Clearly, such rates of growth could not be sustained as reserves became depleted. If nothing else, the costs of recovering the diminishing resources would dampen the rate of consumption. To predict the future of fossil fuels it is necessary to assume that energy use and resource recovery will peak and then decline in a bell-shaped production curve. Long before the last barrel of oil is consumed it will become infeasible, in both energy and economic terms, to produce that last barrel. A resource can be considered effectively exhausted once 80 percent of estimated supply has been recovered.[11] Therefore, the key to the future of industrialism lies in determining when the production peak of energy and other natural resources is reached. Fortunately, this can be done with some precision. Let us take a closer look at the depletion curves for the major fossil fuels.

Geologist M. King Hubbert has projected depletion curves for world and U.S. supplies of oil, natural gas, and coal.[12] While a number of experts take a more optimistic view of fossil fuel supplies, Hubbert's predictions have proven, even to his most virulent critics, to be amazingly accurate to date. If he is wrong it is more likely that he is overly optimistic, because his estimates fail to account for the fact that, once the backside of a production curve is reached, the net energy recovered decreases rapidly. Moreover, as we have seen, significant increases in new reserves add only a small percentage to the projected depletion date under the condition of exponentially increasing demand.

Oil and natural gas

Hubbert estimated a peak in U.S. oil production before 1980 and a decline to half its present output by 2010, at which time approximately 80 percent of U.S. oil will have been recovered and consumed.[13] The effects of Alaskan production will have been absorbed by 1990 and the decline in production will continue unaffected. U.S. natural gas production has already peaked and is steadily declining. By 2020, 80 percent of known recoverable reserves will have been consumed.

Estimates of world supplies of oil and natural gas suggest that world production for both will peak between 1995 and 2015 at which time world demand will exceed supply.[14] Should OPEC decide, as expected, to limit production to husband its remaining reserves, demand will outstrip supply even sooner. The result is likely to tax international diplomacy to its limit.

Coal

Coal is the great hope of many people for a fossil fuel that can push back the timetable for the end of industrial society. Yet as we have seen, this hope is often founded on estimates of depletion based on the static reserve. According to Hubbert, peak production of U.S. coal could be reached anywhere from 150 to 250 years from now at current rates of use.[15] However, if the U.S. were to drastically increase the rate of coal consumption to compensate for declining supplies and escalating costs of other fossil fuels, peak production would be reached in the next century. And this will be accomplished at enormous economic and environmental cost (including the real possibility of major climatic changes).

Regardless of the variability of depletion curve estimates it seems safe to conclude that the era of cheap, readily available, and adequate world supplies of oil and natural gas will be over by 2015 to 2030, and in the U.S. by 1990 to 2015.[16] While coal production will increase rapidly during that time it will decline soon thereafter. Clearly, if the major supplies of fossil fuels, which now provide for 95 percent of the energy needs of the industrial world, will be effectively exhausted within the lifetime of someone born today, we are on the threshold of a major transformation of industrial civilization.[17] When viewed from the perspective of the history of the human species, the Fossil Fuel Age (see accompanying graph) will be seen as the unique and unreplicable anomaly that it is.

Substitutes for fossil fuels

Based on past experience it takes a society at least 20 to 50 years to develop and put into place a new energy system.[18] Consequently, it is important that we begin to seek replacements for conventional fossil fuels. Unfortunately, our addiction to fossil fuel use is so crippling to the imagination of policy makers and energy experts that most alternatives proposed involve the extraction of even more exotic forms of fossil fuels, and the use of dangerous nuclear energy. Many of the proposed solutions to the energy supply problem, such as coal liquification and gassification, require such massive quantities of energy for production and have such a devastating impact on the environment that the expected contribution of these "replacement" fuels will be minimal at best.[19] The mining of coal for these conversion processes would lead to massive pollution problems and greatly increased costs to cover air pollution controls, land reclamation costs, increased shipping costs, and so on.

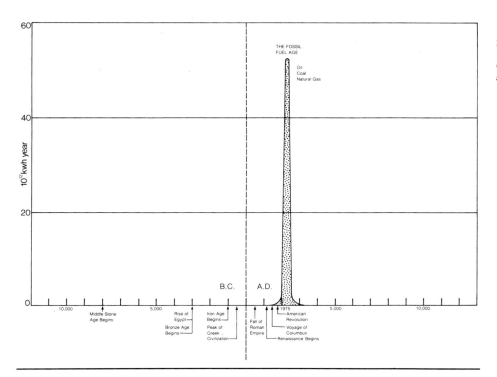

The Fossil Fuel Age

Figure adapted from
Transition. State of Oregon,
Office of Energy Research
and Planning, 1975

The production of oil from shale (our largest unconventional fossil fuel source) is also likely to be less than expected and much more costly than projected. One of the most serious environmental problems is the disposal of the vast amounts of waste rock, which would swell to almost twice the volume of the original shale. A full scale industry producing 3 million barrels of oil per day would generate 4.5 million tons of processed shale per day, requiring 4,640 acres of land each year.[20] Since these wastes are sterile, land reclamation would be impossible without constant fertilizer and water application. Even then, restoration of the natural plant community would be unlikely and nearly 300 species of wildlife in the area of mining would be imperiled. Finally, a full-scale program, 80 percent of which would be located in Colorado, would require almost three-fourths of the water available in the Upper Colorado River Compact area.[21] Clearly, a program of above-ground retorting should be far too destructive to even consider, and the proposed alternative of in-situ recovery, which in some proposals would involve boiling the kerogen out of the shale by the explosion of underground nuclear bombs, would have its own unique problems. While other less destructive production methods may be found, the amount of oil that is likely to be produced will be far short of what is needed to replace conventional oil supplies.

Although oil from the tar sands in the Athabasca region of Canada can be recovered economically, the process is slow and environmentally destructive, and would supply only about 2 to 4 percent of U.S. needs by

1985.[22] (Furthermore, Canada does not intend to export any form of energy to the United States after 1982.)

In conclusion, it can be conservatively stated that the production of synthetic oil substitutes will provide only extremely costly and minimal supplements to diminishing supplies of liquid fossil fuels. It is a short-term strategy with long-term costs.

That makes the entire internal-combustion-engine based U.S. transportation system a multibillion-dollar white elephant. Nevertheless, we are continuing to disassemble our already moribund rail transport system which, if nothing else, will be needed to haul all the coal we expect to mine, in the name of sound economics. As the recent truckers' strike so graphically demonstrated, even a modest slowdown in the rate of flow of goods threatens millions of people in our urban areas with unemployment and even starvation. Without the smooth and continued operation of our irrational system of transportation, our urban-industrial society would be logistically unworkable. Yet the system is completely dependent on liquid fossil fuels whose depletion is most imminent. In the next decade, the beginning of the end of the automobile age will make itself felt in a crisis of major proportions. Given the recent violence over marginal decreases in gasoline supplies one wonders how we will respond to a real crisis.

Nuclear power

An article of faith among technological optimists since the end of World War II is that the fossil fuel age would be replaced by the atomic age, when electricity would be "too cheap to meter." In spite of the disaster at Three-Mile Island and the current economic crisis in the nuclear industry, most American citizens still cling to this myth. (Even if there were any basis for this hope, it would not do much to salvage the transportation sector from serious dislocation.)

The first fact about the potential role of nuclear power is that uranium 235 (U^{235}) needed for conventional fission-reaction plants is itself a scarce natural resource. If present plans for the development of nuclear power were carried out, useful uranium supplies worldwide would be exhausted shortly after the turn of the century. This fact has been known since the beginning of the "peaceful" atom program. The hope for nuclear advocates has always been in the fast-breeder reactor which, in effect, creates more fuel than it uses, thus extending the effective lifetime of uranium supplies by 50- to 80-fold.[23]

It would seem that this is, indeed, the solution to the energy crisis, at least for nontransportation uses. However, like other industrial age fantasies this dream unravels between theory and practice. The first dilemma is cost associated with construction of the plants and protection from sabotage. To date, the prototype commercial fast-breeder in Tennessee has increased in cost from its 1973 estimated $700 million to about $3 billion.[24]

This alone would make fast-breeder electricity unaffordable, but it doesn't even take into account the enormous costs of waste storage or "decommissioning."

After their expected life of 30 to 40 years, even conventional reactors must be "decommissioned." This can be done in one of two ways; (1) dismantling the reactor and storing the radioactive parts (still an unsolved problem), and (2) entombing, encasing the reactor in a protective skin of concrete. It is estimated that the costs for either method could run as high as 100 million dollars or more. Such costs are not now factored into the cost of nuclear-produced electricity. When they are, as they must be, the price of this form of energy will be significantly higher. Even *Business Week,* in a special report on the nuclear dilemma, has expressed grave doubts about the economics of nuclear power.[25]

Based on a thorough analysis of the business potential of the nuclear industry, Saunders Miller, one of the nation's leading utilities investment analysts, has concluded that on purely economic grounds this approach to energy supply should be abandoned.

> . . . the conclusion that must be reached is that, from an economic standpoint alone, to rely on nuclear fission as a primary source of our stationary energy supplies will constitute economic lunacy on a scale unparalleled in recorded history, and may lead to the economic Waterloo of the United States.[26]

Even more serious, however, are problems related to plant safety. This is especially true for the fast-breeder. The reason is amply demonstrated in the following account of the near-tragic incident at the nation's first breeder reactor, the Enrico Fermi Plant in Detroit, which,

> . . . suffered a disabling accident in 1966 in which the fission reaction went out of control and came within a heartbeat of causing a devastating nuclear explosion. Had the explosion occurred, it would have inundated Detroit with a deadly cloud of radioactivity, perhaps killing thousands of people, forced the evacuation of the city, rendered the region "permanently" uninhabitable (the half-life of plutonium 239 is 24,000 years), and effectively terminated the largest single U.S. industry—auto manufacture. The meltdown burned itself out without exploding, leaving in its wake a sobered scientific community and a twisted mass of intensely radioactive molten steel that is still being painstakingly dismantled.[27]

Even if such potential disasters could be controlled by better reactor design and the elimination of all forms of human error (an unlikely prospect), the normal operation of breeder-reactors would create an even more dangerous problem—routine waste disposal. Each plant would produce in its lifetime tons of plutonium fuel that would have to be transported over public routes to reprocessing facilities. Since plutonium is deadly for most higher forms of life on earth (a few millionths of a gram can cause lung cancer when inhaled), it should be clear that the risks of a large-scale program of breeder reactors far outweigh the potential benefits. Even according to nuclear advocates, the danger of plutonium flows being diverted to terrorist groups would require a virtual police state. Furthermore, the problem of waste disposal from conventional plants is, according to many scientists, insoluble in theory. If we haven't figured out how to solve existing long-term nuclear waste storage problems, one wonders why we would want to create more and deadlier wastes.

So, fissionable nuclear power production is economically infeasible, creates a permanent threat to most life forms, and without the fast-breeder, is destined to exhaust its needed fuel supply at about the same time that we run out of conventional fossil fuels. It should not be surprising then, that the U.S. breeder program has been returned to the experimental stage and commercial orders for conventional fission reactors have fallen to levels that could soon cause the collapse of the entire nuclear industry. Rather than replacing fossil fuels, nuclear energy is likely to bankrupt those who use it, and leave behind tons of poisonous substances that must be kept perpetually sealed from the environment and a landscape of entombed reactors that will, no doubt, also require vigilant protection by untold future generations. Only 13 percent of the total U.S. energy supply is electricity. Since our electricity needs can be met far more economically and safely by a variety of renewable and nonrenewable energy sources (for example, wind, photovoltaics, hydro, cogeneration and coal), continued support for electricity from nuclear reactors is unexplainable in rational terms.

Fusion power, which some see as the ultimate energy source, is accompanied by theoretical, technical, and financial problems that make fission look like a trivial engineering exercise for college undergraduates and backyard tinkerers. Even if the problems can be solved, no one expects that the solutions will be found before fossil fuels are nearly gone. Thus, the prognosis for the decline of industrial civilization is altered little by this ultimate magic bullet.[28]

Renewable energy sources

If all forms of concentrated and stored solar energy, from fossil fuels to the energy of the atom, are increasingly costly and scarce, with effective depletion dates clearly in sight, the only viable and attractive alternative for any future civilization is a transition to a low-energy, high-technology metaindustrial culture based on the use of the renewable (income) energy sources of sun, wind, water, and green plants. We must learn to live within the same energy flows that sustain all other life on this planet. Since that is the premise of all the articles in this book, we shall examine the prospects for such a transition when describing the shape of things to come. However, we must first complete the outline of the phenomenon of ecological scarcity. The crisis of industrialism is far more than an energy crisis.

Mineral depletion

While energy from fossil fuels drives the processes that sustain industrial societies, other natural resources must be continually extracted from the earth to be reshaped by energy and technology into manufactured products. Like the consumption of fossil fuels, the use of other nonrenewable natural resources, especially mineral ores, is growing at an exponential rate. Since about half the static reserves of important minerals are less than 100 years, and the average growth rate is approximately 3 percent, exponential reserves of these key materials will be effectively depleted in less than 50 years.[29]

Methods similar to the bell-shaped depletion model applied by M. King Hubbert to fossil fuels have been applied by Arndt and Roper to mineral ores.[30] Using "cumulative depletion" curves, they estimate that U.S production of cadmium peaked in 1957 and reserves will be depleted 75 percent in the year 2000. Chromite peaked in 1955 and will be 100 percent exhausted in 2000. Manganese and zinc will be 98 percent and 67 percent exhausted, respectively, in 2000.[31] Since those metals are crucial to steel production, the continued life of the U.S. steel industry will depend on reliable supplies of imports. Indeed, these depletion curves are already reflected in the fact that, as of 1974, the U.S. depended on foreign suppliers for 98 percent of its manganese and 91 percent of its chromium, as well as 50 percent of a dozen other key metals.[32]

The potential political problems created by such dependencies are obvious. However, problems created by the depletion of world supplies are even more intractable. Peak world production of minerals will be reached around 1990. With demand for those declining resources expected to triple by the year 2000, the crisis of mineral scarcity will rapidly escalate.[33]

Technological optimists like Herman Kahn, who believe that economics creates resources, like to believe that we can mine the oceans for trace minerals. This belief assumes that as demand increases mining will be viable with poorer and poorer ores. However, the theory, which is based on a principle called the *arithmetic-geometric ratio* (A/G ratio), applies only to a few ores under defined limits. According to this principle, as the quality of ore decreases arithmetically, the amount of lower grade ore increases in abundance geometrically. If the principle applied to all key minerals, there would always be enough ore if the price was right. The assumption is that the price of resource recovery would always be low enough to make the effort worthwhile. So, the last hope of superindustrial prophets founders on two facts: (1) the A/G ratio model does not apply to most mineral resources, which means that most reserves simply don't exist in the distributions necessary, and (2) rising energy costs further amplify the recovery costs of lower grade ores, which means that the price will never be right.[34]

While not all minerals are equally affected, the disruptions that are certain to occur as key metals are exhausted will further undermine the continued smooth functioning of industrial activity throughout the world.

Environmental degradation

If energy and mineral resource depletion were the only limits to the continuation of industrial civilization, then it might be possible to play an elaborate mental shell-and-pea game with ourselves, leading to the comforting but false conclusion that if we are clever enough we can manage to keep things going much as they are now. However, the facts of ecological scarcity do not allow us to so indulge ourselves. Even if we could find a cheap, infinite source of energy, which would also allow us to escape the mineral depletion dilemma, industrial society would simply accelerate its decline by another route—environmental degradation. We don't have to wait for the future to experience this constraint. We are already seriously disrupting the major ecosystems of the biosphere and thereby undermining the continued functioning of industrialism.

The atmosphere

Probably the most commonly experienced form of pollution is air pollution. The human health hazards of this growing problem have been dramatized by a number of killer smogs. During the last week of December 1930, the heavily industrialized Meuse Valley in Belgium was covered by an air mass that prevented the normal process of even downwind distribution of harmful sulfur oxides. Over one thousand people became ill and sixty died, ten times more than normal.[35] A similar disaster occurred in October 1948 in the small mill town of Donora, Pennsylvania, located in a valley on the Monongahela River. Six thousand people, nearly half the population, became ill during a thermal inversion that trapped pollutants. Seventeen people died and the lives of many of those made ill may have been shortened. A similar smog which occurred in London in December 1952 reduced visibility to one yard and is believed to have directly accounted for 4000 deaths.[36]

Los Angeles, whose air pollution comes from the operation of motor vehicles, is subject to photochemical smogs that are trapped by temperature inversions, a situation that occurs 80 to 90 percent of the time between June and October.[37] Although the Los Angeles smogs are less spectacular than the killer smogs, the chronic health threat to residents of Los Angeles, San Bernadino, and Riverside counties is so severe that in 1969 leading physicians at UCLA's medical school advised ". . . anyone who does not have compelling reasons to remain to move out . . ." of these areas to ". . . avoid chronic respiratory diseases like bronchitis and emphesema."[38] Air pollution alerts are now a common part of daily life in Los

Angeles and doctors annually advise more than ten thousand people to leave the area as part of their treatment.[39]

But such problems are not limited to a few areas. Every major metropolis in the world has serious air pollution problems. In fact, the entire atmosphere of the planet has been affected: a thin veil of pollution now perpetually encircles the earth. Smog has been reported over the North Pole and the vast unpopulated oceans. It is no longer unusual for small towns downwind of major industrial areas such as the Great Lakes industrial belt to experience serious air pollution problems much of the year.

Even the ozone layer, which filters the deadly ultraviolet radiation of the sun, may already be seriously depleted by the combined effects of nuclear explosions, supersonic aircraft, and the chlorofluoromethane gases used in aerosol propellants and refrigeration equipment. It will be years before we discover whether the ozone layer is already damaged enough to cause extensive harm to organisms crucial to global ecology.

Finally, the intensified use of fossil fuels over the last two hundred years has increased the atmospheric concentration of carbon dioxide by over 10 percent and, if present trends continue, the carbon dioxide content will increase some 25 percent by the year 2000.[40] Since carbon dioxide in the atmosphere traps solar energy that would otherwise be reflected back into space, this effect of industrialism tends to increase global temperatures, and, as we shall see in the section on climate, an increase in global temperatures could lead to a major global disaster.

Apart from causing future major disruptions of the earth's climatic system, air pollution already seriously impairs food production and limits the growth of forested areas. Cotton production in recent years in Fresno, California has been reduced by one-third due to pollution and unfiltered Los Angeles air has cut some fruit crop yields in half.[41] With 13 percent of all U.S. farmland existing within major pollution-producing urban regions, air pollution threatens some of our most productive and strategically crucial food producing areas. It is estimated that urban farmland produces 60 percent of all vegetables, 43 percent of all fruits and nuts, and 17 percent of all corn and accounts for nearly one fourth of all farm income.[42] At present, annual crop losses of a half billion dollars are caused by air pollution.[43] With the increased consumption of fossil fuels projected for the turn of the century, crop losses will become even more serious.

Pollution-related damage to forests has now become a global problem. A comparison of lumber production from Ponderosa pines in the San Bernadino mountains of California during a relatively unpolluted 30 year span (1910–1940) and more polluted period of 30 years (1944–1974) showed a 75 percent reduction.[44] It is relatively well known that the "acid rains" from burning sulphur-bearing fossil fuels have significantly reduced forest production in Sweden, but the effects of a 100-fold increase in the acidity of rainfall in the eastern United States are just now being noticed.[45]

The effects of air pollution, combined with unprecedented and unchecked worldwide deforestation, threaten the long-term viability of a crucial non-renewable resource. Not only does forest damage and depletion signify the loss of an important alternate source of energy and a major source of building materials, but it could also cause other environmental effects ranging from soil erosion and flooding to climate change. We need only look to the barren hills of the Middle East, or the 7000-acre desert in the midst of the lush forest land of Tennessee to see that, once started, such processes of deforestation can be as irreversible as they are devastating.[46]

Clearly, we are taxing the respiratory system of the biosphere beyond its ability to absorb our wastes, thereby threatening the ecosystems which we depend on for survival. Air pollution is far more than a subject for cocktail party chatter; it is a serious and intractable limit to the continuation of industrial civilization in its present form.

Land

The forces of urbanization and industrialization threaten our land in other, more direct ways. Only one quarter of the planet is land, and of that only 11 to 15 percent is considered arable. About half of our arable land is in active cultivation at the present time.[47] Bringing into production any sizeable portion of the remainder will require enormous amounts of capital, energy, and technology, an unlikely prospect in an age of ecological scarcity. Given the current rate of degradation caused by pollution and loss of prime agricultural land to urbanization, the real problem will be to maintain the amount of land now in cultivation.

In the United States we are paving over prime farmland equivalent to the land area of Rhode Island every six months.[48] To date, nearly 10 percent of estimated U.S. arable land has been lost to urbanization.[49] Exploitative agricultural practices over the past 200 years have led to the loss of one third of our rich dowry of topsoil.[50] The loss of topsoil continues unchecked, largely due to the use of chemical fertilizers, which undermine soil structure, and agricultural practices that leave large tracts of land without vegetation for extended periods of time. Irrigation from underground wells has also started a serious decline in soil fertility and productivity due to the build up of mineral salt deposits. Because of soil salinization, the future of some of the most productive wheat land in the Great Plains is looking more and more like that of Pakistan, where 16 percent of the irrigated land has been wholly or partly destroyed in that way.[51]

The future is sure to bring even further problems as the need for new energy supplies forces a tradeoff between energy and land. And, given the crucial role of energy in the functioning of already faltering industrial economies, land will inevitably be sacrificed. Already the Midland Coal Company is strip mining some of the world's most productive farmland in Knox County, Illinois. Even if we could afford to restore these vast tracts of land, which we can't, productivity typically is less than half of what it was before mining.[52]

The implications of soil erosion, fertility reduction, and the loss of farmland to urban and energy needs are staggering in a world where 10 to 20 million people a year starve to death and 460 million are weakened by chronic malnutrition.[53] With world population expected to grow to between 12 and 15 billion by the year 2060, unprecedented levels of famine are virtually certain unless we achieve major changes in world economic patterns. Rather than being able to support 15 to 50 billion people, as some advocates of the "Green Revolution" propose, it is more likely that we shall have difficulty feeding the current population of 4 billion.

Water

Another part of the commons that has become competitively over-exploited is fresh water, the ingredient crucial to all life. From its agricultural system to its vast urban concentrations, industrial civilization is the most water-intensive social form ever created. The depletion of ground and surface water is emerging as one of the world's most serious resource problems. In addition, pollution of fresh water from industrial effluents and agricultural runoff is a chronic and increasingly serious outcome of the industrial organization of life.

There is not a major river system in the industrialized world that does not have serious pollution problems. The Rhine river, known as "Europe's sewer," represents such a threat to health that the city of Rotterdam has been forced to seek its water supply elsewhere. So far, the billions of dollars that have been spent to clean it up have failed to offset the effects of continued industrial development upstream in France, Germany and Switzerland.[54] The Mississippi river is no better. Chlorine from treated New Orleans water combines with organic industrial pollutants in the lower Mississippi to produce a number of carcinogens. Bladder cancer in New Orleans is three times the rate of other southern cities.[55]

But river systems aren't the only bodies of water affected by the "side effects" of urban industrialism. Biologists have described the Chesapeake Bay as a "biological nightmare"[56] and scientists are still arguing about whether or not at least the western basin of Lake Erie is dead or merely dying.[57]

While most examples of fresh water pollution cited so far are the result of wastes created by industry and high population concentrations, the effects of current agricultural practices are equally serious and may prove to be more difficult to solve. The state of Kansas, which is considered very rural, does not have a stream or river safe for swimming or drinking, largely because of the more than 200 feedlots which daily generate the sewage equivalent of 70 million people, most of which is released directly into the water where it becomes a pollution problem rather than a source of nutrients for the land.[58] Agricultural practices also result in the release of large quantities of pesticides, herbicides, and nitrates, which find their way not only into surface water, but also into ground water, where treatment processes are no longer possible.

Nitrate pollution, largely due to the escalating use of inorganic nitrogen fertilizers required by the agribusiness approach to food production, is a particularly insidious problem. While nitrates themselves are not dangerous, they combine with certain bacteria in the digestive tract to produce nitrites, which are extremely toxic. Also any opened container of food can lead to the conversion of nitrates to nitrites. These two conditions are particularly likely to occur in the case of children and farm animals. The absorption of nitrites in the bloodstream reduces the body's ability to absorb and circulate oxygen and can lead to difficult breathing and even suffocation.[59] In many agricultural areas the health hazard is so severe that infants are given only bottled water and, occasionally, entire cities are forced to find new water supplies.[60]

Unlike effluent from feedlots, urban waste treatment plants, and industry, agricultural runoff is so diffuse and widely distributed that there is no feasible way to process it before it enters aquatic ecosystems. As the law of diminishing returns catches up with farmers, more and more nitrate fertilizer, pesticides, and herbicides must be applied to even maintain existing yields. Thus, the poisoning of surface water and ground water is one of the necessary effects of our modern "scientific" approach to agriculture.

Irrigation, another key ingredient in the "success" of the Green Revolution, is causing ground water to be depleted faster than it can be replaced, especially in the valleys of California and the western parts of Kansas.[61] Since underground aquifers often collapse when sufficiently drained, the possibility of desertification of some of the world's major food producing areas is very real.

The prospect of water shortages in major urban areas is equally chilling. Los Angeles survives only by draining the ground water at a rate faster than it is replaced from the Owens Valley 500 miles away through an elaborate system of pumped aquaducts and reservoirs. The time is coming sooner than later when the price of these abuses of a "renewable" resource must be paid. The United Nations estimates that worldwide water shortages will be a major problem by the year 2000, and of course, for the millions in the Sahel and India who have already suffered drought and famine, that time is now.[62]

Oceans

Technological optimists like to believe that we can solve the problem of feeding a growing world population by farming the seas. This idea, of course, depends on maintaining the health of the ocean ecosystem. However, industrial pollution and the mechanized mining of fish by the nations of the world have already reduced the food output from the oceans and may have permanently impaired their carrying capacity.

Contamination of ocean waters by hydrocarbons, most of which comes from routine ship traffic, may have already irreparably harmed the ability of phytoplankton to live and thus produce much of the atmospheric oxygen we breathe.[63] Radioactive wastes from nuclear power plants and underwater "sealed" storage tanks have been found off U.S. coasts.[64] Industrial wastes, such as PCB and Kepone, have accidentally poisoned major commercial fish and shellfish regions along the East Coast, and the routine dumping of toxins by industry into rivers and oceans has polluted beaches, contaminated fishing areas, and is destroying large areas of oceans.[65] These pollution problems are likely to be with us for many decades or perhaps generations, even if all polluting activities stop today.

Even without the further loss of biological production caused by pollution, the ability of the oceans to continue providing historical levels of food output has been eroded by the very efficiency of industrial fishing. Overfishing has reduced the catch below the sustainable yield in 27 of the northwest Atlantic's 30 major fishing areas.[66] This region has sustained Europe's fish needs for centuries, but clearly will be unable to do so much longer. Overfishing of Peru's economically vital anchovy population has caused the collapse of that industry and so far all efforts have failed to restore the fishery's productivity.[67]

It is estimated that yields from the majority of the world's 30-odd most important table-grade fishes may have exceeded maximum sustainable levels.[68] As world catches level off or decline, many nations, especially Japan and the Soviet Union, that depend heavily on fish in their diets, will continue to increase the efficiencies of their already awesome floating factories. The result will be an even more rapid decline in sustained yields. Once again, the counter-productive and tragic logic of industrialism asserts itself.

Climate

The final limit to the continuation of industrial civilization in its present form may be the earth's climate itself. The climate, a complex system composed of the interaction of water, sun, wind, atmosphere, and a host of other variables, is the framework within which all life activity on earth takes place. It is usually taken as a given and ignored, but as recent droughts and severe winters have shown, the carrying capacity of the earth is very much tied to the cycles of climate. Moreover, industrial activity has become so far-reaching that it now must be considered a causal agent in both long- and short-term climatic patterns.

Based on the quantitative analysis of climatic trends over the earth's vast geologic past, climatologists have concluded that the earth's climate is constantly changing in predictable and rhythmic cycles from warm to cold. Ice ages and tropical periods are the result. While the greatest extremes of climate occur on very long-time scales, the short-term cycles which occur within these longer-term trends can have a profound impact on human societies.[69] For example, a "Little Ice Age," which occurred between 1550 and 1850 in Europe and North America, saw the advance of glaciers further south than any time since the Ice Age which ended about 11,600 years ago.[70] The effects of this small scale climatic cycle included the abandonment of farms, the failure of crops, and some of the worst famines in European history. These were accompanied by such ill effects as urban food riots, reports of cannibalism, and massive levels of population decline.[71] (In 1693 one-third of Finland's total population died.)[72] While many inequities and irrationalities in income and food distribution, and other sociopolitical problems, such as an endless series of wars, exacerbated these weather-induced problems, it is important to observe that even relatively minor climatic shifts have been known to stress human societies beyond their capacity to respond effectively and rapidly.

In recent climatic history the Little Ice Age is matched only by the warm peak in the middle of the 20th century for both its abnormality and its impact on human society. (Warm periods favor agricultural production.) What we have come to define as normal is, in fact, the most abnormal period in the last 1,000 years.[73] The earth seems to have recently passed one of its major temperature peaks which occur every 90,000 years and seems to be headed for a cooling trend.[74] In the last two decades the northern hemisphere has experienced its steepest recorded temperature drop and, in February 1978, 74 percent of North America was covered by snow, the highest percentage recorded in 12 years of satellite monitoring.[75] This combination of cold and snow cover is capable of setting in motion a positive feedback process (a cyclical process of self-amplifying change) which can lead in a very short time to a major climatic change. As it gets colder and snowfall increases, the earth's albedo (the reflectance of solar energy back into space) increases. (The earth's albedo has increased 12 percent in the last decade alone, due to the expansion of the polar ice sheets.[76]) As more solar energy is reflected back into space, less sunlight reaches the earth, leading to still colder temperatures, more snow, the further expansion of polar ice, and so on. The result could be a very rapid escalation of the cooling trend that initially began the process. This "ice feedback" effect, as it is called, may have been responsible for the shift to near glacial conditions which developed in less than a century 90,000 years ago.[77] Whether or not such a dramatic shift occurs again, it is clear that the short-term trend in the northern hemisphere (for at least the next decade) is toward cooler weather.[78] If there is indeed a connection between cooler periods and the failure of monsoon rains as some climatologists suppose, the present cooling trend would not have to lead to a little ice age to lead to massive famine.[79]

The prediction of both short- and long-term climatic trends, however, is made more complex by the contradictory effects of industrialism. The average temperature of the earth's surface is determined by two factors: (1)

the earth's albedo, and; (2) the amount and type of gases and aerosols (particulate matter) in the atmosphere. Industrial activity has now become significant in influencing both these factors.[80] On the one hand, the paving of land and the construction of buildings, combined with the heat-generating activities associated with urban-industrialism have led to the urban-heat-island effect. Temperatures at the center of large cities are often several degrees warmer than surrounding areas and weather patterns downwind are dramatically affected. (Generally there is an increase in rainfall due to both heat and increased particulate matter in the atmosphere.[81]) As cities grow together to create regional megalopoli, major changes in regional weather patterns are certain to occur.

The argument that industrial activity is increasing the earth's temperature, and therefore countering the natural cooling trend that seems to be occurring, is also reinforced by an examination of the effects of burning fossil fuels. Not only does the combustion of fossil fuels directly raise temperatures but it also increases the concentration of atmospheric carbon dioxide, which has the effect of increasing temperature (the so-called greenhouse effect). Before the Industrial Revolution the concentration of carbon dioxide was about 290 parts per million (ppm). Now it is 320 ppm and based on current growth curves could be 400 ppm by the end of the century.[82] Such an increase would raise the global temperature 1° Celsius (an increase as large as any in the past 1000 years) and would result in major climatic changes that could, among other things, melt the polar ice caps, flood the earth's major costal cities, and convert some of the world's most productive agricultural lands into arid wastes.[83]

However, another effect of industrial activity is to introduce particulate matter into the atmosphere. This increases the earth's albedo, causing more solar radiation to be reflected back into space. This tends to reinforce the natural cooling cycle we seem to be in.

While climatologists have no idea what will result from this mix, there is a global consensus that a major climatic change is now occurring.[84] Proponents of modern energy-intensive agriculture believe that modern technology and the global food distribution system have forever buffered civilization from the effects of climate-induced declines in food production. Famines and food riots are thought to be a thing of the past. However, rather than local famines due to local crop failures, which has historically been the case, the present globally interconnected food system holds forth the prospect that bad weather in a few of the world's major granaries can rapidly drive the price of grain beyond the ability of the poor nations to pay, creating famines in food-importing nations which aren't themselves experiencing weather-related production shortages.[85] In short, the economies of the world are so interdependent that weather disruptions anywhere in the world can cause massive starvation elsewhere, especially in the poorer countries. Thus, rather than mitigating the effects of weather with modern agricultural technology, we have escalated the scale at which disaster can occur. We are more vulnerable to climate than ever before.

Since the last 50 years have been unusually warm and favorable to food production and since our agriculture has become so dependent on this narrow and passing climatic range, the implications of a climatic shift are staggering. Even the CIA, which recently completed the most intensive study of climate ever undertaken, expects major political and military repercussions.[86]

While the long-term direction of climatic change is still impossible to predict, one thing is certain; climate in the short-term will be turbulent and the current form of industrial agriculture is not capable of adjustment. Even without energy and resource depletion, this fact alone would argue for a major change in industrial food production methods and settlement patterns. Once again, we are intervening powerfully in comlex systems we don't fully understand and upon which we totally depend for our survival. The results may be unpredictable but they will not be trivial.

The ecology of scarcities

So far, we have considered the many limits to the continuation of industrial society in a linear, sequential fashion. But this reflects the structure of language, not the organization of nature. In the real world everything is connected to everything else and, as *The Limits to Growth* so clearly demonstrated, the "world problematique" is an ecology of interacting problems created by exponential growth in population, energy and resource use, and pollution.[87] While the interconnections are so complex that, in theory, no model can accurately predict their combined effects, one thing is certain: the combination of limits makes the prospects for industrialism even gloomier.

For example, we have already seen how the need for more coal to replace diminishing supplies of oil and natural gas creates a conflict between energy and environment. As we continue to strip mine the world's most productive farmland, our ability to feed a growing world population is greatly diminished. Thus, the short-term continuation of existing centralized energy conversion systems creates an even more serious long-term problem. There are many other examples in which the increased extraction and use of fossil fuels leads to the disruption of the ecosystems which sustain us.

The decline in fossil fuel availability also makes it impossible to avert shortages in key metal supplies. The combined effect of energy and mineral ore depletion is far more serious than either problem taken separately.

To avoid even more massive starvation and malnutrition in the future, the conventional wisdom is that we must expand the "Green Revolution." Yet that approach to agriculture relies on increasingly scarce and costly fossil fuels and mineral ores to produce and operate large-scale machinery, and requires the use of chemical fertilizers and pesticides and the intensive consumption of water for irrigation. Yet, as we have seen, all those resources are rapidly being depleted and are needed for energy production and other industrial activities. Moreover, such industrial agriculture destroys soil structure, depletes ground water, and leads to serious soil salinization problems, all of which undermine long-term productivity. There is also growing evidence that the massive application of nitrogen fertilizer, the key to the Green Revolution, may be destructive to the ozone layer, further threatening long-term survival.[88]

It is increasingly clear that the logic of industrialism creates a double bind of the kind popularized during the Vietnam War. In order to save the earth (and ourselves), we must destroy it (and ourselves). As we continue to disrupt the functioning of ecosystems and even the biosphere itself, we are beginning to learn that, in Gregory Bateson's paraphrase of St. Paul to the Galatians, "Ecology is not mocked." As Bateson also observed, the organism that "wins" in a fight against its environment ultimately loses. The basic unit of evolution and survival is the organism-plus-environment. Industrial civilization is destroying both.

Perhaps the most serious limit we confront is time. The risk is that we will fail to perceive and act on the dangers presented by exponential growth. Perhaps the best way to explain this is to use the French riddle made famous by the authors of *The Limits to Growth.* Imagine a farm pond which contains a single lily leaf. The number of leaves doubles each day so that you have one the first day, two the second, four the third, eight the fourth, and so on. If the pond is full on the thirtieth day, on what day is it half full? The answer, of course, is the twenty-ninth day.[89]

This parable illustrates the counter-intuitive nature of exponential growth. As the ever-expanding base continues to build, it reaches such a large number that each future doubling represents an unimaginable increase in the total. The sobering implication is that once the process has continued long enough to become perceived as a problem, there is very little time to act to prevent disaster. Remember, that only half the pond was covered on the twenty-ninth day.

The evidence presented so far strongly suggests that we have already reached the twenty-ninth day, and that industrial civilization will be forced to make a rapid transition from its current business-as-usual growth ethic to a steady-state society. As we shall see shortly, such a transition will require a shift in values, settlement patterns, and institutional forms more profound and rapid than any in recorded history. Moreover, the great cultural transformation must be effectively completed within the next 50 to 100 years. If it is not, we shall experience this turning point in history as the greatest period of violence, suffering, and destruction ever known. Even if we are able to begin reversing current trends today, we shall not be able to escape the disorientation, confusion, and suffering implied by such an unprecedented cultural change.

A scenario for change

Ecological scarcity is the complex system of limits that is forcing the end of industrial civilization. For the end to occur it is not necessary that we actually run out of nonrenewable resources. As a nonrenewable resource, whether a fossil fuel or a metal ore, approaches depletion, it becomes progressively more costly to produce. That, in turn, leads to a rapid and never-ending escalation in price, which has a progressive and pervasive inflationary impact, especially in the case of energy, crucial to every industrial activity and institution. Products that are particularly dependent on increasingly costly energy inputs (such as housing, clothing, and food —all basic necessities), escalate in price most rapidly. This means that the poor suffer first and most. As inflation ripples through the economy, however, everyone's standard of living beings to fall as unemployment increases, new industrial development declines, and capital shortages become chronic. This, of course, is a description of the current dilemma facing the industrial world.

Since inflation is ultimately driven by the escalating costs of recovering increasingly scarce nonrenewable resources, economic growth will continue to be dampened by a cycle of increasingly deep and serious global recessions, accompanied by the growing threat of economic depression and military conflict as every nation scrambles to assure its own supplies of crucial resources. This dangerous situation can be reversed only by a rapid, yet smooth transition to a metaindustrial society based on renewable energy sources. To this possibility and a scenario for its realization we must now turn.[90]

Changing definitions of reality

The first requirement for a cultural transformation of the magnitude required is a recognition that recurring problems will not be solved by the progressive application of remedies based on past conventional wisdom. The energy crisis will not be solved by digging deeper oil wells to increase supplies, nor will the economic crisis be solved by artificially holding the price of energy below its replacement costs. Better health care will not be provided by more hospitals and doctors. More schools will not lead to better education, and a higher standard of living will not be created by increasing the industrial output of goods. For radical change to occur it must become widely recognized that more of the same is not the answer. There must be a new understanding of nature, self, and society. People must come to accept that to maintain what is truly valuable, fundamental changes must be made in existing values, institutions, and practices.

"Business as usual" must be seen as leading toward disaster. Chronic inflation, escalating prices for basic goods and services, and growing doubt about the ability of existing leaders and institutions to perceive accurately and respond effectively to these and other problems, are creating the fertile decay necessary for the rebirth of a positive vision of a future based on a shift to renewable energy sources, and for the creation of a qualitatively different human society.[91]

Every institution and activity that now depends on excessively large machinery, constantly increasing flows of nonrenewable resources, and long distance transportation is already beginning to falter. As more and more people are thrown out of work and public services continue to decline, faith in our economy, institutions, and industrial world view will continue to erode. Many people are already disaffiliating psychically from our dominant institutions and values and are beginning to seek ways to meet more of their basic needs for food, energy, shelter, health, and education through personal, local, and direct action. This process of malaise, altered behavior, and reorientation of values, which began in the 1960s and has continued to grow, is creating a new complex of beliefs, attitudes, and values, or a social paradigm that is firmly rooted in an evolutionary and ecological ethic.

Table 1 summarizes some of the characteristics of this emerging world view and compares them to the industrial-era paradigm it is replacing. While the metaindustrial paradigm is only shared at present by a relatively small number of philosophers, social critics, and political and technological activists, it is clear that popular belief in the industrial paradigm is rapidly eroding. As the full impact of ecological scarcity makes itself felt in the multiple failures and dislocations of the global industrial system, increasing numbers of people will begin to shift toward a more or less consciously articulated constellation of beliefs similar to the metaindustrial vision of reality. When, and only when this begins to happen, will we begin to develop the broad consensus necessary for the major restructuring of our political economy. Fortunately, since the metaindustrial alternative is much closer to the original American ideal of a Jeffersonian democracy in a garden landscape, the fundamental shift in world view will not be perceived as a loss of what is, but rather as a recovery of what could have been.[92] Future generations will, no doubt, marvel at the fact that an ideology as destructive, violent, and authoritarian as the industrial paradigm could ever have been held by such large numbers of people.

The emerging alternative

The shift in world view appropriate to a nonviolent, frugal, and egalitarian society based on the renewable energy sources of sun, wind, moving water, and biomass is creating and being created by changes in technology, institutions, and the pattern and shape of human settlements. It became possible for the majority to believe in the industrial era paradigm only after a world shaped in its image had made it believable. Theory, belief, and action are intertwined through an interactive, mutually causal

(Continued on page 27)

Table 1. *Changing Definitions of Reality*

	INDUSTRIAL PARADIGM	METAINDUSTRIAL PARADIGM
Progress and History	The belief in the inevitable, linear flow of time from a primitive, archaic, and savage past toward an advanced, modern, and civilized future. Newer is, therefore, better. Since the past is seen as inferior to the present, and the present inferior to the future (in material terms), a suggestion that we return to any technology or practice of the past is seen as a regression and a rejection of the ideology of progress. Though other civilizations may have experienced a cyclic rise and fall, the modern world is seen as proof that our scientifically based, technologically advanced civilization will remain forever young. But this belief requires that we sacrifice in the present to achieve even greater happiness in the future.	While some aspects of life have shown improvements, it is not axiomatic that history is a one-way, positive flow from the worse to the better. It is believed that history is a spiral, a progressive movement of recurring cycles of emergence and expression, growth and decay, rather than a linear model of time. You can't return to the past, since your world and images of reality have continually shaped and been shaped by the unfolding of events in time, but there are both necessary and inevitable organic and circular rhythms to the pulse of the individual life as well as the collective biography we call history. To deny and to resist this is to be out of step with time, and the consequences can only be negative. To sacrifice human dignity, freedom, and joy in the present as a means toward some future day of release is, at best, a suspect proposal.
Technology and Industrialization	It is believed that machines are value-free (only their use determines if they are good or bad) and that industrialization is both necessary and inevitable (it is the vehicle of progress), as well as good. If a technology or institution exists it is because it is more efficient than what it replaced, since technology is seen to evolve according to the natural "laws" of evolution such as "survival of the fittest." Large-scale, centralized organizations and machinery, and the subdivision of labor into increasingly specialized roles is the symbol, cause, and outcome of the evolution of society. While we might regret what has been lost, we must accept the verdict of evolution and history. What is, is what is best for humanity in the long run.	Technology is viewed as a language of social action. Built into the structure of various tools and techniques are certain values and assumptions that determine the personal, social, and political outcomes of their use. As the projection of human consciousness onto nature, technology can be either destructive and parasitic or constructive and symbiotic. We can unilaterally impose our will on the landscape or we can enter into a dialogue with climate, slope, and soil to co-create a humanized world. Human beliefs and values shape the nature of the tools and techniques used. The current technologies are neither necessary nor inevitable since they were consciously created to serve the socioeconomic and political needs of the power-elite of a particular form of culture. If we can alter how we think we can alter our technologies. Urban-industrial society is viewed as a failed experiment, an evolutionary cul-de-sac.
Science and Knowledge	Science, as a rational, logical, experimental system of inquiry is the *only* real way of knowing and experiencing the world. All other forms of knowing, such as myth, dream, intuition, and poetry are merely	Science, as one among many modes of inquiry and ways of knowing, is viewed as potentially useful and good. But the view that "objective consciousness" and personal detachment are the only legitimate forms of

Table 1. *Continued: Changing Definitions of Reality*

INDUSTRIAL PARADIGM	METAINDUSTRIAL PARADIGM	
subjective. The ideal of all relationships with other people or the natural environment is a cool, detached, objective observation, an *I-It* relationship. All other expressions of relatedness represent a potentially regressive return to superstition, magic, or worse. Maturity demands objectivity and emotional control.	knowledge is rejected as being hyper-rational and destructive. There are many realities and each has its appropriate way of knowing, including ways that require a "participative consciousness" and active concern for the subject. The goal is to establish an *I-Thou* relationship with all sentient beings and things. *I-It* relationships, like violence in general, should be undertaken with caution and regret.	**Science and Knowledge (continued)**
Growing out of the views on science, it is believed that technically trained, rational, scientific planners and other certified experts, who know more about every aspect of the world than the common man, can and should hold positions of authority and power, and should direct the movement of society (planning *for* people). To introduce democratic principles into the management and design of a technological society is inappropriate and risks the breakdown of society. Ideology and politics should be entirely removed from the world of science and technology.	Given the doubts about the limits of science and scientism and given the respect held for all persons, it is believed that the role of scientists, professional planners, and experts of all kinds should be carefully constrained. To usurp the rule of the people in the name of expertise is to replace democracy with social science. Not only is it wrong but it won't work. Nonexperts are more knowledgeable, as "clients," about the nature of the problems and the effects of the solutions on their lives. To deny this kind of knowledge is to fail to address the problem. The goal should be planning and design by a dialogic, mutually beneficial process (planning with people). People can and should assume responsibility for their own lives.	**Expertise and Power**
It is believed that the domination of nature is both necessary and desirable, since nature is just so much undeveloped raw "stuff" to be used for human ends. Human beings are the end and purpose of evolution, and only people, as self-conscious beings, can be considered fully alive. A moral concern for other sentient beings (rock, soil, plants, and animals) is seen as an atavism from pre-scientific ages. (Nature is a commodity to be used.)	The human domination of nature is seen as an epistemologically false, morally bankrupt concept. The earth and the cosmos are not merely made of dead matter drifting through the voids of timeless space. They are whole and integrated, complex and alive. We belong to and participate in the life of this being, earth, and in the ordered life and rhythm of the universe. (Nature is a community to which we belong.)	**Nature**
In any conflict between the individual and the group, the interests of the group *must* take priority over the individual (the person exists for the company, not the company for the person). Society is like a machine. In order for it to run smoothly, all friction in its parts (individuals) must be eliminated. The group must shape the individual to fit	The primary purpose of any social organization, formal or informal, is to promote the growth and psychic development of the person. Society is viewed not as a machine, but as a complex web of emotionally charged, intimate, and diverse patterns of relationships rooted in shared space and belief. The nature of any group does and	**The Individual versus the Group**

Table 1. *Continued: Changing Definitions of Reality*

	INDUSTRIAL PARADIGM	METAINDUSTRIAL PARADIGM
The Individual versus the Group (continued)	its needs. It is believed that society is inevitably and necessarily repressive of the natural instincts and conditioned tendencies of the individual. Whether through overt power or behavioral engineering (it depends on your views of human nature), society must remake the person in its own image.	should grow out of the interactions and character of its members. Individual persons must participate in the process of shaping society to the needs of the self (not the ego). Society is an organic whole.
Human Nature (the Self)	Since the ideologies represented by industrialism include both capitalism and socialism, as well as liberalism and conservatism, human nature is variously defined as basically good or bad, improvable or not. What links this spectrum is the belief that production and consumption and the improvement of the material conditions of life are the goals of both the individual and the society. You are what you consume, and the more you possess the more you are a success. Happiness, the goal of human existence, is a function of the acquisition of people, goods, and power. The society that succeeds in maximizing these needs of human nature is the best society.	While the ideologies represented by metaindustrialism vary considerably, the basic assumption is that, properly nourished in a healthy cultural milieu, most people will behave cooperatively rather than competitively and will transcend their small and limited egos. To realize this potential, the culture must provide both techniques and opportunities for psychic development. Since the goal of human existence is self-transformation, material goods must be kept to a minimum to avoid breeding attachment. You are what your being is.
The Meaning of Work	The purpose of work is twofold: 1) for the organization it is to maximize profit and productivity (for the state or the shareholders, depending on ideology and socioeconomic form); 2) for the individual it is to make the maximum money for the least effort, or if you are a "professional" to make the most money while providing the greatest service to humanity, advancing your career, and so on. Of course we all work to create more leisure time for which we then spend our money *having fun*. The ultimate end of work is to escape from work into a world of impulse release and fantasy.	The purpose of work is to maximize the welfare of the worker, the productive organization, and the broader community. In producing goods and services the goal should be to serve others while minimizing harm to naturally occurring ecosystems. In assuming responsibility for his or her actions, the worker learns to temper selfish impulses and in so doing promotes his or her own good. The reward for work is not leisure, it is play. Leisure is empty time and space that requires work to fill up. Play is a spontaneous enjoyment of creation that itself is the outcome of right livelihood.
Size, Centralization, and Growth	Big is better. Large, centralized, formal organizations are natural outcomes of an evolutionary process. They are more efficient because of the economies of scale and they are more effective because they exercise more power and control over their internal and external environments. Growth in the	Small is not only beautiful, it is usually better. Although large scale, centralized organizations can be appropriate to some tasks (for example, administering and managing a public utility), large organizations with widespread geographical and political power should be avoided. They are difficult

Table 1. *Continued: Changing Definitions of Reality*

INDUSTRIAL PARADIGM	METAINDUSTRIAL PARADIGM	
size of enterprises (whether economic, governmental, or social), like economic growth in general, is necessary and good. You must grow or collapse. "What's good for G.M. is good for the country," and so on. Small, informal groups, such as clans, neighborhoods, and extended families are archaic, inefficient, and inhibitive of the growth of progressive, modern, rational, formal institutions. While such primary groups may continue to exist due to the inertia of custom and habit, in the future they will necessarily decrease in extent and importance. Many of our current social problems and political abuses can be traced to the persistence of ties to blood and soil.	to control, often impersonal, and frequently insensitive (cybernetically speaking) to feedback from the environments they affect. Since it is well known that there is an appropriate economy of scale for every technology, there is an appropriate size for every enterprise. (Bigger is not necessarily better.) And since many goals besides task efficiency must be achieved by human groups, what's good for profit in the production of automobiles is not necessarily good for the ecology or the country. Small, informal, face-to-face groups are and have always been the substance and foundation of effective and healthy collectivities. Communal organizations, such as families, clans, and neighborhoods should be strengthened, and informal groups within large enterprises should be encouraged.	**Size, Centralization, and Growth (continued)**
Like local societies and other remnants of the past, the uniqueness, character, history, and texture of particular places is more often than not a hindrance to progress. The best kind of space is a flat, empty universal plane that can accept people, buildings, highways, and other "improvements" with minimum alteration. Universal, modern architecture with a uniform year-round microclimate is both a symbol and means toward greater wealth and human betterment. Reduced costs and the promotion of industrialization result from the standardization of building parts and local sites.	The homogenization of place and culture have proceeded hand in hand with industrialization. Like any healthy ecology, an alive, human ecology should aim at maximizing the diversity of landscapes and regions. Architecture and planning should enhance the particular and unique character of localities, creating a symbiosis of nature and culture, earthscape and mindscape. The outcome would be a humanized nature that would represent an acceleration of evolution.	**The Importance of Place**

(Continued from page 23)

process: one cannot be changed without changing the others. Therefore, the metaindustrial image of the future, which is growing out of the failure of the industrial-era world and world view, must become increasingly visible as a concrete, practical, and desirable alternative to business-as-usual. However, before this can happen on a large scale people must believe that the transition to a renewable-energy-based society is possible. It is to this question that we must now turn.

Reducing energy demand

The most pressing problems of ecological scarcity—air and water pollution; land degradation from mining, urban sprawl, and industrial agriculture; and the systematic destruction of global ecosystems through excessive and inefficient production—would all be reduced if we could use less energy more efficiently. Therefore, our ability to create an equitable and sustainable society is directly tied to our ability to do more with less. The key to creating a high-level civilization based on diffuse solar energy rather than concentrated fossil fuels is, similarly, a function of our ability to reduce total energy demand. It is clear that in a solar economy, we cannot practically or economically maintain the levels of consumption or patterns of settlement that have been created and are now maintained by enormous flows of concentrated energy.

If we are to make a transition to a renewable-energy-based society, then, the first question is how much energy do we need, of what kind, and for what ends? The question of energy demand is typically dealt with by a simple process of extrapolation of the recent past into the distant future. However, we have seen that this approach leads to a scenario of resource depletion and economic collapse. The question of energy demand must be based on an entirely different approach, one that begins by asking how much energy of what kind would be needed for what tasks, *if* society were organized to do more with less. With that shift in perspective, the scenario of decline and collapse becomes instead one of opportunity and hope.

Finally, we are recognizing that energy conservation is America's most immediate, cost-effective, and environmentally sound energy source. Rather than recommending the usual expansion of energy supplies from conventional sources (oil, gas, coal, oil shale, and nuclear), a recently completed five-year study by the Harvard Business School concluded that energy conservation is our best alternative for meeting expected shortages and overcoming the highly problematic economic and diplomatic dilemmas of continued reliance on imported oil.

> The United States can use 30 or 40 percent less energy than it does, with virtually no penalty for the way Americans live—save that billions of dollars will be spared, save that the environment will be less polluted, the dollar under less pressure, save that the growing and alarming dependence on O.P.E.C. oil will be reduced, and Western society will be less likely to suffer internal and international tension. These are benefits Americans should be only too happy to accept.[93]

It is important to note that this level of savings could be achieved with little more than good housekeeping and minimal substitutions of more efficient energy conversion systems (for example, increasing refrigerator efficiency, installing heat pumps, industrial cogeneration, and so on). However, through a vigorous program of energy conservation, combined with a substantial but easily realizable reorganization of industry, agriculture, transportation, and settlement patterns, it has been estimated that in the year 2050 we could be operating a full-employment economy with a population of 277 million on as little as 36 percent of the 1975 U.S. level of per capita energy consumption.[94] Moreover, such a radically reduced energy demand could then be easily met by a mosaic of renewable energy sources which are now, or soon will be, economically viable. In fact, our ability to create a sustainable society based on ecological principles and driven by renewable (income) energy sources depends on our success in achieving equal or lower levels of energy demand.

The energy analysis for such a low-energy scenario has been documented in some detail by John S. Steinhart et al.[95] However, since the basic assumptions on which it is based so closely parallel the image of the future outlined in this book, and since any image of the future must be believable before it can energize action toward its realization, it is worthwhile to summarize the kinds of changes that would be required to make a low-energy scenario a reality. (See Table 2 and following outline.)

Settlement Patterns and Changing Communities (Underlying basis for all other energy savings, especially transportation):

- Simultaneous explosion and implosion of population as automobile is abandoned as primary means of transportation, resulting in more compact, distinct urban areas of reduced size (generally 200,000 or fewer residents)
- 30 percent of the U.S. population would live in cities of 2,500 to 25,000 (compared to 21 percent in 1970); 29 percent would live in cities of 25,000 to 100,000 (compared to 17 percent in 1970); 7 percent would live in cities over 100,000 (compared to 28 percent in 1970); 34 percent would live in rural areas of under 25,000 (compared to 34 percent in 1970)
- Settlements designed for maximum accessibility, not maximum mobility, with full pedestrian and bicycle access to all districts and to surrounding food-producing lands
- Resurgence of local neighborhood stores as regional shopping centers decline
- Abandonment of nonviable populated areas (with community gardens and truck farms in their place) and construction of both rural settlements and viable communities in small cities
- Rebuilding of existing regional cities and towns
- National Urban Homestead Act to rebuild cities (especially for the poor) and National Homestead Lease Act to build new settlements

Residential (65-percent reduction):

- Change in the allocation of heat, both spatially and temperally (zoned control, day and night thermostat setbacks)
- Retrofitting of old buildings and careful design of new buildings for energy conservation (including use of solar energy for space and water heating)
- Increased efficiency of appliances
- Energy-efficient building codes on the national, state, and local levels

A Low-Energy Scenario for the United States in 2050

An outline of changes required to achieve a 64-percent reduction of 1975 U.S. per capita energy use. Derived from John S. Steinhart et al., *Pathway to Energy Sufficiency: The 2050 Study* (San Francisco: Friends of the Earth, 1979)

- National and state efficiency standards and labeling laws for energy-using equipment

Food and Agriculture (Energy savings distributed throughout industrial, residential, commercial, and transportation sectors):

- Beef consumption reduced by 50 percent and a shift to pasture and range fed cattle
- Swine diet of poor quality grain and refuse
- Increased production of grain and beans for human consumption on land formerly used for livestock feed (much of this would be exported)
- Increase in fish, chicken, egg, soybean, and dairy product consumption
- 90 percent of fruits and vegetables grown locally by gardening cooperatives, individuals, and local farmers
- Increased grain export
- Dietary shifts toward greater consumption of whole grains, dried beans, potatoes, and vegetables
- Suburban lawns replanted as gardens and orchards, resembling the intensely farmed and carefully tended gardens of England and China

Commercial (70-percent reduction):

- Change in the allocation of heat (and cooling) both spatially and temperally
- Retrofitting of old buildings and careful design of new buildings for energy conservation (including use of solar energy for space and water heating)
- Installation of waste heat recovery systems
- Use of natural ventilation in smaller stores and other moderately sized commercial buildings
- Use of natural light and reduced lighting standards and more careful display of goods (for example, no open freezers)
- Reduced use of lighting for advertising
- Phaseout of fast-food services and "junk" commerce
- Reduction in packaging through a shift to standard sizes and design for reuse and/or recycling
- Virtual elimination of disposable paper and plastic containers as commodities are shipped, stored, and merchandised in bulk, and nonessential junk foods, overprocessed foods, and excessive toiletries and cosmetics are virtually eliminated (A National Container Act would help reduce waste and energy used for packaging.)
- Reduction of local trucking for garbage and waste disposal (one-eighth of all current local trucking)

Transportation (75-percent reduction):

- Shorter car trips through redesigned settlements and alternative modes of transportation (average per capita automobile mileage per year reduced from 8,000 to 3,000 miles)

- Heavy emphasis on rapid intercity rail systems, especially for trips under 500 miles, to greatly reduce air travel
- Rebuilding and expansion of existing rail network
- Energy-efficient speed limits enforced, with lighter vehicles and an average of 25 mpg in town (life use of vehicles 20 years or 200,000 miles)
- 25 percent of energy used for personal travel by electric automobile, rail, and bus
- 50 percent of freight transport (electric trains and trucks) electrified
- Reduced ton-miles for freight through decentralization and localization of food production and processing (At present one-half of all trucks haul food and agricultural products.)
- Reduced ton-miles through decentralized manufacture and shifts in industrial sector
- Citywide delivery systems related to increased use of railroads and decline of centralized, regional shopping centers
- 90 percent of all air freight eliminated and 75 percent of all truck freight shifted to rail carriage

Industry (52-percent reduction):

- Thirty-percent decline in production in energy-intensive industries (for example, reduced automobile production due to decreased auto ownership and greater auto durability)
- 50 percent reduction in food and related industries and primary metals industries
- Conservation in space heat and cooling and production processes through housekeeping measures and careful matching of energy quality to task requirements (for example, the introduction of small-scale multi-purpose power plants, and cogeneration systems). (A Depletable Fuels Tax Act would make such changes economically attractive.)

Employment, Social Welfare, and Leisure Time (Full employment and social justice as possibility of low-energy society):

- Average workweek in 1990 at 30 hours to increase total employment and allow more free time for offsetting decreased cash income with potentially profitable leisure time (assisted by a Full Employment Act for federal and state jobs)
- Substantial interregional and interindustrial shifts of labor, with transfer of population and industry from North and Northeast to South and Southwest to continue (Appropriate Skills Retraining Act to ease transition)
- Increase in construction job opportunities (especially related to alternate energy systems) as older cities are renovated and rehabilitated, increasing labor demand for persons still living there
- Significant increase in labor demand as railroads and mass transit systems are rebuilt and expanded
- Slack in declining automotive industries taken up by manufacture and installation of single-unit and centralized solar and wind systems

A Low-Energy Scenario for the United States in 2050 Continued

- Labor demand for recycling industries significantly increased
- A turn in labor to agriculture, horticulture, and silviculture in new, less physically demanding roles, as energy becomes more and more costly
- Guaranteed Annual Income to ease transition to new employment and settlement patterns of a low-energy society

International Considerations

- Reduction of balance of payments problem and strengthening of dollar
- End of commercial nuclear power program, making the United States the leader in creating a non-nuclear world order
- Emergence of the United States as the technological leader in solar and wind technologies and a partner in development of energy and economic self-reliance among poor nations (rather than a major arms supplier of the world)
- Reduction in gap between haves and have nots, thereby reducing chance of global conflict

New patterns of human settlements

The key to achieving a radically reduced energy demand in the United States by the year 2050 is the reorganization of the existing pattern of human settlements. Over the last 200 years industrial civilization has literally reshaped the surface of the earth. Modern America is a creation of cheap, concentrated fossil fuels. But the pattern of megalopolitan sprawl that has resulted is completely maladapted for our future survival. Without massive, constantly increasing flows of conventional fossil fuels, the energy-addicted, hyperactive metabolism of our existing urban–industrial habitat would be logistically impossible to maintain. Since conventional fossil fuels will soon be depleted, we must begin now to plan and implement major changes in the spatial distribution of basic life-support systems.

Rather than engaging in a futile attempt to maintain the existing structure of our human habitat with diffuse renewable energy sources, the only reasonable strategy is to destructure megalopolis into a multinucleated pattern of energy-efficient, compact, and humanly scaled cities, towns, and neighborhoods. Rather than trying to overcome the distances between home, work, commerce, and school that have been created by fossil-fuel-based automobile transport with similar vehicles operated on electricity or liquid fuels from organic conversion processes, megalopolis should be restructured so that irrational separations of life functions no longer exist. This implies the decentralization of center-city employment concentrations, the redistribution of commercial and residential areas in a pattern of mixed-use land development, and the diversification of transportation options with a heavy emphasis on electrified mass transit (for

Table 2 *Overview of low energy scenario final energy use 1975–2050*

	1975 Primary* Energy Per Capita 10¹⁰ Joules	2050 Primary** Energy Per Capita 10¹⁰ Joules	Primary Energy Savings Per Capita 10¹⁰ Joules	1975 Total Primary Energy 10¹⁸ Joules	2050 Total Primary Energy 10¹⁸ Joules
Residential	6.9	2.4	4.5	14.6	6.7
Commercial	5.9	1.8	4.1	12.6	4.9
Transportation	9.2	2.3	6.9	19.6	6.5
Personal	(6.0)	(1.4)	(4.6)	(12.7)	(3.8)
Freight	(3.2)	(1.0)	(2.3)	(6.9)	(2.7)
Industrial***	13.0	6.2	6.8	27.6	17
Total	35.0	12	22	74.4	35

2050 primary energy per capita is 36% of 1975 primary energy per capita.

2050 total primary energy is 47% of 1975 total primary energy.

Source: 1975 total primary energy from News Release March 14, 1977, "Annual U.S. Energy Use Up in 1976," Office of Assistant Director—Fuels, Bureau of Mines, U.S. Department of the Interior.

Notes: The division of energy into residential and commercial from Bureau of Mines figures follows Amory B. Lovins. "Scale, Centralization and Electrification in Energy Systems," a paper presented at Oak Ridge National Laboratories, October 1976. Totals may not add due to rounding.

  * 213 × 10⁶ population.

  ** 277 × 10⁶ population.

  *** Miscellaneous and unaccounted for in Bureau of Mines data included in industrial.

Reprinted, by permission, from John S. Steinhart et al., *Pathway to Energy Sufficiency: The 2050 Study* (San Francisco: Friends of the Earth, 1979), p. 15.

example, busses, trains, and trolleys) and personally powered movement systems (for example, walking and riding bicycles). Such a shift in the scale, texture, and organization of urban areas would bring about the re-emergence of neighborhood stores and cottage industries as well as such energy-efficient amenities as home delivery of goods.

Unlike megalopolis, which is the physical, social, and spiritual outcome of a single-minded search for profit based on maximum mobility, the urban community of the future would be based on the principle of maximum accessibility with minimum energy and effort.[96] Besides being inherently energy-efficient, such a compact pedestrian-intensive human habitat would tend to be richer in opportunities for the recovery of a sense of community based on shared passage in a common space. It would also encourage a richer interpersonal, visual, and environmental experience within smaller geographic areas than is now possible in urban, suburban, and exurban ghettoes. (Street farming and cafe life might come to replace endless hours of solitary commuting and hurried meals at the fast-food drive-in.) In short, urban decentralization would not only decrease energy demand for transport, but it would also transform the neighborhood and

Figure 1.
Energy Supply:
1980–2050

Reprinted, by permission,
from John S. Steinhart
et al., *Pathway to Energy
Sufficiency: The 2050 Study*
(San Francisco: Friends of
the Earth, 1979), p. 55.

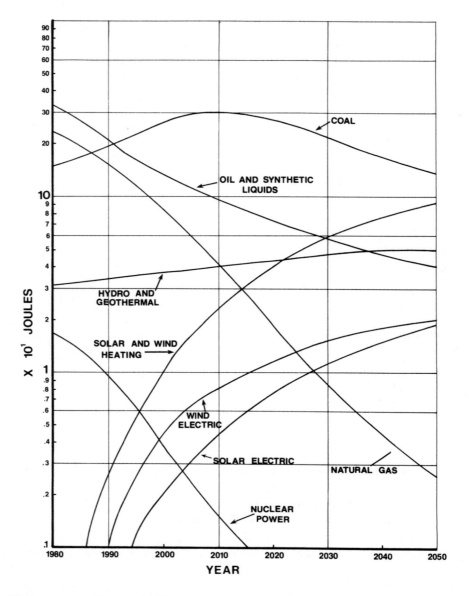

We have separated low- and high-temperature energy supplies to further illustrate the necessity of thermodynamically matching supply and demand.

community into a more balanced, whole, and satisfying miniworld capable of being powered by integrated community solar energy systems.

The restructuring of megalopolis into a regional network of smaller-scaled urban communities cannot, of course, be accomplished without some redistribution of population. Thus, this scenario not ony implies the implosion of population within megalopolis as the automobile is abandoned as the primary means of transport, but it also means that existing

	1975	1980	1990	2000	2010	2020	2030	2040	2050
Solar electric, including photovoltaic	—	—	—	.20	.43	.80	1.1	1.5	1.9
Wind electric	—	—	.10	.44	.80	1.1	1.5	1.8	2.0
Hydro and geothermal	3.3	3.4	3.5	3.8	4.1	4.4	4.7	4.9	5.0
Solar and wind heating	—	—	.25	1.0	2.3	4.0	6.0	7.6	9.0
Coal	14.1	15	19	26	27	25	21	17	13
Oil—imported*	12.9	12	7.0	2.0	—	—	—	—	—
domestic	21.4	21	14	11	9.5	7.0	5.5	3.4	2.0
Synthetic liquids**	—	—	—	.10	.12	.20	.50	1.2	2.0
Natural gas	21.1	21	15	8.3	4.0	1.8	.80	.44	.25
Nuclear electric generation***	1.6	1.6	.95	.37	.15	—	—	—	—
Total	74.4	74	60	53	48	44	41	38	35

Table 3
Overview of projected energy supply, 1975–2050 (10^{18} joules)

Note: Figures may not add up because of rounding. For estimated future amounts only two significant figures are presented.

  * No oil for U.S. imports available approximately 10 years after expected world peak production.
 ** Synthetic liquids from coal, oil shale, bioconversion, and others will increasingly be used for transportation, combined with domestic oil.
*** Last nuclear power plant construction in 1985; approximate lifetime 30 years.
Reprinted, by permission, from John S. Steinhart et al., *Pathway to Energy Sufficiency: The 2050 Study* (San Francisco: Friends of the Earth, 1977) p. 54.

regional cities, small towns, and rural communities would experience a growth in population as nonviable areas of megalopolis are abandoned. Thus, an urban policy for a renewable-energy-based society is simultaneously a program of urban decentralization and rural repopulation. While in some cases this would call for rural new towns,[97] most shifts in population distribution would be absorbed in incrementally restructured existing communities.

All those changes would have to occur within a planning framework aimed at achieving more balanced and integrated regional economies, and they would have to be constrained by the need to match energy and food demand with bioregionally based renewable energy supply and food production potentials.[98] The overall objective of such changes in settlement patterns would be to create a more balanced population distribution within the limits established by the needs of the land and the criteria of sustainability. The pattern of development would tend to enhance the natural biological potential of the earth while meeting the legitimate (and prudent) requirements of an information-intensive, frugal, and advanced civilization. The overall effect would be the evolution of an historically novel expression of human culture as a symbiont rather than a parasite of naturally occurring systems.

Renewable energy systems and appropriate technology

Through such a coordinated program of urban decentralization, rural repopulation, and bioregional develoment it would become logistically possible to meet our greatly reduced energy demand with renewable energy sources and a technology appropriate for a democratic society. Table 3, the following outline, and Figure 1 summarize the supply scenario as projected to 2050 by Steinhart et al. Since the world's major reserves of fossil fuels will soon be exhausted and since every previous shift to a new energy base has been subsidized by the fuel being replaced, a process which has typically taken 20 to 50 years, the development of a renewable-energy-based technology is the central and most urgent task of our generation.

Energy Supply Scenario, 1975–2050

An outline of changes required to meet greatly reduced energy needs from conventional domestic and renewable energy sources. Derived from Steinhart et al; *Pathway to Energy Sufficiency: The 2050 Study* (San Francisco; Friends of the Earth, 1979)

- By the mid–1980s, rising costs and public concern over safety halt nuclear plant construction (including breeders).

- A diverse and innovative electric generation system emerges to replace existing systems, with solar (photovoltaic), wind, hydro, and geothermal electric generators meeting most of the electricity demand. (As cryogenic storage and electrolysis become less expensive, solar may assume a base-load function.)

- Marginal-cost pricing and other load management techniques carefully fit demand curve to supply.

- Trend toward small (300 megawatts or less), multipurpose coal plants and the development of coal-solar and coal-wind hybrid plants.

- Industrial cogeneration plants provide industrial process heat and electricity, with surplus sold as district heat and electricity to residential and commercial sectors.

- Solar heating for space and water in widespread use by 2050 and supplying, together with wind, most low temperature energy needs (including the 16 percent of total U.S. energy use for industrial process heat that is below 350°F).

- Widespread use of wind-thermal and wind-electric systems and combinations of these (both centralized and decentralized applications).

- Total coal consumption slightly lower than total industrial energy consumption by the year 2050.

- In one of the few technological breakthroughs projected, photovoltaic cells are expected to cost $1,000 (in 1976 dollars) per installed kilowatt of capacity by 1990. (This is a little less than the current cost for nuclear electric plants. Capital costs per installed kilowatt capacity of wind machines and conventional electric generators are presently of the same order of magnitude.)

- Several changes would facilitate this shift to a renewable-energy-based society, including: (1) a nuclear moratorium, an end to nuclear subsidies, and an end to the federal commercial breeder program; (2) improved techniques and mass production to reduce cost of solar and wind energy systems (both thermal and electric); (3) increase in number and variety of demonstration projects to help provide necessary production demand; (4) a tax and loan-guarantee incentive program for the use of renewable resources (at both state and federal levels) to encourage shift to new energy systems and production processes; (5) a stringent national strip-mining act that guarantees restoration of the landscape; (6) rising costs of depletable fuels, plus a progressive depletable-fuels tax, to help conservation efforts and make renewable-energy-based alternatives economically viable.

Of necessity, a technology based on the income energy of the sun would be ecological in nature. Rather than being centralized to take advantage of the presumed economies of scale characteristic of concentrated energy sources, such a system would be decentralized to tap the varied forms and sources of energy in specific biogeographic areas. New England, for example, might rely on a mix of wood, hydropower, and solar energy. The Great Plains would more heavily utilize wind power and solar energy. Coastal areas might emphasize ocean currents, thermal gradients, wind, and biomass (for example, kelp plantations). Waste products in all regions would tend to be used as energy and/or nutrient sources. The conversion of diverse and region-specific energy flows is the basic strategy of nature, and a human ecology based on such technologies would tend to be more varied and less disruptive of ecosystems.

But reliance on renewable energy does not, in itself, guarantee an appropriate technology or desirable society. Rather than shaping human values and institutions as side effects of technology, as is presently the case, a steady-state human ecology implies the need for the social and political control of technology based on human values. A technology appropriate for the future, therefore, would (1) make use of locally available energy and natural resources and locally available labor skills to satisfy community energy needs; (2) increase community economic and energy self-reliance; (3) minimize the disruption of ecosystems; and (4) conserve nonrenewable resources. It would also tend to be low-cost, small-scale, durable, and simple to install, operate, and maintain.

Physicist Amory Lovins has persuasively argued that we could make a transition from our inherently brittle and fated "hard" energy path toward a "soft" path. It would require a serious commitment to energy conservation, the development of renewable energy sources matched in scale and energy quality to end-use needs, and the selective use of transitional fossil fuel technologies.[99]

The strategy of matching energy quality to end-use needs is central to the soft path approach. Because our present system of energy supply and distribution fails to take this principle into account, only about 15 percent of the total energy used in the United States is actually applied to the tasks for which it is consumed.[100] For example, a typical central power station converts three units of fuel into only one unit of electricity. The rest of the energy is dissipated into the environment as "waste" heat, where it becomes a serious source of pollution. Moreover, since much of the electricity produced is applied to tasks for which it is inappropriate (for example, space heating), the total mismatch between energy quality and task requirements is even greater. As Lovins points out, "Where we want only to create temperature differences of tens of degrees, we should meet the need with sources whose potential is tens of hundreds of degrees, not with a flame temperature of thousands or a nuclear reaction temperature equivalent to trillions—like cutting butter with a chainsaw."[101]

A decentralized, carefully planned energy supply system, based on the principle of maximizing on-site production and consumption wherever possible, would eliminate such absurd energy waste and allow more accurate matching of supply capacity to demand. (Large centralized supply systems increase supply to meet projected demand in large jumps, whereas demand increases in small increments and frequently varies considerably from long-term projections.)

To make the transition from our current fossil-fuel-based, centralized energy supply system to a renewable-energy-based, diverse, and geographically dispersed system, the soft path proposes the introduction of transitional technologies such as coal combustion in fluidized beds and the cogeneration of electricity and space heating and cooling from industrial process heat. Not only is such technology more efficient thermodynamically, but the energy supply potential is substantial. It has been estimated "that with the present requirements for process steam enough electricity could be produced as a by-product not only to meet the electricity needs of industry, [about one third of U.S. electricity use] but to have a surplus to sell."[102]

If the transitional systems were built at a suitable scale, renewable energy technologies could be substituted over time. For example, a neighborhood-scale district heating system that uses heat from fluidized bed combustion could easily be run by neighborhood-scale solar collectors, wind electric plants, or geothermal wells, as appropriate and when economically feasible.

Ecologist and solar energy advocate Barry Commoner has proposed similar scenarios in which small gas-fired cogenerators would be used as part of an urban rebuilding program. Such total energy systems, which would be capable of efficiently supplying a neighborhood with electricity, space heating and cooling, and hot water, would offer immediate energy cost savings. Later, as "solar methane" from urban and agricultural wastes, and hydrogen and methane from solar and wind electric plants replaced natural gas in the pipelines, the entire system could operate on renewable energy supplies, thereby permanently eliminating escalating fuels costs and assuring the urban poor of basic necessities in a future solar economy.[103]

But the important point is that a commitment to such flexible, integrated, and thermodynamically efficient transitional technologies implies a long-term commitment to and planning for a reorganized habitat based on renewable energy sources.

Unless we make such a commitment now we shall forever lose the energy subsidy necessary to do so. As Lovins has pointed out, the only barriers to change are the few powerful institutions that now benefit from our centralized, environmentally destructive energy system and a host of contradictory and outdated building codes, inappropriate tax and fee structures, and other institutional barriers. A shift toward a soft energy path is uniquely compatible with our basic democratic and humanitarian values:

> Instead of trading off one constituency against another—unemployment versus inflation, economic growth versus environmental quality, inconvenience versus vulnerability—a soft path offers advantages for every constituency. . . . [it] simultaneously offers jobs for the unemployed, capital for business people, environmental protection for conservationists, enhanced national security for the military, opportunities for small business to innovate and for big business to recycle itself, exciting technologies for the secular, a rebirth of spiritual values for the religious, traditional virtues for the old, radical reforms for the young, world order and equity for globalists, energy independence for isolationists, civil rights for liberals, states' rights for conservatives.[104]

Since ecological scarcity implies the allocation of resources through political process, any policy that allows diverse constituencies to agree, albeit for different reasons, is likely to become the direction for change. As this book so clearly demonstrates, the compelling appeal and logic of the shift to a soft energy path is already beginning to assert itself at every scale of the environment.

Ecological agriculture

Because energy and its use is so strategically central to the functioning of society, the decline in the availability of cheap and abundant fossil fuel will create changes in every aspect of our lives. Our present system of industrial agriculture is highly dependent on massive amounts of fossil fuel. It requires an input of between five and twenty calories of nonrenewable energy to get one calorie of food energy output. Current farming methods are also eroding topsoil and depleting ground water at an alarming rate. The real costs of this antiecological and unsustainable approach to food production are now becoming apparent.

The end of the fossil fuel age implies the end of the historical trend of substituting energy and machinery for labor. A significant percentage of the population over the next 25 to 50 years will have to become more directly involved in food production. The unbearable cost of highly processed foods and long distance transportation will force us to grow more food nearer to its point of consumption. This will mean the decentralization of agriculture and the emergence of a new pattern of urban agriculture. As the articles in this book demonstrate, the process has already begun. It is also likely that our diet will shift in the direction of less energy-expensive food sources such as root and grain crops, soybeans, rice, corn, and potatoes.[105] The production and consumption of grain-fed beef will decline radically as diet shifts to reflect the real costs of food production.

Not only will food production become less energy-intensive and more decentralized, but farms will once again become more diversified and ecologically balanced. In such a system of organic agriculture, the basic strategy will be to create domestic ecosystems, where human needs are supplied on a sustained yield basis. Short-term production from relatively simple pioneer plant communities (annuals) will have to be balanced against the need for long-term soil protection provided by more mature and diverse plant communities (perennials).[106] This will require the development of novel forms of agriculture, horticulture, and aquaculture along the lines described later in this book.

Decentralized industry

Our industrial economy, like our physical habitat, is the product of cheap energy. As energy and resource costs increase, large centralized energy- and capital-intensive manufacturing operations, especially those that depend on cheap transportation, will become less and less competitive with small-scale, labor-intensive, regional and local enterprises. Decentralized businesses will also tend to be more responsive to the needs of workers and customers. In many cases, they will be owned and operated by workers or cooperatives of producers and consumers. They will be inherently more flexible and adaptive in the face of the uncertainty and turbulence that will characterize the period of transition, which will further amplify their competitive advantage. Unlikely as it would appear today, the age of the multinational corporation may well be coming to an end.

Resettling America: the fifth migration

While these changes in our existing paradigms, technologies, energy systems, agriculture, industry, and settlement patterns will be essential parts of any process of radical change, a better society will not come about by an approach directed solely toward changes in parts and details. Only an interconnected whole of reforms carried out with a collectively shared, wholistic vision, a strategic plan aimed at an easily imaged goal, will effect the needed transformation of consciousness and culture, mindscape and landscape. The resettling of America is the end toward which these changes converge, as well as the means by which they shall take place.

This book shows by theory and example how the process of resettling America is already emerging as a creative response to the end of industrial civilization. However, the theme is not new. The dream of a middle landscape of balanced and healthy communities living close to the earth has haunted the American imagination since the landing of the first settlers. Before describing the organization and contents of this book, let us look at this vision of possibilities as it was articulated at the beginning of this century.

In a remarkable essay entitled "The Fourth Migration," first published in the "Regional Planning Number" of *Survey Graphic* in May 1925, historian Lewis Mumford described the history of America as an initial settlement followed by three great internal migrations. The first America, the America of the settlement, was a nation of small communities along the Eastern seaboard and the major river valleys. By 1850 those communities had reached their peak development in a balanced pattern of industrial and agricultural life based upon the ". . . fullest use of their regional resources through the water-wheel, mill, and farm."[107]

The initial flowering of the American Dream, which, as Mumford observes, was also expressed in the writings of transcendentalists Emerson and Thoreau and the literature of Melville, Whitman, and Poe, was followed by the second America, the America of the internal migrations. The first migration was a great westward expansion that cleared the virgin forests west of the Alleghenies, and dispersed a farm population fairly evenly across the continent. The second migration was the direct result of the process of industrialization, as the farm population moved to the small factory towns that grew up in the valleys. Those communities were often little more than work camps clustered around the mine, timber stand, or railway station. They were almost completely unburdened by the cultural amenities of settled life. The "unsettling of America" had begun.

The railroads reinforced this pattern, and the continued explosion of industrial activity after the Civil War created the third migration, the movement of population from the small industrial towns and farms to the great financial and manufacturing centers of the industrial age. That produced the basis of our present framework of congested urban centers and depopulated rural landscapes.

With the mounting social, economic, environmental, and human costs of the flight to the city clearly in view in 1925, Mumford and his colleagues in the Regional Planning Association of America (RPAA) sounded a call for the fourth migration which, it was hoped, would redirect the already emerging pattern of cancerous metropolitan sprawl. These practical visionaries believed that the potentially decentralizing technologies of the automobile, telephone, radio, and the emerging national electrical energy grid would make it possible to replace the overly centralized metropolitan civilization with a nation of decentralized urban centers and environmentally balanced regions. The fourth migration was seen as a movement that would be created by a process of democratic planning informed by scientific insight and guided by humanistic ideals, a movement that would restore the failed potential of the American experiment. Unlike many social reformers and city planners of his day, Mumford did not believe that the existing framework of settlements, which was the result of the first three migrations, was either complete or satisfactory.

> But the mold of America has not been set; we are again in another period of flow, caused like the flows of the past by new industrial methods, new wants and necessities, and new ideals of life, and we have before us the great adventure of working out a new pattern so that the fourth migration will give to the whole continent that stable, well-balanced, settled, cultivated life which grew out of its provincial settlement. We can hinder this tidal change and rob ourselves of its potential benefits by adjusting our plans to the forces that were dominant in the recent past; or we can remold our plans and guide our action in terms of a more desirable future.[108]

Unfortunately, the vision of Mumford and the RPAA went unheeded, and the fourth migration became a mere extension of the third. Rather than decentralizing America, the technologies that were the hope of the future in the 1920s helped to accelerate the concentration of power and wealth in the major industrial and financial cities on the coasts and along the Great Lakes. However, the negative reaction to the problems of the cities, rather than giving impetus to the move toward decentralized regional centers, was harnessed to the centrifugal force of the automobile in a massive but ultimately unsuccessful flight from the city. The expanding rings of suburbia that now imprison the decaying cores of our major urban areas have created problems unimagined a generation ago. Suburbanization, not regionalization, is our legacy from the fourth migration.

The vision of the fourth migration still stands before us today as the unfinished agenda of the American Dream of a middle landscape. However, what may have been merely a utopian ideal 60 years ago has now assumed the status of a practical necessity. The destructive tendencies of metropolitanization so accurately described by Mumford and the RPAA have now become the grim realities of megalopolitization so graphically depicted by Theodore Roszak:

> The supercity . . . stretches out tentacles of influence that reach thousands of miles beyond its already sprawling perimeters. It sucks every hinterland and wilderness into its technological metabolism. It forces rural populations off the land and replaces them with vast agri-industrial combines. Its investments and technicians bring the roar of the bulldozer and oil derrick into the most uncharted quarters. It runs its conduits of transport and communication, its lines of supply and distribution through the wildest landscapes. It flushes its waste into every river, lake, and ocean or trucks them away into desert areas. The world becomes its garbage can.[109]

As we have seen, the world can no longer absorb such abuse. There is neither the energy and raw materials, nor the ecological resilience necessary for urban industrialism to long continue. Our choice today may well be utopia or oblivion.

As the contents of this book suggest, we have already begun the fifth migration, a redistribution of population and a restructuring of habitat without precedent in human history. While the great transition from an industrial civilization to a metaindustrial culture is taking place world-wide, the focus here is on America, a land that has embodied the archetype of industrial civilization more completely than any other. America is still a land of hope, the repository of the dreams of Western civilization for a future world finer than any yet dreamed or experienced. And since the rest of the world still seems to be competing to see who can most rapidly and completely follow our lead into the wasteland culture of consumerism, perhaps a reversal of the past 200 years of industrial destruction and wasted opportunity in America can offer the peoples of the world a better model for future development. In resettling America we might once again become the visionaries and pioneers of a new world. But as Lewis Mumford so eloquently observed, this new exploration of the human potential will require of us a new depth and maturity and a more complete vision than that which has brought us to our current crisis. Since Mumford's prophetic vision of the fourth migration has yet to be achieved, and since events have since proven that his vision of possibilities continues to be our best hope for the future, it is, perhaps, worth quoting in some detail:

. . . the field of adventure is no longer that of the old explorers and pioneers, swiftly staking out the surface of the earth: we must now tunnel downward in chosen areas and deal intensively with many matters that the New World mind, in its first moment of expansion, could touch only superficially, if in-deed it did not completely neglect. In this concentration and intensification of interest, the New World ideology must itself undergo a change that will rescue it from the shallowness of its original vision and technique. Not expansion and conquest but intensive cultivation, not "freedom from" but "freedom for," not wholesale mechanization for the sake of power, profit, productivity, or prestige, but a mechanization measured by human need and limited by vital norms—this will dictate the nature of economic and social enterprises. This means a general change from a money economy to a life economy.

The old exploration is now at an end. Under One World guidance "the new exploration," as Benton Mackaye has called it, will begin: the assemblage of all existing knowledge and values toward the creation of an integrated plan of life. This new exploration has a wider province than the geographic one; but its application to the earth is important. For a survey of the possibilities of human existence, in a new ecological pattern, region by region, is the necessary basis for the resettlement and recultivation of the planet . . .

This new adventure demands psychological maturity, as the boyish heroism of the old adventures did not; for it is an exploration in depth, to fathom all the potential resources of a region, geologic, climatic, vegetative, zoological, his-toric, cultural, psychological, aesthetic, and to assess its possibilities for contin-ued human enjoyment and for further improvement. The kind of intensive study of the local environment that Henry Thoreau began now needs to be done systematically throughout the planet; and, though it necessarily enlists all the resources of science, it need not, as Patrick Geddes showed through the regional survey, be the work of specialists alone: it is above all an instrument of education in which every member of the community may be enlisted, not least school children.

. . . Perhaps not the least contribution of New World civilization, once it transfers its impulses into more humane common channels, will be in the reversal of its original mistakes: the resettlement of people, the replenishment of resources, the recultivation of landscapes: in short, a general undoing of its blind assault upon both the biological environment and the cultures of primitive peoples, and its present wiping out, by heedless urban expansion, of the very rural background necessary to the enjoyment of life in cities. At last sufficient knowledge is available to rectify the results of importunate greed and to remodel an environment that has been degraded by the engineer's over-confidence in machine-made plans.[110]

THIS BOOK

Taken as a whole, this book attempts to describe how Mumford's neglected vision is being brought into existence in contemporary America. In E. F. Schumacher's words, it shows a "viable future visible in the present." It is divided into three major sections; *Vision, Expression,* and *Reflection,* an organization which itself speaks to the need for an ongoing dialectic between idea and reality that is informed by the critical evaluation of what is and what has been in the light of what should be.

Vision

Part One, *Vision,* contains two articles that present an image of a future of meaningful work, localized economies, diversity and richness of community, place, and region, with a technology and architecture in symbiosis with the ecosystems that sustain them.

Expression

Part Two, *Expression,* comprises the bulk of the volume. It explores the multitude of ways such a society is now being brought into existence throughout America. The major ways are reflected in the four subsections of Part Two: Contemplative Community, Rural New Towns, Urban Decentralization, and Biotechnology and Regional Integration. The majority of articles in the four subsections are case studies that exemplify the ideals of Part One. The many projects represented make it clear that we have already begun the process of resettling people, replenishing resources, and recultivating landscapes that is called for in Mumford's vision of the American future. And, from the many specific proposals for policy and action aimed at enhancing this grass-roots process of cultural transformation, the reader should be able to see more clearly where we could be headed and how we might get there, should we have the vision and courage to make the effort.

This book has a format designed to guide the reader: all of the editor's introductory material in each section is set in this wide column format. The articles contributed by other authors are set in a more narrow two-column format.

Contemplative community

America, since its initial discovery, has held up to the world the possibility of creating a "new heaven and a new earth." In the 18th and 19th Centuries this vision led to the creation of a profusion of communitarian experiments aimed at transforming the nation by providing living models of ideal communities that transcended the contradictions of industrial life. The recent upsurge of interest in creating small, self-reliant, intentional communities, often rooted in spiritual practices and beliefs, can be seen as a vital thread of continuity that stretches back to an age when optimism about a better future was less blunted by the realities of failed dreams. As we attempt to come to terms with our inner landscape of compulsive anxiety and our outer landscape of failing institutions, the spiritual community that attempts to heal the division of self and society by applying spiritual ideals to the organization of everyday life is likely to once again become a model for the larger society. The case studies of Zen Center in California and The Abode of the Message, a Sufi community that is literally resettling a Shaker village in upstate New York, represent this growing movement and illustrate its relevance and potential for the restructuring of the American landscape and mindscape.

Rural new towns

If we are to resolve the crisis of our overpopulated and unsustainable urban concentrations, we must simultaneously confront the problems of our depopulated rural areas. This section presents two case studies: one addresses the problems of rural blacks who have resisted the migration to the cities and wish to create a better life in the country, and the other describes an ongoing attempt by future residents to create a village community that is based on ecological planning methods and participatory design processes. Together the studies present concrete and innovative strategies for land reform, financing, design, and planning within a policy framework that would make it possible to facilitate and enhance the growing movement of people back to smaller towns and rural areas. As energy and resource scarcities, reflected in escalating costs, continue to erode the quality of life in the major cities and threaten the viability of our industrial agriculture, the need to plan and coordinate the return of large numbers of people to primary production will become a major national challenge. With adequate financial support and coordinated planning and land reform at the regional and national levels to support future efforts of this kind, Cerro Gordo and New Communities Inc. could well be remembered as pioneers of a new pattern of human settlement.

Urban decentralization

It has become painfully evident that our cities are not working and, with their complete dependence on increasingly scarce and costly fossil fuels, it is certain that they neither can nor should continue to exist in their current social and physical form. If radical changes do not occur soon, we are likely to experience even more serious problems and a more violent collapse at some point in the not-so-distant future. The articles in this subsection demonstrate that such a scenario need not occur; that it is possible for our cities and towns to be restructured into a network of more self-reliant, energy- and resource-conserving neighborhoods and communities. Through case studies, a variety of strategies for locally-initiated, social, political, and environmental change from the lower east side of New York to the college town of Davis, California, are described. Each reflects a unique and appropriate response to the problems and opportunities of its particular context, yet, taken as a group, the articles outline a range of approaches that are applicable to the whole gamut of city problems and types in America today.

Biotechnology and regional integration

To build more self-reliant cities and ecologically derived new towns, we will have to rethink what a building is, and what a city is, and how a restructured human ecology can be integrated gracefully and gently into the ecosystems and bioregions by which it is sustained. Among other things, this will require us to develop a sustainable and productive agriculture and a bioregionally based system of food production and distribution within an overall matrix of renewable energy systems. This subsection addresses those issues from a theoretical perspective, in terms of goals, and from a pragmatic perspective in terms of means. It will not be hard for the perceptive reader to begin to envision an America composed of bioregional economies evolving out of this emerging dialogue with the soil and wind, sun and water, trees and land forms of our native ecosystems.

Reflection

Finally, Part Three, *Reflection,* is an attempt to address some of the broader theoretical issues that arise out of such a vision of problems and possibilities. The crisis of industrial civilization is not new. Perhaps 30 civilizations have come into existence and then perished, unable to effectively adapt to social, political, economic, and environmental crises spawned by their very success. Rather than moving toward greater diversity, symbiosis, and stability, as is the case in organic evolution, human ecologies guided by conscious purpose have systematically evolved in the direction of simplicity, homogeneity, competitive exploitation, and fragility. If we are to avoid making the same mistakes again, we must come to a better understanding of why that has happened and learn what is necessary to avoid repeating the same dull round of growth and decline. How, in the words of Gregory Bateson, is it possible to maintain "flexibility" in social systems, to institutionalize the capacity for evolutionarily adaptive behavior in individuals and groups?

From an acceptance of paradox and a theoretical foundation based on the insights of ecology, general biology, cybernetics, and various branches of archaic and mystical thought, Part Three shows how such dilemmas can be resolved and how enduring solutions to the crucial problems of contemporary society, if not probable, are at least possible in the coming metaindustrial world order. In fact, evidence of such a possibility is contained in the ideas and actions embodied in this book.

References

1. Theodore Roszak, *Where the Wasteland Ends: Politics and Transcendence in Postindustrial Society,* (Garden City, N.Y.: Anchor Books/Doubleday & Co., 1973), p. xvii.

2. Erich Fromm, *To Have or To Be?,* (New York: Harper & Row, 1976), p. 1.

3. Eds., The Ecologist, *A Blueprint for Survival,* (Middlesex, England: Penguin Books, 1972), p. 15.

4. William Ophuls, *Ecology and the Politics of Scarcity,* (San Francisco: W. H. Freeman and Co., 1977), p. 9.

5. Ibid, p. 127.

6. G. Tyler Miller, Jr., *Energy and Environment: Four Energy Crises,* (Belmont, Cal.: Wadsworth Publishing Co., 1975), pp. 45–46.

7. W. Jackson Davis, *The Seventh Year: Industrial Civilization in Transition,* (New York: W. W. Norton & Co., 1979), p. 47. This book makes the most complete, carefully documented and persuasive argument for the immi-

nent and inevitable decline of industrial civilization since the landmark publication of the Club of Rome, *The Limits to Growth.* Obviously, I am greatly indebted to Davis for much of the factual information used in developing the brief overview of this same argument in my general introduction. However, my presentation is a poor substitute for reading Davis's superb book, which not only goes into far greater detail but places the crisis of resource scarcity within an interdisciplinary framework firmly rooted in ecological theory. *The Seventh Year* should be viewed as necessary reading for anyone seeking a better understanding of the phenomenon of ecological scarcity and its implications for the postindustrial age we are now entering.

8. Ophuls, *Ecology and the Politics of Scarcity,* p. 88.

9. Ibid., p. 88.

10. This scenario for coal depletion is taken from Davis, *The Seventh Year,*

p. 39.

11. Miller, *Energy and Environment,* p. 45.

12. M. K. Hubbert, *U.S. Energy Sources, A Review as of 1972.* Document no. 93–40 (92–75) (Washington, D.C.: U.S. Government Printing Office, 1974). For those who find such technical reports difficult to digest, useful summaries of Hubbert's studies can be found in Chapter 3 in: Davis, *The Seventh Year,* "Facts and Trends," in *Transition: A Book on Future Energy: Nuclear or Solar?,* (Portland, Ore.: Prometheus Unbound, Specialty Books, 1977), Office of Energy Research and Planning, Office of the Governor, State of Oregon, P.O. Box 42261, Portland, OR 97242; and Chapter 5, in Miller, *Energy and Environment.*

13. Miller, *Energy and Environment,* p. 47.

14. Davis, *The Seventh Year,* p. 47.

15. Ibid., p. 44.

16. Miller, *Energy and Environment,* p. 46.

17. Davis, *The Seventh Year,* p. 37.

18. Miller, *Energy and Environment,* p. 46.

19. Ibid., p. 49.

20. Wilson Clark, *Energy for Survival: The Alternative to Extinction,* (Garden City, N.Y.: Anchor Press/ Doubleday & Co., 1974), p. 264.

21. Ibid., p. 265.

22. Ibid., p. 266.

23. For a concise and readily understandable discussion of nuclear power, see Davis, *The Seventh Year,* pp. 58–67. Also see Barry Commoner, *The Poverty of Power: Energy and the Economic Crisis,* (New York: Alfred A. Knopf, 1977), pp. 76–112.

24. Davis, *The Seventh Year,* p. 60.

25. "Nuclear Dilemma: The Atom's Fizzle in an Energy Short World," *Business Week,* 25 December 1978, pp. 54–68. See p. 65 for a discussion of the potential costs of decommissioning.

26. As quoted in Barry Commoner, *The Politics of Energy,* (New York: Alfred A. Knopf, 1979), p. 46.

27. Davis, *The Seventh Year,* p. 60. While conventional fission plants cannot explode, breeder reactors can.

28. For an overview of the problems associated with the development of fusion power see Davis, *The Seventh Year,* pp. 63–67.

29. Ophuls, *Ecology and the Politics of Scarcity,* pp. 65–66.

30. R. A. Arndt and L. D. Roper, *Depletion of United States and World Mineral Resources,* (Blacksburg, Va.: University Publications, 1976) and L. D. Roper, *Where Have All the Minerals Gone?,* (Blacksburg, Va.: University Publications, 1976).

31. These examples of depletion schedules for key metals are taken from a concise summary of Arndt & Roper's studies in Davis, *The Seventh Year,* p. 131.

32. See Davis, *The Seventh Year,* p. 138.

33. Ibid, p. 140.

34. Paul R. Ehrlich, and Anne H. Ehrlich, *Population/Resources/Environment: Issues in Human Ecology,* (San Francisco: W. H. Freeman and Co., 1970), p. 59.

35. Richard H. Wagner, *Environment and Man,* 3rd ed., (New York: W. W. Norton & Co., 1978), p. 429.

36. Ehrlich and Ehrlich, *Population/Resources/Environment,* p. 120.

37. Wagner, *Environment and Man,* p. 437.

38. As quoted in Ehrlich and Ehrlich, *Population/Resources/Environment,* p. 119.

39. Ibid., p. 119.

40. Stephan H. Schneider, *The Genesis Strategy: Climate and Global Survival,* (New York: Dell Publishing Co., 1977), p. 9.

41. Davis, *The Seventh Year,* p. 110.

42. Ibid., p. 110.

43. Ehrlich and Ehrlich, *Population/Resources/Environment,* p. 118.

44. Lester R. Brown, *The Twenty Ninth Day: Accommodating Human Needs and Numbers to the Earth's Resources,* (New York: W. W. Norton & Co., 1978), p. 42.

45. Ibid., p. 43.

46. Wagner, *Environment and Man,* p. 447. For a vivid explanation of how a desert was created amidst the lush woodlands of southeastern Tennessee by a copper smelting operation, see Chapter 5, in John H. Storer, *The Web of Life,* (New York: Mentor Books/New American Library, 1953). This little book is still one of the best introductions to the study of ecology.

47. Davis, *The Seventh Year,* p. 112.

48. G. Tyler Miller, Jr., *Replenish the Earth: A Primer in Human Ecology,* (Belmont, Cal.: Wadsworth Publishing Co., 1972), p. 73.

49. Davis, *The Seventh Year,* p. 114.

50. David Pimentel et al., "Land Degradation: Effects on Food and Energy Resources," *Science,* 8 October 1976, pp. 149–155.

51. Davis, *The Seventh Year,* p. 115.

52. Wayne Slater, "Monster Machine Chews up Farmland—Farmers, Citizens Fight," *The Manhattan* (Kans.) *Mercury,* 11 July, 1979.

53. See Ehrlich and Ehrlich, *Population/Resources/Environment,* p. 2, and Catherine Lerza and Michael Jacobson, *Food for People Not for Profit,* (New York: Ballantine Books, 1975) p. 3.

54. Brown, *The Twenty Ninth Day,* p. 40.

55. Wagner, *Environment and Man,* p. 380.

56. Brown, *The Twenty Ninth Day,* p. 40.

57. Wagner, *Environment and Man,* p. 393.

58. Ibid, p. 381.

59. Ehrlich and Ehrlich, *Population/Resources/Environment,* p. 127.

60. Ibid, p. 127.

61. Davis, *The Seventh Year,* pp. 104–105.

62. Ibid, p. 106.

63. Davis, *The Seventh Year,* p. 106.

64. Brown, *The Twenty Ninth Day,* p. 52.

65. Davis, *The Seventh Year,* pp. 107–108.

66. Brown, *The Twenty Ninth Day,* p. 20.

67. Ibid, p. 20.

68. Ibid, pp. 20–21.

69. Schneider, *The Genesis Strategy,* p. 65.

70. Ibid, p. 71.

71. Ibid, p. 72.

72. Ibid, p. 72.

73. Ibid, p. 77.

74. Davis, *The Seventh Year,* p. 101.

75. Ibid, p. 101.

76. Ibid, p. 101.

77. Schneider, *The Genesis Strategy,* pp. 130, 66.

78. Ibid, p. 79.

79. Ibid, p. 79.

80. Ibid, p. 125.

81. Ibid, p. 137.

82. Ibid, p. 135.

83. Davis, *The Seventh Year,* p. 111.

84. Ibid, p. 102.

85. Schneider, *The Genesis Strategy,* p. 90.

86. For a Reprint of two CIA reports on climate change as well as a good introduction to the dynamics of weather and climate, see The Impact Team, *The Weather Conspiracy: The Coming of the New Ice Age,* (New York: Ballantine Books, 1977).

87. Donella H. Meadows, et al., *The Limits to Growth,* (New York: Signet Books/New American Library, 1972). This book, which startled the world when it was first published, is still one

of the best explanations of the systemic nature of the "world problematique."

88. Schneider, *The Genesis Strategy*, p. 13. The use of nitrogen fertilizer leads to an increase in nitrous oxide (N_2O) in the soil. When this gas works its way into the atmosphere it destroys ozone.

89. Meadows et al., *The Limits to Growth*, p. 37.

90. For a realistic, yet hopeful, study of energy and resource problems and their implications for social, economic, political, technical, and cultural changes, see Warren Johnson, *Muddling Toward Frugality*, (San Francisco: Sierra Club Books, 1978). In many important respects, Johnson's scenario for change is similar to that presented in this volume.

91. For a more detailed study of contemporary images of the future see Gary J. Coates, "Future Images, Present Possibilities: Revisioning Nature, Self, and Society," in this volume.

92. For a more detailed analysis of the historical roots of the Jeffersonian pastoral ideal, see Gary J. Coates, "Future Images, Present Possibilities: Revisioning Nature, Self, and Society," in this volume.

93. Robert Stobaugh and Daniel Yergin, eds., *Energy Future: Report of the Energy Project at the Harvard Business School*, (New York: Random House, 1979), p. 182.

94. John S. Steinhart et al., *Pathway to Energy Sufficiency: The 2050 Study*, (San Francisco: Friends of the Earth, 1979), p. 14.

95. See Steinhart, et al., *Pathway to Energy Sufficiency: The 2050 Study*, for documentation of this low-energy scenario.

96. Ibid., p. 76. The central thesis of the 2050 Study is the principle of "maximum accessibility, not maximum mobility."

97. See the sections, "Contemplative Community" and "Rural New Towns" in this volume.

98. See the section, "Biotechnology and Regional Integration" in this volume.

99. See Amory Lovins, *Soft Energy Paths: Toward a Durable Peace*, 2nd ed., (New York: Harper & Row, 1979).

100. Commoner, *The Politics of Energy*, p. 50.

101. Amory Lovins, *Soft Energy Paths: Toward a Durable Peace*, (New York: Harper & Row, 1979), p. 40.

102. Steinhart et al., *Pathway to Energy Sufficiency*, p. 50.

103. Commoner, *The Politics of Energy*, p. 60.

104. Lovins, *Soft Energy Paths*, p. 23.

105. Davis, *The Seventh Year*, p. 196.

106. See Earle A. Barnhart, "Agricultural Landscapes: Strategies Toward Permanence" and Wes Jackson, "New Roots for Agriculture" in this volume.

107. Lewis Mumford, as quoted in Carl Sussman, ed., *Planning the Fourth Migration: The Neglected Vision of the Regional Planning Association of America*, (Cambridge: MIT Press, 1976), p. 55. This book reprints the entire issue of *Survey Graphic* as well as a number of other papers by RPAA members. It should be required reading for everyone concerned with the issues raised in this book.

108. Ibid., p. 56.

109. Theodore Roszak, as quoted in Miller, *Energy and Environment*, pp. 23–24.

110. Lewis Mumford, *The Transformations of Man*, (New York: Harper & Row, 1956), pp. 159–161. Reprinted by permission of the publisher.

VISION

Where there is no vision, the people perish

−Proverbs 29:18

1 | Future Images, Present Possibilities: *Revisioning Nature, Self, and Society*

Gary J. Coates

TIME IS THE REALM of change, a succession of timeless moments between past and future, between memory and desire. In memory we hold the image of what has been, and through the observation of its absence, we perceive and desire what could have been. And while it may be true, as T.S. Eliot has reminded us, that, "time past and time future, allow but a little consciousness," the awareness of the gap between possibility and realization, what is and what could be, is the creative tension that has given form to the shape of time.

Social change can be thus perceived as "a push-pull process in which a society is at once pulled forward by its own magnetic images of an idealized future and pushed from behind by its realized past."[1] The image of the future, as the collective expression of a desire for a better world, is the driving force behind the process of historical change. Just as the genetically patterned ends contained in the structure of DNA guide and direct the unfolding potential of the organism, the image of the future organizes and guides the sequence of events that leads to its realization. "The primary forces in history

are not propelled by a system of production; nor by individual or military might but rather by the underlying ideas, ideals, values, and norms that manage to achieve mass appeal."[2]

In his exhaustive study of the role of images of the future in Western history, sociologist Fred Polak has discerned a number of characteristics typical of such images. First, images of the future are always aristocratic in origin. They can be created by prophets, philosophers, poets, saints, or scholars, but always the author of the image belongs to the creative minority of a society. Certain of these images of a radically different world in another time seem to combine intellectual insight, aesthetic appeal, and spiritual power in such a form that they resonate to the needs and desires of the masses at a particular time and place. When this happens, as for example, in the powerful images of Zarathustra, the Jewish prophets, Christ, and St. Augustine (whose book *The City of God* shaped the next four or five centuries of Christendom), society is drawn together to direct its collective actions toward creating that other and better future.

Besides being aristocratic in origin

Time Present And Time Past Are Both Perhaps Present In Time Future, And Time Future Contained In Time Past.
T.S. Eliot

Eternity Is In Love With The Productions Of Time
William Blake

We look at the present through a rear view mirror. We march backwards into the future.
Marshall McLuhan

53

and charismatic in their mass appeal, images of the future are dialectical in nature. As the image of the future passes into history, it undergoes a series of transformations in a process of self-correction, change, and renewal. Thus, images of the future both shape and are shaped by history.

The authentic image of the future both grows out of and contains an image of the past. It explains who we are, where we have come from, and where we are headed. It is an attempt to give meaning to the flow of time by discerning the pattern that reconciles human performance with human potential. By giving meaning to the failures of the past, the suffering of the present can be endured in the expectation of a better world to come.

So in the current competition among images of the future, we are experiencing a battle over the shape of things to come. What we expect we will look for, and what we desire we will seek to realize. The new world will be created in the image of the new world view.

Contemporary images of the future

Figure 1 is a map of the field of images that dominate current speculations about the future. The horizontal axis represents a continuum from optimism to pessimism while the vertical axis presents a range of societal types according to whether their organizing impulse is basically centralizing or decentralizing.

Quadrants 1 and 2 present optimistic possibilities for both decentralized and centralized social forms. Depending on your views about the aims of history and the relative roles of divine and human intervention, these quadrants can embody both utopian and eschatological projections. Since there is little

disagreement about the centralizing tendencies of the present sociotechnical order, individuals representing Quadrant 1, the metaindustrial vision, tend to believe that while the present reality is indeed powerful, it is not good for people or the planet. Images falling in this quadrant portray the future as an inversion of the present order. Images falling into Quadrant 2 project the future as fulfilling the promise of the present. Representatives of the superindustrial visions see the present as good and seek to extend it into the future by enhancing the power of existing paradigms and institutions. Again, both these scenarios can be viewed as inevitable or subject to varying degrees of human intervention.

Quadrants 3 and 4 are merely flip sides of the optimistic images of Quadrants 1 and 2. When a liberal technocrat finds the evidence for the decline of industrial civilization overwhelming and his belief in the perfectibility of human nature shaken, the superindustrial vision of possibilities becomes its mirror opposite, a grim scenario of apocalypse without the redemptive possibility of the millennium. For representatives of the superindustrial images, who have dedicated a lifetime to the celebration of the power and goodness of the world created by the industrial revolution, the prospect of its inevitable decline in power only serves to erode an already weak faith in the goodness of creation. In the present stage of industrial crisis, many former optimists are confronting the existential pain which is the result of too complete a faith in the virtue of the present and too narrow a vision of human possibilities.

The pessimistic images are neither criticisms of the present nor visions of what could be. They are merely more or less bitter eulogies for the death of

Figure 1: *Images of the Future*

Metaindustrial	**Decentralized**	**Preindustrial** **(A new, final dark age)**
Long-range prospect: World-wide decline of urban-industrial civilization eased by return to local and regional economies. Integration of classical economies of the past into a new structure of civilization. *Prophets:* William Irwin Thompson, Murray Bookchin, E.F. Schumacher, Amory Lovins, Theodore Roszak, Lewis Mumford, Ivan Illich. *Cultural expression:* The metaindustrial village and the planetary city, decentralized biotechnologies, a symbiosis of nature, self, and society.		*Long-range prospect:* World-wide collapse of interconnected global economies. Massive drop in population. Chronic cycles of plague and famine. A return to savagery. *Prophets:* Roberto Vacca, Paul Ehrlich. *Cultural expression:* A decimated landscape of deserted cities, mined for their "raw" materials, tribal bands wandering the countryside. Chaos and conflict over scarce resources.
Optimistic	**1** / **3** / **2** / **4**	**Pessimistic**
Superindustrial		**Hyperindustrial**
Long-range prospect: World-wide development of postindustrial economies. Fifteen billion people earning $20,000 a year. Elimination of poverty and disease. Infinite supply of energy and materials through the exploitation of space. *Prophets:* Herman Kahn, Gerard O'Neill, Daniel Bell, B.F. Skinner. *Cultural expression:* On earth we would have the "city of efficient consumption," a Disneyworld of manufactured fun and adventure. In space, we would have efficient industry and fantasy islands.		*Long-range Prospect:* World-wide freeze on industrial growth. Revolt of the masses requiring massive, often severe, centralized control by state. Technical elite and military join together to prevent collapse of civilization. Privilege of the few maintained at the expense of the many. *Prophets:* Robert Heilbroner, H.G. Wells. *Cultural expression:* "Federal" architecture, poorly serviced, joyless "Pentagons" and bare necessities with zones and pockets of opulence. A "1984" police state.
	Centralized	

Adapted from the Alternative Futures Matrix in Nigel Cross, David Elliot, and Robin Roy, Designing the Future *(London: Hutchinson & Co., Open University Press, 1975), p. 27.*

what has been: they fail to tell us who we are, where we have come from, and where we should be headed. Thus, they are not even images of the future, since our definition assumes that viable images of the future guide and direct action in the present toward the realization of an ideal. The only positive function of the pessimistic images of the future is to create the psychological impasse, the fertile decay, out of which the unconscious urge for wholeness can project compensatory images of the transcendence of crisis, visions of a new order of nature, self, and society.

So the remainder of this paper will explore the dominant images of Quadrants 1 and 2, the optimistic images of a future on the far side of the conflict and disorder of the present.

Herman Kahn and the Americanization of planet earth

All images of the future involve an imaginative return to the past, in a new synthesis that explains the present and suggests a course of action by which the new perfected future will be realized. Futurist Herman Kahn and his associates at his "think tank," the Hudson Institute, view history as a linear progression from the technology of the cave man to the technology of the space man. According to this view, we are currently standing at the inflection point of this upward trend of history, and unless we suffer a failure of nerve, we shall soon realize the fruits of the original millenarian New World vision in its modern, secular and scientific form. Not surprisingly, then, Kahn projects, in *The Next Two Hundred Years,* a scenario that sounds like an extension of his idealized image of the past:

> The scenario presented, elaborated and tested in this book can be summarized with the general statement that 200 years ago almost everywhere human beings were comparatively few, poor and at the mercy of the forces of nature, and 200 years from now, we expect, almost everywhere they will be numerous, rich and in control of the forces of nature. The 400-year period will thus have been as dramatic and important in the history of mankind as was the 10,000-year period that preceded it, a span of time that saw the agricultural

revolution spread around the world, giving way finally to the birth of the Industrial Revolution. At the midway mark in the 400-year period, we have just seen in the most advanced countries the initial emergence of superindustrial economies (where enterprises are extraordinarily large, encompassing and pervasive forces in the physical and societal environments), to be followed soon by postindustrial economies (where the task of producing the necessities of life has become trivially easy because of technological advancement and economic development). We expect that all countries eventually will develop the characteristics of super- and postindustrial societies.[3]

To characterize the changes wrought in society by the two great watersheds of history, the Agricultural Revolution of 10,000 years ago and the Industrial Revolution, which began 200 years ago, Kahn distinguishes four kinds of economic activities; primary, secondary, tertiary, and quaternary.

Primary economic activities are basically concerned with extracting raw materials from the environment and include agriculture, mining, forestry, and fishing. During the worldwide spread of the agricultural revolution, societies were based on these kinds of labor-intensive activities. Only a small proportion of the population could be supported by the excess production of the masses and, consequently, cities tended to be small and widely scattered.

Secondary economic activities are primarily those of urban people—construction and manufacturing. As societies became increasingly urban, especially after the onset of the industrial revolution, more and more people shifted their efforts into this economic sector.

The emerging postindustrial economies are characterized by tertiary economic activities such as transportation, finance, management, insurance, education, and government. In the United States, 65 percent of the population is currently involved in such pursuits. Other industrialized nations are rapidly approaching such a concentration in the services sector.

As envisioned by Kahn and his associates, the future superindustrial economies of the world will be dominated by quarternary economic activities. In such a situation, the primary and secondary economic sectors will be almost completely automated and the need for tertiary activities greatly diminished. Consequently, most of the population will be engaged, for their livelihood, in what today would be described as leisure activities such as reading, writing, painting, camping, hiking, gourmet cooking, and eating.

In this image of the future Kahn is suggesting that the direction of history is a return to the pattern of work and leisure characteristic of pre-industrial, hunting and gathering economies. But instead of small bands of people living within the eternal round of nature, the future life of abundance and leisure will occur within the totally remade, totally human-defined artificial environment to be completed within the next two hundred years.

Not that such a world would be without its own problems—Kahn is clear on this. "Of course there will be problems. Some of them are likely to be: wishful thinking, illusion, decadence, educated incapacity and a kind of violence-prone boredom."[4]

Moreover, Kahn believes that this final fulfillment of the modern quest for the domination of nature will be achieved with known or soon-to-be-developed technologies and managerial skills. Assuming that we do not succumb to the demoralizing influence of doomsayers and limits-to-growth fanatics, the population, economic growth, energy, raw materials, food, and pollution problems of this historically momentous "transitory era" will be solved within the near to medium-term future. However, to provide a margin of safety, Kahn presents his future scenario with two perspectives, one "earth-centered" and the other "space-bound." The second perspective would involve the "establishment of large autonomous colonies in space involved in the processing of raw materials, the production of energy and the manufacture of durable goods— both for indigenous consumption and as exports back to earth or to other solar-system colonies."[5] Given the enormous implications of this perspective, Kahn cautiously advises that no realistic future scenario can be projected at this time.

However, the two perspectives complement each other nicely, providing a "dual-purpose lifeboat for spaceship earth."[6] For example, should the earth-centered scenario succeed as outlined, there is likely to be a small minority of adventurous and intractable sorts who will feel smothered by the easy comforts of a superindustrial world economy. For them, the exploration and settlement of space will provide an appropriate (and socially useful) outlet. Should some major unexpected catastrophe, such as nuclear war or a massive disruption of world climate, result from the pursuit of the earthly millennium, space colonies would act as genetic banks and medieval monasteries, preserving knowledge and life against the darkness that would follow. Then, like an updated story of Noah and the Ark, the earth could eventually be repopulated by these latter-day elect who would have been spared the calamity of world destruction.

Of course, Kahn sees this possibility as infinitesimally small, but it is comforting to know that even the worst fears of the present have been accommodated by a fail-safe plan for the future. Whether by the earth-centered path or the space-bound trajectory, or both, it would seem that on the far side of this age of troubles, the real enduring problems of the future will be how to survive the successes, not the failures, of the urban-industrial experiment. Indeed, as we look beyond the present to the world to come we might well be moved to ask, along with Kahn and his colleagues:

> What kind of life will a genetically engineered, vital-organ-replaceable, mental-state-adjustable, computer-robot-assisted human being want to live? Will he find satisfaction in the postindustrial era? Will he seek even more to test himself in the combat of sport, the risk of adventure or the challenge of exploration? Or will he be able and prefer to experience all of this—and more—through artificial stimulation?[7]

Sobering questions indeed.

Gerard O'Neill and the colonization of space and time

It is time to leave behind such timid and hard-nosed images of the future and look to the stars with the eyes of a truly visionary scientist for clues about the destiny of humankind. Not all advocates of superindustrialism share Kahn's boundless faith in the ability of science and technology to solve the serious problems created by the current earth-based industrial economy. While the Hudson Institute image of the future offers the exploration of space as either a backup system for the failure of an earth-centered scenario or the tantalizing reward for its success, there is a growing movement that sees the colonization of space as the *only* solution to the double-binds of industrialism.

Kahn poses a black-and-white choice between his "realistic" description of the shape of things to come and the hysterical, if well meaning, visions of such doomsayers as the Club-of-Rome,[8] Robert Heilbroner,[9] and Roberto Vacca.[10] Rather than accepting the devitiating effects of a negative image of the future, Kahn assumes that a caring America (his book was addressed to America on its 200th anniversary as a vision of possibilities for the next two centuries) would choose to see finer possibilities than a return to barbarism.

Physicist Gerard O'Neill has demonstrated that a second possibility for superindustrial optimism exists, a possibility based on accepting the so-called limits-to-growth argument that an industrial economy that demands infinite growth is ill-suited to the bounded horizons of a finite planet. To Kahn, acceptance of such an argument is equivalent to a repudiation of rationality, technology, progress, and the American Way of Life, but to O'Neill it implies the opposite: it is the ultimate justification for all scientific-technological revolutions, past, present, and future. The exploration and settlement of space now becomes the final solution to the problems created by the exploration and settlement of the New World which began nearly 500 years ago.

This remarkable synthesis harnesses the energies of the doomsayers to the boundless enthusiasm of the technophiles in a united effort to transform the forces of darkness into a final triumph for the forces of light. But the catch is, in order to save the planet earth, we shall have to leave it. As we shall see later, this vision is a secularized and modernized version of archetypal mythical content and is the final consummation of the world view that has shaped the American experience and brought us to this point in history. Whether or not we agree with O'Neill and his followers that space colonies will literally be our redemption, a careful examination of the idea of space colonies could well have a redemptive effect on our thinking about the future.

The new millennium under corporate management

Like Kahn, O'Neill justifies his image of the future by a brief and revealing, if overly simplified, recounting of history up to the present moment of crisis and decision:

> Through many tens of thousands of years human beings were few in numbers, and insignificant in power over the physical environment. Not only war but famine and plague decimated populations whenever they grew large; centuries passed without great increase in the total human population. The quality of life, for most people in those preindustrial years, seems to have been low even in times of peace. Although there were, nearly everywhere, small privileged classes enjoying comparative wealth, most people lived out their lives in heavy labor, many as slaves.
> . . . Very suddenly, in a time less than two hundred years, our human status as passengers on a giant planet, lost in its immensity and powerless before its forces, has changed dramatically. The beginnings of a science of medicine, and the rapid development of chemistry have made fatal disease a rarity among children in the wealthy nations, and have even reduced its power in the poorer nations. With that one radical change we suddenly find ourselves growing in numbers so fast that Earth itself cannot long sustain our increase.
> At the same time, our power to change the surface of Earth has increased: our activities can and now do alter the planet and its atmosphere. We

achieve every year a greater degree of control over the natural environment, and we change it more in attempts to suit our liking. The result though does not always please us.[11]

Note how this history contains an explanation of the present, as well as logically compelling guidelines for the future. If the pre-industrial past was characterized by war, famine, plague, slavery, and the existence of privileged and wealthy elites, we certainly would not want to solve the problems of overpopulation and environmental degradation created by the industrial revolution with "a retreat to a pastoral, machine-free society."[12] No, that would be throwing out the baby with the bath water. Somehow we must carefully and rationally identify the admitted evils, the necessary side-effects of industrialism, and devise a strategy to eliminate them while keeping the benefits such as increased life expectancy, freedom to travel, and democratic access to the evening news and other forms of mass education.

What then does O'Neill see as the evils to be eliminated? While environmental damage is certainly a problem, the greater evils are the "sharp limits on food, energy, and materials [which] confront us at a time when most of the human race is still poor, and when much of it is on the edge of starvation."[13] Incredibly, the evils of industrialism, then, would seem to be the limits set by a finite planet on the expansion of industrialism to the whole planet. Such a conclusion implies that evil resides in the world to be exploited rather than in the works of the exploiters. Here we have the American tendency to "blame the victim" elevated to its logical conclusion in a cosmic justification of the ways of man to god.

If we follow O'Neill's history carefully, we will see that the Creation has been evil and inappropriate to our needs since the beginning of time. First we were helpless and impotent in the face of nature and now that we have gotten the better of her, she begins to deny us by her very defeat. There is only one thing to be done: to find a way to inflate our human power even further in order to remake the world in our own image. We must move our industrial economy into space so that we can exploit the infinite resources of the solar system. Such an extraordinary conclusion, especially in the face of the current evidence of our enormous destructiveness, sounds ironically like the fulfillment of prophecy from the book of Genesis.[14]

In that story, it will be remembered, history begins with the murder of Abel by Cain, after which Cain is summoned by God and cursed. The curse is that Cain shall become a homeless fugitive but with the proviso that God's mark shall serve as a final protection against his harm. But Cain, in his pride, is completely dissatisfied with the security granted him by God, and he searches for a security of his own making completely beyond the presence and without the help of God. So Cain leaves the presence of God and begins a life of struggle against hostile forces, devising ever more clever means to dominate men and nature. To recover eternal life, Cain fathers a son, Enoch, and to replace Eden, he builds the first city and names it after his son.

The rest of the biblical record can be read as the ongoing quest of the sons of Cain to find security by creating ever more grand cities and fathering ever more numerous progeny. If the account had been written today, no doubt there would be a chapter that tells of O'Neill and the latest scheme to escape the curse of Cain by leaving the bounded horizons of planet Earth to create totally human-defined worlds,

some with as many as ten million people, floating in space between earth and moon.

While O'Neill betrays no conscious awareness of the mythical content of his proposal, the rest of the space colonies story reveals a clearly millenarian quality. But it should be noted that this secular myth of progress cleverly inverts the biblical prototype. Rather than having the millennium grow out of the period of decadence, misery, and global destruction of the "Last Days," the new heaven and new earth becomes a strategy for avoiding the apocalypse foreshadowed by the limits to growth. Eschatological tension gives way to boundless optimism as the idea of unlimited and, it is suggested, predestined progress replaces the gloomier prophecies of our primitive pre-industrial and prescientific biblical story tellers.

And what will the millennium be like? First of all, the planet earth, so inadequate to the needs of an industrial economy, will be restored to its primeval wholeness as a new, humanly created Garden of Eden. With the infinite energy of the sun beamed to earth by the first space colonies, the poor nations will be able to achieve within the next 100 years the same high standard of living as that of the United States. Then, gradually, all the polluting and resource-consuming heavy industries will be moved to the growing number of internationally controlled space colonies where the nasty side effects of such necessary functions will be rigorously controlled and easily diffused into interplanetary space.

With the foundation of this new heaven, the work of creating the new earth will begin. The possibilities of this resettling of the earth are described by the new age engineer and rocket specialist G. Harry Stine, in his book on the future, *The Third Industrial Rev-*

olution.[15] While Stine is not as sophisticated a prophet as O'Neill, his eschatological expectations for a future filled by space colonies are no less enthusiastic.

Beginning with the premise best expressed by author Robert Heinlein that, "We've just about used up this planet; time to find another one," Stine rebuts the conclusions of the limits-to-growth advocates by positing the emergence of the Third Industrial Revolution. Whereas the First Industrial Revolution replaced human muscles with the machine and the Second Industrial Revolution substituted the computer for limited human mental processes, the Third Industrial Revolution is replacing the earth with the whole solar system. With the wealth generated by exploiting the heavens we shall achieve an industrial base that will allow the time and resources to "return the planetary ecology to something like it was one hundred thousand years ago when we were biologically attuned to it."[16]

By his estimates, Stine expects that this work of restoration will begin within the next 100 years with an earthly population of more than 6 billion people. For those people left behind in the rush to the "high frontier," Stine does not, as does Kahn, suggest the prospect of a boring existence amidst unimagined wealth. Rather:

> Our return to the Garden of Eden will find us keeping a large number of industrial operations with us right here on the ground. This, again, will keep a lot of people busy. These "Eden industries" are going to be considerably different from those we transfer into space. They will involve the final fabrication and assembly of products whose basic raw materials have come from space factories. These will be nonpolluting industries, assembly industries, permitting a considerable amount of individual craftsmanship. Remember that the Second Industrial Revolution will have matured so that nearly all repetitive operations are handled by automation and computers.[17]

Paradoxically, while Stine admits that the Third Industrial Revolution must, of necessity, be implemented by large, capital-intensive, multinational corporations, the result will be a resurgence of updated cottage industries on earth. He explains: "The opportunities for new products that can be made by these little firms will be vastly increased because of new materials, devices, and products that will fall to earth like manna from the space factories."[18]

Moreover, the age-old dilemma of equitable distribution of goods will be solved by the universal wealth generated by the Third Industrial Revolution and the ease by which products can be dropped anywhere on the surface of the earth from the necklace of hovering space factories.

There will also be proliferation of service industries, Kahn's tertiary economic activities. While Stine admits that a service economy in a limited world could rapidly evolve into "the closed-system situation of everyone taking in one another's laundry,"[19] even this possibility will be transcended by the constant economic growth injected into the planetary economy by the space colonies.

With six billion people on earth, agriculture and mariculture will return to the status of major employers, since it would be uneconomic to import food from space. One can almost see Jefferson's yeoman farmer waiting in the wings of history for a return performance.

Again, like Kahn, Stine does not want to leave the dangerous impression that the world to come will be without its own problems. He is too keen an observer of the tendency for human beings to create new problems which become the challenge of future generations. But, the Third Industrial Revolution *will* solve the one problem identified by O'Neill, the problem of limited energy and resources, "and permit us to solve our remaining ones without entering the New Dark Ages of gloom, doom, famine, pestilence, death, and nuclear warfare that are the consequences of continuing closed-system Earth."[20]

Like a New England puritan, chastened by having witnessed the undermining of the work ethic by advanced capitalism, Stine's image of the future very wisely ends with the promise, "Yes, it will be a garden planet again with work for all and plenty of problems yet to solve for the future."[21]

Superindustrialism reconsidered

It would be easy, perhaps too easy, to reject these two images of superindustrial bliss for America and the world as unrealistic fantasies. A systematic and more realistic review of the food, raw materials, population, and energy problems confronting urban industrial society would, for example, clearly demonstrate that Kahn 's belief that all of these problems can be solved, even without space colonies, by the very processes and organizations that have created them is very far from the truth. (See the General Introduction.) Nowhere has Kahn shown an understanding of the interactive, whole-systems character of these problem areas and, typically, his optimism is rooted 10 to 20 years into the future when "inevitable" solutions will have been found. He also fails to deal with

the issue of timing, with the very real probability that problems will escalate to genuine crises before it is possible to effect new technological changes on all fronts. And, finally, he utterly fails, by his total lack of regard for them, to see the social, political, and moral dimensions of the "world problematique." His is a world where possibility is fact and value is not even an issue.

The point is that the leadership of all the world's governments and corporations, as well as the majority of its citizens, now *act* as if such an incredible parody of possibility is established fact. So, in Kahn's image we see the faith of the past that has created the present and is shaping the future.

But even superindustrial true believers such as O'Neill and Stine can see that the emperor has no clothes. There are indeed serious and intractable dilemmas facing industrial societies, problems that will not be solved by the next technological fixes. But, like addicts who have reluctantly accepted the fact that local supplies of heroin are about to be used up, O'Neill and other advocates of the "high frontier" can only imagine a new, infinite supply of fixes beyond the stars. But then, the junkie is the last person to accept the necessity of going cold turkey.

We might accept the space colonies idea as a serious proposal and attempt to analyze its practical potential as a solution to our problems, but as biologist John Todd has pointed out, we do not even know how to model, let alone maintain, even a relatively simple, semiclosed ecosystem on earth.[22] To believe that we can create a self-regulating, atmosphere-sustaining complex of ecosystems in a tin can floating in space is clearly a case of *hubris,* the Greek sin of overweening pride. And even if we could do so, as Ecologist Howard Odum pointed out years ago, the land area required to support one space colonist would be a minimum of 2½ acres.[23] Thus, only 40 people, not the 10,000 estimated by O'Neill, could in theory be supported by Island One, his proposed Prototype Space Colony.[24] So, if only on the grounds of its unrealistic and naive understanding of biology and ecology, the space colony idea could be eliminated as a serious proposal.

Another kind of critique, based on the issue of economic feasibility, could also be made. Biologist Garrett Hardin, for example, citing Hitch's Rule, which states that any new enterprise always costs from 2 to 20 times the initial estimate, points out that O'Neill's space program would cost thousands of billions of dollars rather than the hundreds of billions estimated.[25] One can imagine a scenario where space colonies could become an infinite economic sink, absorbing the last precious resources of an already declining industrial economy.

But even granting that the theoretically problematic biological issues and the practically impossible economic problems could be solved and the first space colony built, the political contradictions implicit in the motivation to build it would become frighteningly evident.

First, the necessity for rigid and hierarchical social control increases in direct proportion to the risk of failure and the penalty for error. For a large, humanly operated ecosystem floating in space, the penalty for human error, let alone acts of sabotage, would be large indeed, and the risks of such a catastrophe always present. Rather than serving as outlets for aggressive and idiosyncratic misfits, inventors, and adventurers, as Kahn, O'Neill, and Stine suppose, it is more probable that space colonies would select inhabitants for their ability to conform, follow orders and, in general, fit the needs of the habitat and its multinational corporate designers. Steward Brand, the enthusiastic countercultural advocate, would not be likely to get a chance to do somersaults on Island One's hilltops.

In fact, the necessity to completely control behavior to protect the space colony from disaster would give us the ultimate form of Herbert Marcuse's one-dimensional world, a "comfortable, smooth, reasonable, democratic unfreedom . . . a token of technical progress."[26] Social control would become invisible; it would become a necessity of natural law, a "given" beyond human challenge. This is hardly what the space colony advocates have in mind, but such a "friendly fascism" would be necessary for a successful space colony program.[27]

Since the space colony proposal is seen, in part, as an escape from the harsh necessities for authoritarian social and political control predicted by economist Robert Heilbroner and many others for an earth of diminishing energy and raw material supply, this feature of space colonies would be particularly disheartening for those who initially conceived the idea. So, as Hardin observes, "the whole project fails by reason of a pair of paradoxes. (1) The people who can conceive of this clever solution cannot be a part of it. (2) The reasons for seeking the solution—refusal to accept political control—require that the solution be rejected."[28] Hardin suggests that the space colony proposal exemplifies the logical properties of a *Reductio ad Absurdum* proof in geometry, where an issue is considered to be settled once and for all if it can be shown that the assumptions necessary for a proposition lead to a logical absurdity. Hardin calls the analogue of this situation in the field of futurology a *Reductio ad Paradoxum.*

But, in spite of the fact that space colonies can be shown to be biologically impossible, economically infeasible, and politically undesirable, the idea is rapidly gaining adherents and respectability in the United States, both in the usually skeptical scientific community and among well-meaning and intelligent individuals from a broad cross section of the general population. The National Aeronautics and Space Administration (NASA) is now accepting research proposals for the study of ways to create self-regulating and self-generating closed-system ecologies, and L-5 Societies (groups of citizen advocates) are sprouting up in most major American cities. Clearly, there is something far more powerful in the idea of space colonies than would be expected if it were just another scheme for a technological fix. To discover what it is, we must first trace the history of this new heaven and new earth and then explore its mythological and psychological implications.

Superindustrialism: Historical roots

All superindustrial images of the future are an extension of the scientific, technological, social, political, and spiritual revolutions initiated 500 years ago in the West in the Age of Exploration. Lewis Mumford has referred to the image of the future that propelled these changes as the New World Vision—a vision of a new heaven and a new earth, the inevitable result of using science and technology to exploit resources for the creation of material wealth. Like most of the powerful ideas of history, the New World Vision grew from the chaos created by the failure of an existing reality to provide the majority of people with the psychological, material and spiritual foundations for a fully realized existence:

In the west the beginnings of the new culture date back to the great catastrophe of the fourteenth century, the Black Death: a plague that wiped out between one-third and one-half the population of Western Europe. This was the century that witnessed the schism in the Christian Church, with two rival popes contending for power, while the repeated efforts of protestantism (Waldo, Wycliffe, Fox) to return to a simpler Christianity deepened that fissure. Within the span of a few centuries the focus of interest shifted from the inner world to the outer world: from a disordered and contentious subjectivity to a rigorously ordered objectivity, whose very method guaranteed agreement.

To torn, divided souls, this new order came as a blessing: and the new goods and powers brought forth by the machine briskly offset the dwindling energies of the spirit. The measurement of time and space, the multiplication of nonorganic sources of energy, the reduction of distances by speeding transportation, the quickening of the processes of production—all these acts of the New World economy advanced together, at first slowly, but presently with increasing momentum.[29]

By the beginning of the 17th century, Sir Francis Bacon, in his unfinished utopia, *The New Atlantis,* consolidated these shifts in consciousness in a vivid image of an ideal society transformed by the application of scientific knowledge and technical invention to practical purposes. In his portrayal of an unknown island kingdom, Bacon described a society that grew in health, wisdom, and riches due to the judicious introduction of knowledge and invention by a kind of freemasonry of scientist-engineers who worked in isolation from the rest of the population in an establishment called Soloman's

House. The purpose of this Foundation was the "knowledge of causes, and the secret motions of things; and, the enlarging of the bounds of human empire, to the effecting of all things possible."[30] And, it would seem from Bacon's description that more things were possible than had been dreamed by the scholastics and priests of medieval Europe. Bacon described techniques for the prolongation of life; the curing of incurable diseases; the engineering of new plants and animals; the acceleration of time in the life cycle of organisms; the creation of new materials, both organic and inorganic; the creation of air conditioning; and the manufacture of all forms of new engines of war, from flying machines to ships that traveled under the water.

Against the backdrop of the morally corrupt and materially poor world of Western Europe, Bacon's description of what was possible once the methods of science were developed for human good had an enormous influence, not only on subsequent Western thought, but on the action of the original pioneers of North America. In fact, it would not be stretching credibility to say that Bacon's "New Atlantis" has, in large part, been realized in the form of the modern U.S. technocracy. But the result would, no doubt, dismay even Sir Francis. Perhaps this is because Bensalem, Bacon's island kingdom, was at root a Christian state, and its scientists were ruled by the highest ethical ideals of that tradition as well as the methods of science. What Bacon failed to anticipate was that the decline of Christendom would be the price paid for the rise of a secular scientific state.

In any case, the immediate effect of the new world view formulated by Bacon, Descartes, Newton, Locke, and others was an intoxicating sense of the limitless potential of human beings to create an artificial environment more splendid than any offered by the creator.

With the discovery of an entirely new hemisphere, this new world view found the material foundation for the creation of a concrete utopia, a real New Atlantis, where the very idea of limits, so much a part of the world view of Medieval Christendom, would be abolished. Once again, Mumford provides a vivid and condensed summary of the threads of the New World Vision that has created out present American landscape:

> The fantasy of a New World, seized by Western man in so many forms after the fifteenth century, was, then, an attempt to escape time and the cumulative effects of time (tradition and history) by changing it for unoccupied space. This took many forms: a religious form by breaking away from the established church and its orthodoxies, a utopian form by founding new communities, an adventurous form by conquering new lands, a mechanical form by substituting machines for organisms, and physical changes, in which time exists only as wear and tear, for organic changes, in which time leaves a permanent record: finally, the "New World" took a revolutionary form; an attempt to make over the ways and habits and goals of a large population, in which all these modes of escape were more or less combined in a single complex—the new heaven and earth that would come into existence once royalism, feudalism, ecclesiasticism, and capitalism should pass away.[31]

The current crisis of industrial society suggests that the new heaven and new earth is yet to come, or if this is it, that it is not what we had in mind. But for some, this delay in the approach of the millennium has not dulled the passionate belief that, with the application of still more science, the development of still more marvelous technologies, and the discovery of even more boundless new territories, we might not live to see the final consummation of the real New Atlantis, perhaps as an island kingdom in the vast ocean of interplanetary, or even intergalactic space.

This possibility, in fact, is the space colony solution to the limits-to-growth dilemma which is now proposed by advocates of superindustrialism. And while such latter-day prophets of progress as Herman Kahn and Gerard O'Neill may lack some of the breadth of scholarship and the sense of the mystery of life of their predecessor Sir Frances Bacon, they do have his uncompromising faith in the magical power of science to effect all things possible. Bacon's description of the marvels of Bensalem pale in comparison to Kahn's projection of a world 100 years from now with 15-billion people each earning $20,000 per year, or O'Neill's vision of space colonies mining the moon and asteroids in an industrial economy fueled by the inexhaustible fires of the sun. But, as Bacon said, "knowledge is power," and we have accumulated much power-knowledge since the 17th century.

That dreams of unlimited power should be revived now, when the limits to the mechanical New World Vision have become so evident, attests to the remarkable ability of ideas about the future to outlive their creators and become detached, like the keepers of Solomon's House, from the unpleasant realities and more limited views of the mass of humanity. Since superindustrial prophets Kahn and O'Neill are both Americans, the explanation for the staying power of their visions might well be found in our own history.

From the machine in the garden to the garden in the machine

More than any other modern nation, the United States is the product of the eschatological and messianic hopes of Western Europe. Even the discovery of the new world had eschatological implications. In his *Book of Prophecies,* Columbus predicted that the end of the world would be preceded by the conquest of the new continent, the conversion of the aborigines, and the destruction of the Antichrist. And he felt that he had been chosen by God to initiate this sequence of events: "God made me the messenger of the new heaven and the new earth, of which he spoke in the Apocalypse by Saint John, after having spoken of it by the mouth of Isaiah; and he showed me the spot where to find it."[32]

The colonization of both Americas thus began as a movement for the renewal of the Christian world and the fulfillment of Christian prophecy, and the renewal was to involve a return to an earthly paradise. In particular, coming as it did on the heels of the Protestant Reformation, the creation of an earthly paradise was seen as the outward sign of the completion of the renovation of the Christian church, of its return to the purity and simplicity of the early church.

This widespread belief led to a view, clearly evident in the diaries and travelogs of early settlers, that America was an Edenic paradise, a land blessed by God and made ready for their salvation. This notion became the basis for the geographical determinism which formed the foundation for thought of Thomas Jefferson, an idea to which we shall return shortly.

But there were other expressions of the millenarist expectations of the pioneers. Rather than a garden paradise waiting to be nurtured by the elect, some colonists, specifically the Puritans who settled the harsher Northeast coast, saw the New World as a wilderness occupied by demons. But that view still confirmed their eschatological expectations, since the taming of this wilderness was seen as a moral and spiritual trial to be completed before they would be allowed to enter the Promised Land. This view is the root metaphor of what, in our day, has become the superindustrial image of the future.

It was a logical step from the idea that the American landscape was a desert for testing moral worth to the idea that the New Jerusalem would, at least in part, be the result of human works. That movement of thought eventually transformed the millennial expectations of the early settlers into the modern American belief in unlimited progress through the application of science and technology. It is this secularized and decayed myth which now animates the fervor of the Herman Kahns and the Gerard O'Neills and accounts for their certainty about the ultimate victory of the machine.

These two images of the American landscape, that of a garden and that of a wilderness, formed the basis for two distinctly different attitudes toward the machine technologies that were beginning to transform England and Europe by the time of the American Revolution. By then the initial religious zeal and millenarian expectation was becoming secularized into the more civilized form of a pastoral ideal. Rather than a dialectic between Christ and the Antichrist, as the earlier conflict between Protestant England and Catholic France and Spain over control of America had been perceived, the new polarity that engaged the American mind was the conflict between the be-

atitude of the rural life and the decadence of the city. The American dream came to be seen as an ideal middle landscape, standing between, yet transcending, the opposing forces of civilization and nature, the city and the desert. And, as the machine technology and instrumental knowledge of science began to reshape the very form and idea of the city, a new dilemma arose. In the powerful metaphor of the brilliant literary critic and historian Leo Marx, this was the problem of the "machine in the garden": How was the new technology to be reconciled with the idea of a garden paradise?

The history of America can be read as an evolving series of attempts to reconcile the Edenic myth of its founding with the emerging reality of a technological society. More than any other person, Thomas Jefferson embodied the American ambivalence about the role of the machine in American destiny, an ambivalence that we still see in our dominant images of the future.

On the one hand, Jefferson saw the machine as an emissary of the devil, a force that would spoil the purity of the American middle landscape and precipitate a fall into the degraded form of an industrializing and urbanizing Europe. Arguing against the prevailing opinion that each nation should endeavor to become self-sufficient in manufactures, Jefferson asserted that America, which had an immensity of land awaiting cultivation, would be better off leaving the sweatshops in Europe to cultivate itself as a democratic society of small, independent landholders. In mythopoetic language, Jefferson states the case for such an agrarian republic:

> Is it best then that all our citizens should be employed in its improvement, or that one half should be called off from that to exercise manufactures and handi-

craft arts for the other? Those who labour in the earth are the chosen people of God, if ever he had a chosen people, whose breasts he has made his peculiar deposit for substantial and genuine virtue. It is the focus in which he keeps alive that sacred fire, which otherwise might escape from the face of the earth. Corruption of morals in the mass of cultivators is a phaenomenon of which no age nor nation has furnished an example. It is the mark set on those, who not looking up to heaven, to their own soil and industry, as does the husbandman, for their subsistence, depend for it on the casualties and caprice of customers. Dependence begets subservience and venality, suffocates the germ of virtue, and prepares fit tools for the designs of ambition. This, the natural progress and consequence of the arts, has sometimes perhaps been retarded by accidental circumstances: but, generally speaking, the proportion which the other classes of citizens bears in any state to that of its husbandmen, is the proportion of its unsound to its healthy parts, and is a good enough barometer whereby to measure its degree of corruption. While we have land to labour then, let us never wish to see our citizens occupied at a workbench, or twisting a distaff. Carpenters, masons, smiths, are wanting in husbandry: but, for the general operations of manufacture, let our workshops remain in Europe. It is better to carry provisions and materials to workmen there, than bring them to the provisions and materials, and with them their manners and principles. The loss by the transportation of commodities across the Atlantic will be made up in happiness and permanence of government. The mobs of the great cities add just so much to the support of pure government, as sores do to the strength of the human body. It is the manners and spirit of a people which preserve a republic in vigour. A degeneracy in these is a canker which soon eats to the heart of its laws and constitution.[33]

In the space colony scenario for the future one can clearly see the reappearance of this initial Jeffersonian pastoral ideal for America. Instead of leaving the workshops of industrialism in Europe, O'Neill and Stine place them in their true home beyond the too-fragile envelope of this emerald planet. But the effect is the same: with the dirty work of industry safely at a distance, supplying the material needs of a basically agrarian and thoroughly blessed people, first the United States and now the entire world can be maintained as a purified landscape of pastorial bliss.

What began as the problem of the machine in the Edenic American garden has ended with the problem of how to manufacture the garden within the machine. On the surface, at least to a people captivated by mechanism and the machine metaphor, the idea of creating a wholly new earth (or earths, if we choose) seems to represent a final solution to the dialectical tension between the city and the wilderness, the machine and the garden. With the space colony scenario, we are promised infinite wealth and power, as well as a reconciliation with mother earth, a mother who, admittedly, has suffered much until now at the hands of reason. In Biblical terms, we find a renewed hope that Cain's search for a world without pain, a world beyond the presence of God, might yet turn out to have been a viable strategy, especially if we believe ourselves capable of creating our own new worlds, yet compassionate enough to restore the one God gave us.

Although unrecognized in its secular form, the American New World Vision, in its simplest archetypal form, bears the characteristics of the primal myth described by mythologist Joseph Campbell in his masterful crosscultural study of the myth of the hero. First there is a separation from the world, a retreat away from civilization in the direction of the wilderness, then a penetration to a source of power, followed by a triumphant and life-enhancing return. In the case of America, the trials presented by the frontier led us to the discovery of the power of the machine, and with that power we have returned to the city to remake the earth in the image of a garden.[34] The space colony proposal is merely a new variation of the radically secularized American myth of the eternal return.

But this is what the poet William Blake would have recognized as a spectral parody, a confusion of similitude and identity. To literally enact such a degraded myth, to inflate the power of ego and intellect to such cosmic dimensions, would in Blake's terms, lead to the creation of the hermaphroditic Covering Cherub. In Blake's apocalyptic vision, the Cherub incarnates the form of our enslavement to our own selfhood.[35] A space colony with an "earthly" paradise contained within, would easily fit Blake's image of the Covering Cherub which encloses and obscures the New Jerusalem, the form of our human freedom. Its resemblance to the new heaven and new earth anticipated since the founding of America suggests that what keeps us from re-entering Eden is our vulnerability to its simulations.

Since the entire superindustrial space colony scenario has been offered as an alternative to the pain and suffering of the "Last Days" as described in the original apocalypse, we should be alert to the possibility that the enactment of this vision may lead to the very war of all against all that its advocates fear. This possibility can, perhaps, be seen more clearly in an analysis of the psychology of transformative experience.

Superindustrialism as myth

All images of the future, especially those that attract large numbers of enthusiastic followers, are expressions of religious myths, archetypal impulses, that arise in the psyche to restore order and meaning to the experience of everyday life. It is one of the conceits of modernism that such religious and mythological tendencies are a thing of the prescientific and primitive past. But, as the eruption of the unrecognized Nazi myth of apocalypse and self-destruction clearly demonstrated, we may be free to "despise mythologies and theologies but that will not prevent [us] from continuing to feed upon decayed myths and degraded images."[36] In fact, it could be argued that the repression of genuine religious myth has led to the leading neurosis of our time, "to a primitive mythologization of secular values, to a pseudoreligion of material prosperity, monetary greed, and sexual thrills."[37]

During periods of collective stress, when a culture no longer meets the psychic, social, and material needs of its people, unconscious content of the psyche, long repressed, breaks to the surface in new images of wholeness, new images of the future. The eruption of such visions of reconciliation and transformation seems to be the expression of an innate integrative function.

The voice of this partly unconscious urge to wholeness and integration is loudest when integrity is most deeply threatened, when the contradictions and failures of the social order create divisions within the self which demand, for their resolution, the creation of a new, more harmonious biological, psychological, and social order.

As we experience the multiple failures and contradictions of urban-industrial institutions and values, we can see the urge to wholeness in the form of images of the future, a time when current crisis is transcended in a new order. Even in the superindustrial visions of Kahn, O'Neill, and Stine we can see the need expressed as prophecies of a new millennium through the final victory of science and technology. Viewing our current troubles as the result of a failure to complete the secularization of life begun over 500 years ago, the new priests of the industrial state are now calling on us to renew our faith and redouble our efforts. But, as we have seen, there is at least some cause to doubt whether more of the same will save us from the problems this view of reality has already created.

But such images from the repressed and unconscious layers of the psyche do not automatically provide literal solutions to the problem that may have generated them. Images that may appear to justify the past and offer new hope for the future can lead to delusion and self-destructive Ghost Dances and Cargo Cults as well as to wholly new and more adaptive cultural forms.[38]

Notwithstanding the accidents of circumstance and history, the misunderstood or unexpected responses of other individuals or groups, the pathology of certain prophets, and the exploitative use of authentic vision by unscrupulous individuals, the power of a dream-vision of reconciliation to work its healing effect depends on whether the vision is first assimilated in symbolic terms and subjected to the ethical and moral cannons of the individual and his or her group. If the vision is blindly enacted as an escape from the pain of the present, the result is likely to be disastrous.

The charismatic appeal of the space colony myth, even in the face of all rational arguments against it, suggests the operation of such unassimilated

forces, and the literal enactment of either Kahn's earth-centered or O'Neill's space-bound scenarios holds the prospect of amplifying the present problems and anxieties to new levels of despair. Thus, it is particularly disturbing that many people of the world's most scientific and "rational" society should now find their best hope for survival in a myth of cosmic escape. We have seen how the superindustrial images of the future are the *Reductio ad Absurdum* of the New World Vision of a return to Eden through science and technology. Now, to complete our analysis of these secularized myths, we must examine their psychological roots to discover the source of their charismatic appeal during these troubled times and to see why action based on them is likely to be so counterproductive.

Initiation and the crisis of industrialism

As seen so clearly in the poetry of William Blake, the psychology of C.G. Jung, and the mystical traditions of all peoples, the internal structure of the psyche is interpersonal: the gods and demons, the guides and antagonists, and the forces of darkness and light are experienced by the conscious ego as persons engaged in a struggle for the human soul. Consequently, the integration of any one person implies and includes the integration of society into a differentiated, yet harmonious, social whole. In the macrocosm of human society we see a reflection of the microcosm of the human self. To realize the full human potential is to simultaneously create a fully humanized world. Thus, all images of the future are simultaneously personal and social visions of reconciliation.

Whether in a shaman's descent to the underworld, the birth, death and resurrection of Christ, or the spontaneous efforts of a schizophrenic trying to re-gain his wholeness, the separation, ini-tiation, and return cycle of the hero myth describes the process of rebirth and the integration of the self. In the course of such transformative proc-esses the ego must first experience an impasse (Bateson's double-bind), a sit-uation where both action and inaction seem to make the problems worse. Such an impasse should, therefore, be welcomed, for all its pain, as an indica-tor that one is on the path. The im-passe, like a Zen koan, must then be lived consciously as a symbol of one's inherent personality conflicts. In the Christian variant of the myth, one must suffer the crucifixion willingly, learning not to act compulsively to avoid suffering or to willfully attempt to do away with the impasse.

Premature action at this point can lead to a situation similar to that of the paranoid schizophrenic who "unable to comprehend or tolerate the stark ter-rors of his inner world, prematurely di-rects his attention to the outside world. In this type of abortive crisis solution, the inner chaos is not, so to speak, worked through, or is not capable of being worked through."[39] The result of repressing the demons is to drive them back into the unconscious where they retain their primitive and compul-sive power and, because they are un-conscious forces, become subject to displacement and projection. When this occurs, we become, like the para-noid schizophrenic, captives of the pro-jections of our own evil, in a solipsistic world outside of which there is no es-cape.

If, however, the conflict within the self can be endured with conscious dis-cipline rather than escaped through compulsive action, the unconscious and repressed forces, which have until now been experienced as antagonists,

as forces of evil, are suddenly trans-formed into helpers through the recon-ciling power of a genuine archetypal symbol of wholeness. At this point, and only at this point, is productive ac-tion possible and the rebirth experience genuine.

The space colony parody of rebirth and wholeness, based as it is on both a desire to escape the suffering of the present and an awareness of the suf-fering and violence of the industrial past, is a case of compulsive projection, an attempt to escape the experience of initiation. In Jungian terms, it repre-sents the assimilation of the Self into the ego, a state of megalomania and paranoid delusion in which one loses sight of concrete, personal, and human limitations in an attempt to play God. Rather than accepting impasse as a de-feat, the ego inflates itself to cosmic proportions in a last, final effort to es-cape the necessity for change. And its rage for order organizes the very forces of chaos it is seeking to escape. The re-sult is a more violent defeat for the ego.

So the attempt to literally enact the space colony myth is likely to increase human suffering and planetary destruc-tion to new levels, rather than serving to avoid them. One can imagine that space stations would become floating islands of nuclear destruction, raining death rather than consumer products on an earth drained of its last resources by the very effort to build them. This scenario for the "end of days" would surely be a bitter and ironic fulfillment of Columbus's expectation that his dis-covery would lead to the completion of the prophecy of Saint John. But given our recent experience with the Nazi myth of world destruction,[40] such a possibility should not be taken lightly.

Jefferson's other vision

We have seen how Jefferson's rejection of technology as an evil influence from Europe is ironically transfigured by the space colony myth into a vision of factories floating in space around a garden planet tended by updated yeoman farmers. But to fully understand the parallels between Jefferson's thought on the place of technology in the future of America and current American images of the future, we must examine his other vision, a vision of reconciliation with the machine. If we had only his early account from *Notes on Virginia* it would appear that Jefferson was an idealistic dreamer, a technophobe who completely failed to grasp the enormous impact the emerging machine technology would have on the American experience. But Jefferson was an enthusiastic tinkerer, as well as a statesman and philosopher, and a quarter of a century later, in 1812, he had come to see the machine's potential for realizing his initial pastoral vision. Rather than leaving "manufactures" to the Europeans, who could, as shown in the War of 1812, cut America off from its vital supplies, Jefferson came to believe, along with a growing segment of American leaders, that the very machines that had created the cruel capitalist factories of Europe would, in the Edenic landscape of America, produce just the opposite effect. He believed that the new engines of production would allow the increased decentralization of production, making the idea of household manufactures by a nation of yeoman farmers a real possibility rather than a wistful dream. With a shortage of labor, an abundance of land on an ever-expanding frontier, and a belief that the American landscape could purify the ideas and immigrants of Europe, Jefferson hitched his dream of an American middle earth to the rising star of science and technology.[41]

Ironically, it was that decentralist vision that later philosophers, statesmen, and industrialists reforged into the American belief in unlimited moral and material progress through the growth of science and technology. In the process, the original belief that America was to become an earthly paradise was transformed into the secular faith that the new heaven and new earth would grow inevitably out of the marriage of mechanization and Republican virtue. But the synthesis became a radical inversion of Jefferson's hope that technology would make possible an historically unprecedented society of economically self-reliant, self-governing, small communities firmly rooted in American soil. Just as he had feared in his first naive vision, the importation of capitalist technology from the sweatshops of Europe brought far more than its potential as a decentralizing source of motive power.

If Jefferson were alive now to see how his pastoral vision of a nation of yeoman farmers and household manufactures had first justified and then been subverted by the juggernaut of technology, he would perhaps remind us that we had not yet attempted to create the kind of middle earth he had in mind. Looking at Kahn's scenario of a nation where less than one percent of the population tills the earth with monstrous air-conditioned machines, he might well respond in language reminiscent of his discourse on the place of farming and the role of manufactures in his *Notes on Virginia*. And, with perfect hindsight, he might well admit the error of his naive belief that somehow the use of the machine technologies of Europe would not, on this Edenic continent, lead to a capitalist economy and a nation of cities. He might now be able to see that technology is not neutral, that it is a language of social action that shapes consciousness as well as the material environment. He might be moved to ask the question posed by E.F. Schumacher:

> If our technology has been created mainly by the capitalist system, is it not probable that it bears the marks of its origin, a technology of exploitation, a technology that is class-oriented, undemocratic, inhuman, and also unecological and nonconservationist?[42]

And his answer might sound like Schumacher's comment on the idea, held by many developing countries today, that it is possible to have the West's technology without its ideology, patterns of settlement, life styles, and so on.

> The implicit assumption is that you can have a technological transplant without getting at the same time an ideological transplant; that technology is ideologically neutral; that you can acquire the hardware without the software that lies behind it, has made the hardware possible, *and keeps it moving*. Is this not a bit like saying: I want to import eggs for hatching, but I don't want chicks from them but mice or kangaroos?[43]

But Jefferson, like all Americans before and since, probably would not have lost his belief that we might yet create a garden paradise. The mythological substructure of national ideologies runs very deep. Jefferson might counsel us that, rather than making the same mistakes on a larger scale, we not attempt another beginning or construct grand visions for a great society without first confronting past mistakes and living through the trauma of that confrontation in a spirit of voluntary and conscious suffering. He might agree with Mumford that, "Until every generation did this consciously, examining its hoary tradition in the light of new experience, evaluating and selecting every part of its heritage, man [can]

make no fresh start."[44]

So, realizing that some form of an optimistic image of the future is necessary to energize action toward its realization, we shall close by offering a variant of Jefferson's second new world vision, a myth that may prove appropriate to our present global crisis.

William Irwin Thompson and the metaindustrial vision

When Kahn and O'Neill look at the current crises of industrial civilization, their belief in the goodness of science, technology, and modern institutions is so complete that the only future world they can imagine is one created by increasing the current power of industrial beliefs and processes. Consequently, when they survey the field of images of the future (see Figure 1), they see only the one-dimensional choice of superindustrialism or savagery. The metaindustrial alternative, as a positive image, completely escapes their attention.

But if the current industrial civilization is seen as being somewhat less than good, as the cause of the tragedies confronting humankind, then more of the same would be viewed with horror as a path leading to an even more violent collapse. Such a picture of the present is the foundation for the metaindustrial images of the future.

Cultural historian William Irwin Thompson believes we are experiencing the sunset effect of industrial civilization, and his negative scenario for the future requires only the continuation of things as they are. According to his view, if we do not see the growing dilemmas of industrial civilization as the signs of its decline, and attempt instead to sustain economic growth in a last mad rush to consume the earth, we are likely to experience the future as a negative destruction rather than as a joyful destructuring.

Revisioning the effects of following Kahn's proposal for the next 200 years, Thompson sees the escalation of impasse rather than its resolution. As the economic contradictions of inflation and unemployment increase with our attempts to heat up the economy, we would begin to see the bankruptcy of New York as the future for the entire nation. As more and more people are thrown out of work and the value of the dollar continues to plummet, there would be a move to establish a strong presidency along the lines of those in Brazil and Argentina. Such a regime would seek a new marriage of labor and management as the multinational corporations frantically attempted to maintain high levels of employment along with their vast power and autonomy.

Desperate to secure new sources of concentrated energy to maintain our centralized utilities and government bodies, we would abolish standards for environmental quality in a mad rush to strip mine the Dakotas and to supply electricity with dangerous nuclear power. As the number of nuclear plants increased during such a period of social turbulence, the need for a garrison state to protect us from terrorists would become commonly accepted and fully implemented.

In an atmosphere of fear and confusion created by chronic brownouts, blackouts, and widespread eruptions of violence like that witnessed in the recent truckers strike, people would gladly begin to surrender their civil liberties to a paternalistic state which offered to:

. . . become the guarantor of the pension funds and the savior of the middle-class dream of security. But the more people surrender their civil liberties in return for government paternalism, the

more the terrorists of Right and Left will seek to disrupt the government. The more terrorism there is, the more the government will seek to protect the population through strong emergency powers. The people will clamor for security and demand to be driven to work in tanks, but the more authoritarian order is imposed, the more revolutionary anarchy will be stimulated. And so the whole culture will spin downward to darkness in a tightening spiral.[45]

As the contradictions of industrialism are heightened, the climate would be ripe for increasing conflict with other nations as everyone scrambled to secure their own share of diminishing stores of energy and raw materials. At this point, the recent CIA studies of the possibility of seizing oil wells in the Middle East and using food as a weapon to extort raw materials from the developing world would be dusted off and presented as the only means to protect national security. Since other nations would be experiencing similar crises and responding with similar tactics, the stage would be set for Heilbroner's wars of "pre-emptive seizure" or "wars of redistribution."

In his sketch of a future of authoritarian government, resource shortages, massive crop failures, and wars among and within nations, created by "more of the same," Thompson is projecting the very world O'Neill and Kahn expect to avoid through the Third Industrial Revolution. From the narrow perspective of a liberal technocrat like O'Neill, who sees history as a linear ascent from savagery to civilization through increasingly powerful and destructive technology, such a scenario is unthinkable. But to a cultural historian like Thompson who remembers that at least 30 civilizations have experienced such an age of dissolution, the real possibility that such events can occur again is at least plausible:

> And so, by pressing onward to Herman Kahn's superindustrial society, our culture becomes overextended and directed toward an even greater civilizational collapse.
>
> And yet nothing seems to be able to stop industrialization. The revolt of romanticism against industrialization did not stop it. Marxism did not stop it. Anarchism did not stop it. The disintegration of the British Empire by tribal nationalism did not stop it. Like an enormous flood sweeping through a narrow valley, the torrent seems to pick up everything which stands in its way to include it in its own behavior. As you see romantic poet, anarchist, communist, and hippie swept up and floating in the rushing stream, you can see that revolt cannot stop the flood but only lend a little color to the floating debris of history.
>
> Now the mystical movements of the seventies seem about to be swept up in the torrent. Planetary mysticism, the romantic rejection of post-industrial civilization, seems about to be absorbed to become part of the ideological camouflage of planetary management . . . Hip management has now moved from Esalen to EST and even Indira Gandhi has been credited with using Kundalini Yoga to help her save the nation from the perils of an unbridled freedom.[46]

Thompson interprets the decline of industrial civilization in a way that gives meaning to the suffering we are experiencing, and proposes a positive scenario for the present period of cultural transformation. However, his alternative vision of the future is not based on a willfully ignorant optimism nor an unrealistic belief that the pains of change can be avoided by adopting his alternative. Rather, his vision is an affirmation of possibilities for personal and social renewal as a result of, not an alternative to, the death of a civilizational form that no longer serves the purposes of life.

Thompson properly sees the present period of confusion and suffering as a rite of passage necessary for the birth of a new form of human culture and a more integrated human self. And, since it is seldom possible for those who are participating in such a profound cultural change to see what is happening, Thompson chooses to see the signs in the present which suggest that we are experiencing a transition "from civilization to planetization, from a materialistic industrial society based upon production and consumption to a contemplative culture based upon consciousness and ecological symbiosis."[47]

Cycles of change

All processes of organic and adaptive social change progress through a four-part cycle. First, there is a period of stability within a guiding paradigm or world view. The map fits the territory. Gradually, as the gap between expectation and experience widens, people begin to experience doubt about the truth and goodness of dominant ideas and institutions. If anomaly cannot be resolved, the next phase is a stage of crisis where the map clearly does not fit the territory. New descriptions of reality begin to compete for popular acceptance. Eventually, this period of radical change is replaced by a new period of stability and developmental change within the new paradigm that has emerged as the successor to the old world view. If we were to take this circular process and stretch it out on a line, we would have a representation of Thompson's understanding of the spiral of time we call history: "we turn back to the past, reconstitute it, and then turn away from it in a new direction."[48] If, as Thompson believes, we are now experiencing the radical transformation of a culture of giantism, centralization, and imperial power, we might expect that the future will be characterized by a shift from industrial factories to craft-guild workshops, from massive cities of fragmented individuals to decentralized communities of mutual obligation, and from a secular to a sacred world view. But such a return to earlier expressions of human culture does not imply a simple linear regression, as the one-dimensional image of history held by Kahn and O'Neill would predict. Rather, as Mumford has said,

> As with every other fresh integration, each part must die to its old form, in order to be born anew within a larger whole, and become viable in terms of the new self and the new culture we are putting forward.[49]

In formulating his image of a metaindustrial alternative to Kahn's superindustrial state, Thompson includes all the earlier expressions of human culture in an imaginative reconstruction of a new world out of the present chaos—a cosmos that unites past and present, the real and ideal, and the individual and society in an image of wholeness on the far side of a creative heightening of conflict, through the destruction of the present to a new resolution in a perfected future. In short, Thompson's image of the future has all the characteristics of an apocalyptic-millennial vision. Rather than ignoring the dilemmas and double-binds of industrial civilization in a cosmic myth of escape, he chooses to transcend them in a vision of rebirth and renewal. And, since America has given the world the charismatic archetype of the powerful industrial state, Thompson proposes that the way for Americans to work for the creation of a new heaven and new earth is to stay at home to create the forms of a new metaindustrial synthe-

sis. In short, it is our role to create a new elite with a new mythology to give meaning to the process of change and to provide new models for human culture.

Revisioning the past in a transformed future

If, as Mumford has observed, it is impossible to make a complete break with the past, and if we are to avoid making our earlier mistake of thinking we could forget the old world of European culture in the creation of the new world, then we must form our image of the future by remembering the past.

Unlike the parochial histories of Kahn and O'Neill, Thompson's history includes the evolution of consciousness as well as the development of technology. In his view, the earliest forms of human culture were the hunting and gathering societies, small tribes that moved through space in the circular flow of time. Within the seasonal round of nature and the containing security of the circle of the small band, life was a unity of nature, self, and society in symbiotic harmony. But the price of this harmony was the lack of development of the individual self, since the group and the animistic deities of nature were the sources of personal worth and identity.

So, with the Neolithic and the Urban Revolutions, which occurred over a period from 10,000 to 4,000 years ago, there was a profound revolution in consciousness as well as culture. By staying fixed in space, and changing nature to suit the needs of the group, time became a line described by the calendar, and the primal unity with nature was severed to create a world where unity was now experienced in the conflict of opposites: nature versus culture, the individual versus the group, the ego versus the self, and the urban power elite versus the rural hick. With the invention of writing, knowledge became disconnected from mind, body, and communal group and was stored, like the grain of its large-scale agriculture, in the containers of the city. And while the rise of large urban concentrations generated the evils of slavery, compulsory labor, economic exploitation, social regimentation, environmental degradation, and organized warfare, it also created the basis for the development of the ego and initiated an intensified process of individuation.

But if the city, which is the vehicle for and definition of civilization, makes the ego possible, the resulting split in consciousness also generates the increasingly desperate and ultimately futile effort to achieve the lost unity of the tribe through the accumulation of wealth, status, and power. And so, in the intensification of civilization brought by the Industrial Revolution, we find ever more desperate attempts to escape the curse of Cain through the domination of man and nature.

This process has continued until the present and at this moment in history, which is the point of the maximum spread of civilization and cities to every corner of the globe, we are experiencing the limit of the very dialectic of center and periphery, city and desert, initiated by the urban revolution. Facing an explosion of fragmented information, we have reached the limits of knowledge initiated by the discovery of writing in the first urban centers. Confronting the end of the age of fossil fuels and easily recoverable raw materials, we have now reached the limits of the urban-industrial concentration of wealth, power, and material culture. And, in our rage to order the chaos we have created, we are discovering the limits to the dialectic of chaos and control. Our very search for a unity with the world has become the cause of the fragmentation and dissociation of consciousness that drives us to establish ever more elaborate and authoritarian modes of being and organizational hierarchies of social control.

If then, as Thompson so argues, we have reached the limits to the contradictions of civilization, we might look for the signs of a countermovement, a turning away from the imperial animus of empire toward the cultural forms of our earlier identity with creation. Rather than seeing a continuation of Kahn's multifold trend toward increasingly large-scale impersonal organizations, more powerful technocratic elites, and an increasingly secularized and fragmented consciousness, ending in a global ecumenopolis and world-ringing necklace of space colonies, Thompson sees a return to a new form of an earlier expression of human culture—the Neolithic village.

The Neolithic village or its modern variant, the preindustrial village, was based on certain internalized images of space and time. Through the identity of the family name, the individual was rooted in his or her past through a linear progression of generations stretching from past to present. And, through attachment to place through family land, the image of space linked the person to the pulse of sun and wind and the cycles of seasonal time. But if the individual was contained within the comforting bounds of time and space through the attachments of blood and soil, he or she was also imprisoned by tradition and bound to a limited world by the demands of endless production and reproduction. And it was this too-narrow confinement which created the "idiocy of rural life" which, in turn, provided the impetus for the rush to the city with its lure of freedom and its own form of cosmopolitan servitude.

So, if we are to return to some form of the preindustrial village in compensation for, and as an alternative to, civilization and its discontents, we must do so in an historically novel way that avoids the weaknesses of this social form while providing the urban benefits of mobility, the free flow of information, and a wider human identity and a deeper human self. Otherwise we shall simply repeat the same endless round of flight and confinement which has reached its limits in our present age.

It is this possibility that animates Thompson's hopes for the future. Toward this end he sees four archetypal forces at work in the present which suggest the possibility of such a transformation: (1) the planetization of nations, (2) the decentralization of cities, (3) the miniaturization of technology, and (4) the interiorization of consciousness.

The planetization of nations

In a planetary human ecology, where everything is connected to everything else, we can no longer continue to have a world made up of nation-states, each claiming total autonomy in relation to other nations. The proliferation of nuclear weapons to the presently absurd levels among the superpowers and the imminent spread of this capacity for destruction to dozens of other nations, has created a situation in which global destruction becomes more probable every day. A world facing limits to growth can no longer afford to spend massive proportions of its wealth in preparation for a war of all against all. As Thompson points out, the alternative to a new planetary world order is

thermonuclear war or economic collapse, or both.

The belief in the necessity of creating a world community is a defining characteristic of advocates of a metaindustrial future. Mumford, for example, bases his hopes for humankind on one assumption,

. . . the destiny of mankind, after its long preparatory period of separation and differentiation, is at last to become one. Our survey of man's successive transformations has disclosed the fact that the widening of the base of human community, though fitful and erratic, has nevertheless been one of the cumulative results of human history. This unity is on the point of being politically expressed in a world government that will unite regions and nations in transactions beyond their individual capacity: it will be spurred to these difficult tasks of political and economic unification by common ideals of human development. The words that G.A. Borgese applied to one aspect of this movement may now be applied to the whole task of building a world culture: "It is necessary; therefore it is possible."[50]

While the goal of world unity transcending the divisions of competitive nation-states is also a goal of the superindustrial scenario, the unity envisioned by Thompson, Mumford, and other advocates of the metaindustrial alternative is one that "seeks to enrich and enhance, in the very transactions of world society, the human values that differentiation has brought into existence."[51] This vision of unity through diversity is the exact opposite of the kind of technocratic homogeneity and authoritarian management that a world unified by mechanization and space colonies would create.

The decentralization of cities

The possibility of establishing a truly planetary civilization is directly related to our ability to overcome the accelerating trends of massification in impersonal organizations and giant megalopolitan concentrations:

> The more readily we conceive the planet as a single unit and move about it freely on missions of study or work, the more necessary it is to establish such a home base, such an intimate psychological core, with visible landmarks and cherished personalities. The world will not become a neighborhood, even if every part of it is bound by instant communication and rapid transportation, if the neighborhood itself as an idea and a social form is allowed to disappear.[52]

So, in a metaindustrial return to the past we must begin to destructure our vast and anonymous cities into coherent and meaningful social and territorial groups. We must recreate, in historically novel forms, the opportunities to experience the nurturing bonds of place and the primary face-to-face group—family, household, and neighborhood. We must rediscover the preindustrial and Neolithic village in the midst of our urban wastelands.

Such communal groups, formed for no special purposes, as are secondary associations such as interest groups, are crucial to the development of balanced and healthy human personalities. Rather than the "communities of purified identity" we have created in suburb and ghetto, the true place-centered urban community of the future must be characterized by a mixture of age groups, world views, life styles, and values. If we are to reverse the modern tendency to create narrow communities of like-minded people, the city, with its historically crucial role of confronting the individual with the fact of "otherness," must be given new meaning and new form.[53] A planetary civilization can only be rooted in communities made up of people who are different from each other, who sometimes disagree. We cannot make the mistake of the original new world visionaries of thinking that it is good (or even possible) to start completely fresh, leaving the cities and their problems behind to live in new communities among mirror reflections of our own partial selves.

The image of the city as a federation of interdependent urban villages is a far cry from Kahn's dream of a single, world-circling ecumenopolis. According to Kahn's extrapolation of his "multifold trend" we are headed toward (and therefore should seek) an ecumene rather than a community, a world city rather than a global village, and a world market rather than a marketplace. But, by elevating trend into destiny in his image of the world as a global shopping center run by multinational corporate elites, Kahn is proposing a path of development that would subvert his expectation of a growing "sense of 'world public opinion' and of shared responsibility for all human beings."[54]

As psychologist Erich Von Neumann has pointed out, such an acceleration of massification will only create more dissociated and power-oriented egos, intensifying the process of alienation from the unconscious. This alienation, in turn, would increase the probability of another occurrence of recollectivization, similar to that which took place in Nazi Germany. The genuine day-to-day experience of communities of shared space and mutual obligation is the only hope we have of avoiding such a destructive regression to primitive personality disorders and social pathologies:

> The group contains its own regulator, not only in the form of the ruling canon, but in the mutual knowledge all members have of one another. The very ano-

nymity in the mass intensifies the action of the shadow side.[55]

So, if we don't decentralize our cities into coherent and recognizable social, political, economic, and technological units, we will only continue the dialectic of the mass and the fragmented self. The result, as Thompson so vividly describes, will be unmanageable cities and disconnected individuals:

> The opposite force to decentralization is, of course, urbanization, and if we do not decentralize, then all our cities will become like Calcutta, and the center-periphery dialectic of civilization will reach its extreme polarization in dictatorship and terrorism. If civilization is not transformed, it will explode.[56]

The miniaturization of technology

Until the last world war, the direction of technology had been toward increasingly large, centralized production units. But in the last 35 years, there has been a countermovement with the development of small-scale multipurpose machinery, miniaturized communications equipment and highly durable and efficient renewable energy technologies.[57] The shift in the scale of technology, Thompson believes, has profound implications for cultural evolution:

> If the machines are small and people can once again hear the trees, then the sensibility goes through a profound revolution and the relationship between culture and nature changes dramatically. The miniaturization of technology enables us to reduce the scale of the impact of industrialization on the biosphere. In a shift from hardware to information, from capital-intensive economies of scale to communal forms of regional production, from consumer values to contemplative values, the industrial maladjustment to nature is corrected and the neurotic compulsions of modern society are alleviated.[58]

The opposite of a culture based on small-scale, decentralized, but often highly sophisticated renewable energy technologies is a culture in which giantism, centralization, and hierarchy combine to create a mechanized state suitable only for habitation by Mumford's "post-historic man."[59] Such a society would be the ironic completion of Bacon's scientific-technological utopia—a world in which all human behavior, even the functioning of ecological systems and climate (as in the case of O'Neill's space colonies) would be subject to the control of multidisciplinary teams of experts operating from a position superordinate to the masses.

So, we can choose now to create the material conditions for a modern, technological culture of abundance based on the values of frugality and voluntary simplicity, rooted in the practices of democratic decision making, and supportive of diversity of place and local culture, or we shall instead experience as fate the world painted by Kahn. And since Kahn's expectation that such a world would be compensated by universal material wealth is likely to be grossly wrong, we would end up with a less than friendly fascism.

The interiorization of consciousness

The final force Thompson sees operating in the world today is the tendency for people to look within for a source for their values:

> In the emergence of the modern world in the sixteenth century, there was a shift from the concentric, centripetal orientation of medieval Christendom to the centrifugal expansions in the age of humanism, exploration, and science. This orientation still continues in the exploration of space. The externalization of consciousness leads the individual to look for all values outside: the next fron-

tier contains the solution to all the disappointments of the last frontier. You move to the New World, cut down its forests, pollute its great lakes, and then look to Australia, Brazil, or LaGrange Place V in space. Now, however, we can sense the beginning of the end of the masculine mode of externalization.[60]

Whether in the religious conversion experience of a Russell Schweickart floating free in space, seeing and knowing the whole earth for the first time, or in the widespread experimentation with Yoga, Zen, Sufism, Celtic animism, and mystical forms of Judaism and Christianity, the exploration of outer space has been accompanied by a renewed search for mystical or nondualistic modes of being. This adventure of consciousness is a return to modes of human understanding that join art, science, and religion in a new synthesis. And such a turn on the spiral of history from the secular worldview of industrialism to the sacred consciousness of the archaic traditions and the great universal religions is exactly the counterforce needed to humanize our technology.

Thompson makes the point that this return to ancient and forgotten wisdom is not simply a regression to old forms, but rather, a new expression of that repressed part of the modern psyche:

In a Hegelian dialectic of *aufheben* America is swallowing up and absorbing the traditional Eastern techniques of transformation, because only these are strong enough to humanize its technology. In the days before planetization, when civilization was split between East and West, there were basically two cultural directions. The Westerner went outward to level forests, conquer nations, and walk upon the moon; the Easterner went inward and away from the physical into the astral and causal planes. Now, . . . we can glimpse the beginnings of a new level of religious experience, neither Eastern nor Western, but planetary.[61]

So, in addition to returning to the earlier forms of human community most completely expressed in the preindustrial village, Thompson suggests that we are also returning to earlier modes of a unitary consciousness of reality first experienced by the hunter and gatherer, and later extended to a universal ideal by the great religious traditions of early civilization. But we are doing so with the full consciousness of the modern postindustrial world, and a full awareness of the limitations of earlier historical expressions. The result of this new synthesis of past and present is a new form of sacred world view.

Mumford, for many years, has made the same argument:

Now this change toward world culture parallels a change that seems also on the point of taking place within the human personality: a change in the direction of wholeness and balance . . ., parts of the human organism long buried or removed from conscious control will be brought to light, recognized, accepted, reevaluated, and redirected. The ability to face one's whole self, and to direct every part of it toward a more unified development, is one of the promises held forth by the advance both of objective science and subjective understanding.[62]

Thus, in the metaindustrial vision of possibilities there is a mutually supportive and reciprocal relation between the planetization of nations, the restoration of the earth, and the historically unfulfilled promise of a fully developed, unified, and integrated human self. In the words of Theodore Roszak, the "needs of a planet and the needs of the person have begun to act upon the central institutions of our society with a force that is profoundly subversive, but which carries within it the promise of cultural renewal."[63]

But, like the other three societal forces, the interiorization of consciousness has an equal and opposite force:

If we do not achieve the interiorization of consciousness in our culture, then the result will be the continuing externalization of our sickness in pollution and catastrophic disruption of the biosphere from industrial and nuclear wastes. The law of opposites will play itself out, and the heating up of the atmosphere from global industrial development will alter the biosphere and disrupt the whole basis of industrial civilization.[64]

The metaindustrial village as cultural strategy

Assuming that we can avoid a nuclear holocaust or a massive disruption of world climate and biological support systems, Thompson suggests that in the next generation or two we shall return to an economy in which a larger percentage of the population will be involved in primary production. This prediction is, as might be expected, the exact opposite of Kahn's multifold trend toward a superindustrial society dominated by quarternary economic activity.

Thus, rather than extrapolating the emerging postindustrial economy of the United States to its *Reductio Ad Absurdum* completion in the superindustrial future of Kahn, Thompson imagines a return to an occupational structure similar to that of the United States around the turn of the last century. In projecting this dialectical reversal of the spiral of history, Thompson assumes that the four societal forces, the planetization of nations, the decentralization of cities, the miniaturization of technology, and the interiorization of consciousness will have

gained adherents and momentum enough to begin the process of reshaping the American landscape, culture, and consciousness:

I am assuming that by the year 2000 the electronic decentralization of information and the miniaturization of technology will enable people to move from New York, Detroit, and Los Angeles to live in rural areas. I am assuming that the production of good small tools will enable communities to produce goods and services in small workshops rather than large factories. I am assuming that the existence of electronics, as expressed in informational flow and miniaturized technology, will enable society to appreciate the prophetic visions of Piotr Kropotkin rather than Karl Marx. I am also assuming that, as human beings begin to move out of the concrete world of New York to live with the trees, the consciousness of the individual will undergo a profound transformation in a scientific return to animism.[65]

Noting the key role in past cultural transformations played by small groups, such as the monastery school of Lindisfarne founded in 634 A.D. on an island off the coast of Northumbria, and Pythagoras's school at Crotona,[66] Thompson calls for the creation of living models of the metaindustrial village:

Evolution occurs in small populations of *demes* in which a mutation has taken place. The metaindustrial village is just such a deme; it is a place in which the four cultural forces are completely expressed.[67]

Thompson believes that by absorbing the four major cultural and economic forms of history and miniaturizing them so they are visible in a single, comprehensible social form, the movement toward a metaindustrial culture can be hastened. So, in this imaginative return to the past, the metaindustrial village would express the form of a culture yet unborn.

The hunting and gathering economy would be expressed in the gathering of wood, wind, and sun, and perhaps in the harvesting of nuts, berries, and small game from carefully managed multistory polyculture tree farms.[68] The agricultural economy would be expressed in the labor- and information-intensive cultivation of organically cultivated crops, after the fashion of current experiments in French Intensive/Biodynamic gardening. The industrial economy would be found in the form of small scale workshops in converted barns like those envisioned by Jefferson and realized in the last century by the Shakers. The postindustrial economy, with its emphasis on research and development and education, would exist as a basic characteristic of the community. With a planetary information flow with other communities throughout the world, and a communal life rooted in the practice of transformational disciplines such as Zen, Sufism, Yoga, and esoteric Christianity, the small community would inhabit a very large space and time. Like the Greek notion of *padeia,* education would be looked upon as a lifelong process of self-transformation in which every aspect of community life, from nonviolent birth to contemplative death, would play a part.

While there are now partial expressions of this vision of the metaindustrial village in such communities as Zen Center in California,[69] the Sufi community in New Lebanon, New York,[70] Findhorn in Scotland, and Auroville in India, none of these communities has succeeded in expressing the four classical human economies in a single deme:

> The importance of such miniaturization is that this compression makes

human evolution visible in a new way, and thus allows a new evolution of consciousness to take place. When you look back at something, you are already out of it and moving into a new environment. The four economies already exist together on the planet, and the planet from an evolutionary point of view is a single deme, but this planetary level of awareness is not available as a direct experience for many people. . . . By making the small human community into a microcosm of the planet, the community itself becomes a *yantra,* an object of contemplation for insight into universal processes of evolution and transformation. What M.I.T. was to postindustrial society, the metaindustrial village will become for the new culture.[71]

In contrast to the microcosm of the space colony, Thompson advances the image of a terrestrial village as a metaphor for the metaindustrial culture of the future and as a strategy for its realization. Despite their similarities as self-contained ideal types, Thompson believes that the space colony and the metaindustrial village represent two mutually exclusive modes of consciousness and paths of development. To pursue the path toward a superindustrial future would not only usurp the resources necessary for the creation of the metaindustrial alternative, but would also channel the social imagination in such a way that the ability to image alternatives to the blueprints of space engineers would atrophy. For Kahn and O'Neill the choice is between civilization and savagery, but for Thompson it is the alternative of civilized savagery or a reconciliation with the past in a new heaven and a new earth:

> By 1984 we should be at the fork in the road. Then everyone should be able to see clearly the choice we need to make. One road will lead toward nuclear power, strip mining, and authoritarian

governments, which can underwrite the contracts for the corporations and the pension funds of the labor unions, as well as protect industrial society from revolution and terrorism. The other road will lead toward a spiritual awakening on the level of the great universal religions that have guided the cultural evolution of humanity. This path will be expressed by a change of heart and mind, a new wedding of nature and culture, and a new kind of human community which can express the resacralization of the earth. With solar collectors contrasted with smog, smokestacks with windmills, meditators with teenagers with radios blasting in their ears as they walk the crowded streets, I hope that Americans will look at the two roads and choose the wisdom of the poet Gary Snyder, "to live lightly on the earth."[72]

Colonizing space or resettling the earth

Blake said that "Everything possible to be believed is an image of the truth." Both optimistic images of the future, the superindustrial and the metaindustrial, contain a surprising number of similarities. Both images see the crises of the present as a prelude to a great cultural transformation, a major revolution in the history of life on the planet. Both assume that the direction of this change is toward a higher form of human unity, relationship, and cooperation with nature. Both see the necessity to restore the health of the planet and to ensure equity in the distribution of life's basic necessities to all the peoples of the earth. Both eschew either the possibility or the desirability of a rejection of the gains of knowledge, technical skill, and scientific understanding made in the last 500 years. And, both suggest that the measure of our success in this great transformation is our ability to create a form of human culture that is sustainable. These shared

goals and understandings are what the philosopher and theologian Paul Tillich would call the truth of both propositions about the future.

But the differences in underlying assumptions and the means of achieving these shared goals betray a fundamental split in world view between the two images of the future. Whereas the superindustrial scenario proposes that the great cultural transformation will be the result of an escape from limits through the exploitation of space, the metaindustrial alternative envisions the emergence of an entirely new form of human culture through the acceptance of limits on this earth at this time. The metaindustrial vision reaffirms the ancient belief that we achieve our freedom in recognizing the limits of what is necessary and possible.

The superindustrial vision of world unity is rooted in the metaphor of the machine: it is an image of unity through the imposition of order by abstract intelligence and civilized elites. While the parts of a machine differ, the differences are an expression of predetermined and narrowly prescribed functions. Any conflict between the parts or between the parts and the whole would undermine the very purpose of the machine. The notion of mechanical order is appropriate for a machine but when the machine becomes a model for the organization of society, its meaning changes. Individual human beings do not exist as means to serve social ends: they are the ends for which society exists. Ultimately, a society conceived as a product of social engineering reduces people to the status of objects: if they cannot be made to fit the needs of the social machine, they must be retooled or replaced. Individuals existing in one of O'Neill's space colonies would become the ultimate expression of this inverted relationship between the needs of the individual and the needs of the group, since such artificial worlds would be the ultimate machine.

In contrast to this mechanized vision of unity through conformity, the metaindustrial scenario is rooted in organic metaphors of unity through diversity. Rather than being a whole made up of pre-engineered and hierarchically ordered parts, society is viewed as the pattern of relationships created by the evolving interactions of its parts—human and nonhuman. The social whole is seen as existing to serve the needs of the person, not the other way around. And unity is seen not as the expression of a lack of conflict between the part and the whole, but as the embodiment of higher levels of organization, order, and cooperation which grows out of the conflict among a diversity of self-regulating subsystems.

In the superindustrial future the earth is to be restored to an Edenic paradise by the expansion of technology and the inflation of the ego to cosmic proportions. In the metaindustrial option, the earth is to be restored to a state of health and balance through the reduction of our demands for material growth and expansion and through the selective application of technologies that serve the purposes of life. To O'Neill the exploitation of space is the prerequisite to the end of the degradation of the earth. To Thompson, the exploitation of space is an extension of the problem, not its solution. Violence only breeds more violence.

The problems of equity and distributive justice are solved for the superindustrialists by realizing the dream of unlimited wealth. But their metaindustrial counterparts would argue that the trickle-down theory of justice has not worked yet, that abject poverty still exists in the wealthiest country on earth, and that the gap between the poor and the rich within nations is increasing as is the gap between poor and rich nations.

The superindustrial image of the future is premised on the development of ever more powerful and complex technology, comprehensible to fewer and fewer highly trained specialists and controllable by no one. The metaindustrial proposal is to select and develop technologies that are simple, durable, affordable, and comprehensible, and controllable by political process. This vision of the role of technology recalls Jefferson's vision of an American democracy based on the use of tools that promoted household manufactures and community self-reliance, rather than the factory system with its vast cities and debased proletariat. O'Neill would now place these factories in the sky under transnational management—Thompson would restructure the productive enterprise on earth under community control.

And while the space colony myth would suggest that a sustainable culture is possible only by the infinite expansion of production and consumption, the metaindustrial vision is premised on Gandhi's belief that the "Earth provides enough to satisfy every man's need, but not enough for every man's greed."

So, what appears at first to be merely two paths to shared goals turns out, upon closer inspection, to be two separate paths to very different goals. As mental construct and material reality the two visions of the future stand before us, expressing the historical contradictions of industrial society. By making the choices so clear, they point toward the decision that we must and will make in the next 50 years. As Thompson has said, "Whichever choice we make, we will get what we deserve."[73]

References

1. Fred Polak, *The Image of the Future,* (San Francisco: Jossey-Bass, 1973), p. 101.

2. Ibid., p. 14.

3. Herman Kahn, William Brown, and Leon Martel, *The Next Two Hundred Years: A Scenario for America and the World,* (New York: William Morrow and Co., 1976) p. 1.

4. Ibid., p. 24.

5. Ibid., p. 4.

6. Ibid., p. 224.

7. Ibid., pp. 225, 226.

8. See Donella H. Meadows et al., *The Limits to Growth,* (New York: Signet Books / New American Library 1972). This book has had an enormous impact on speculations about the future and is still an excellent source of insight into the systemic crisis of industrialism.

9. See Robert L. Heilbroner, *An Inquiry Into the Human Prospect,* (New York: W.W. Norton & Co., 1974). A brief but powerful book about the end of industrial civilization. Since Heilbroner believes that human nature is basically selfish, fearful, and given to authoritarian solutions to problems, the human prospect is portrayed as entirely negative, without hope of transcendence.

10. See Roberto Vacca, *The Coming Dark Age,* (Garden City, N.Y.: Anchor Press / Doubleday & Co., 1974). As mathematician and electronics specialist the author is able to see the limits of technology but unable to present a plausible image of the future after the collapse of industrialism.

11. Gerard O'Neill, *The High Frontier: Human Colonies in Space,* (New York: William Morrow & Co., 1977), pp. 19, 20. Reprinted by permission of the publisher.

12. Ibid., p. 21.

13. Ibid., p. 4.

14. For a thorough and thought-provoking analysis of the symbolism of the city in scripture, see Jacques Ellul, *The Meaning of the City,* (Grand Rapids, Mich.: Wm. B. Eerdmans Publishing Co., 1970). While Ellul sees the city as a spiritual power that tends to destroy the human being for the sake of human works, he does not see the resolution of this dilemma in a return to an idyllic Eden. Rather, he believes the fulfillment of history is to be found in communion with the divine in the city transfigured.

15. G. Harry Stine, *The Third Industrial Revolution,* (New York: G.P. Putnam's Sons, 1975).

16. Ibid., p. 26.

17. Ibid., pp. 161, 162.

18. Ibid., p. 162.

19. Ibid., p. 163.

20. Ibid., p. 165.

21. Ibid., p. 168.

22. See John Todd's letter to the editor in *The Co-Evolution Quarterly,* no. 9, (Spring 1976), pp. 20, 21.

23. Howard T. Odum, "Limits of Remote Ecosystems Containing Man," in *The American Biology Teacher,* vol. 25, (1963), pp. 423–443.

24. Todd, *The Co-Evolution Quarterly,* p. 21.

25. See Garrett Hardin's response to the space colony proposal in his letter to the editor in *The Co-Evolution Quarterly,* pp. 28–29.

26. Herbert Marcuse, *One-Dimensional Man: Studies in the Ideology of Advanced Industrial Society,* (Boston: Beacon Press, 1964), p. 1.

27. For a superb analysis of how a uniquely modern and American form of totalitarianism is contained as both reality and possibility in our advanced technological society see, Bertram M.

Gross, "Friendly Fascism: A Model for America," in *Social Policy,* (November/December 1970), pp. 44–52. I am suggesting that the space colony would completely embody such a new style fascism, and, following Marcuse, that by its very nature such total social control would be invisible, and therefore unproblematic to its inhabitants.

28. Hardin, *The Co-Evolution Quarterly,* p. 29.

29. Lewis Mumford, *The Transformations of Man,* (New York: Harper & Row, 1956), pp. 97–98. Reprinted by permission of the publisher.

30. Henry Morley, ed., *Ideal Commonwealths,* (New York: The Colonial Press, 1901), p. 129.

31. Lewis Mumford, *The Pentagon of Power: The Myth of the Machine, Volume II,* (New York: Harcourt Brace Jovanovich, 1964), p. 14.

32. As quoted in Mircea Eliade, "Paradise and Utopia," in *Utopias and Utopian Thought,* ed. Frank E. Manuel, (Boston: Houghton Mifflin Co., 1966), p. 262. I am indebted to Eliade for this analysis of the eschatological roots of American history.

33. As quoted in Leo Marx, *The Machine in the Garden: Technology and the Pastoral Ideal in America,* (New York: The Oxford Univ. Press, 1964), pp. 124–125.

34. Ibid., p. 228. I am indebted to Leo Marx for this insight. For a masterful study of the relationship between technology and American civilization that complements that by Leo Marx see John F. Kasson, *Civilizing the Machine: Technology and Republican Values in America 1776–1900,* (New York: Penguin Books, 1977).

35. See the poems, "Milton a Poem in 2 Books," (pp. 94–143) and "Jerusalem: The Emanation of the Giant Albion," (pp. 143–256), in *The Poetry and Prose of William Blake* ed. David V. Erdman, (Garden City, N.Y.: Doubleday & Co., 1970).

36. Mircea Eliade, as quoted in Edward C. Whitmont, *The Symbolic Quest: Basic Concepts of Analytical Psychology,* (New York: Harper & Row, 1969), p. 80.

37. Ibid., p. 102.

38. There is a broad and growing literature on the relationship between myth and history. See, for example, the brilliant historical survey by Norman Cohn, *The Pursuit of the Millennium: Revolutionary Millenarians and Mystical Anarchists of the Middle Ages,* 2d ed., rev. and enl., (New York: Oxford Univ. Press, 1970). The classic study of revitalization movements within "primitive" tribal groups as they confront modern civilizations is by Kenelm Burridge, *New Heaven, New Earth: A Study of Millenarian Activities,* (New York: Schocken Books, 1969). One of the best studies of the role of the apocalyptic-millennial imagination in movements for personal and social reintegration is by Eleanor Wilner, *Gathering the Winds: Visionary Imagination and Radical Transformation of Self and Society,* (Baltimore, Md.: John Hopkins Univ. Press, 1975).

39. Julian Silverman, "Shamans and Acute Schizophrenia," *American Anthropologist* 69, no. 1, (February 1967), as quoted in Joseph Campbell, *Myths to Live By,* (New York: Viking Press, 1972), p. 213.

40. For a description of the Nazi myth of world destruction and an analysis of its role in the last World War, see Whitmont, *The Symbolic Quest,* pp. 80–82.

41. For an analysis of this aspect and potential of technology see Marx, *The Machine in the Garden,* pp. 146–150, and Kasson, *Civilizing the Machine,* pp. 22–25.

42. E. F. Schumacher, *Good Work,*

(New York: Harper & Row, 1979), p. 40.

43. Ibid., p. 41.

44. Mumford, *The Pentagon of Power,* p. 14.

45. William Irwin Thompson, *Darkness and Scattered Light: Speculations on the Future,* (Garden City, N.Y.: Anchor Press / Doubleday & Co., 1978), p. 28.

46. Ibid., p. 33.

47. Ibid., p. 34.

48. William Irwin Thompson, *Evil and World Order,* (New York: Harper & Row, 1976), p. 7.

49. Mumford, *The Transformations of Man,* p. 143.

50. Ibid., p. 142.

51. Ibid., p. 142.

52. Ibid., p. 150.

53. For a discussion of the potential of the city as a vehicle for overcoming narcissism and promoting human community rooted in diversity see Richard Sennett, *The Uses of Disorder,* (New York: Vintage Books / Random House, 1970).

54. Kahn et al., *The Next Two Hundred Years,* p. 183.

55. Erich Von Neumann, *The Origins and History of Consciousness,* (Princeton, N.J. Princeton Univ. Press, 1954), p. 444.

56. Thompson, *Darkness and Scattered Light,* p. 83.

57. See Murray Bookchin, *Post-Scarcity Anarchism,* (San Francisco: Ramparts Press, 1971), pp. 83–141.

58. Thompson, *Darkness and Scattered Light,* p. 83.

59. See Mumford: "Post Historic Man" in *The Transformations of Man,* pp. 120–136, and *The Pentagon of Power,* pp. 311–320.

60. Thompson, *Darkness and Scattered Light,* p. 85.

61. Thompson, *Evil and World Order,* p. 53.

62. Mumford, *The Transformations of Man,* p. 144.

63. Theodore Roszak, *Person / Planet,* (Garden City, N. Y.: Anchor Press / Doubleday & Co., 1978), p. xix.

64. Thompson, *Darkness and Scattered Light,* p. 86.

65. Ibid., pp. 89–90.

66. See Thompson, *Evil and World Order,* p. 8.

67. Thompson, *Darkness and Scattered Light,* p. 92.

68. For a presentation of such a form of sustainable agriculture see Earle A. Barnhart, "Agricultural Landscapes: Strategies Toward Permanence" in this volume.

69. See Richard Baker-roshi, "Sangha-Community" in this volume.

70. See Elizabeth Rechtschaffen, "Resettling the Shakers: The Abode of the Message" in this volume.

71. Thompson, *Darkness and Scattered Light,* p. 97.

72. Ibid, pp. 101–102.

73. Ibid., p. 102.

2 | Sharing Smaller Pies

Tom Bender

Becoming slaves to energy

THERE IS NO LONGER any doubt that our age of affluence, based upon depletion of our planet's non-renewable energy and material resources, is at an end and that *major* changes must be made in every aspect of our lives. The United States, in particular, has used up much of its own non-renewable resources and has come to depend upon consumption of the resources of other countries at a prodigious rate. Americans currently consume more than a third of the world's oil, and must import nearly 100 percent of many essential materials. Such patterns of resource use cannot be continued either physically or politically, as other countries require more of their own resources and realize the absurdity of allowing us to consume their irreplaceable source of wealth to support an unnecessarily wasteful way of life.

We have prided ourselves on our affluence, believing that it has been brought about by our hard work and ingenuity. Beneath all the hocus-pocus of our monetary system, our true wealth lies in the quality of life available to us in return for work. Our recent affluence has been possible because of the great amounts of work done for us by fossil fuels, which until recently have required very little of our actual work to obtain. For one unit of our work we have been able to obtain 50 units of work done for us by fossil fuels. We have been using approximately 10 percent of our work to obtain this energy, which means fossil fuels have had the effect of temporarily increasing our total ability to do work by almost six times.

The low cost to us of energy-work has also made possible our massive exploitation of the work of people who lack "energy-slaves." They have had to use human labor to compete against the cheap work of our fossil fuels, thus lowering the return for their work to the pittance we have had to pay for this concentrated form of energy. It is this ability to do work, the power it has given us to exploit the work of others, and our rapid consumption of material resources on a global basis that has temporarily given us much greater wealth than other societies.

The energy and material resources that have supported our wealth are being rapidly exhausted, and remaining world reserves are requiring increasing amounts of work to obtain.

Earth provides enough to satisfy every man's need, but not enough for every man's greed.
Mahatma Gandhi

89

We have assumed that these lower grade energy reserves would become economically feasible to develop as richer, lower cost sources were exhausted. We have ignored the fact, however, that our ability to afford any significant use of such expensive energy is dependent upon wealth generated from inexpensive energy sources, and as these are exhausted, we will become increasingly less able to afford more expensive ones.

Global population is still increasing beyond the earth's capability to sustain the greater demands for increasingly limited resources. At the same time, political actions are being taken to slow the rate of depletion of these resources and to assure longer benefit from their use, further decreasing their availability. These events make our continued dependence on vanishing non-renewable resources impossible, and require that we move to the use of renewable resources such as solar energy, agriculture, and human work, and move to the lower levels of activity renewable resources can support.

Scarcity of non-renewable resources is a fundamental and permanent change in our condition that even our wildest dreams of fusion power and unlimited energy cannot alter. Even if such dreams prove technically possible, they would only postpone the necessity to meet the same impossibility of infinite growth in a finite world. We must face the reality that any attempts to sustain our growth, or even to maintain our lifestyle, without basic changes will result in a steady, if not catastrophic, worsening of our quality of life.[1,2]

Events are already underway which will, in a very few years, transform the United States from one of the richest and most powerful nations on earth into one of the weakest and most dependent nations—unless fundamental changes are made in our economic and social processes.

Economic and political independence cannot be maintained when we are dependent upon other people for resources to operate our society. Yet, we have built a structure of cities, agricultural and industrial production, educational and professional services that requires the importation of massive amounts of energy and materials to operate.

Rapid exhaustion of our domestic resources will make us totally dependent upon the resources of other nations—available only on *their* terms, if at all. Even if those nations were willing to supply us with energy and materials, we would not be able to afford them or to remain competitive with them because of our overcomplex and expensive industrial and agricultural processes, institutions, and physical structure. Even if we are able to become independent of direct foreign power, the availability of low-cost energy and material resources in other countries means that they will have the same absolute advantage over us in economic trade that we have enjoyed over them in the last century. We have shown that goods produced with inexpensive energy sources are tough competitors in the world market. Countries that try to compete with products made with inexpensive energy sources are vulnerable to economic and cultural ruin and exploitation. Now *we* will be on the bad end of that relationship unless we can establish the controls on trade that we have thus far prevented other countries from establishing.

Changing possibilities

Plentiful resources have, until recently, freed us from having to say, "This will not be good for us." Having the ability to mask the effects of unwise actions, to rebuild structure cheaply, and to introduce exotic sources of materials and energy, has permitted us to try anything that held the promise of immediate benefit, regardless of its eventual cost. This has had a positive aspect, for it has given us an opportunity to test our ethical and moral wisdom, and through our mistakes to come to a more sane basis for the choices we make.

Cheap energy has allowed us to explore new technologies, social and political organization, and to test assumptions about our world. From testing past assumptions, and through being able to repeat the evolutionary dead ends that nature has already abandoned, we have had the opportunity to come to a closer understanding of the possibilities and limitations of our world. Such understanding can give us greater and more precisely defined freedom and a more thorough understanding of what we can and should do and not do. The closer we move our arbitrary human laws to natural law, the less arbitrary and more meaningful our way of life will become. Within natural law is total freedom, for it defines the realities through which we must move.

Such a period of testing is always limited, and ours is coming to an end as the inexpensive energy to support our experimentation becomes less available. This is forcing us as individuals and as a society to develop values and ways of living, working, and relating, which offer the greatest benefit to our survival and well-being.

Value judgements seem ephemeral when considered beside profit and loss statements. Yet profit and loss statements hold little meaning when viewed from the next generation, or when viewed beside the irreplacable re-sources upon which the continuing support of our lives depends. Values are a complex and compact depository of survival wisdom, expressions of the attitudes, actions, and relationships we have found to be most essential to our well-being. Those values become touchstones from which we determine ways of dealing with specific situations. Under conditions which allow growth and great wealth, our values, and resulting actions, shift to take best advantage of those conditions. When material growth is no longer possible or desirable, our values and actions must adjust to harmonize with new realities.

Our present assumptions reflect conditions of plenty and expectations of even greater plenty. As a result, we have believed that human work could and should be replaced by machines, and that such changes would contribute to our well-being. We have considered that enlargement of our material wealth offered the primary if not sole means to improve our quality of life— to the point of equating measurement of our material productive capabilities with quality of life.

The novelty and excitement of our new abilities to change the conditions of our lives through massive use of resources has made evaluation of such actions difficult. We have shown little concern about the economic and social effects of our actions on each other and even less concern about effects on people of other cultures. We assumed that any problems would be resolved through greater production of goods and services, or were unimportant because of our relatively great material wealth and assumed equity of opportunity for everyone. We also have had great confidence that the apparently powerful tools of our science and technology could apply, and have as positive an effect on other aspects of our lives, as they have on our material well-being. We have felt that we could beneficially institutionalize our individual responsibilities for caring for ourselves and others, for seeing to our health, education, and safety, and for seeing to the effects of our actions.

Such assumptions have proven wrong.

We have plunged headlong, for more than half a century, into development of a technological direction unprecedented on this planet, and are now finding that this direction is unsustainable, its effects undesirable, and its replacement necessary if we are to ensure the soundness, stability, and permanence of our society.

Freedom is always possible

We need new assumptions about what we are and what we wish to accomplish. We must now establish new perceptions of how our institutions actually operate, and what changes need to be made. The steps necessary to adjust our values and institutions to what will be required of them must be laid out so we can begin to make changes. There are only a few critical actions that must be taken. It is inherent in their nature that these actions be made on local or regional levels, though timely action on a national or international level could speed and assist the changes.

Our dependence on massive resource use has been so total that most Americans cannot conceive of operating on as little as one third the present energy use—though civilized countries such as New Zealand, Switzerland, Japan, and France do so quite well. It remains totally incomprehensible to us that a society can operate adequately on ten, five, or even one per-

cent of the energy and wealth that we demand, yet hundreds of millions of people do so. Ironically, our wasteful use of energy (and the increasing inefficiency of our institutions) has resulted in a deterioration in the quality of our lives. Our standards of health, the quality of our environment, and the efficiency of our industry have all fallen below that of many other countries consuming only a fraction of the energy we consume.

We know that good and viable societies can exist with much fewer resources and less wealth than ours, and there is considerable precedent and experience to examine and build upon. The experience of traditional societies, such as Chinese and Tanzanian, and the experience of sectors of own society that have already chosen to change their lifestyle, can contribute both directions and cautions for future changes.

Any affluence that we can now achieve must come about through prudent use of our resources. It requires the development of new production processes as well as educational and governmental systems, professions, and other institutions that can: (1) operate successfully on the scale and with the resources possible; (2) conserve and sustain our non-renewable resources, and; (3) generate rather than consume resources. Most importantly, it requires the development of sufficient self-discipline to limit our numbers and our demands in order to maintain a way of life above the subsistence level to which it must otherwise sink.

Fundamental changes in our institutions are necessary —resource crisis or not —and can offer us the quickest, longest lasting, and most effective ways to move to a better quality of life while adjusting to the new resource and economic conditions with which we are faced.

Harmful servants

The resources of American society have always appeared so plentiful that no reason seemed justified for restraint in their use, for concern about what would happen when they were exhausted, or for consideration of the pervasive effects of plentiful and inexpensive resources on seemingly remote and unrelated aspects of our society. The effects of abundant resources upon the nature and operation of our institutions are both pervasive and invisible because they have always been there. Our institutions have all been formed under conditions of plenty and have never before faced serious prospects of operation under scarcity.

Every institution in our society is organized to encourage growth, and every institution has developed patterns of organization and operation that require unaffordable quantities of our resources and wealth. Our tax laws stimulate growth of corporations at the expense of individuals. Our monetary regulations force growth. Our legal system permits the instability of contractual relationships. Our government ignores responsibilities for sustaining our biosystems. Our schools teach consumption and our cities demand it. We permit public communications media to be conduits for private advertisement for furthering consumption.

We only consume, and do not produce, while learning. Our building codes require structural strength, electrical capacity, thermal control, and lighting levels that are totally unnecessary. Our land use patterns demand ever-increasing costs of transportation. Trucks carrying widgets from New York to Los Angeles pass trucks carrying the same widgets from Los Angeles to New York. Agriculture consumes energy instead of producing it. It is all unsustainable.

With fossil fuels doing most of our work, the effect of inefficiency in our own work and our institutions has been relatively unnoticeable. The value of, and respect for, human work and skills is relatively small when energy slaves will do our work for only two percent of the cost of the human work. As remaining fossil fuels require more work to obtain, the relative value of human work increases. As material costs increase, so does the value of our immaterial resources, and the effectiveness of all our institutions and processes becomes more and more important.

If energy wealth has made the inefficiency of our institutions temporarily unimportant, the measurement of our quality of life, the effectiveness of our production, and the progress of our society through the single measure of "Gross National Product" (GNP) has given such inefficiencies the appearance of improving our lives. This focus on production has ignored the reality that most production and consumption is actually the *cost* of replacing and maintaining our stocks of goods and services rather than a measure of our wealth. Even now less than 10 percent of our production goes for increasing the stocks of goods and services available to us. The other 90 percent goes for maintaining and replacing our existing ones.

It seems strange at first to say that a smaller GNP, or less expenditure for transportation or medical costs, could improve our quality of life. Yet we recognize that any time we can eliminate a need for transportation we have to spend less of our time, work, and income to pay for it, and whenever we can maintain the same quality of medical service on a smaller budget, we increase our options for spending the time or income that otherwise would go to supporting those services. Satisfying our needs with the least expenditure of time, energy, and dollars is only good common sense.

Efforts have been made to determine the timetable for the end of our affluence and the degree of reduction in our energy and wealth to which we must adjust. Accurate determinations are largely impossible, because factors such as political decisions, the amounts of energy that further prospecting will discover, technological developments in using renewable energy sources, changing rates of population growth, and possibilities of economic collapse are all crucial and unknowable in advance. Exact timetables and levels are also relatively unimportant, because the *directionality* of events is what is important, and that is fundamentally unchangeable. We know that the minimum rate for changing things is the replacement rate for present equipment and the rate necessary to maintain employment. Faster change will be to our ongoing advantage. Most of the changes we must make are beneficial to our quality of life whether or not reduction in our wealth makes them unavoidable. Most of the changes are also cumulative. The sooner we are able to implement them, the greater the benefits. We need to know only that in 10 or 15 years—20 years at the most—we will be living in an extremely different world and it will be extraordinarily difficult for us if we have not exerted our fullest efforts to prepare for that world.

We have been told countless times that growth is necessary to the health and well-being of our economy and our society. That assumption is even truer than imagined. If we stop growing and consuming, the collapse of our whole system is unavoidable. The system is inherently unsustainable and must be changed, as the resources to support growth become unavailable.

We have never paused to critically examine the nature and effects of our institutions, or to impose ethically and morally based restraint on those that lessen the quality of our life, or which have a negative effect on society as a whole. Many of our institutions are based on incorrect assumptions that actually impair their intended goals and achievements. Our transportation system, for example, often proclaimed the finest in the world, proves on analysis to be less *effective* than systems of societies where people walk everywhere:

The typical American male devotes more than 1,600 hours a year to his car. He sits in it while it goes and while it stands idling. He parks it and searches for it. He earns the money to put down on it and to meet the monthly installments. He works to pay for petrol, tolls, insurance, taxes, and tickets. He spends four of his sixteen waking hours on the road or gathering his resources for it. And this figure does not take into account the time consumed by other activities dictated by transport: time spent in hospitals, traffic courts, and garages; time spent watching automobile commercials or attending consumer education meetings to improve the quality of the next buy. The model American puts in 1,600 hours to go 7,500 miles; less than five miles per hour. In countries deprived of a transportation industry, people manage to do the same, walking wherever they want to go, and they allocate only three to eight percent of their society's energy and monetary budget to traffic instead of 28 percent. What distinguishes the traffic in rich countries from the traffic in poor countries is not more mileage per hour of life-time for the majority, but more hours of compulsory consumption of high doses of energy, packed and unequally distributed by the transportation industry.[3]

Our institutions have become counterproductive—producing less health, less transportation, less learning, less justice—while consuming more energy, dollars, and time. Education is required that is never used. More money is spent administering welfare than is received by the poor. Freeways use so much land that places are farther apart and require more freeways to get to. Air conditioning makes cities hotter, necessitating more air conditioning.

The counterproductive nature of our institutions has arisen from a mistaken belief that individual responsibility in supporting, regulating, and using such institutions, and in avoiding dependence upon them, can be replaced, without harm, by organization, regulation, and equipment.

It remains the responsibility of people within an institution to use it as a means of heightening their ability to serve, not as an excuse to not serve. Responsibility for being aware of the effects of our actions from the receiving end—what it is like to apply for a job or unemployment, to be sick, to be in a hospital, to need aid—cannot be replaced by regulations. Responsibility to perceive misdirection of institutions and the power to correct it cannot be replaced by any program or organization. Only individual responsibility can maintain health instead of restoring it. Only individual responsibility can ensure that we learn rather than are educated.

Medicine, architecture, law, education, transportation, social work, and civil engineering have all followed the path of increasingly professionalized, more restricted, and less beneficial applications of their skills. Our reaction to their increasing failure to achieve their purposes has been to escalate their technological and bureaucratic growth. Such fundamentally wrong assumptions can be countered only by deprofessionalizing the social agencies, setting limits to their operation, and reassuming individual responsibility for their purposes.

The spiraling costs of repairing institutionally-caused damage quickly becomes unaffordable, even for societies with vast resources. The wisest and least costly way to maintain health and learning, control population, and obtain goods must be based on personal rather than institutional responsibility for actions. When people are prevented from having viable options to satisfying their needs, institutions concerned with delivery of services or goods are effectively insulated from evaluation of the effectiveness of the processes used or the assumptions upon which these processes are based.

When we have already been required to pay for social security, public schools, or our highway system; when tax advantages for large corporations prevent viable competition from small businesses; when union regulations, building codes, and drug prescription laws prevent alternative means of satisfying our needs, then our consumption of existing goods or services is, for all practical purposes, compulsory.[4,5]

Old problems

In determining new directions, we must face and resolve a number of problems we have long been able to ignore.

Per capita wealth, and indeed, survival, is almost totally tied to population size. With fixed or decreasing resources, population control is absolutely necessary if our quality of life is not to drop to a subsistence level. The only humane way to control population and poverty without repressive central control is to restore to people the responsibility and control of their lives and their world, so they directly understand their ability and that of society to support more or fewer children. This requires an absolute reversal of our present trend towards institutionalization of our responsibilities and broadening institutional control over our lives.

Trade and other economic and social relationships with other regions and nations must be controlled to prevent our exploitation and loss of independence. "Free" trade is possible only among equals. The work of our people cannot compete with the work of fossil fuels of other nations. Trade among unequals is exploitive, as we have long known to our benefit. Our resource depletion will leave us in a dependent and exploited trade relationship unless we are aware of the meaning of our changing resource realities and ensure that our trade relationships are correspondingly regulated. Control of relationships is necessary to maintain independence and viability, buffer internal commerce against massive external disruptions, and prevent the exploitation of the work and livelihood of our people. Unrestrained trade also makes control of political and economic systems less possible and makes control of exploitation of ecosystems virtually impossible. Localization of economic activity is necessary to reduce costs, regain control of productive systems, and make more effective use of our resources as well as to maintain independence and freedom. *Dependence* on trade results in loss of independence.

Problems such as equity must be resolved now. We have been able to avoid them through the assumption that increasing wealth would solve everyone's problems—that there would be bigger pie to share and that everyone's absolute share would increase. That is no longer possible, and arguments for inequality in wealth as neces-

sary for investment and growth have lost their force. It is hard to see how ethical appeals for equal shares can any longer be countered. Achieving equity will require not only redistribution of wealth but also redistribution of the means for producing wealth.

We must reduce our wants to correspond more closely to our needs, which are but a small fraction of our current demands. Unless we can determine more accurately what is possible at any time, and adjust our dreams and demands to that reality, increased frustration, damaging economic policy, and problems of civic unrest and disruption can become overwhelming.

Fewer resources, coupled with more work and dollars necessary to get remaining resources, leaves substantially fewer total resources to operate the rest of our society. All institutions must soon be able to operate on a small fraction of the energy and dollars that have been available to them. Conservation —more efficient use of energy and dollars in existing systems—can afford some relief. Reduction in resource use on the order of 40 percent is both necessary and possible through conservation. But without fundamental changes in our institutions, conservation alone is more likely to restrict than improve our quality of life in the process.

We have reached the point where the economics and logistics of improvement of our life quality through physical and institutional means have become less beneficial than through new values and expanding individual responsibility and initiative.

New values

Our ability to develop a culture that can endure beyond our own lifetime depends upon our coming to a new understanding of what is desirable for a harmonious and sustainable relationship with the systems that support our lives.

Stewardship, not progress

We have valued progress highly during our period of growth. Progress assumes that the future will be better, creating dissatisfaction with the present and telling us that *now* isn't good. As a result, we are prompted to work harder to get what the future can offer, but lose our ability to enjoy what we now have. We also lose a sense that we ourselves, and what we have and do, are really good. We expect the rewards from what we do to come in the future rather from the *doing* of it, and then become frustrated when most of those dreams cannot be attained. The "future" always continues to lie in the future.

Stewardship, in contrast to progress, elicits attentive care and concern for the present—for understanding its nature and for best developing, nurturing, and protecting its possibilities. Such actions unavoidably ensure the best possible future as a byproduct of enjoyment and satisfaction from the present.

The government of a society has a fundamental responsibility, which we have neglected, for stewardship—particularly for the biophysical systems that support our society. It is the only organ of society that can protect those systems and protect future citizens of the society from loss of their needed resources through the profiteering of present citizens. The government's fundamental obligation in this area is to prevent deterioration in the support capacities of the biophysical systems; to maintain in stable and sound fashion their ongoing capabilities, and whenever possible, to extend those capabilities in terms of quality as well as quantity. Present and past governments, and those who have profited from their actions, must be accountable for loss to present and future citizens, and to the biophysical systems themselves.

Austerity, not affluence

Austerity is a principle which does not exclude all enjoyments, only those which are distracting from or destructive of personal relatedness. Affluence, in contrast, does not discriminate between what is wise and useful and what is merely possible. Affluence demands impossible, endless growth, both because those things necessary for good relations are foregone for unnecessary things, and because many of those unnecessary things act to damage or destroy the good relations that we desire.

Permanence, not profit

Profit, as a criterion of performance, must be replaced by permanence in a world where irreplaceable resources are in scarce supply. The only way to place lighter demands on material resources is to place heavier demands on moral resources. Permanence as a judge of the desirability of actions requires first that those actions contribute to, rather than lessen, the continuing quality of the society.

Responsibilities, not rights

A society based on rights rather than responsibilities is possible only when the actions involved are not significant enough to affect others. Our present society is based upon rights rather than responsibilities, and upon competitive distrust and contractual relationships rather than upon the more cooperative kinds of relationships common in other cultures. These relationships have given us the freedom to very quickly extract and use our material resources, settle a continent, and develop the structure of cities and civilization.

Any enduring relationship, however, must balance rights with responsibilities to prevent destruction of weaker, yet essential, parts of relationships—whether with other people, with the biosphere that supports our lives, or with the various parts of our own personalities.

Contractual relationships, rooted as they are in distrust, are the easiest to escape and the most expensive to maintain—requiring the development of elaborate and expensive legal and financial systems—and cannot be the dominant form of relationship in societies that do not have the surplus wealth to afford them. Moral or ethically-based relationships; relationships based on cooperation, trust, and love; and the relationships encompassing more than just work, family, educational, recreational, or spiritual parts of our lives are more rewarding and satisfying. They are also more stable in their contribution to society, vastly easier to maintain, and harder to disrupt. They have always been the most common kinds of relationships between people except under the extreme duress of war or growth.

People, not professions

Our wealth has made it possible for us to institutionalize and professionalize many of our individual responsibilities—a process which is inherently ineffective and costly, which has proven destructive of individual competence and confidence, and which is affordable only when significant surplus of wealth is available.

We have been able to afford going to expensively trained doctors for every small health problem, rather than learning rudiments of medical skills or taking care to prevent health problems. We have been able to afford expensive police protection rather than handling our problems by ourselves or with our neighbors. We have established professional social workers, lawyers, and educators—and required that everyone use their services even for things we could do ourselves and that are wastes of the time and expertise of the professionals. As the wealth that has permitted this becomes less available to us, it will become necessary to deprofessionalize and deinstitutionalize many of these services and again take primary responsibility for them ourselves.

We have to take responsibility *ourselves* for own lives, actions, health, and learning. We must also take responsibility ourselves for our community and society. There is no other way to operate any aspect of our lives and society without creating dictatorial power that destroys and prevents the unfolding of human nature and that concentrates the ability to make errors without corrective input. No one else shares our perceptions and perspective on what is occurring and its rightness, wrongness, or alternatives. We are the only ones who can give that perspective to the process of determining and directing the pattern of events.

Our institutions can be tools that serve us only when they arise from and sustain the abilities of individuals and remain controlled by them.

Betterment, not biggerment

Quantitative things, because of the ease of their measurement by external means, have been sought and relied upon as measures of success by our institutionally-centered society. We are learning the hard lesson that quantity is no substitute for quality in our lives, that qualitative benefits cannot be externalized, and that a society that wishes betterness rather than moreness, and betterment rather than biggerment, must be organized to allow individuals the scope for determining and obtaining what they themselves consider better.

Enoughness, not moreness

We are learning that too much of a good thing is not a good thing, and that we would often be wiser to determine what is enough rather than how much is possible. When we can learn to be satisfied with the least necessary for happiness, we can lighten our demands on ourselves, on others, and on our surroundings. Our consumption ethic has prevented our thinking about enoughness, in part out of fear of unemployment problems arising from reducing our demands. Employment problems are only a result of choices of energy versus employment-intensive production processes and arbitrary choices we have made in the patterns of distributing the wealth of our society —both of which can be modified with little difficulty. Our major goal is to keep happy with the least production of goods and services necessary and with the greatest opportunity to employ our time and skills for good rather than for survival. The fewer our wants, the greater our freedom from having to serve them.

Localization, not centralization

Centralization, in all kinds of organization, is important during periods of growth when ability to quickly marshall resources and change and direct an organization is important. It is, however, an expensive and ineffective means for dealing with ongoing operations when an excess of energy to operate the system is unavailable. As effectiveness in resolving problems on the scale and location where they occur becomes more important, organization must move to more localized and less institutionalized ways of operation. Even with sufficient resources, the power concentration of centralized systems overpowers the rights of individuals, and has proved to lead to inevitable deterioration of the quality of life.

The size and centralization of many of our organizations has nothing to do with even alleged economies or benefits of scale, and is actually often associated with diseconomies of scale, and deterioration of quality of services. Size breeds size, even where it is counterproductive. It is easier for any organization to deal with others of the same scale and kind of organization, and to create pressures for other organizations to adapt their own mode of operation.

Equitization, not urbanization

Uncontrollable urbanization has accompanied industrialization in every country where it has occurred. The results of that urbanization, which has occurred in spite of the desires of both the people and the governments involved, have been twofold: the destruction of traditional means of livelihood by energy slaves along with the market control of large corporations, and the unequal availability of employment opportunities, educational, medical, and other services. Neither of these outcomes is necessary. The inequity of services has resulted from conscious choices to centralize and professionalize services rather than to manage available resources in a way to ensure equal availability of services in rural as well as urban areas. The destruction of traditional patterns of livelihood has been equally based on conscious and unnecessary choices.

Equity is not only possible, but is necessary to restore choices of where and how one lives. It can be achieved through introduction of appropriate technology; control of organization size; equalization of income and available wealth; establishment of equal access to learning opportunities, health care, justice, and other services; and by assurance of the opportunity for meaningful work for everyone. Equity can be achieved by returning to individuals the responsibility and control of their lives, surroundings, and social, economic, and political systems; by ensuring freedom to not consume or depend upon any systems other than one's own abilities; and by encouraging the ownership of the tools of production by the people who do the work, thus increasing the chances of developing a balanced, affluent, and stable society.

Work, not leisure

We have considered work a negative thing—that the sole function of work is to produce goods and services. To workers it has meant a loss of leisure, something to be minimized while still maintaining income. To the employer it is simply a cost of production, also to be minimized. Yet work is one of our greatest opportunities to contribute to the well-being of ourselves and our community—opportunity to utilize and develop our skills and abilities, opportunity to overcome our self-centeredness through joining with other people in common tasks, as well as opportunity to produce the goods and services needed for a dignified existence. Properly appreciated, work stands in the same relation to the higher faculties as food to the physical body. It nourishes and enlivens us. It furnishes a medium to display our scale of values and develop our personality. To strive for leisure, rather than work, denies that work and leisure are complementary parts of the same living process.

Opportunity for meaningful work, rather than merely a share of the products of work, needs to be assured to every member of our society.

Tools, not machines

We need to regain the ability to distinguish between technologies which aid and those which destroy our ability to seek the ends we wish. We need to discriminate between tools and machines.

A tool channels work and experiences through our faculties, allowing us to bring to bear upon them the full play of our nature and dreams, and to give the fullest possible opportunity for our physical and mental faculties to experience, experiment, and grow.

Our culture has valued devices that are labor saving and require little skill to operate. Such devices are machines which rob us of our opportunity to act, experience, and grow. We need skill-developing rather than labor-saving technologies.[6,7,8,9,10,11,12]

Independence and interdependence

Many of the basic values upon which we have tried to build our society have become weakened through the ways they have been interpreted, and now face the prospect of further weakening through the pressures inevitable in adapting our society to new conditions.

Independence cannot be maintained when we are dependent upon other people or other nations, when we are forced to work on other's terms, to consume certain kinds of education to qualify for work, to use automobiles because that kind of transportation system has made walking dangerous or physically impossible. As long as we must depend upon resources other than ourselves and the renewable resources of our surroundings, we cannot be independent.

We have also discovered, through the power that our wealth has given us, that slavery is as enslaving for the master as for the mastered. By becoming *dependent* upon the abilities of the slave, whether the slave is a human, animal, institutional or energy slave, we forego developing our own capabilities to be self-sufficient.

Two things are important. 1) We must have the *capability* for self-sufficiency to have options, alternatives, self-confidence, and knowledge of how things are related and work and to be able to lighten our demands on others. 2) We must also have the *ability* to contribute our special skills to the development of interdependent relationships which can benefit all. Trade, as giving of surplus, of what is not necessary, is the only viable resolution of the interrelated problems of independence, interdependence, and slavery.

As we begin to actually make changes, the things we come to find of value are almost the opposite of what we value today. That which contributes to stability, soundness, and to valued relationships is exactly what prevents and hinders disruption, change, and growth. Meaningful work, localized economies, diversity and richness of employment and community, controllable, clever, human–centered technologies will become important. Community will become more important than individualism. Strong roots and

relationships will become more important than mobility. Buildings and equipment with long life and lower total costs rather than low initial costs will be favored. Cooperation will be seen as more positive, wiser, and less costly than competition. Skill-using will replace labor-saving. We will soon discover that all our present sciences and principles are not unbiased, but are built upon values promoting growth rather than stability, and will need to be modified when quantitative growth is no longer possible.

Appropriate technology

Fear of technology is an understandable reaction to a technology that serves values antithetical to our wellbeing, that destroys personal capabilities and initiative, that requires unsustainable quantities of resources, that degrades our surroundings, and enriches the few at the expense of many. But such fears need to be qualified if we are to move on to new dreams. Every society develops a technology appropriate to it, and for every dream there are techniques that make it attainable or unattainable. What is necessary for us is to replace our present technology with one appropriate to our new dreams and new conditions. Appropriate technology, in this sense, is not merely a question of machines and tools, but of the nature of all the organizational, conceptual, political, physical, and spiritual tools and techniques which are brought into play by our actions.

Continuation of present technologies is neither possible nor desirable. The technologies themselves are proving socially, environmentally, and spiritually damaging, and often uncontrollable. The values they support are no longer desired, and their products no longer seen as the primary wants of our society.

Technology appropriate for our emerging needs must fulfill the following requirements:

- Provide full employment and meaningful work.
- Substitute human resources for energy and material resources.
- Operate capably within the levels and patterns of activities sustainable with renewable energy sources and material recycling.
- Promote equity, independence, soundness, stability, and other values appropriate to a sound and enduring society.
- Be easily applicable on a broad scale and to both urban and rural areas.
- Be affordable in terms of money, energy, materials, and human, environmental, and social costs.
- Establish a self-sustaining and expanding reservoir of skills and self-confidence.
- Permit easy control of political, economic, and social systems.
- Establish a small enough scale of operations to permit social, economic, and environmental diversity, stability, and control.
- Provide the best possible support for not only our material comfort, but our psychological, cultural, and spiritual growth as well.
- Reduce economic, social, and political dependency among individuals, among regions, and among nations.
- Permit ownership of the means of production by those who do the work.

Such technologies provide better responses to our emerging scarcities, are fundamentally better ways of doing things, and are necessary to protect our freedoms and other basic values. They permit lower investment costs for good production, wider potentials for entrepreneurship, and more appreciative attitudes towards human skills and work.

Such technologies do in fact exist and have been widely tested under stringent conditions in many developing countries where resource limitations have always been severe and social questions of equity and distribution have not been avoidable by assuming that plenty would soon be available for all. Their even greater value, when applied to overdeveloped countries, is rapidly being proven. Ironically enough, this is occurring in places such as England, Canada, and Japan— where large scale, energy and capital-intensive technologies have been most successful and have most clearly shown their shortcomings and negative effects upon the quality of life.

Technologies that ensure employment, independence, comfort, and quality of life are the normal outcome of almost any healthy cultural development. They have been displaced by our oversized mechanized systems because of the short-term availability of massive energy and material resources and our accompanying assumptions concerning economies of scale and the benefits of institutionalization. We have been willing to allow large organizations the freedom to prove their assertion that they are the best possible avenue for improving our lives. The consequent energetic, economic, and political power of large organizations to secure advantages for themselves has given those systems the appearance of being natural outcomes of economic activity rather than the expensive, unsustainable, and damaging systems that they are.

The assumptions upon which present production processes have been built are no longer supportable:

- Means of production that return the greatest short-run profit are a better choice than ones that are sustainable.
- Continuously increasing capital intensity of production is both possible and the best way of increasing production and minimizing costs.
- Political and social effects of how we do things are less important than the "economic" effects—that "efficient" production gives greater social benefit than ways which cost more directly but offer greater social benefits and fewer social costs.
- Our capacity to purchase goods and services will continue to increase.
- Production is the primary importance and role of work.
- Inequality of income, wealth, and control of production and political processes is necessary for sound business operation.

Our assumptions that larger and larger scales of organization would prove more economical has been conclusively disproved through more comprehensive accounting practices (inclusion of externalized and secondary costs, energy accounting, etc.) and through the development of new and more appropriate small scale technologies over the last dozen years. Where economies of scale have existed, they have long ago been passed by the increasing size of our industrial and other organizations. This has occurred because it has been more *profitable* (not efficient) to do so, because power is a more central goal of such organizations than economics, because diseconomies of worker morale, internal organization, and energy use were not accounted for, and because it has been

possible to externalize or transfer costs (such as pollution) to consumers and to the public at large.

The *profitability* of large organizations has been fundamentally based upon centralization of profits, monopolistic market pricing and control, and taxation and other legislative advantages that the power of large organizations has obtained—*not* fulfillment of their purpose at the lowest cost to society.[13]

Technology is political as well as economic

The implications of the way we choose to do things are far wider and more significant than the criterion of the dollar cost of immediate actions. Smaller scale and regional autonomy in the ways we produce our goods, make available our services, and control our social processes is possible. Such technology is necessary to our political and economic health for many reasons:

- It permits more knowledgeable meeting of local needs.
- It prevents centralization of production and therefore removal of profit from the region concerned, permitting full benefits of work to remain within the community.
- It allows the ability to buffer a region from effects of outside economic changes.
- It increases the diversity, stability, and soundness of local employment opportunities and community life.
- It maintains a comprehensible and controllable scale of activities, organization, and mistakes.
- It permits people to retain responsibility for the social, political, economic, and physical environment where they live, and the power to meet that responsibility.

- It allows more economical operation through minimizing transportation, allowing greater interaction of local industry, and permitting greater use of local resources.
- It allows more people to be employed directly in production rather than in secondary services, thus permitting fuller employment and more viable operation under conditions of lower resource availability.
- It makes unnecessary many expensive or unavailable finance, transportation, education, advertising, management, and energy services.

Small is beautiful

Even before the energy costs of transportation and operation became an important aspect of patterns of production, the realization that a smaller scale of operation was often more effective than larger ones was becoming apparent. When forced several years ago to design small scale oil refineries for oil producing nations, the U.S. petroleum industry was surprised to discover that small refineries could actually operate less expensively than large ones.

It has now been repeatedly demonstrated that, given competent engineering design, capital-to-output ratios of present facilities can quite commonly be equalled or improved by mini-plants that have often only one or two percent of what has previously been considered minimum economic capacity, yet which substantially increase employment opportunities. In other cases, much of the real efficiency of large organization has been its ability to apply inexpensive energy to do our work, yet we now have technologies that permit equally effective use of energy in small applications. As energy becomes less available, economic bene-

fits of small industry become much greater than large industry because of less need for transportation and greater ability to substitute human resources for energy resources.

Egg carton plants with a capacity of less than one percent of previous economic minimums are now in operation. Other mini-plants have been designed for producing wood particle board with a capacity of $6\frac{1}{2}$ tons per day as opposed to accepted minimums of 1000 tons per day. More than 900 small scale sugar production plants have been set up in India, Pakistan, and Ghana that produce only 100 tons per day, as opposed to a former size of more than a thousand tons per day. They offer four times the employment capacity and cost only one-fourth as much per ton to operate as larger mills. They also reduce transportation needs and impart greater diversity and strength to local economies.

In many cases we have also been reminded that our needs can be met much more effectively merely by elimination of self-indulgent demands. Very good, high quality soap can be produced inexpensively by small scale processes. It is only when we demand *perfumed* soap that complex, expensive, and large scale production is necessary. Perfumed soap requires the removal of the glycerine, a complex and expensive process.

The fundamental reason we need so much energy and complex technology is that we have developed patterns of production and use which are indirect, inefficient, and untrustworthy. Much of the cost of production is necessary only because it is divorced from the user. When we examine the costs involved in standardization and regulation of products, shipping, preservation, packaging, management, advertising, buildings and equipment, and employee commuting, we can see why lower technical costs of production are often more than offset by higher secondary costs.

The weight of a loaf of bread is totally unimportant if you make it yourself because you eat it by the mouthful, not by the pound. Yet expensive weighing machines are necessary in commercial bread production, because the interest there is in maximizing profit—you must give people what they pay for, but you don't want to give them the least bit more than that. Advertising is unnecessary if you know the people you are buying things from, but it forms a major part of production costs in present processes.

Developments in appropriate technology have so far clearly demonstrated that great enlargement of human abilities can be achieved at low cost and with simple yet ingenious and well-designed tools that remove the drudgery but not the skill from work. It has also been shown that simplification of unnecessarily complex ways of production are possible and can offer affordable, controllable, and sustainable ways of doing things.

Simplified, low-energy clothes washing machines and spin-dryers have been developed. Hand operated washing machines are in production to sell for less than $1. Hand tractors for farmers, electric mortise drills for carpenters, bicycle ambulances, water conserving flush toilets, domestic solar water heaters, and low-energy, more nutritious fast food restaurants only suggest the range of low-cost, low-energy, and easy to use tools and appliances that have been developed in the last twenty years. Even some of our present complex devices such as telephones and sewing machines fit the definition of appropriate tools.

Appropriate technology implies the adoption of people-intensive tools, but not regression to inefficient tools. It requires a considerable reduction of all kinds of now compulsory use of goods and services, but not the elimination of teaching, guidance, healing, or manufacture for which individuals take personal responsibility.[14]

Serving whom?

Our professional services are as unsupportable under emerging conditions as our industrial production. We have never faced the inherent limitations in providing services to people or in providing people the fullest opportunities for good health, legal protection, learning, and material well-being. We have felt that, given time, we would produce enough doctors, hospitals, schools, and lawyers to be able to give everyone any desired medical care, education, or other service. We have assumed that we had the resources and that it was only a question of making them available. Such assumptions ignore both our resource limitations and the dynamics of professional practice. The resources don't exist for unlimited services, while for any level of health or education made available to rural areas more resources are diverted to urban areas to develop "new frontiers," maintaining or exacerbating the inequity.

Equity is impossible when limited resources are allocated to provide the "best" services rather than the broadest and most widely needed. The best invariably requires relatively capital-intensive services, more exotic equipment and more highly trained personnel, and inevitably leads to centralization, with services going to the urban, the rich and the more powerful. The "best" is never possible for everyone. Combined with unequal ability of people to pay for services, vast disparity in actual availability of affordable services is inevitable. The most equitable distribution of services requires allocation of resources in terms of benefit to society rather than to the professions, and expansion of service frontiers which can provide more widespread benefit to society rather than expansion of exotic research frontiers such as organ transplants and sex changes which can be of benefit to only a few.

Exclusive "professional" standards are harmful to both the professionals and their clients. Professionals must spend most of their time doing routine things that make poor use of their skills, while clients cannot obtain or afford the expense of "professional" skills for routine needs. Levels of service result that are generally higher than needed and higher than can be delivered to the entire community. Professionals inherently place greater importance on their skills than on others with which they are less familiar. When allowed to establish professional standards themselves, they demand higher standards than necessary and without regard for the many needs and limited resources of most people. Such standards also result in training costs as well as salaries of professionals being substantially higher than necessary to deliver services. They lead to restricting rather than disseminating skills and prevent everyone from learning the skills to take care of their own needs.

Basing responsibility for health, learning and other services outside the individual inherently multiplies the cost of maintaining any level of performance. Individuals then have no incentive to maintain their own health or to educate themselves and no skills to do so. Any profession or service based on assuming a responsibility that should remain with the individual will inherently fail. It will be unable to fulfill such responsibilities and efforts to do so will become unaffordably expensive.

The development of human services in developing countries with extremely limited resources has produced benefits equally effective as the introduction of appropriate technology to production processes. Resources are allocated to programs with the greatest social benefits, such as public health and sanitation measures which have produced mortality rates lower than those of our own immensely richer country. Medical, legal and educational programs based on community and village clinics, self-help schools, and "one-teach-one" programs have permitted professions to disseminate their skills to the greatest number of people—raising the range and reservoir of skills in every individual and in society as a whole and making skills most easily available to everyone.

The advances in medical care in China in recent years are legendary in demonstrating the advances that are possible. "Barefoot doctors," local people trained in elementary medical skills, have made basic services available in every village and hamlet. Para-professionals have been trained in large numbers to handle routine medical problems and to take care of innoculations, birth control services, and public health measures. Widespread educational campaigns have been conducted to raise everyone's awareness of general problems and enlist their aid in eliminating problems such as VD, tuberculosis, and various endemic diseases. Urban-based doctors and other technicians have been required to spend part of each year in rural areas learning of the people's actual needs, spreading their skills, and training medical practitioners.

Both traditional Chinese herbal and preventive medicine and Western curative medicine have been employed and taught, and both scrutinized to determine their benefits and shortcomings. The synthesis of the various medical traditions, particularly in areas such as healing broken bones, treating burns, and use of anesthetics, has proven far better than either previous tradition, and has resulted in the development of an equitable and adequate medical care program on a larger scale, with a speed, and at a lower cost than ever before achieved (to say nothing of resolving problems, such as VD, which our medical profession has proven powerless to affect).

Similar potentials exist through careful resource allocation, deprofessionalization, and education to permit dramatic improvement in the level and equity of all our professional services, developing greater self-reliance and knowledge in the general population, achieving better use of time and skills of professionals, and substantially reducing costs.

These approaches have been so much more successful than application of our traditional technologies that countries such as China, Tanzania, Pakistan, and Indonesia have largely rejected "Western technology" and are firmly basing their development on more appropriate, low-impact, and people-centered technology. Many other countries in both "developing" and "overdeveloped" areas are now building such programs. Local programs have recently been established in every county of England, and are being established in Canada and the U.S.[15,16,17]

Big things are paper tigers

The changes necessary to refocus our society into ways that are sustainable and beneficial can be significantly affected by our individual actions. They are based upon four interrelated concerns:

Resources: Conservation of scarce energy and material resources, and wiser use of renewable human resources.

Scale: Adjustment to the smallest viable scales of organization and activity.

Control: Reduction of complexity and capital costs of systems.

Wisdom: Sustainable values, less violent processes, meaningful goals, new means of evaluating tools and institutions so that we might determine and employ only ones that extend and deepen our own capabilities and experiences and unify them with those of others and with our surroundings.

The necessary changes must and can be made ourselves—through our consumption, work and living patterns; through our community and political activity; and through our community, state, and regional government. We cannot expect large scale government, business, or other organizations to make these changes for us, for it would require them to perceive themselves as harmful to society and require their yielding enormous power and wealth. The trend towards a smaller scale of organization implicit in resource scarcity requires that such smaller organizations *assume* their authority and *demonstrate* their ability and rightness through appropriate actions.

This is already happening.[18]

References

1. Amory Lovins, *World Energy Strategies: Facts, Issues, and Options,* (Cambridge, Mass.: Ballinger Publishing Co., 1975). Available from Friends of the Earth.

2. For an overview of depletion schedules for domestic and global material resources see Nicholas Wade, "Raw Materials: U.S. Grows More Vulnerable to Third World Cartels," *Science,* 18 Jan. 1974, pp. 185–186.

3. Ivan Illich, *Energy and Equity,* (New York: Harper & Row, 1974), pp. 18–19. Reprinted by permission of the publisher. Also available as an essay in Ivan Illich, *Toward A History of Needs,* (New York: Pantheon Books, 1977).

4. For an excellent analysis of the claimed and actual effects of large scale organizations on our societies see Richard Barnet and Ronald Muller, *Global Reach: The Power of The Multinational Corporations,* (New York: Simon & Schuster, 1974).

5. For the clearest overview of our needs for changes and the framework within which changes can best occur see Ivan Illich, *Tools for Conviviality,* (New York: Harper & Row, 1973).

6. For an exploration of the principles and operation of ecosystems under conditions of growth, steady-state, and contracting energy conditions see, Eugene Odum, "The Strategy of Ecosystem Development," *Science,* 18 April 1969, pp. 262–270.

7. See Howard T. Odum, *Environment, Power, and Society,* New York: Wiley-Interscience, 197. A difficult but powerful analysis of the principles relating energy and social operations. For a continued analysis see Howard T. Odum, and Elizabeth C. Odum, *Energy Basis for Man and Nature,* (New York: McGraw-Hill Book Co., 1976).

8. For a sensitive and perceptive study of the meaning and value of work in a traditional society see, Ananda K. Coomeraswamy, *The Indian Craftsman,* (London: Probsthain & Co., 1909). Out of Print.

9. See Francis Fitzgerald, *Fire in the Lake: The Vietnamese and the Americans in Vietnam,* (Boston: Little, Brown & Co. 1972). The cultural interfacing of the traditional Vietnamese, modern Communist, and our own American societies in Vietnam. Very perceptive views of the fundamentally different base from which three cultures arise, act, and affect their people.

10. See William Hinton, *Fanshen; A Documentary of Revolution in a Chinese Village,* (New York: Monthly Review Press, 1966). A study of one of the 30 experimental villages on which the Chinese have tested their new policies before enacting them on a national level. Revealing documentation of the changes in a village during land distribution and establishment of democratic government.

11. See J. S. Horn, *Away with all Pests: An English Surgeon in People's China, 1954–1969,* (New York: Monthly Review Press, 1973). Probably the best book available to give a feeling for the revolutions in Chinese medicine and the effects on the people involved.

12. See Tom Bender, *Environmental Design Primer,* New York: Schocken Books, 1973. Explorations of changes in attitudes, ways of working, and of making changes related to our emerging conditions. See also "Living Lightly," and other papers by Tom Bender available from *RAIN: The Journal of Appropriate Technology,* 2270 N.W. Irving, Portland, OR 97210.

13. See E.F. Schumacher, *Small is Beautiful: Economics as If People Mattered,* (New York: Harper & Row, 1973). This book is our soundest basis for

making changes in our present production and consumption patterns.

14. See the journal *Appropriate Technology* and other publications available from The Intermediate Technology Development Group (I.T.D.G.), Parnell House, 25 Wilton Rd., London SWI. See also, *The Village Technology Handbook,* and other publications of V.I.T.A. (Volunteers in Technical Assistance), 3706 Rhode Island Avenue, Mt. Rainier, MD 20822. For a comprehensive overview of sources on appropriate technology see, *Rainbook: Resources for Appropriate Technology,* (New York: Schocken Books, 1977) and Lane de Moll and Gigi Coe (eds.), *Stepping Stones: Appropriate Technology and Beyond,* (New York: Schocken Books, 1978).

15. For a careful documentation of the effectiveness of innovative health services in developing countries, see David Morley, *Paediatric Priorities in the Developing World,* (London: Butterworths, 1973). Available from I.T.D.G.

16. For a good study of the principles of organizing equitable health services under conditions of scarcity, see I.T.D.G., *Health Manpower and the Medical Auxiliary.* Available from I.T.D.G.

17. See Ivan Illich, *Energy and Equity,* (New York: Harper & Row, 1974) and Ivan Illich, *Medical Nemesis: The Expropriation of Health,* (New York: Random House, 1976).

18. See Lane de Moll and Gigi Coe, (eds.), *Stepping Stones: Appropriate Technology and Beyond,* (New York: Schocken Books, 1978). Community actions for adjusting to emerging resource conditions.

EXPRESSION

*Not the saying
but the doing
is the essence*

—Abot 1:17

Contemplative
Communities

THE UTOPIAN VISION of a middle landscape, a harmony of opposites which synthesizes the polarities of nature and culture, spirit and matter, the city and the desert, has haunted the human imagination throughout history. It is an image of a world where cooperation and mutual aid has replaced competition and mutual exploitation, a social order where the needs of the individual are congruent with the interests of the group. Underlying all such visions of a harmonious and unified psychosocial order is the assumption that the evils of self and society are, to some extent, the result of the distortion of human nature created by imperfect, and therefore perfectible, human institutions. The genuine utopian vision, then, starts as a critique of the existing social order and ends in an image of the possibilities for its improvement.

Since its founding, America has been the repository of the spiritual hopes and utopian ideals of Western civilization. With the opening of a vast continent for settlement, these dreams became translated into concrete proposals for the actual creation of ideal communities. In the 19th Century alone at least 100,000 people were engaged in the attempt to create hundreds of living models of communal ideals.[1] Three kinds of critiques of society have provided the moving force behind this utopian search: religious, politico-economic, and psychosocial. Sociologist Rosabeth Moss Kanter describes the history of these American experiments in community building as a series of three historical waves roughly corresponding to each of the three critiques of the existing social order.

. . . the initial impetus for building of American communes has tended to stem from one of the three major themes: a desire to live according to religious and spiritual values, rejecting the sinfulness of the established order; a desire to reform society by curing its economic and political ills, rejecting the injustices and inhumanity of the establishment; or a desire to promote the psychosocial growth of the individual by putting him into closer touch with his fellows, rejecting the isolation and alienation of the surrounding society. These three threads vaguely correspond to the three historical waves of American utopian communities: the first lasted from early days to about 1845, when religious themes were prominent; the second, stressing economic and political issues, ran from 1820 to 1930, flourishing especially in the 1840s; and the third, psychosocial period emerged after World War Two and became especially important in the 1960s.[2]

While the commune-building efforts of the late 1960s and early 1970s often ended in failed dreams and metaphysical disillusionment, the personal, social, and spiritual needs that gave rise to the attempt to create a more nurturant and supportive framework for personal growth and social expression are still very much with us. And as industrial civilization continues to split and crack and break apart at the seams, the desire to create a communitarian culture based on "Buddhist economics," non-violence, and spiritual growth is likely to assume increasing relevance, especially in a nation founded on the belief that the creation of a new heaven and a new earth was a practical possibility.

The articles in this section describe two contemporary American communities that give substance to this hope. In many ways these communities combine the three historical themes, the religious, the politico-economic, and the psychosocial, in a unified critique of industrial civilization and a holistic vision of a metaindustrial alternative. This vision of possibilities, beyond the age of having and getting, has been called the "new American monasticism." In his book, *Living Together Alone,* Charles A. Fracchia summarizes his impressions of the nature of this growing movement toward spiritual community:

What is happening in the United States today is a significant revival of both Western and Eastern monasticism in their "pure", or historic, forms, as well as the development of new forms of monasticism.

Although sociological studies of the "new monks" are, as yet, lacking, there have been sufficient studies, coupled with my own observations, to allow me to make some general statements about those men and women entering spiritual communities; many of them are products of the countercultural revolution of the 1960s and 1970s. They were politically radical, questioning the material values of their parents, and seeking altered states of consciousness through drugs, unconvinced of the doctrine of self-fulfillment through successful careers or higher education.

. . . . Experimenting during the freedom of the 1960s and 1970s, and exposed to a broad array of the luxuries of the consumer economy, these young men and women have eschewed drugs and multiple sex experiences and have turned their backs on color television, suburban-style ranch homes, the "get ahead" mentality, sports cars, and digital watches.

They also have turned away from social and political activism. It was as if an entire generation had "burned out" in trying to make "the world a better place to live in". The end of the war in Vietnam and the loss of energy in "the great society" signaled an end to activism—but not to the aspirations of this generation. Many of them asked, "Is that all there is? There must be more." And many of them discovered this "more" in religion and in spiritual communities.[3]

For those radical political activists, pop sociologists, and silent majority conservatives who believe that the search for personal growth and spiritual development must necessarily regress into a dead-end of narcissism and an other-worldly escape from social and political responsibility, Zen Center and the Abode of the Message provide important lessons about the central paradoxes of the monastic tradition. Both communities are founded on the principle that the claims of the person for spiritual growth be accorded the highest priority; that is the reason they were created and the justification for their continuation. Yet both communities, in the process of creating conditions supportive of this goal, have succeeded in establishing a communitarian fellowship which, itself, is a vehicle for transcending the selfish claims of the limited ego. While the members of these communities have detached themselves from the demands of the consumer society in a search for spiritual growth, they have, paradoxically, created service-oriented, self-reliant domestic economies that restore dignity to work and minimize the disruption of the natural economy of nature. And while withdrawing from the outer world of overt political activism to explore the inner world of the self, they have also joined with others in their local communities to share their knowledge and skills in projects of service and neighborly aid.

These seeming paradoxes have characterized the phenomenon of monasticism throughout its history, in both its eastern and western forms. In his call for a revitalization of this ancient tradition, historian and social critic Theodore Roszak suggests that the key to resolving these paradoxes of contemplative communities is to be found precisely in their commitment to the sanctity of the person and their devotion to individual spiritual growth.

> For what are we to make of the seeming paradox that people who did not put social obligation "first" or make it the monopolistic concern of their lives, nevertheless achieved one of the most culturally vital forms of egalitarian fellowship? And further: that people who did not allow practicality to dominate their lives nevertheless developed an economic style of astonishing inventiveness and productivity? I suggest that the key to the paradox lies in recognizing how much can be achieved if we once allow the social and economic necessities to become "secondary" considerations, trusting that they will draw their best motivations from a psychology of wise indirection. Then we allow other energies to rise within us—energies that are born of personal need, but which unfold naturally into the surrounding world.[4]

Community out of solitude, public service out of self-development, right livelihood out of spiritual practice. These are the paradoxes that define and give meaning to the new monasticism. In its unique ability to "synthesize qualities of life that have become fiercely polarized in our world,"[5] the contemplative community is once again pioneering ways of being and means of livelihood that offer a viable alternative to the anomie and alienation that is our legacy from the impersonal organizations and rootless "communities" of the industrial age.

No community better exemplifies the relevance of the monastic tradition to the needs of contemporary America than Zen Center in California. Zen as a way of life, philosophy, and meditational discipline in the 2,500-year tradition of Buddhism is concerned with the development of integrated, calm, and centered individuals whose every thought and action reflects an understanding of the interconnectedness of all beings and things. Since the nature of a society is a reflection of the consciousness and character of the individuals of which it is composed, Zen serves the needs of society by helping the person to discover his or her own wholeness and essential identity with all creation. Because Zen is not a religion in the western sense of that term, it has found ready acceptance as a meditational practice within a wide range of religious and cultural traditions. The Catholic monk Thomas Merton explains:

> Zen is not theology, and it makes no claim to deal with theological truth in any form whatever. Nor is it an abstract metaphysic. It is, so to speak, a concrete and lived ontology which explains itself not in theoretical propositions but acts emerging out of a certain quality of consciousness and of awareness. Only by these acts and by this quality of consciousness can Zen be judged.[6]

Zen Center as a community has grown out of this "quality of consciousness and of awareness," a mode of being that is rooted in the daily practice of zazen—just sitting. All the external forms of the community, from its hand and horse cultivated farm at Green Gulch to its many self-supporting businesses in San Francisco and its mountain retreat at Tassajara (Figures 1 and 2), are merely the outward expression of this inner life of meditation, this disciplined search for a centered mindfulness of existence in the here-and-now of the present. That Zen Center is also a model for a balanced and sane life in a metaindustrial future is a tribute to the timeless relevance of the contemplative tradition of Zen and the unqualified success the members of Zen Center have had applying their spiritual ideals to everyday life.

Just as the small mystical communities of Cistercian monks of 12th and 13th Century Europe revitalized a sagging spiritual tradition while draining swamps, clearing forests, and terracing hillsides to provide the agricultural foundation for Western civilization, Zen Center is now creating the basis for a spiritual renaissance in America while pioneering new methods of biologically-derived agriculture, experimenting with a variety of renewable-energy-based technologies, and evolving new patterns of economic activity that respect the needs of the person as well as the planet. The result is a new form of community that is uniquely adapted to the

economic, political and ecological needs of contemporary America.

It is hard to describe Zen Center. It is a monastic community rooted in daily meditational practice that includes both men and women as well as families with children. It is an economically self-supporting community where work is a form of spiritual practice as well as a means to serve the larger community of which it is a part. It is a service community that attempts to create activities and places that build trust and improve the lives of those who are not a part of Zen Center. It is a community-scale experiment in appropriate technology and a meeting ground for dialogue in cross-cultural awareness and understanding. And it is part of a planetary network of communities that share a commitment to the ideals of non-violence, justice, and equity for all the peoples of the world and seek to realize these ideals in every aspect of community life. In short, Zen Center is a model for the creative dis-integration of industrial civilization and the imaginative, yet practical, re-structuring of the American landscape, a

Figure 1
Zen Center Mountain Retreat at Tassajara Springs. The Zen community includes men and women of all ages as well as families with children.
(Photo by Gary Coates)

Figure 2
*Tassajara dining build-
ing and outside eating
area.*
(Courtesy of Zen Center)

model that includes the urban neighborhood, the rural farm community
and the isolated monastic retreat in a unified whole which includes, yet
transcends, these historically polarized opposites.

Like Zen Center, the Abode of the Message in New Lebanon, N.Y., reflects the recent infusion of eastern spiritual traditions into the life and
thought of modern America. Sufism, like Zen, is nearly impossible to describe, for it too, is neither a religion nor a doctrine. Rather, it is a meditational practice that seeks to lead the student to an experience of the unity
of life. Hazrat Inayat Khan, who brought Sufism to the west, has explained the Sufi belief in the brotherhood of humankind in the following
way.

If there is any moral principle that the Sufi movement brings, it is this: that the whole of humanity is like one body, and any organ which is hurt or troubled can indirectly cause damage to the whole body. And as the health of the whole body depends upon the health of each part, so the health of the whole body depends upon the health of every nation.[7]

Because of this universalistic perspective, and its respect for the essential truth of all the world's great religions, Sufism has flourished among Hindu, Christian, and Buddhist cultures throughout its history. The Abode of the Message, as a community, is an attempt to apply Sufism to the experience of everyday life in contemporary America.

Unlike Zen Center, which is a community in three locations, The Abode is a residential community located on the site of a former Shaker community in New Lebanon, N.Y. The Shakers were perhaps the most successful and certainly the longest-lived American spiritual community group. During their 184-year history the Shakers recorded 17,000 members and at their height (1830–1840) they counted 6,000 members in 18 villages throughout the Northeast.[8] The Shaker example of simplicity, hard work, inventiveness, careful husbandry, fine craftmanship, and practical spirituality has established a standard of excellence for communal groups for all time.

In resettling the Shaker village in New Lebanon, the Sufis, who share many Shaker ideals and spiritual practices (including sacred dance), have had to find a way to respect the spiritual tradition of the Shakers while developing physical and social patterns of community life appropriate to the evolving identity of the community. For example, the Shakers were celibate and lived in dormitory housing that carefully segregated men from women and minimized opportunities for casual intermingling. For a growing community with families and children these physical patterns soon proved disruptive of community goals and personal needs. However, rather than radically restructuring the historically significant Shaker buildings, the Sufis have chosen to gradually create a more diverse and balanced set of living options. Over time, the central Shaker building complex, now being restored, will become a village center serving the needs of visitors and providing a gathering place for the community at meals and meditations, and for meetings and study groups.

This respect for the legacy of the past is also characteristic of the Abode's approach to interpersonal relationships and community economic development. In their effort to become self-supporting, the ideals of quality craftmanship and community service are more important than any considerations of short-term economic expediency. All community businesses, from the large organic farm and orchard to the highly successful natural foods bakery, Volkswagen repair shop, and alternate energy systems store, as well as the many small crafts businesses, are oriented toward providing high quality at low prices. Service programs such as the Mountain Road Children's School and the holistic healing center are not only open to community members but they also serve the needs of surrounding communities. The Abode is not, nor does it seek to become, a self-sufficient survival community. Like Zen Center, the Abode recognizes the fact that there is no such thing as complete autonomy for any living entity. The community goal of economic self-reliance reflects a desire to provide meaningful work opportunities for community members that simultaneously meet the genuine needs of outside groups for goods and services.

For both the Abode and Zen Center, community is seen as a strategy for experiencing and expressing the wholeness and interdependence of life. It is as much a state of consciousness of relatedness as it is a social or physical form. Community thus becomes an educational process, a "yoga of relationship," that can help to reintegrate the self and reunify the self with the world. Charles Fracchia sees this as one of the enduring contributions of contemporary spiritual communities:

> What is it, then, that the "new monasticism" has to teach us about relationships? It is perhaps the sanctity of other humans as the basis of a relationship. The analogy to things may not be too far-fetched: we should not pollute the air or the water, we should not destroy fish or animals needlessly, we should not deplete the fertility of the soil, we should not proliferate ugliness in nature. Why? Because creation is sacred—and if we diminish ourselves by consuming more than we need, by damaging the environment—how much more do we lessen our humanity by using other human beings for our gratification? It is this paradoxical lesson of attachment through detachment that the "new monasticism" offers our society.[9]

The growing number of small, decentralized contemplative communities that are seeking to create a high quality, low-consumption lifestyle based on skill-intensive occupations and supported by the renewable energies of sun, wind, and soil can be seen as a microcosm of the emerging alternative to industrial civilization.[10] The contemplative community is a domestic household, a production economy, a political entity, and a religious association. However, unlike the larger society where all these functions are now separated in time and space, these life functions are telescoped into one small, comprehensible, geographically bounded entity that is responsible for their integration and ongoing vitality. By thus miniaturizing society, the contemplative community makes, in E. F. Schumacher's words, "a viable future visible in the present."

As pioneers of the new landscape of postindustrial America, Zen Center and The Abode of the Message are confronting, and in many ways solving, the multiple problems that we as individuals and a nation must face in the decades ahead. At the heart of their search for answers is a commitment to the sanctity of the person and the sacredness of creation. In the midst of a society that cultivates inner compulsions and fears in order to harness them to the wheels of production and consumption, they are attempting to confront and transcend existential anxiety through a life of meditation and voluntary simplicity. Within an industrial economy dedicated to the mindless and meaningless production of shoddy and harmful products for the sake of endlessly increasing profits, there is an effort to create an "economics of permanence" where durable, useful and carefully crafted goods are produced to meet basic needs in contemplative workshops where manual labor is once again practiced as a spiritual discipline. In a society where the exploitation of people and environments has become the prerequisite for survival, there is a consciousness of spiritual and ecological interdependence and a commitment to non-violence in every aspect of community life. And while the contemplative community cannot help but participate in the destructiveness of the larger society of which it is a part, there is at least a recognition of this and an active search for a way to live more responsibly.

As the large, complex, overspecialized and interdependent institutions of industrial society continue to consume the people and the nonrenewable resources upon which they depend for survival, we can expect increasing numbers of people to turn to the example of the contemplative community for inspiration and practical advice. In the coming transition to a metaindustrial culture we are likely to see an explosion of similar efforts at community building. Some will be rooted in meditational practice and religious beliefs. Others will be more specialized associations aimed at meeting basic needs for goods and services, such as producer-consumer food co-ops, and neighborhood energy utilities. Some will be communities of self-managed workers. But regardless of their form, the inevitable end of industrial civilization will mean the rebirth of community as a fundamental expression of human identity and an enduring foundation for human culture.

What, then, is the meaning and relevance of these small tentative experiments in spiritual community to the task of resettling America? Charles Fracchia provides the answer in his assessment of the future of the "new monasticism."

> At the risk of ridicule for being a visionary, I believe that the "new monasticism" will provide a catalyst for change, will be a conscience for the nation, will change the values of many with regard to work and money, relationships, and the environment. I see the "new monasticism" as institutionalizing the ferment of the 1960s and 1970s: the consciousness of non-violence, the ecological movement, the desire for relationships that see the essence of each encountering the other, the wish for a contemplative life. In this institutionalization will come, hopefully, a source of vitalizing our society, of holding forth the possibility of a life that is both sane and full.[11]

References

1. Dolores Hayden, *Seven American Utopias: The Architecture of Communitarian Socialism, 1790–1975,* (Cambridge: MIT Press, 1976), p. 9.

2. Rosabeth Moss Kanter, *Commitment and Community: Communes and Utopias in Sociological Perspective,* (Cambridge: Harvard Univ. Press, 1972), p. 8.

3. Charles A. Fracchia, *Living Together Alone: The New Monasticism,* (San Francisco: Harper & Row, 1979), p. 8. Reprinted by permission of the publishers.

4. Theodore Roszak, *Person/Planet: The Creative Disintegration of Industrial Society,* (Garden City, N.Y.: Anchor Press / Doubleday & Co., 1978), p. 290.

5. Ibid., p. 290.

6. Thomas Merton, *Mystics and Zen Masters,* (New York: Dell Publishing Co., Inc., 1967), p. ix.

7. Hazrat Inayat Khan, as quoted in Elizabeth Rechtschaffen, "Resettling the Shakers: The Abode of the Message, New Lebanon, N.Y." in this volume.

8. Rosabeth Moss Kanter, *Communes and Utopias,* p. 246.

9. Charles A. Fracchia, *Living Together Alone: The New Monasticism,* pp. 20–21.

10. Zen Center and The Abode of the Message are at least partial embodiments of what cultural historian William Irwin Thompson has referred to as the "metaindustrial village." See Gary J. Coates, "Future Images, Present Possibilities: Revisioning Nature, Self and Society," in this volume for a more complete explanation of this idea.

11. Charles A. Fracchia, *Living Together Alone: The New Monasticism,* p. 21.

3 | Sangha-Community

Richard Baker-roshi

INDIVIDUALS AND THE STATE have an identity in America, but all other associations are seen as limited to a particular purpose such as business, education, fraternity, athletics, research, worship, and so forth. Community is not seen as a fundamental expression of personal and social identity. And community is not simply an amplification or extension of personal identity; it is an identity in itself, an identity that is more than and other than the individual alone plus other people. Community is certainly a more real and functioning identity than the political, economic and trade unit called the state. The state is primarily defined by its extent and its control of transportation and resources, and very little defined by the emotional and psychological needs of individuals. The state is threatened by real bonding in communities and particularly threatened by any community approaching self-sufficiency or autonomy. (In pre-

modern Japan the military dictatorship consciously tried to wipe out the economically nearly self-sufficient small cross-village units called *buraku* by getting their members into debt— tempting them with Tokyo goods not produced by their household and village economy.)

Zen Center is a traditional and innovative Zen Buddhist community that is not exactly similar to any Buddhist community in Japan, China, or Tibet. At the same time Zen Center is a direct descendant of a tradition of meditation and communal life that goes back more than 2500 years to Buddha's own way of life with his disciples, and back more than 1200 years to the specific ways and rules of Zen communal life begun by Pai-chang (Hyakujo) in the 8th Century. (His most famous statement was, "A day of no work is a day of no eating.")

Zen meditation is called zazen. Za means sitting, and Zen means that concentration or absorption in which you are one with everything, in which there is no subject-object distinction. Shunryu Suzuki-roshi, my teacher, came from Japan in 1959. He never started a group, but he meditated every

Reprinted by permission from Michael Katz et al., eds, *Earth's Answer,* (Lindisfarne Books / Harper & Row, 1977), p. 44–57. Copyright Zen Center.

Figure 1

The three main sites of the Zen Center: (a) The City Center in San Francisco is located in an historic building designed by Julia Morgan in 1922. It provides student housing, facilities for communal meals and meditation and a library-bookstore; (b) The Wheelwright Center at Green Gulch Farm was built by Zen Center carpenters as as place for guests to stay, for retreats, and for workshops; (c) Tassajara's temporary Zendo or meditation hall was built by Zen Center carpenters in 1978 after the original Zendo was destroyed by fire. The building will be used for traditional religious services when the permanent Zendo is rebuilt.

(Photos *a* and *c* by Gary Coates; photo *b* courtesy of Zen Center)

A

B

C

day and people just began to join him in meditation. In those early days when there was no community, we thought only one or two people might practice successfully for a long period of time. That it was actually possible or feasible to make a lifetime commitment to Zen practice had not occurred to us. We felt lucky to imagine that we could practice even for a short time, especially since it always seemed imminent that Suzuki-roshi would have to return to Japan. Also, the economic and material circumstances that would permit us to practice for a long period of time were not available, or seemed not to be available.

However, soon there were many people staying a year or two or longer. Then with the starting of Tassajara Zen Mountain Center in 1967, the number of students who were staying a long time and who had an actual feeling for and understanding of Zen practice dramatically increased. In fact, now we find we have to limit the number of students in order to maintain our goal of remaining a face-to-face community of about two hundred residents in our three locations of San Francisco, Green Gulch, and Tassajara (Figure 1). In addition to the residents there are about a hundred more students who live in apartments near Zen Center in the city and a few who live near Green Gulch Farm and Tassajara. There are many more people who come to the public lectures in San Francisco and Green Gulch. Beyond these people in the Bay Area, there are quite a few thousand people throughout the country who correspond with us, or who come to Zen Center as students for various lengths of time, or who come to the summer guest season at Tassajara. So the size of the extended Zen Center community is quite large and varied.

Let me define Zen Center more clearly and establish some of the vocabulary for this talk. Zen Center is a practice and study center in three locations. In San Francisco there is a public meditation hall; a seminary, the Shunryu Suzuki Study Center; and a neighborhood community and service center, The Neighborhood Foundation. In the mountains near Carmel and Big Sur is Zen Mountain Center at Tassajara Springs, the most well-known part of Zen Center. It is a traditional Chinese-Japanese style Zen monastery with a four-month summer guest season open to the public. In Marin County, just north of the Golden Gate Bridge, near Muir Woods and the town of Muir Beach, is Green Gulch Farm (Figure 2). At the farm are a public meditation hall, a large hand-and-horse-cultivated produce and egg farm, beginning experiments in alternative energy systems, and a meeting and retreat center called The Wheelwright Center. Zen Center also includes the Green Gulch Greengrocer (Figure 3), a produce and neighborhood store in the city; the Tassajara Bread Bakery, a general bakery, pastry, and coffee shop in the city; and the Alaya Storehouse, a factory and store where we make and sell clothes, cushions, and mats for meditation and comfort.

While the number of residents is a little under two hundred, the immediate Zen Center community is about 250 persons who have been together for many years—the average is over seven years, and some people have been with Zen Center eighteen years. This cumulative experience in how to live and do things together makes possible everything we do. Faced with our gathering community and the increasing number of married couples and children, in the mid-to-late 60s we concluded that we were not a transient stu-

Figure 2

Green Gulch Farm, a 115-acre farm 17 miles north of San Francisco near Muir Beach, provides Zen Center with an opportunity to explore the practicality of organic farming and a variety of other appropriate technologies in a way that is extraordinarily accessible to the public. Zen Center takes care of the Green Gulch Valley as a private extension of the surrounding Golden Gate National Recreation Area and has an average of eight to ten thousand visitors a year, including many groups of urban poor and suburban high school students who have participated in a special six-to-eight-week summer program in organic gardening methods, livestock care, cooking and bread making, carpentry, and other skills.

(Courtesy of Zen Center)

dent body but a community (with tenure and stability) that we must recognize and make (its existence and support) an integral part of our practice.

Although Zen Center is a community, it is a practice community and not primarily a residential community. In a Buddhist practice-community, a Sangha, you leave if you stop practicing, while in a residential community, it is residence and not practice that establishes your participation. Exceptions can be made for a person to experiment with stopping practice for a time or for one member of a couple not to practice, but usually if you stop practicing meditation you leave. A Buddhist community or Sangha is not society at large, so it can exclude people. It does not need prisons. A large part of early Buddhist literature details this communal process of how and on what grounds someone not practicing or disturbing the community life and practice is excluded.

Buddha, Dharma, and Sangha are called the Three Treasures of Buddhism. Throughout history people have found the world undependable, painful, and full of suffering, so in Buddhism it is said that we should not take refuge in this conditioned world of suffering; instead we should take refuge in the unconditioned Buddha, Dharma, and Sangha. Buddha is understood as your identity or oneness with the truth. Dharma is the phenomenal world or form itself as the teaching, or your oneness with all things. Sangha is your identity with all being. In a limited communal sense, Sangha means those who acknowledge this identity and make their life intention and work the enlightenment of all beings.

Implicit in the idea and practice of Sangha is that the prevailing society of every period of history will be to some degree corrupt, misguided, or chaotic; and that the antidote to this, the fundamental social action, the only hope, is the maintenance of a tradition that produces realized, enlightened, radically

Figure 3
The Green Gulch Greengrocery, the first of Zen Center's businesses, opened in 1975 as a general neighborhood store with three purposes: to provide good, low-cost food (especially produce from Green Gulch Farm) to the neighborhood; to help local residents meet, creating conditions in which a face-to-face community could develop; to provide income for Zen Center.

(Courtesy of Zen Center)

sane individuals. Society needs the presence and companionship of such individuals and of groups of people trying to live this way—people who are trying to find as their first priority the optimum way to live together. In this sense Sangha is a kind of potential or capacity of society to live together —if a few people can find a way to live together, then many people can find a way to live together. At least we ought to throw our shoulders to the wheel.

It is this effort and example, not really the scale of its success, that opens and allows a society to breathe and deepen its expression, singly and together. A community can help us become free from viewing our lives as dramas of success or failure requiring a leading actor and a series of emotional scenes. A community can give us the space and support to express ourselves individually and with others in the simplest, most continuous and adequate way.

The Buddhist Sangha is one of the oldest continuing institutions in the world. It is not local or limited to any particular age, country, or century. So a Buddhist community usually has a very open and precise feeling. Everything does not have to be done in one generation. This large-scale and open-ended time frame is exceedingly important. People need a scale of time and history that allows them to understand how things happen, allows them to feel their own lives continuing and to see the lives of those around them as understandable and accessible. Without an accessible, understandable scale there is likely to be a build-up of frustration, oppression, and social violence.

Culture is produced by people living and doing things together, so the intensity, interactions, and time scale of people living together in a community are extremely potent. This also means that a community must have the capacity and sophistication to absorb, widen, and extend the development of its members who by living together change and themselves become more sophisticated. For us it is Buddhism which broadens the community beyond our personal needs and teaches us to share resources without possessiveness. It cannot be done just by morality and good intentions, for that will pale, bore, or repress, especially the most imaginative and energetic people. A community needs a wise, wide, intentional, philosophical, and practical base that is expressed not so much by rules or philosophy itself as by the nature, details, and trivia of the daily physical activity, attitudes, and way of life.

Buddhism poses a transient world which you cannot grasp, as the Diamond Sutra states, "with past, present, or future mind." Being transient, it is suffering. The world posed is not only ecologically interdependent, but extended in all ways, in all directions, without obstruction. In this changing vast world the identity of everything is found under your own two feet. Human beings are makers. If we pick up a beachstone, we have made something. We enjoy a beachstone that someone has given us. We are always making things, and for somebody who practices meditation there is an awareness of the fullness and emptiness of the background out of which things are made, out of which things arise. When things are examined carefully, even in the physical terms of modern physics, they rest on the edge, the entry of arising and disappearing.

The process of meditation is to identify our self or to find our own center of balance in that space, in that emptiness that includes form and emptiness; in that activity that is the moment of expression; in that danger and security of being without support and also not needing support. The Large Sutra on Perfect Wisdom states that "a Bodhisattva who courses in perfect wisdom should survey conditioned co-production through the aspiration for space-like non-extinction." You, your aspiration, your making, is the center of existence. "Making" in this sense is another word for form itself, for the intentional identity of the phenomenal world.

What can you actually possess? How do you possess anything? I remember Suzuki-roshi taking his glasses off and saying, "These are your glasses, but you know about my tired old eyes so you let me use them." There is that kind of feeling about possession in a Buddhist community—that you cannot actually own something, that you use things through the assistance, through the kindness of others. We do not want possessions that exclude, that cause envy, that are not easily accessible to others. If you have something unusual, it is best if someone gave it to you. Everything can be understood this way, by our continuity with everything, by our inextricable oneness and place.

The second precept of Buddhism is a good example of this. It is sometimes translated as "do not steal," but actually it means "do not take what is not given." More strictly, the "do not" of all the precepts means that what you have already is enough, that you do not need anything more. Already is enough. Precepts are boundaries that only exist when they are crossed. Looking at someone you may feel a direct contact. But as soon as you wonder what kind of person or what the person is thinking, good, bad or indifferent, you have lost the contact and broken the precepts.

The first precept, "do not kill," means do not interfere with what you cannot repair or replace (including this moment). For example, it would extend to minimizing the use of non-renewable resources—try not to use so much gasoline, propane, and so forth;

try to use replaceable fuels such as wood or wind (Figure 4). In the Sangha this is expressed through physical activity, attitudes, and rules. When Dogen-roshi, one of the greatest Zen masters of Japan, used water from a running stream to wash his clothes, he put the water that was left over back into the stream. In a Zen monastery when you pour out waste water, you should pour it toward yourself. You will treat the water very carefully. In this way you will be aware and careful with everything, treating everything as yourself, even waste.

This physical care and expression of your situation and life are very important in Zen practice. It is a kind of field or ecological perception and proprioception. For example, although breaking a cup is a loss, it is also an opportunity for someone to sweep it up and an opportunity for someone else to mend it or to make another cup. This perception of the real as the relationships of things, rather than the isolated object, is characteristic of Buddhism and the emphasis on physical practice.

The question of what are the relationships among people that create a community which is more than just neighbors, friends, or associates would require a more extended discussion than is possible here. But at least we can say that the kind of community we are talking about is a group of people who make all major and most minor decisions communally, who share some or most of their daily activity, and who live together or in very close proximity.

The dominant bonding and controlling aspect of the Zen Center community is that we meditate together and share a daily schedule. Sharing a schedule produces the feeling of a common life, which is further reinforced by the contrast with the outside world. The

Figure 4
Sailwing windmill at Green Gulch Farm, designed and built by Ty Cashman (formerly of the New Alchemy Institute) and Zen Center students. Rotating on a free-floating, 3/4-ton axle from an old truck, the mill can pump up to 10,000 gallons of water a day to hillside storage ponds that supply the farm's drip irrigation system.
(Courtesy of Zen Center)

schedule should also be somewhat demanding, should cause some feeling of difficulty or inconvenience. A schedule that realistically requires something from us will help a community stay together. People seldom go back twice to a movie, book, painting, or poem that makes little demand on them.

But the essence of our schedule is the zazen meditation. The deep feeling, openness, and space of zazen absorb most of the problems that would otherwise occur in a community, reducing pettiness and quarrels almost to zero. The challenge and high priority of practicing and meditating together make the problems of kitchen and grounds, of personal interactions seem relatively unimportant.

Another essential function of meditation in a community is that it is a mode for personal change in much the same way as the encounter group process works for the Synanon Foundation and Delancey Street Foundation. In a community people are always confronted with how well or poorly they function personally and with others. This would be very upsetting and would make everyone defensive if there were not a continual process of personal change and self-awareness.

The thinking, decisions, and visions of a Zen Sangha flow from the mind-of-zazen, the mind of meditation. This zazen mind is grounded in our breathing, in the physiology of heart and lungs, in concentrated attention and related thinking, expressing what the Greeks called "the unshakable truth of the well-rounded heart."

While zazen is the priority by which we relate all other aspects of the daily life, still zazen alone would not be enough. The rest of the life of the community must be a support and an extension of zazen. I have already mentioned two of the precepts, a little of the philosophy, and the importance of physical care and attention to the details of our relationships to people and things. Other examples are such important and difficult rules as not gossiping or criticizing others—rules which are often repressive or nearly impossible to follow unless you are practicing meditation. It is encouraging to find that it is possible to enjoy people and express everything we want to without gossip and the many things we often do to undermine each other. (The minute attentive practices of Abidharma psychology and mindfulness are necessary extensions of zazen

too, but too much to go into in this talk.) The fundamental expression of zazen in our life is a capacity for compassionate attention to people and details.

The two most important rules of the Sangha-community are "do not hurt others" and "do not deceive others." These are especially important in guiding members of the community in love and sexual relationships. When these two common-sense rules are honestly and carefully observed, almost all of the sexual problems that beset and in fact often destroy most communities are avoided or solved. But you must be able to find the general community's good—the priority, ethics, and ethos of everyone finding a way to live together—above your own particular satisfactions. In a community it usually becomes very clear that when the price of personal satisfaction is deception and pain, it is not worth it.

These two rules will lessen the tendency of people, particularly new people, to raid the community to satisfy their pre-community fantasies and values. A community cannot survive if it is used as a source of status, sexual partners, or convenient living in a manner that is primarily meaningful in the outside world or in exclusively personal terms. There needs to be an adjustment period available for new members to find out and open themselves to the responsibilities, unique intimacy, and deep satisfactions of living in a community.

The glue or bonds of a community are different from the glue of friendship or marriage. The usual bond of marriage or friendship often will not survive time or individual personalities, and even at its best and most consistent will not sustain or hold together a community. The attempt to build a community on the basis of friendship, personality, or likes and dislikes will destroy friendships and marriages as well as founder the community. It is a mistake that has been made by numerous communes, experimental schools, growth centers, and extended living arrangements.

The actual physical space is a very important part of what makes people able to live together and develop the bonds of community. By physical space I mean also the space of sound, sight, and physical passage. The bells, drums, and sounding boards of a Buddhist community articulate and relate space and events. It is a mostly unknown environment in the West. The visual space should be varied, related, and if possible visually interlocking. The space of physical passage should be thought of according to whether people are or should be walking slowly, quickly, quietly, with care, and so forth. In Japan, temples and other buildings of some dignity are often up a flight of outside stairs that are paced to change your pace. Level stone walkways are similarly paced and often bring you a long way around a building so that you enter it with familiarity. Most important, passage within and between buildings should be understood according to how often people will meet each other and the significance of the activities and buildings joined by the passage. It is best if people meet and greet each other regularly and appropriately in their passage through the day. Passage in this way can make manifest and develop the common experience of work, priorities, and associations that are the actual bonds and intentions of a community.

It is helpful if the schedule and rules work with life outside the community. The diet should not be too different from what people grew up with and what is eaten in restaurants and people's homes. How to bring up children and include non-parents, and how to maintain the nuclear family and at the same time share community life, are best developed in a way that is integrally related to the larger society. Without this, life for school age children may be especially difficult, confusing, and even disabling. In general, the way of life and schedule should permit easy access and flow between the community and the world outside the community. This should be especially true where members have outside jobs, as do the students at our San Francisco center.

Work itself, both inside and outside the community, is an essential part of practice, a way to realize the nature and needs of our environmental and social existence. Within the community we would not dream of or consider replacing a person by a machine. It is an offensive and ridiculous idea. The work we do together is too valuable to sacrifice to machines or to the saving of time (Figure 5). Work is our "making," the activity, the making of our being and of our material and psychological survival.

In Buddhism the physical body is not viewed as something separate from or other or lesser than mind/spirit; and the physical world is not viewed as other than being itself, inextricably separate and joined. This is far from the physicalist view of the world as an inanimate and windable clock, far from the attempt of reductive and deterministic behaviorism to eliminate consciousness and will, and far from the attempt by many people to synthesize experience with chemicals. In Buddhism we start existentially with just what is in front of us and is effective now. Life continues from this spot and is complete on this spot. Life is not a picture in front of you, a destiny, not

Figure 5
At Green Gulch Farm, community members are experimenting with traditional forms of farm management, including horse-drawn cultivators rather then fossil-fuel-dependent machines. This requires more human labor and attention, but it also contributes more to human psychological survival.
(Courtesy of Zen Center)

something you can synthesize. The aspects of your present situation are actually you and your path. ("Mind only" or "material only" comes to the same, if we actually try impossibly to "account for," to take everything into account. Cybernetics and Buddhist logic can come together here.)

It is from this premise that we started the Neighborhood Foundation —start sweeping the streets in front of the building. Start somewhere immediately. Right in front of you. The poet and Zen teacher Gary Snyder's own Zen teacher, shortly before he died, told Gary that "Zen is only two things —zazen and sweeping the temple, and it does not matter how big the temple is." The Neighborhood Foundation is part of the permeable membrane of the Zen Center community and now in-

cludes a neighborhood track team, a low rent program, special assistance to many neighborhood groups and individuals, neighborhood and park maintenance, a local community garden, tree planting, recycling, food distribution, and many other things—all begun from starting to sweep the street (Figure 6).

The various ways we are becoming self-supporting also started as extensions of what we were already doing. Right Livelihood is the fifth step of what is called the Eightfold Path in Buddhism. The eight are Right Views, Right Thought, Right Speech, Right Conduct, Right Livelihood, Right Effort, Right Mindfulness, and Right Concentration. Right Livelihood means that whatever you do should not in any way harm or deceive people.

Suzuki-roshi insisted that we protect other people's livelihood before we think of our own. For a number of years he would not let us start a bookstore. He said, with a force critical of our thoughtlessness, that we should support the local bookstores. It was not until we had a library that he allowed us to start a bookstore as part of the library.

In a similar way we should be careful not to use our advantages as a community with extended connections and inexpensive labor costs in a way that hurts the competitors of the Tassajara Bread Bakery and the Green Gulch Greengrocer. Rather than lowering prices too much, we should offer more service and better products made with better ingredients (Figures 7 and 8). The emphasis in a Buddhist community is on cooperative and not competitive interdependence. Competitiveness is usually motivated by an attempt to create some static safe unchanging situation. Actual interdependence is more

dangerous than that. We can take pleasure in other people's success.

A Sangha-community is organized and defined in a way that does not produce winners and losers. We are not always trying to turn verbs into nouns, process into gains, learning into education (a tendency Ivan Illich has pointed out). In a Sangha, status is not determined by skill, talent, or winning. Status is determined primarily by seniority, commitment, kindness, flexibility, receptivity and similar attitudes. Authority and decision-making are based on consensus through seniority—for example, members of five years have roughly the same participation and authority. Positions are rotated, giving everyone a chance to develop. It means that you may be head cook at some point, even though you do not know how to cook, and that you can expect people to support you in doing the best you can.

Without this approach the most talented people, or those with the most

Figure 6
Daniel E. Koshland Community Park in San Francisco was completed in July 1977 after four years of work by neighborhood and city groups and Zen Center's Neighborhood Foundation. The Foundation was created as a way of responsibly participating in and improving the quality of life in the twenty-square-block area within which the City Center is located. Existing now as a separately incorporated entity with its own Board and Neighborhood Council, the Foundation focuses on programs in: (1) community resource development; (2) low-cost housing and building rehabilitation; (3) youth programs.
(Courtesy of Zen Center)

Figure 7
Tassajara Bread Bakery in San Francisco, started in 1976, is part of Zen Center's effort to be fully self-supporting. Designed by Edward Avedisian, the bakery provides a place for regular customers and neighborhood workers, shoppers and students to shop and to meet with friends over coffee or tea.
(Courtesy of Zen Center)

Figure 8
Greens, Zen Center's new restaurant, which opened in 1979 at Fort Mason on San Francisco's north waterfront, offers a gourmet vegetarian menu. The restaurant contributes significantly to community self-support while providing new work opportunities for students.
(Courtesy of Gary Coates)

desire or need to excel, or those with developed social skills, will take over the community and decision-making very rapidly. When talent or winning is the premium, a fairly new member with great talent, but without experience or wisdom, can take over a community that is not articulated through consensus and seniority. Leadership by talent alone develops leaders and followers but not leaders who develop. When development of all the members of the community is emphasized, then the wisdom of the community can flow through everyone. Community can awaken our capacity to know and experience the reaches and great satisfactions of our mental and physical life, of our individual and extended life.

In this talk I have tried to touch on many aspects of community that may be useful to anyone and any community. Our society needs every kind of community, every meaning of the word community, if it is to survive. Laws and wealth alone cannot hold us together.

In America the identity and good of the individual has been given such singular priority that everything else, every association, all agencies, the government, the land, even the environment and the planet are seen as serving the individual, his or her property and opportunities. (On the other side in the Orient the emphasis is too much on everything serving the community.) Much of our urban and rural population sees the government, business, and the church as personal sources of welfare payments, employment, and charity. Few people understand or act through the responsibility and originality of association and mutuality.

We have made opportunities for free enterprise and individual liberties; now we need to make opportunities for the enterprises and identities of community to develop new liberties and new individual identities. We fear this idea, but there is no alternative. Laws are meant to arbitrate; you cannot legislate the common good, that is the province of community, of living together with kindness and practicality.

Community is that compassionate good will and realistic regard for others, for ourselves, that makes laws mostly unnecessary to enforce the common weal, the common good. Without this regard, as it arises and is developed by community, our society will not establish or maintain humane order—a social order that is the natural expression and necessary basis of individual freedom.

4 | Resettling the Shakers: *The Abode of the Message, New Lebanon, N.Y.*

Elizabeth Rechtschaffen

The Abode vision

The spirituality of our time is not to be found in reaching away from life, but in realizing the divinity of man in the midst of life. It is no longer a personal experience, but a global one.

Pir Vilayat Inayat Khan

IN 1975, Pir Vilayat Inayat Khan, head of the Sufi Order in the West, announced a vision of a community he planned to build. This community was established at the site of a former Shaker settlement in New Lebanon, New York, and is home to more than 110 adults and 30 children (Figures 1 & 2). The community, called the Abode of the Message, was envisioned by Pir Vilayat as a place where people could come to live and to apply the principles of Sufism in their own lives.

Sufism is not easily defined, for it is neither a religion nor a doctrine. It is not made up of a body of dogma which one must follow, and it does not require its constituents to rely upon specific, prescribed rituals or techniques as part of a spiritual practice. It is not for a particular race, nation, or church.

This does not mean that Sufism is without structure in its spiritual life. Indeed, just the opposite is true. Traditional Sufism is very structured, and at the Abode, the community practices Sufism as brought to the West by Hazrat Inayat Khan in the early 1920s. His teachings include daily prayer and meditation, weekly universal worship, whirling, listening to sacred music and making music and dance.

Sufism is a way of looking at the world and a way of living in the world. It is a way of understanding the relationship of the individual to himself (both physically and spiritually) and to all things outside himself. It has existed across centuries and across cultures, and even if, because of its nature, its substance takes no one particular form that can be precisely defined, it is possible to describe some of its characteristics:

1. Sufism is "of the world." It is not a spiritual practice which requires withdrawal from the world, but rather, immersion in it. It is a way to bring the highest ideals into everyday life. It is a way for humanity to awaken to the true meaning of life, to discover the divinity of humanity, not only individually, but together in religion, science, energy, business, health, government, education, art, and every aspect of life on this planet.

Figure 1
Located on 450 acres in the Berkshire Mountains of upstate New York, The Abode of the Message is the site of a 200-year-old Shaker settlement.
(Courtesy of Michael R. Young)

Figure 2
Razzaq Manzil, "The House of Abundance" (left), houses the kitchen and dining room on the first floor and the library on the second floor, as well as private living quarters. Dowla Manzil, "The House of Wealth" (right), provides living space and a snack kitchen.
(Courtesy of Michael R. Young)

2. It is contemporary. It is responsive to the needs of the time and culture within which it exists.

3. Hazrat Inayat Khan said of Sufism: "If there is any moral principle that the Sufi movement brings, it is this: that the whole of humanity is like one body, and any organ which is hurt or troubled can indirectly cause damage to the whole body. And, as the health of the whole body depends upon the health of each part, so the health of the whole of humanity depends upon the health of every nation."

The Abode of the Message was founded with the vision and hope that it would provide a place where people could live in harmony with each other, with nature, and with the evolution of the planet. Pir Vilayat referred to the establishment of the Abode as "a vast project . . . of great relevance to the problems of our time."

While the vision of the community was to provide a living spiritual center, promoting the unity of all religions, and providing an environment conducive to the unfoldment of the individual by replacing competition with cooperation, it was also envisioned as a place which could provide a means of livelihood for its members. It was toward this end, in 1975, that the first 20 people began the work of building a community.

Building the community
Finding a location

The first step in building the new community involved finding a suitable place. The early planners began their work in California, but soon initiated a search for land on the east coast. Pir Vilayat's vision called for 100 people and 500 to 1000 acres. A location was sought in the southeast, which offered a gentle climate and long growing season as well as reasonable land prices. Just before final action was taken on a site in North Carolina, the planners learned of the availability of 450 acres in the Berkshire Mountains of upstate New York. This land, the site of a 200-year-old Shaker settlement, was expensive; the area had a harsh climate and short growing season; the buildings were neglected and in need of repair. Despite the drawbacks, the obvious began to be manifest. The Sufis were being sent to resettle the Shaker community.

After some study of the Shaker way of life, many similarities in worship were discovered. The communal ideals of simplicity, work, perfection, daily prayer, dance and whirling were akin to the ideals held by the Abode. It was in the spirit of continuing the work begun by the Shakers that the decision was made to purchase the land in New Lebanon.

Early days at the abode:
Operation survival

The early days at the Abode were characterized by hard work on all levels. The first crew of 20 people, who started work in May 1975, began the task of making the new community an appropriate living place for the 75 people who were expected to be living there by the end of the summer.

The spirit of the Shakers was very pervasive in those early days and the earliest spiritual work of those first pioneers was to find a way to work harmoniously with the spiritual tradition that seemed to accompany the land. Besides dealing with the spiritual atmosphere of the village, the Sufis were faced with the immediate task of restoring buildings to a livable condition, and plowing the fields and planting the garden that could feed the anticipated 75 members of the community (Figure 2). It was also necessary to establish a plan for community governance, to organize the inner life of the community, to begin community cottage industries which would provide support for the community, and to lay the groundwork for the education and health centers, part of the vision of the community.

Things did not go smoothly at first. The adjustment to communal life, the lack of space and privacy, and hard work and lack of money took a tremendous amount of patience for all community members, most of whom did not initially know each other and many of whom had contrasting visions of the purpose and direction of the community. Only by delving into Sufism and using its teachings as guidelines did the new community begin to take form. Out of the application of Sufi beliefs and practices grew the ideals that guide community members in their everyday interactions. Among the most important ideals was *tolerance.* Tolerance of many points of view within the community led to a greater respect for human spirit and a greater support for each other among community members. The application of tolerance served as a bridge over many stormy times in the early development of the community.

Another aspect of tolerance is the question of helping each other to see personal shortcomings. In keeping with the ideal of tolerance, the community members try not to criticize each other because "there are many sins, great and small; but to recognize sin is the greatest sin." Of course, it is recognized within the community that this approach cannot be carried too far and that, if necessary, criticism that comes from love, compassion, and wisdom will be right.

Another ideal of the community, which gives the Abode its inner direction is, according to Hazrat Inayat Khan: "the awakening of humanity to the divinity of man." This is a very pure statement of the philosophy of the Abode and means as Pir Vilayat has stated: "the spirituality of our time is not in reaching away from life, but realizing the divinity of man in the midst of life."

Faith is another ideal that guides the Abode. Through faith in the purpose of their work, the Abode community has been able to accept the difficulties encountered in building the new community.

Spiritual life

The spiritual life at the Abode takes the form of daily meditation, prayers, evening classes, group and individual retreats and seminars given by Pir Vilayat and visiting teachers. Sufism is the core of the community's spiritual practice as the Abode is the home of the Sufi Order of the West.

Daily meditations are led by Pir Vilayat, Taj Inayat, Pir Vilayat's spiritual partner who spiritually guides the community with him, or by other family members trained by Pir Vilayat (Figure 3). The sessions are usually

Figure 3
Daily meditations, such as this during the homecoming celebration in May, are held in the Meditation Hall and led by Pir Vilayat Khan, the spiritual leader of the Abode.
(Courtesy of Stephen Hawkins)

Figure 4

An important part of spiritual practice is Sufi dancing or whirling.
(Courtesy of Stephen Hawkins)

readings, meditations, dances and practices and often each day of the week is dedicated to a different religion, in a rhythm recommended by Pir Vilayat, reading from the scripture and doing practices, chants, and songs of that religion.

The family meets three times a day for meditation and prayers, although this is not mandatory and attendance fluctuates. Two evening classes are offered each week. One, for initiates to the Sufi order, focuses on the teachings of Hazrat Inayat Khan. The other, open to the full community, takes the form of music, dance, whirling, and selected readings (Figure 4). Music is an important expression of the divine for the community.

Sunday is a day set aside for welcoming visitors to the community and sharing a Universal Worship. This service was transmitted by Hazrat Inayat Khan, and is an expression of reverence and gratitude for the light brought to humanity through all religions, known and unknown. Attendance at Universal Worship has grown over the years, and neighbors and friends from all over the area now attend. In the spirit of Universal Worship, visiting teachers from different faiths share with us their experience and knowledge. On religious holidays, those who have dedicated their lives to the particular faith are especially welcome to lead the community in traditional services.

Spiritual retreat is one of the most important parts of the practice. Dotting the hillsides of the Abode are little huts where Abode members and visitors take 3-, 6-, or 12-day retreats. Retreats provide an opportunity to break from daily life to do the more important instead of the more urgent. Retreats are a time when one can completely immerse oneself in uninterrupted spiritual practice (meditation and mantra). Pir Vilayat has used the six-stage formula of alchemy to develop a schedule for the retreat, and has trained several Abode members as retreat guides. A guide visits each person on retreat once or twice a day to briefly review the practices for the next day, to bring a light meal, and to take care of any other needs that the retreatant might have. The retreat program is open to all family members and to other persons interested in deepening their spiritual life. The program grew to the point where the six retreat huts were no longer sufficient. A separate retreat center was built on the Abode land, at a distance from the main buildings. This center has its own kitchen, a stone chapel and retreat huts. It serves as the Abode Sanctuary, where members who feel a strong calling to isolate themselves from a worldly life can live for extended periods of time in a retreat-like atmosphere. These people can, in turn, serve as retreat guides for others wishing to take a short retreat in one of the huts.

Another aspect of the spiritual work being done at the Abode is counseling. Counseling can take the form of helping a person with spiritual practices, being available to listen to someone facing a problem, or helping two people in a relationship to see each other's point of view. Several people at the Abode have been designated by Pir Vilayat as being able to guide people in their spiritual practices. These people and some others, who naturally fit the role, help family members with personal problems. Since family members work to deal as openly as they can with their changing personality, seeking help is not considered a weakness. Rather it is seen as another way to bring insight into their lives.

Probably the most significant spiritual work is the way the community puts its ideals into practice. The spiritual ideals of love, harmony and beauty, of tolerance, balance and global consciousness deepen with time and experience and bring to the Abode an atmosphere of sincerity and joy.

Community governance

The community's system of government was another major task needing to be completed during the first year. Reliance on the spiritual ideals of the community helped carry members through this very difficult exercise.

Prior to starting the community, Pir Vilayat had designed the basic structure for leadership and administration at the Abode. The system, a merging of democracy and hierarchy, required considerable effort and some reorganization for its implementation since none of the community members had ever worked with the system before. The system represented the efforts of community founders to respect the need of each individual to express his or her desires and insights while also recognizing that some individuals, due to their wisdom and experience, can be trusted with leadership roles and be given the responsibility to make decisions that affect the whole community.

The community recognized that, at its extreme, democracy can become tedious, ineffective, and overly encouraging to the expression of the individual will, while hierarchy can become oppressive, uncreative, and damaging to the development of the individual. It is the balance between these extremes that Pir Vilayat sought when he designed the initial system of government for the Abode.

The hierarchical structure of the Abode consists of The Elder, Pir Vilayat, responsible for the direction of the community; Arif Rechtschaffen a

"vice-president" to the Elder with responsibility for steering the community on a day-to-day basis and guiding the community in Pir Vilayat's absence. With the help of Taj, who acts as the community's esoteric guide, Arif has been the one most responsible for the community's course. His other duties include: chairing the Piloting Committee (the community's chief decision-making body), chairing family meetings, and attending all committee meetings integral to the organization of the community. In all aspects of his job, the Guide must view the community in its wholeness and make decisions with the guidance of Pir Vilayat in mind.

All major decisions at the Abode must be considered by the Piloting Committee, a representative body of community members which meets weekly. Any controversial matter, after consideration by the Piloting Committee, is then brought before the family meeting for changes, additions, and decisions. The Piloting Committee symbolizes the cohesive nature of the community as it works to deal with the events of everyday life in a specific way.

Besides the Piloting Committee, there are several other vehicles set up to help govern the Abode. These include: the Admissions Committee, which interviews all people interested in staying at the Abode for longer than three days, the Business Committee, the Esoteric Committee, the Housing Committee, and the Planning Committee. These groups meet only when a need arises. The largest governing body is the Family itself which meets together bimonthly at the Family Meeting.

Community finances

The economic system of the Abode has been the most difficult aspect of the governing structure. The current system is a product of much modification and adaptation and is still in a developmental phase. The goal of the community is to develop an economic structure that will allow each individual to meet financial needs while also contributing equitably to the welfare of the community.

The basic components of the economic structure were planned well in advance of the establishment of the community. The system, which was planned to encourage cooperation, not competition, allowed for shared work as well as individual incentive. The original economic plan included a credit system whereby difficult, highly skilled, and undesirable jobs earned the highest amount of credit, as did more productive jobs. Individuals also retained the system of earning private income. In addition, the system included the principle of Karma Yoga—the idea of selfless service—for work done solely for the benefit of others (Figure 5).

Initially, each community member was asked to donate $500 to the Abode as admissions fee in addition to paying $500 for five months rent and food. It was hoped that at the end of five months, the community would have achieved economic self-sufficiency. Because of the great financial needs of the community, (large mortgage, high taxes, building repairs, new businesses in need of capitalization) the goal of achieving economic self-sufficiency required a year and a half.

Despite this, the community began experimenting with a credit system at the end of five months. At the beginning, this was a very simple system with all work given one credit per hour. The value of the credit was determined by dividing the total community income by the number of credits earned each month. Credits earned by each person were tallied, rent deducted and the balance deposited in a Credit Pool Bank from which it could be withdrawn, on demand, in cash.

After several months, it became obvious that some changes were needed. Money was scarce and in order to earn sufficient credits to meet rent and basic needs, it was necessary for each adult to work more than 50 hours per week. This proved untenable for families with children. To deal with this problem, profit-sharing was instituted. This allowed those whose work directly brought income to the community to keep a percentage of the gross amount earned. This encouraged people to bring in more money since it benefitted both the individual and the community.

This, however, negatively affected some of the ideals of sharing since there was little incentive for doing jobs (without profit sharing) that earned only credits. There was a constant move toward a higher percentage of profit sharing. Other problems arose. Total credits increased faster than total income. There was also a problem with Karma Yoga or donated labor. Some people felt their work was so vital that extra time given to it should be a con-

tribution toward Karma Yoga. This was allowed but was later seen to be a mistake which undermined the idea of selfless service to the community as a whole.

By the end of the second year, the community felt that the credit system had become hopelessly complex and it was abandoned for a system which paid cash salaries for specific jobs. Other jobs were done by true Karma Yoga.

With this new system, all members donate, after payment of rent and medical expenses, 40 percent of the remaining profit to the community. This provides a source of support for the community and helps link members financially as the credit system did.

Its is difficult to assess the effects of changing economic systems. Shortly after the change, the Abode experienced a substantial increase in income through a large influx of visitors, new memberships, stabilization of family businesses and support, and through work opportunities for family members in local private businesses. The success of the new system may be better measured by its impact on community goals. The ideal of Karma Yoga was restored and, as people ceased to view Karma Yoga jobs as sources of income, they were performed with greater joy. The system's simplicity and the reliability of income made it more popular with family members.

One aspect that may be considered a disadvantage is a move away from communal resources. With the credit system, people were closely linked economically and personal gain was gain for all. On the cash system, people are financially more independent of each other. The community is still searching for better ways to combine the ideal of shared economics with the incentive and efficiency of the more capitalistic approach, which will probably mean further modification of the present economic system.

Concrete economic goals now include: group health insurance, total self-sufficiency through Abode businesses, and better support for families. Currently, acute financial needs of individuals are met by an emergency fund, made by monthly family member donations. This fund is administered with no questions asked and no expectation of immediate repayment.

Work at the Abode

The Shakers left a heritage of workmanship that has served as a model for the community of the Abode. While the initial work began with a pioneering enthusiasm and the unique emotional tone of beginning a new adventure, the seemingly endless work that needed to be done, combined with the fact that hard work was seen as synonymous with dedication to the Abode, led to an unhealthy situation when community members began making harsh judgments about the amount of work done by fellow members. The atmosphere became somewhat oppressive until the spiritual work of the community, along with changes in the organization of work, helped members to approach work more objectively and to view each other without the blinders of their own egos.

The organization of work at the Abode can be divided into two categories: Karma Yoga (service work), and work done to earn a living. Every Abode member, at some point in the day, does both kinds of work. The Works Commissioner oversees and coordinates all the work of the community. This person takes responsibility for the

smooth running of the community, and for the integration of each member into the daily work pattern. The Works Commissioner also keeps an overall view of the priority of work projects and the allocation of funds. One important job of the Works Commissioner is to help new family members to become accustomed to the rhythm of work at the Abode and to help them find a job best suited to their talents, skills, experience, and needs. This could mean exploring the possibilities of finding a job within the Abode, or looking for one in the outside community. The Works Commissioner has a demanding job, and more people have rotated in and out of it than any other administrative position. It requires involvement with each person's daily routine, without overbearance or insensitivity to the varying temperaments and needs of each member of the community.

Karma Yoga work is voluntary, non-paying, and done in the interest of the whole community. Most tasks that have to do with the essentials of everyday needs are organized under Karma Yoga. Cooking, kitchen clean-up, housecleaning, grounds work, weeding and harvesting on the farm, woodgathering, and other special work projects are jobs for Karma Yoga volunteers. Each person is expected to sign up for two Karma Yoga jobs each week to supplement the work of the paid cleaning and kitchen staff.

In addition to daily Karma Yoga, every Saturday the whole community participates in Saturday Abode Purification, a major house and grounds clean-up or a concentrated community effort to complete a big work project such as cutting and hauling wood in preparation for winter.

More difficult to organize is the work each member does to earn a living. The community has experimented with several different systems, each being centered around the economic system in use at the time. Presently there are four different ways to earn a living at the Abode. One can work in a community business, a privately owned business, an outside job, or be an Abode staff member.

Community businesses

Community cottage industries, or businesses, have grown over the years to the point where they may soon completely support the Abode. They all derive from a particular ideal that the community wishes to see manifest in the material world: the purpose of the community businesses is to offer products and services that benefit people and the planet, and to support the community. The profits accruing to each industry are used by that industry for reinvestment and wages. These industries are incorporated under a for-profit corporation (separate from the Abode) called The Winged Heart Corporation.

The Reza Quality Bakery was the first of the Abode's cottage industries. In Persian, Reza means the divine provider, reflecting the desire to make available to everyone pure and natural foods. Over its years at the Abode, the bakery has experimented with new products and methods best suited to the Abode and its area customers. It now supplies health food stores and supermarkets, within a large radius of the Abode, with seven kinds of whole-grain breads and other products. The bakery also supplies the Abode kitchen with all of its baked goods.

The Heart and Wings Volkswagen Repair Shop was another early enterprise. A family member from Kansas had supported himself for several years

running a VW garage and wanted to do the same at the Abode. He set up shop in Pittsfield, Massachusets (nine miles from the Abode) and today the VW shop is well known throughout the area for honest and reliable service. It has been one of the most successful businesses (Figure 6).

Unlike the bakery and the shop, the Winged Heart Energy Systems (WHES) developed entirely at the Abode. Interest in heat conservation and energy efficiency first began in the search for a better way to heat and insulate the Abode buildings. Finding the best available products was the goal. This led to research in the varied fields of energy—wood, solar, methane, insulation, and fuel-saving devices. The community then formed the Winged Heart Energy Systems, offering the same quality materials and installation. WHES are suppliers of woodstoves, fuel-oil-saving devices, wood-splitters and flush toilet alternatives. It is hoped that WHES can expand into other forms of alternative energy, as knowledge and experience grow. WHES employs many Abode family members.

Mt. Lebanon Natural Foods is the community's natural foods distribut-

Figure 6
Heart and Wings Volkswagen Repair Shop, Pittsfield, Massachusetts. Community cottage industries have grown over the years to the point where they may soon support the Abode.

(Courtesy of Omar Manuelian)

ing company. This business is introducing natural foods (whole grains, juices, dried fruits, nuts and other organic and unrefined food products) into area supermarkets. It also serves as an inner Abode food co-op for those living in houses on the land.

The Springs Health Center, located in Lebanon Springs, three miles from the Abode, is a holistic health center staffed by the Abode resident doctor, Arif Rechtschaffen, and other community health and healing professionals. It offers town residents, as well as family members, a complete health care system. It has plans to expand into a residential health center and spa.

Part of the health center involves home birth and prenatal care and classes. Three midwives work with Dr. Rechtschaffen, attending births, running classes, and being available to pregnant women and new parents for help and advice.

An Abode family member may choose to start a private enterprise which is not incorporated under the auspices of Winged Heart. Businesses such as these are privately owned and controlled, but most fall within certain guidelines set up by the Business Committee. They must be capitalized by the individual, and profits are split 50/50 with the Abode. Any large-scale recapitalization must be approved by the Business Committee. Most of community craftspeople have set up their businesses in this manner. The most successful of these are: stained glass, weaving, jewelry making and sewing. Goods are sold at local stores, at the Abode and at traveling art shows.

Other private businesses continue to grow slowly. Earthworks (a heavy equipment operation) owns a backhoe, a bulldozer and a tractor, and works for the Abode as well as private construction companies in the area. Another

successful private business is a farrier (horse-shoeing) service, owned and run by a family member trained in that skill. Several family members have small private importing businesses.

The need for family members to hold outside jobs has lessened as the businesses have grown and become more stable. However, it still benefits the Abode financially for family members to bring in outside money and some members prefer to work in neighboring areas, finding the service and stimulation fulfilling. Until the Abode develops its own outlets for some professional members of the community (such as social workers and computer technicians) many of these trained people have to work in neighboring towns.

The Abode itself, as an economic entity, employs Abode members to run the kitchen, the Abode store, and the food preserving concentration. There is a staff for the maintenance and renovation of the buildings, for running the farm, and filling the administrative roles of the community. There is also an office staff for the reception and information office. Abode staff all receive the same wage, which varies according to the financial situation of the community.

The kitchen staff is responsible for ordering food, keeping the kitchen budget, planning menus, organizing food storage and heading up the cooking of each meal. The cooking staff has become very knowledgeable about natural foods preparation for large numbers. They are beginning to take this knowledge and experience outside the community. Recently a few Abode cooks were hired to run the kitchen at a large camp for emotionally disturbed children, to see if diet can help those with emotional problems. They were very well received, and are continuing the project at the camp and at area schools.

The Abode hires people to run the farm, gardens, and orchard and to preserve the produce raised. This is a fairly large operation, involving many members, visitors, and farm machinery. The Abode cultivates approximately 10 acres, 5 in vegetables and 5 in grain. In addition, there is one acre planted in fruit trees, one in strawberries and asparagus, and one-half acre in herbs. As the community expands its cultivated land it hopes to raise more grains, beans, and some cash crops. During the summer, Abode members eat entirely from the gardens and freeze and can as much as possible for winter. Several organic farming methods are used. The farm workers feel the importance of attuning themselves to the plants they are raising, and have held several celebrations in the fields at different times during the farming season. Only organic fertilizer from the compost is used. Insects are controlled by planting herbs and flowers as pest controls, by rotating crops and (in extreme cases) by using organic sprays on infected plants.

Every family member is expected at some point to put in some Karma Yoga time on the farm. Usually, several weekends are put aside for community farm work. Sometimes the farm crew will organize a planting or weeding or harvest festival. The major farm work — planning, plowing and a good portion of the planting, weeding and harvesting — is done by a farming crew employed by the Abode.

Building maintenance and renovation is also supported by the Abode. Family members are employed to do the continual tasks of keeping the common areas maintained, the plumbing, electricity and heating functioning, and other general outside and inside build-

Figure 7
A grant from the New York State Preservation League allowed the Abode to restore many of the Shaker buildings.
(Courtesy of the Abode)

ing maintenance. Ground work, including landscaping, lawnmowing and gardening falls under this category also. The Shaker buildings of the Abode have had little or no attention for nearly 30 years. When the Abode first moved into them, the family had to completely rebuild the kitchen, install a new heating and hot-water system, rewire much of the electrical system, and do extensive work on the septic system. The community's financial situation had allowed only a minimum of historic preservation until the receipt of a grant from the N.Y. State Preservation League, which has allowed work to proceed in restoring the buildings to their original beauty (Figure 7). The Sufis feel a commitment to the Shaker spirit and wish to bring out the simple perfection expressed in the village. Further funding toward this aim is being sought from a number of foundations.

Also supported by the Abode are the office, visitor-hosting, the Store, and various administrative posts. The office is the main communication center for the community. It handles visitor registration, mail, telephones, the Bank, typing and the organization of the Abode records. In the office, family members may sign up in advance for the use of an Abode vehicle—the Abode "fleet." This is a service for those who do not own a personal car. The cars are used for both official Abode business and personal use, and are maintained by Abode mechanics. A fee per mile is charged to cover the cost of parts, maintenance, and gas.

The Abode Store is available to visitors and family members. It features crafts made at the Abode, Sufi Order tapes, books and pictures, a large selection of spiritual books from all over the world, and assorted gift items.

Family life

In addition to being a community, an organization, and a spiritual center, the Abode of the Message is a family consisting of those who have committed themselves to the community. There exists between members a bond of love that results in a willingness to forgive faults, strive for harmony, and to serve each other.

The family changes and the number of family members has risen over the years, yet the bond of the family remains. This aspect of family life has been an important lesson in community living. In the early days of the Abode, every family member's decision to leave represented a failure in community living. At that time the Abode's identity was still in a very formative stage. Some members were new to the Sufi way of life while others had been leaders of Sufi centers in other parts of the country. Consequently, there were many different points of view concerning the directions the

community should take, and it became clear that the Abode could not fill some of the expectations of all the original members. To the community now, the departure of a family member is seen as a sign of growth, not of failure.

Presently, the family consists of 110 adults and 30 children. Approximately half the adult population is single, and the other half is couples and parents. Most members are in their late 20s and early 30s. The youngest members are newborn, and the oldest are in their 50s. It is hoped that the community can maintain a broad spectrum of ages, attracting older members as the years go by.

Children are an important part of Abode life. Although the nuclear family is maintained, everyone in the community is involved with the children. This involvement can take the form of spontaneous play, organized child care, or financial support for Abode children's schooling. Everyone at the Abode feels that children add another dimension to community life and spiritual work. Among themselves, children learn responsibility in taking care of the younger ones and cooperation through playing together. In the greater community, the presence of the children makes everyone ever mindful of their influence on the future.

The question of children and the nuclear family is just one aspect of family life at the Abode. Learning how to live intimately with 100 people is a process that involves many changes for all involved. Many questions arise when people come together to share their lives. How can people communicate on a meaningful level when they are meeting in large groups? How can they get to know each other on a friendship basis when their lives are scheduled and living arrangements are institutional? Can people accept that within a large group of people, smaller units form, and it is not possible for everyone to share the same intimacy? How can individuals share creatively as a family? Is it possible to put aside "matters of importance" to play together?

It has been found that if a conscious effort at getting together in a social way is not made, the phenomenon of loneliness in a crowd develops. Mostly it is due to living arrangements and busy schedules. The Shaker buildings were not constructed with socializing in mind. There are few common spaces, and the rooms are organized in a way that does not encourage an open door atmosphere. The work and prayer schedule often leaves little time to relax together. The day begins at 6:00 A.M. with morning meditation at 6:15 A.M. Breakfast is at 7:00 A.M. and work meeting at 7:30 A.M. Work usually begins between 8 A.M. and 9 A.M. Midday prayers are at 12:00 Noon and lunch is at 12:30 P.M. Evening meditation is at 5:30 P.M. and dinner at 6:00 P.M. Classes generally begin at 7:30 P.M.

One way of dealing with this lack of space and time for the cultivation of personal relationships is by following Pir Vilayat's advice:

Sometimes one just has to find one's own rhythm and one's own vibrations, and that is very difficult when one is with many people, for one wants to be alone or to be able to do things that don't matter, not like meditating, which really matters. One wants to perhaps read a newspaper or play ball or let the children play horse on one's back, or even just laugh without any meaning, like the Tibetan and Christian monks who have a time in the day when they laugh for half an hour without any reason. We don't have to institutionalize laughter. I think that something that's called for is having a time during the day when it's not kosher to work. Much as

we have things to do, we just do something else.

Besides breaking out of routine, there are other ways of sharing developing at the Abode. One of these ways is through music and dance. A family concert series has been started, where each month family members present an evening of music and poetry. This has encouraged musicians to spend more time practicing and playing together. The Abode classical choir meets twice a week and performs at community celebrations. Several dramatic presentations are also presented each year.

Sports also bring family members together. A basketball team has formed, and in the summer people hike and swim and play volleyball together. In the winter, cross-country ski treks are organized.

The Abode softball team is part of the Lebanon Valley Softball League, an activity which provides a very important contact with the surrounding community as well as fun for Abode members.

House-building has had a profound effect on family life. With more and more people moving out of the main buildings into hand-built homes on the land, the atmosphere of the Abode changes, and gives more accommodation to the growth of personal relationships. Several people have grouped together to live in smaller communal houses, or in clusters of houses. Although it may seem that by moving away from the community center one becomes more isolated, the long-range effect is that family members are now able to be together in a more peaceful and relaxed setting, without the constant pressure of the Abode's schedule. This is especially true for those living in clusters of houses. Small groups of people living together within the community at large provide a great oppor-

Figure 8
A house building pro-
gram helps people build
private homes. Shown
here is a home under
construction for Pir
Vilayat and his family.
(Courtesy of Omar
Manuelian)

tunity for exploring a tighter social unit. A house-building program has been developed that helps individuals to build private homes and also organizes and carefully plans the building of clusters to make the best use of the land. Family members who build their own homes finance the operation themselves and are paid back by the Abode after two years. They may sell the house for building costs should they move elsewhere within the community or leave the Abode. Some community-built houses financed by the Abode are available to individuals through the Housing Committee (Figure 8).

Family members living in houses away from the main complex may choose to remain on the Abode meal schedule, and eat in the communal dining room, or they may go off the food plan and prepare meals in their own kitchens. A rent reduction is given to those who prepare their own meals. All family members are encouraged to eat one meal a day in the dining room, as it preserves the family feeling.

School at the Abode

The Mountain Road Children's School is the Abode-run preschool and elementary school for Abode children and children from the surrounding area. The school is financed and staffed by the Abode. Abode parents pay tuition, as do parents of outside children, and the community supplements this by helping to pay the teachers' salaries. The school is not on the Abode property, but is located about nine miles away, in a large space that was once a Catholic retreat camp. About 40 children—half of whom are from the Abode—are enrolled. They range in age from 2½ to 8 years. The school is divided into three separate programs, one for the preschoolers and kindergartners, one for the first and second graders, and one for the remaining children in the upper grades. The curriculum for each program is different and is taught by different teachers, but the staff works together and every morning meets to attune themselves through meditation to the school and to each other. There is a certain amount of mingling between the three programs—older children helping the younger ones and the younger ones cooking a snack for the older ones, all of them taking a hike together. The teachers also participate in each other's programs, sharing music, science and other special interests with the children.

The curriculum for the elementary grades follows the guidelines set by the state of New York. The school has an open-classroom style of teaching. Teaching is child-oriented, with the child/teacher ratio small enough for personal attention. The relationship between spirituality and education is one that Mountain Road School experiments and grows with.

The teachers share the belief that spirituality for the young must be a natural and integrated process. Children do not feel comfortable with organized ritual and have less of a tendency to separate spirituality from everyday life. Rather than teaching about God, the school tries to make every subject an example of how life and learning are full of interest, discovery, beauty and perfection. There is a focus on heroes and heroines throughout the ages who have exemplified human potentials, and have reached beyond accepted human limits. Holidays are celebrated, and saints and prophets from the various religions are brought to life through stories, dramatic play, and song. Another way the teachers use their spiritual training to bring harmony to the school is by meditating upon a child when teacher/child conflicts arise. Seeing the child in his or her perfection can break a pattern of relationship that might be hindering the teacher's abilities to guide the child.

It has been difficult for nuclear families to make a living at the Abode, and this has been an opportunity for single people as well as parents to try to see life from each other's point of view. Areas where steps have been made in this direction are: group child care, school support by the whole family, and a reduction in rent for families. Occasionally the parents meet together to discuss mutual problems. They might plan the construction of a play area or study together the teachings of Hazrat Inayat Khan on child-raising.

The Abode as a center for visitors

In addition to school at the Abode, three other programs, the Apprentice Program, the Omega Institute for Holistic Studies, and spiritual retreats and seminars, represent aspects of education encompassed by the practice of the Sufis at the Abode.

The goal of the Omega Institute is to create an environment that encourages the serious pursuit of a particular subject while presenting each subject in the light of a larger whole. Omega's course of study is geared toward the practitioner, professional, and continuing student who wishes to bring to his or her experience a fresh understanding of how his or her work can integrate holistically with the current directions of life and culture.

Directed by Pir Vilayat Inayat Khan, Omega is located in Hoosick, N.Y. It offers 5-day intensive study sessions and weekend seminars. Each 5-day session is staffed by a group of teachers working together to provide an in-depth study opportunity that is rich in diversity of method and background. Guest teachers offer classes as well as weekend seminars.

Classes offered include medical and healing arts, science and spirit, music, art, dance and drama.

The Apprentice program of the Abode represents the third educational endeavor undertaken by the Sufis. Its purpose is to offer participants the opportunity to become proficient at a meaningful, useful skill while taking part in community life, establishing regular meditation and spiritual practices and sharing the community's evolution as a model of balanced life.

The program offers four one-month sessions beginning in June. Participants may choose the minimum one-month experience or may continue for as long as four months. Course offerings include: stone masonry, nutrition and natural foods cooking, esoteric carpentry, herbs and flower gardening, organic agriculture, and commercial organic baking.

Finally, at various times of the year, spiritual retreats and special seminars are given by Abode members, Pir Vilayat and visiting teachers representing various intellectual disciplines and spiritual traditions

The Abode and the future

The meaning of the Abode today is not complete without understanding the community's collective dreams for the future. Pir Vilayat teaches the importance of having one foot always in the future—never to linger in the past or get stuck in old patterns.

In the coming years, the Abode will grow to 200 to 300 members. The main center will continue to function more as a village structure, and less as a housing unit. It will be used for seminars, guests, businesses, food co-ops, music school, studios, a research center and spiritual gathering place. The Sufis will continue to restore the Shaker buildings. Their sanctuary on top of the mountain will be turned into a permanent retreat area, and will become the spiritual center of the community. The Abode also hopes to have more artists and to find a way of integrating art into community life. In this area, there are plans for a music school, recording studio, and expansion of the printing press.

The farm will eventually produce enough food to make the community self-sufficient in that respect, and the family hopes to have enough to share with those who are less fortunate. The plan is to start new businesses that reflect Sufi ideals and are of service to humanity. In the energy field, the community wants to convert as much of its energy consumption as possible to alternative sources, such as wood, sun, wind and water.

The most important ideal is to continue to be a channel for the Message of love, harmony, and beauty, and to spread that message to all those who wish to hear it. The community's goal is not to isolate itself in a living situation suited only to a few, but rather to build a center that is an example to the world of human potential. The ideal of what is and should be changes as the community changes. It is a process of evolution and it takes guidance and intuition to be able to see the next stepping stone on the path. Recently, Pir Vilayat said, "The next step is always the important thing. One has to move ahead, and not get stuck in a certain way of life. Vision is meaningfulness. The Abode has gone through all of its birth pangs. I'm very glad we were prepared to play it by ear and give up preconceived ideas for reality. I used to think that the Abode was to develop my vision, and now I see that my vision has developed with the development of the Abode. And I find it more beautiful than my vision."

Rural New Towns

INDUSTRIALIZATION, urbanization and rural depopulation are linked phenomena that have, in the unbelievably short space of 300 years, profoundly transformed the shape and pattern of human settlements. Until this century, for some 15,000 to 20,000 years of human existence in organized groups and recognizable settlements, 90 percent of the world's peoples have lived out their lives in hamlets, villages, and small towns.[1]

At the time of the American Revolution, 90 percent of the people in the United States were living in communities of 2,500 or less. In fact, it has only been in the latter half of this century that this millennial ratio of rural to urban people has been reversed. At the beginning of the 20th Century, only 15 percent of the total world population of 1.65 billion were living in towns larger than 20,000 people.[2] However, by 1960 there were 1 billion people out of a total of 3 billion living in urban areas, a ratio of only two rural people for every one urban resident. Since World War II the United States has become a predominantly urban nation. At present, 80 percent of our population is classified as urban, with more than half the total U.S. population living on only 1 percent of the available land.[3] Most other nations are rapidly following the same pattern. By the year 2000, if present trends continue, there will be, for the first time in human history, more urban than rural people in a world population that will have swelled to between 6 and 7 billion.[4]

This astonishingly rapid shift in the distribution of human population and the structure of human habitat has been made possible only by the availability of cheap fossil fuels and mineral resources, and a host of natural resources ranging from clean air and fresh water to the existence, over the past 50 years, of perhaps the most stable and favorable climatic conditions in the past 90,000 years. As we have seen, these conditions, which have made the urbanization of the earth possible, are not likely to prevail much past the beginning of the next century.[5] Thus, the emerging age of ecological scarcity implies the reversal of the seemingly inevitable and irresistible trend toward population concentration which has prevailed over the past three centuries, and a return to a pattern of settlements more characteristic of the human species throughout the vast eons of its evolutionary development.

Why is this so? In the first place, the modern city far exceeds the carrying capacity of the earth. In order to import the food, minerals, energy, and water necessary to support such vast concentrations of people and to export their mountains of solid, liquid, and gaseous wastes, the modern city must systematically exploit ecosystems on a continental, and, indeed, a global scale. This grossly exploitative metabolism is entirely dependent upon concentrated sources of energy, soon to be effectively exhausted. As the costs of energy and resources increase, our ability and our desire to continue such an ecologically, socially, and economically destructive form of human habitat will be effectively curtailed. In short, we shall simply be unable to afford to maintain the modern industrial city.

Without cheap energy, our present system of industrial agriculture will no longer be able to economically produce or distribute food to concentrated and dependent urban populations. If a disastrous decline in food production is to be avoided, this implies a shift toward a more skill-and-labor-intensive, ecologically-derived agriculture with a much larger percentage of the population directly involved in food production. It also implies that food will have to be produced much closer to where it is consumed. Without cheap energy in the form of concentrated fossil fuels it will also become increasingly impossible to heat, cool, or light the glass and steel office towers of the central city or to transport people 20 to 60 miles daily to work in them. In fact, without our low cost, fossil fuel-based system of transportation our entire urban-based economy of mass production for mass markets becomes logistically awkward and economically infeasible. Thus, the end of the fossil fuel age implies the end of the age of cities. It will force us to destructure and reorganize existing urban areas (along the lines indicated in the next section on Urban Decentralization) and to redistribute population in a regional network of decentralized local production. For the pattern of human settlements to come into balance with the carrying capacity of the earth, cities must be smaller, population less concentrated and more evenly distributed. And this means that a much larger percentage of our population will have to be redistributed among existing rural villages and small towns and that many more new and innovative rural communities will have to be formed.

The issue of rural development, then, must come to be seen within the context of an urban policy which takes as its first premise the need to reshape human habitat to conform to new energy and resource realities. Any urban policy that is not simultaneously a policy of large-scale population redistribution and rural revitalization will prove to be maladaptive. We must develop an integrated and imaginative approach to resettling America based on a clear acceptance of the inevitable decline of the city as we know it today.

So, rather than being a nostalgic and romanticized longing for the quaint but outdated small communities of our preindustrial past, the search for a modern variant of the rural village and small town reflects a deep evolutionary wisdom and represents a development strategy well suited to the energy and resource realities that are likely to prevail for the remainder of our development as a species on planet earth. Megalopolis, not the rural village, is the historical anomaly, the evolutionary dead end. Our ability to create a sustainable culture out of the chaos of the present is directly tied to our ability to effectively formulate and successfully implement a coherent policy of rural new towns.

The two papers in this section, by both theory and example, provide a solid foundation for the search for an integrated approach to a rural/urban settlements policy for the postindustrial age. Both New Communities, Inc. (NCI), a rural new town for former black sharecroppers in southwest Georgia, and Cerro Gordo, an ecologically based, user-designed and financed new village in Oregon, are based on the idea that the problems of our depopulated rural areas will not be solved by a continuation of policies which encourage migration to urban centers. Neither do they see much hope for the thoughtless continuation of a pattern of suburban development that creates still greater distances between work and home while paving over our most fertile and productive farmland. Rather than a continuation of business as usual, NCI and Cerro Gordo present two very different approaches to the problem of how to create new communities which will provide satisfying and sustainable living environments based on the renewable energy sources of sun, wind, water, and green plants. They are based on the integration of work and home, industry and agriculture, the urban and the rural in a new synthesis of nature and culture. They represent an historically new expression of the millennial pattern of small-scale human settlements.

The idea of rural new towns, as defined by Shimon Gottschalk and exemplified in NCI, is addressed specifically to the plight of the rural poor who have chosen not to join the ranks of the urban unemployed in our nation's ghettoes, but who still remain trapped in a vicious cycle of racial prejudice and poverty in our rural areas. It is addressed to the people and places left behind in the flood-tide of urbanization that has accompanied the industrial revolution in America.

The organizing principle behind this pproach to rural new towns is as simple as it is bold. It is to provide the land, investment capital, and expertise necessary for the rural poor to become economically, politically, and culturally self-reliant. The rural new town is modeled on the Israeli *moshav,* which is a small-scale settlement that balances individual family production for use and cooperative production for sale. The land for the rural

new town is held in common by a community land trust and can never be
sold. Individual plots are leased on a 99-year renewable basis for family
use—they can neither be sold nor subleased. These privately managed
tracts are grouped around a larger communally owned and operated parcel
of land which provides a resource for cooperative agricultural and industrial enterprises.

Because the land as a whole is held in trust, it is effectively removed
from the speculative market. Not only does this prevent profiteering in
land values but it also protects the residents of the rural new town from
being separated from their land should crops or business fail in any given
year. In this way the community land trust provides an innovative and effective grass roots approach to land reform that is well suited to the problems and needs of disposessed rural people. This concept, combined with
Professor Gottshalk's other proposals for the use of community development corporations (CDC's) and new financing and credit institutions, is
capable of providing a nationally coordinated yet locally planned and
managed policy of rural development (Figure 1). As the escalating costs of
energy and resources continue to undermine the viability of existing urban
concentrations, the search for appropriate alternatives will be greatly facilitated by the courageous example of NCI and the thoughtful policy formulations described in this paper.

For those who are familiar with the projects developed under the auspices of the Subsistence Homestead Division of the Department of the Interior during the Great Depression, the rural new towns idea will seem
strangely familiar. When it is realized that economist and author Ralph
Borsodi had a hand in formulating both projects, this similarity becomes
easier to understand. Compare Professor Gottschalk's rural new towns
proposal with Borsodi's description of the Homestead Unit plan for resettling the area around Dayton, Ohio in the 1930s:

. . . In the Homestead Units, which are to be located within a fifteen-mile radius of the city, the families belonging to each unit will build their own homes and grow their own crops in addition to carrying on the group activities which the unit as a whole may decide on. Each tract will be owned by the unit as a whole; the homesteads will be granted to members under perpetual leaseholds and will consist of about three acres each. The pasture, wood-lot, and community buildings will be owned by the unit and used by the members under rules and regulations established by the whole group. Each family in the unit is expected to build its own home, poultry-house, cow-shed, and workshop; to cultivate a garden, set out an orchard and berry patch, and become as nearly self-sufficient as were the pioneers of a hundred years ago. Trades and crafts will be permitted to develop toward specialization as far as the members desire, but there will be no emphasis on specialization as a good in itself. Large-scale farming operations may be carried on by the group as a unit, . . .[6]

Through such "appropriate technologies" as rammed earth construction and homesteads planned for family weaving and other crafts, it was Borsodi's hope that the Dayton project would make the "home, rather than the factory, the economic center of life."[7] The Dayton plan called for fifty such Homestead Units which would have enabled 1,750 to 2,000 families to become self-sufficient and secure even during the difficult conditions which prevailed during the depression. While a start was actually made in implementing this scheme, the U.S. Government failed to take Borsodi's advice that it should limit its role to providing financing to the homesteaders and making funds available for an educational program administered by the state universities aimed at helping the new farmers to adjust to their new life. In clear violation of prior contracts which had placed the entire Dayton project under local control, the Secretary of the Interior "federalized" all projects under his control in spring of 1934. Without the knowledge and understanding of local problems and possibilities which had characterized the beginnings of this experiment, the entire project degenerated into a program of centralized social engineering.

Since the shift of decision-making authority from the local to the federal level undermined the bright promise of this earlier experiment in establishing "rural new towns" it is especially important to keep in mind Professor Gottschalk's warning that the resettling of America must begin with the people and proceed as the result of radical initiatives which "emanate from action which includes people at the roots." Community, like freedom, is not a commodity that one group can give to another. Rather, community is something that people do together as they attempt to create a common life together based on mutual aid and shared obligations.

This is also one of the central ideas underlying the effort of the future residents of Cerro Gordo to design and finance an ecological new town near Cottage Grove, Oregon. Like NCI, Cerro Gordo is being developed on the assumption that the act of planning and designing the new town is the first step in the ongoing process of creating a true community. Long before Cerro Gordo becomes a fully developed town it will have already come into being as a face-to-face, self-organizing and self-managing community.

While this may appear to be an obvious principle for the successful creation of a new town, it is one that has been systematically ignored in every other new town development this century. Typically, the design of a new town is viewed primarily as a problem in physical and economic planning, i.e. how to create an infrastructure that will promote "community." Thus, the town comes first and then the people. Whether it is the bureaucratically administered socialism of the British new towns or the corporately administered capitalism of the American new towns, the issue of resident participation in design and planning is seen as totally irrelevant to the process of development. Perhaps that is why most new towns, whether British, American, or European, are consistently described as lacking a warm and vital sense of human life. Community building involves far more than laying out roads and utilities, designing housing and attracting large-scale industry. If the physical community is not the expression of the interpersonal relations and decisions of the social community, it becomes a mere shell that lacks meaning for the residents. It becomes a process of social engineering that is imposed on people. It might be possible to create new towns in this way but such a process can never create new communities.

In addition to being planned and developed by its future residents, Cerro Gordo is unique in its comprehensive ecological approach to land use planning and physical design. The intent is to demonstrate that it is not only possible to create a human habitat that enhances rather then destroys the natural environment, but that such a community can be more desirable as a place to live than towns which are conceived out of an ignorance of local ecosystems and implemented with a bulldozer technology. To achieve their goal of reintegrating the village and the natural environment, the Cerro Gordo design process began with an extensive search for a site that satisfied the community's desire to be able to meet its needs for energy, water, food, and other necessities largely from its own land. This concern for the resource base of the new village continued as the future residents joined with a professional planning firm to conduct an extensive ecological inventory of the site. In this way the Cerro Gordo planners were able to create a land use plan that reflected the problems and potentials of the site as well as the goals and intents of the community. This plan, combined with a limit on population that was established by an estimation of the carrying capacity of the land, has become a kind of covenant with the land that ensures the long term viability of the total system of the village-in-the-environment.

This same respectful approach to land use planning has been carried through consistently in all other areas of physical planning and design, from the policy which bans cars from the community to the decision not to build on prime agricultural land. It shows up in the solar heated duplex which has just been built, and the plans for the homestead which is now under construction. In fact, there are few developments of any scale which exhibit such a deep concern for the integrity and importance of natural ecosystems.

Cerro Gordo will also become a center for a wide range of social, economic, and educational innovations including: a participation system of community governance; a law enforcement system modeled on British constable and Native American approaches which emphasize reconciliation rather than retribution; a community health system that focuses on wholistic health care, preventative medicine, and health education; a rich and diverse cultural life that supports both individual excellence and community participation through community holidays and festivals; a diverse village economy that includes both primary and secondary economic enterprises which can provide support for all community members who seek to work near where they live; a learning system in which the entire community participates regardless of age or formal education; an experimental college in which students from outside the community can join with the residents to help plan and develop the physical infrastructure as well as the other innovative programs and institutions.

Whether or not such a comprehensive project can succeed in its goals is still very much to be decided. Both Cerro Gordo and New Communities, Inc. have survived from crisis to crisis. From their experience it should be clear why most new town efforts do not attempt to involve future residents in all phases of project development. Not only is decision making difficult for democratically constituted groups, but the entire problem of financing is a constant source of problems. Yet, in spite of the many real and serious crises each community has faced, both have managed to survive. Just this fact alone would suggest that they may one day succeed in realizing their visions.

Fortunately, we have much to learn from their pioneering efforts to date. Authors Gottschalk and Canfield attempt to communicate these experiences and to indicate the kinds of personal, interpersonal, and policy changes that would facilitate future efforts of this kind.

As the idea of population redistribution continues to gain currency as a necessary and desirable national goal in the face of declining resources and shifting economic patterns, it is hoped that the true value of the idea of rural new towns will become more generally recognized, as it was during the last Great Depression. Perhaps then the United States, as well as other nations, will choose to develop a policy framework that is rooted in a commitment to grass roots community building efforts and supportive of rural new town development projects similar to the case studies described in the following pages.

References

1. Barbara Ward, *The Home of Man,* (New York: W. W. Norton and Co., 1976), p. 3.

2. Ibid., p. 3.

3. W. Jackson Davis, *The Seventh Year: Industrial Civilization in Transition,* (New York: W. W. Norton and Co., 1979), p. 233. The argument that there must be a reversal in this trend is fully developed and carefully documented in this important book.

4. Ward, *The Home of Man,* p. 3.

5. See the General Introduction to this volume.

6. Ralph Borsodi, *Flight From the City: An Experiment in Creative Living on the Land,* (New York: Harper & Row, 1933. Reprint. Harper Colophon Edition, 1972), pp. 156–157.

7. Ibid., p. 159.

5 | Rural New Towns for America

Shimon S. Gottschalk

RURAL POVERTY is a problem that remains largely overlooked in late 20th Century America. The rural poor are virtually unseen, and offer no major threat to the civil order. In some strange way, we have a tendency to romanticize their plight. Despite the fact that nearly half of all Americans officially defined as poor reside in rural areas, the designers of most social, economic, and welfare programs have taken only scant notice until recently.

The nation's principal approach to the alleviation of rural poverty has been a non-policy—the hope that the problem will vanish as a result of continued migration toward the urban centers. We are beginning to realize that we may have passed the end of an era. The old solution has turned sour. The cities, overwhelmed by the complexity of their problems, offer little hope to additional late arrivals from the countryside.

The aim of this article is to discuss an experimental alternative to urbanization for rural poor families. The idea of rural new towns has emerged from an awareness that social problems are almost never simple, that they tend to be interrelated and complex. Therefore we have taken into account not only concerns of economic development but also ecological survival, political realities and cultural sensitivities. The factors of efficiency as well as social purpose must also be considered.

Rural new towns (RNT) is a term referring to the establishment of new communities in the relatively underpopulated agricultural areas of the United States. Such communities would have a mixed agricultural, commercial, and industrial economic base. Their populations would be drawn largely from the region in which they are located. Granted sufficient autonomy in order to be able to search out their individual character, yet supported with adequate resources in the form of land, technical assistance, loan guarantees, and preferential treatment in the allocation of governmental services, such rural new towns may offer a new hope for those who have been dispossessed by modern industrial technology in agriculture and the ideology which accompanies it.

A pilot project employing these ideas was established in Southwest

Georgia approximately ten years ago. The discussion of a proposed policy of rural new towns for America, which constitutes the major thrust of this article, has been importantly influenced by this first experimental effort. The projection of policy proposals is therefore closely interwoven with a critical examination of our practice experience to date. It helps us to raise many issues that might never have occurred to us otherwise:

1. How can a plan for an RNT be developed that will assure the inclusion of those who are genuinely poor and yet include those who have essential talents and skills?

2. What shall be the role of the planners and the technical experts? How can social engineering be avoided? Must planners sacrifice technical rationality for sensitive responsiveness to the people's ever changing perceptions of need and opportunity?

3. What shall be the economic base of such a community? Are there alternatives to the small rural village and the factory town? How might such a community become a genuine part of a post-industrial society?

This article does not claim to offer total solutions to these or the many other related questions which will be raised. Its aim is limited to thinking through the major issues as they affect RNTs, to describe some initial successes and failures in one unique setting, and to look into the future with the purpose of identifying and partially specifying one of the many possible paths to travel toward a more humane, more liberating social order.

Background

Non-metropolitan areas comprise 27 percent of the U.S. population. In 1977, out of a total of 24.7 million persons designated poor according to the Social Security Administration standard, 9.9 million (39.8 percent) of them lived outside of the major metropolitan areas. Or to put it differently, almost one out of ten persons (9.5 percent) lives in poverty in urban areas compared with nearly one out of five persons (17 percent) in rural areas.[1] These are the "surplus people," by-products of modern, industrialized society.

Rural poor people tend to be older, less well educated, less adequately housed, and less healthy than their urban counterparts. Their children, when and if the opportunity arises, move into the central cities, where, as often as not, they serve their lifetime in poverty and deprivation. Many suffer the additional scourge of racism, though the overwhelming numerical majority of both urban and rural poor are white. The migration of the young is like a double-edged sword, for it not only imposes new burdens upon the central cities, but it also deprives rural areas of their best manpower and leadership potential.

It has been suggested, but not statistically validated, that the urban-rural tide may be turning. There is no question that it has slowed down.[2] Whether this will turn into a major and more permanent shift, such as occurred during the Great Depression in the 1930s, is too early to predict.

Edward Banfield has proposed that the best solution to most contemporary social problems is to simply wait them out.[3] Do nothing, he suggests, and the solution that will evolve is as good or better than any that might have been devised by plan. While this may be a defensible view under some circumstances, as a general principle it overlooks the fact that in modern America, most social problems are the consequence of social policies, and that doing nothing implies perpetuation of harmful policies.

During 1979, 30,000 to 40,000 small farms were expected to disappear.[4] In 1960 the U.S. farm population stood at 15.6 million, by 1976 it was halved, to 7.8 million. It is inconceivable how, by means of a do-nothing policy, this trend can be reversed. The farms disappear and the individuals who farmed or operated them join the human surplus.

One of the more encouraging pieces of legislation languishing in the U.S. Congress in recent times is the Family Farm Development Act.[5] This legislation, which is given slim chance of passage in its present form, aims to turn around some of the major policies of the United States Department of Agriculture, which has consistently promoted the interests of large and corporate farmers over small, family farms.[6] Even if this legislation should pass, however, it will benefit primarily the small entrepreneur, not the dispossessed sharecropper and unemployed farm hand.

The policy of rural new towns proposed here is a fresh start. It proceeds from the somewhat idealistic assumption that, contrary to most existent social welfare policy in America, in order to reduce poverty it is not necessary to make the rich richer. It further assumes that important, lasting successes can be achieved only by the people themselves. Those who have the power and the wealth in society will not intentionally produce social revolution.

The rural new town idea and the community land trust

The RNT, ideally speaking, grows out of the ideas and hopes of the potential residents. These are people living in a defined rural region who have been economically dispossessed, primarily as a result of the dramatic changes in agriculture in the 20th Century. The rural new town aims to bring them together in an area close to their place of origin, and to make available to them resources that are most likely to enable them to build a new life, primarily: land, investment capital, and to a limited extent, expertise. The rural new town begins with people who, because they have not been physically uprooted, because their families are still more nearly intact, are more likely to share a generalized sense of community, even before the task of community building has begun.

The RNT is similar to new towns generally in that it brings people together in a new, partially planned environment. Its difference lies in that it begins with the people, rather than with the place. The planners serve as advocates of the potential or actual residents, not as experts in the employ of a distant authority. The RNT emphasizes community well-being, not only individual satisfaction. It is not a suburb, but also not a city. Its closest analogue in American history goes back to colonial times, to the first settlements of the Massachusetts Bay Colony and to Plymouth. These early settlements, too, began with a problem and a need, with a hope and a dream, and with the support of meager resources from abroad.[7]

Central to the rural new town idea is the concept of the community land trust. A community land trust (CLT) is a legal entity that serves to hold land in stewardship for perpetuity. Land which is either purchased by or donated to the trust is "decommoditized" by being taken permanently off the market. The trust is permitted only to lease land, never to sell it. Land leases, at nominal cost, are made available only to actual or potential direct users. Thus usership rights, rather than the rights of ownership, become paramount. Subleases are not permitted and the possibility of absentee landlordism is permanently avoided. Whereas the community land trust idea does not demand the parallel existence of cooperative social institutions and economic enterprises organized within a community development corporation (CDC), it is highly compatible with such undertakings.[8]

One of the advantages of the CLT is that it serves as a step toward the elimination of speculation and profiteering in land values, principal sources of inflation in our society, and main reasons for the demise of millions of small family farms during the past half century. Marginal farm operators are frequently forced to put up their land as collateral for operating loans; when harvests fail, their tenure to their property is easily endangered. This problem has been especially severe among southern black farmers.[9] As leaseholders within a community land trust, small farmers cannot be similarly dispossessed.

Usership rights in the CLT can be inherited, though they cannot be sold, leased, or mortgaged. Under this new arrangement, the question of who owns the land eventually becomes as irrelevant as the question of who owns the air or the view of the mountains. In theory, the community land trust offers a decentralist, grass roots approach to land reform in America. In order to gain a larger foothold in our society, it requires primarily community organization, not governmental initiative or national mobilization for political action.

The community land trust and the rural new town ideas are based upon a variety of precedents, both in this country and abroad. The village "commons" in England and in colonial New England encompassed an idea of shared land ownership and usership. The Homestead Act of 1862 also included the principle of usership, in this case, as a precondition of ownership. During the Great Depression, in the 1930s, several efforts were made to establish cooperatively owned rural villages under federal government sponsorship.[10] The belief that land is a God-given trust to be treasured, cherished, and shared, not owned and exploited, is indigenous to this continent in the tradition of the Native Americans. Thus, contrary to popular myth, the Indians had no idea that they were "selling" Manhattan island to the Dutch settlers; they simply agreed to share its use with them. In modern times the need has arisen not only to return to these beliefs but also to give them practical institutional form. That is, in large part, what the rural new town and the CLT are about.[11]

The policy matrix

Daniel Patrick Moynihan, U.S. Senator, urban policy planner, and advisor to several presidents, has criticized the decade of the 60s as having been excessively obsessed with programs and insufficiently concerned with the development of what he calls true policy. "Programs," suggests Moynihan, "relate to a single part of the system; policy seeks to respond to the system in its entirety."[12] Our farm programs, for example, have greatly expanded productivity—and created poverty, hunger, and pollution. In the development of a rural new towns policy, therefore, it is necessary to examine not only the meaning and impact upon the problems of rural poverty, but also the relationship to such issues as urban policy, population growth, population distribution, agricultural and industrial production, and ecological survival.

Melvin Webber, writing in *Daedalus,* pronounced a seemingly obvious truth that to date has been largely ignored by policy makers: the idea of urban is not synonymous with the idea of city.[13] Whereas city is a spatial concept, urban refers to our modern, industrialized, bureaucratized social order. It is quite evident that today, some of the least urbanized populations live in the central city, and many highly urbanized individuals reside upon their huge farm estates in the Great Plains, or in Texas.

Urban policy in the light of Webber's redefinition refers to the issue of bringing non-urban, left-behind groups into more meaningful and mutually beneficial contact with the remainder of society.[14] The issue is not merely one of physical, or even of social mobility in the usual sense of the word. Rather, it is a matter of the reduction of basic inequality on a multiplicity of levels. It means creating opportunity and reducing excessive privilege. Within the framework of urban policy in this sense, rural new towns are to be viewed as one of a variety of potential strategies.

Today, the approximately 25,000 square miles of urbanized land which contain about 70 percent of the American population, constitute less than 2 percent of the nation's land area. Whereas a policy of rural new towns can not be expected to have a profound impact upon this imbalance of population distribution, at least it will not constitute a continued contribution to it.

Economic policy, agricultural policy, and problems of ecological survival are becoming increasingly intertwined. Whereas simple population increase creates its own environmental problems, Barry Commoner and others have demonstrated that in America this threat to the environment is not nearly as important as that of uncontrolled and unlimited industrialization. Between 1946 and 1968, the U.S. population increased by about 43 percent, while pollution in the United States during the same period increased over a range from 200 to 1,000 percent.[15]

But industrial development is not the only villain in the battle for a sane environmental policy. In agriculture, the pollution of streams and lakes caused by the excessive use of nitrates, the contamination caused by feedlots, the poisoning of the air, soil, water, and food with sprays, the destruction of ecologically vital insects and wildlife, and corporate factory farms which practice our historically unique system of monoculture are the major sources of severe problems. The answer lies not in the development of new or better technology but in the re-establishment of more intimate, personal relationships between individual farmers and their land, an approach that will not permit the attitude that land and the seemingly commonplace gifts of nature are a resource to be mined.

Ray Marshall, before becoming Secretary of Labor in the Carter administration, convincingly argued that it is less economies of scale than the politics of bigness that have driven the small farmer out of farming.[16] Government policy, following dominant values of society, has viewed the farm primarily as an economic production unit rather than as a way of life, and as a home.

It is within the context of these policies, these perceptions of existing programs and ideas, that the first RNT in America was brought into being.

The story of New Communities

New Communities, Incorporated (NCI), founded in 1968, constitutes an

Figures 1, 2 and 3
New Communities,
Inc. (NCI) is the larg-
est landholding con-
trolled by a black com-
munity group in the
United States. While
most of them do not
live on the land, the 35
families that comprise
NCI earn their living
from the land, held in
common through a
community land trust.
(Courtesy of Joe Pfister)

effort to create an attractive, feasible alternative to urbanization for marginal, rural, black families (Figures 1, 2, 3). Located in Lee County, Georgia, NCI is in possession of some 5,000 acres of (heavily mortgaged) farm and woodland. It lays claim to being the largest landholding controlled by a black community group anywhere in America. Its annual operating budget exceeds half a million dollars. Some 35 families are currently earning their livelihood from NCI, though most of these families do not yet physically live on the land. The major operation is agricultural, growing peanuts, corn, soybeans, cattle, hogs, and some vegetables. NCI also operates a roadside farmers' market/grocery store, a daycare center, and a remedial education program (Figure 4). In its alliance with the Southwest Georgia Project, NCI

3

4

Figure 4
Construction of a new wing on the Day Care Center.
(Courtesy of Joe Pfister)

conducts a variety of community organization activities such as voter registration drives, and sponsors occasional cultural events such as a black fashion show and an annual Fourth of July community outing (Figure 5).

For the author, the story of NCI is a very personal tale, a long, often joyful, and sometimes stressful series of experiences in which he participated over the past decade, and more. Therefore, the account which follows is both analytical and subjective. Its aim is both to enlighten and to bear witness. There is no other way to write about NCI and its (and our) unique romance with social revolution.

Rationale

Why did any of us ever get into this? A major social undertaking such as

NCI invariably emerges from a complex of objectives. There are collective goals and personal goals, political goals and ethical goals. There are the goals that sparked the beginning and those that evolved as a result of experience. As we proceed, we will touch upon most of these points, but for the moment let us focus on two primary ideals, or visions, as they apply to NCI: the ideal of the good life, and the ideal of freedom.

The good life

In a practical, concrete way, probably the essence of what most people call the good life is captured by the idea of home. Home includes house, and family, and neighborhood, and community. Home, regardless of its objective content, connotes comfort, security, and well-being. Even if for a particular individual it is not, and perhaps never has been, a positive reality, it remains an emotion-charged, often romanticized ideal.

One of the primary goals of NCI has been to create a new opportunity for rural black families in southwest Georgia who have resisted the flight to the city because, despite the hardships, they have preferred to remain at home. The aim is clear and simple, to create the material and social basis for a meaningful, good life upon the land.

Freedom

Freedom is not a commodity that one individual or group can transfer to another. Freedom is created by concrete acts of self-liberation from the symbolic and material constraints imposed by others. Though such a highly abstract notion has hardly been the topic of daily conversation among the members of NCI, its practical implications are evidenced throughout:

1. NCI aims to achieve maximal economic autonomy. The goal is to make NCI an economic success, not simply another charitable enterprise. Americans have a way of re-

Figure 5
Annual Fourth of July outing. Through its alliance with the Southwest Georgia Project, NCI conducts a variety of community organization activities.
(Courtesy of Joe Pfister)

sponding to (or in fact avoiding) every conceivable social problem by continually inventing additional social services. NCI is not a social service agency. It is an approach involving the restructuring of people's lives and their livelihood.[17]

2. From the very beginning NCI was viewed as a place where black people might give expression to ideas and life styles, independent of those imposed by the dominant white society from without or above. This meaning of the word freedom, essential to the building of a sense of dignity, is to be viewed not in individual terms alone. It is a collective enterprise and experience, a goal, as we shall illustrate below, easier to express than to put into practice.

NCI cannot be understood except as a part of the contemporary struggle for racial integrity, identity, and liberation. If there is a common ideology that binds the many varied people who have become a part of NCI then it is this shared vision, which for lack of a better term, we call black liberation. For the former farm hands, day laborers, and domestics its meaning is very specific and concrete; for black leaders its meaning is much broader; and for those of us who have come from afar it is part of a large vision that includes the liberation of all people, not excluding ourselves.

3. First and last there is the land. In recent years much has been written about the need to learn again how to live within the world as a part of nature rather than as exploiters of nature. But for rural black people who have never physically left the land, who have been largely excluded from modern technology and are strangers to bureaucratic ways, the call for a return to the land has an entirely different meaning. For generations they have been squatters, tenant farmers, sharecroppers, hired day laborers working other people's land. The erosion of land ownership among rural blacks during the present century is a largely unknown chapter in the long sad history of these people upon the North American continent.[18] But here at NCI, for the first time in their memory, poor black people can say that this is *our* land to build and make prosper, and to hold in trust for future generations.

Origins

The origins of NCI can be traced to two entirely separate sources. The first is primarily intellectual and ideological, and the second is uniquely individual. In 1967–68, while liberal forces in the nation were perceptively beginning to disengage from the euphoria of "we shall overcome," while the forces of opposition to the war in Vietnam were beginning to gain momentum, a small group (including the author), representing a variety of academic and professional disciplines, began to gather in Exeter, N.H., under the leadership of eighty-year old Ralph Borsodi. Borsodi had been active in the back-to-land movement of the Great Depression. He, and others in the group, were influenced by the 19th Century American social philosopher Henry George and his theory of the single tax on land.[19] George suggested that the increased value of land over time, which was socially produced, should accrue to the community as a whole, rather than fortuitously to a small number of private individuals.

Another ideological strain which contributed to the thinking of the group was the Gandhian notion of "constructive program." Gandhi taught that *satyagraha* (Sanskrit for truth force), is to be given expression not simply as a method of protest, but also in the creating of liberating institutional alternatives.[20] This theme of alternative institutions has since become one of the major radical forces of the 1970s and 1980s.[21]

Gradually, plans for what would eventually be called a rural new town emerged. As suggested above, the RNT has both a social, and a unique land use component. Our social model leaned heavily upon the precedent of the Israeli *moshav,* a somewhat modified form of the *kibbutz.*[22] Whereas the *kibbutz* permits of no private property (only personal property), in the *moshav* some property is held privately. In the *kibbutz* all work is done collectively, in the *moshav* not all work is collective. In the early *kibbutzim* children lived in children's houses whereas in the *moshav* they live with their parents in the home.

In its physical layout the *moshav* resembles a small village. One or more clusters of houses are arranged in the midst of a large tract of land. The houses, though not the land on which they stand, are privately owned. Adjacent to, or within walking distance of each home, is a small plot which serves the family as a kitchen garden, perhaps with a few chickens, and a cow or a goat. Beyond these plots are large fields cooperatively farmed, utilizing modern machinery, where appropriate, and producing cash crops. The *moshav* (as well as the *kibbutz*) might also include cooperatively owned and managed industrial and commercial enterprises (see Figure 6).

In applying this idea to black people in the rural South, the thought was that the rural new town might, among

other things, function as the social, cultural, and recreational hub of a much larger geographic area. There was no thought that this community would become an isolated enclave. Non-residents might well be employed within it and its residents, in turn, might commute elsewhere to seek employment. The rural new town, like the *moshav,* would include collectively owned as well as private enterprises. One of the early ideas was that the rural new town might, in addition to its agricultural undertakings, enter the prefabricated housing field. Whereas initially it would serve primarily its own residents, in the long run it would provide housing for a much larger geographic area.

While formulating the rural new town idea and contrasting it with land reform efforts in other parts of the world we found that such undertakings often foundered due to their limited, unidimensional approach involving land redistribution only. We learned from others that the success of land reform can be assured only if in addition to land, capital resources are made available to the newly liberated peasants, to facilitate agricultural, as well as commercial and industrial development. In the case of the rural new town the original idea was to raise the necessary development capital partly from governmental, but primarily from private sources on an eleemosynary investment basis. Charitable foundations, corporations, organizations, and individuals would be called upon to make "social investments" in the rural new town on a long-term, low interest-rate basis. Outright grants would be sought only for purposes of land purchase. The theory was that loans, in the long run, help make the recipient independent of the lender. By contrast, gifts have a way of perpetuating depen-

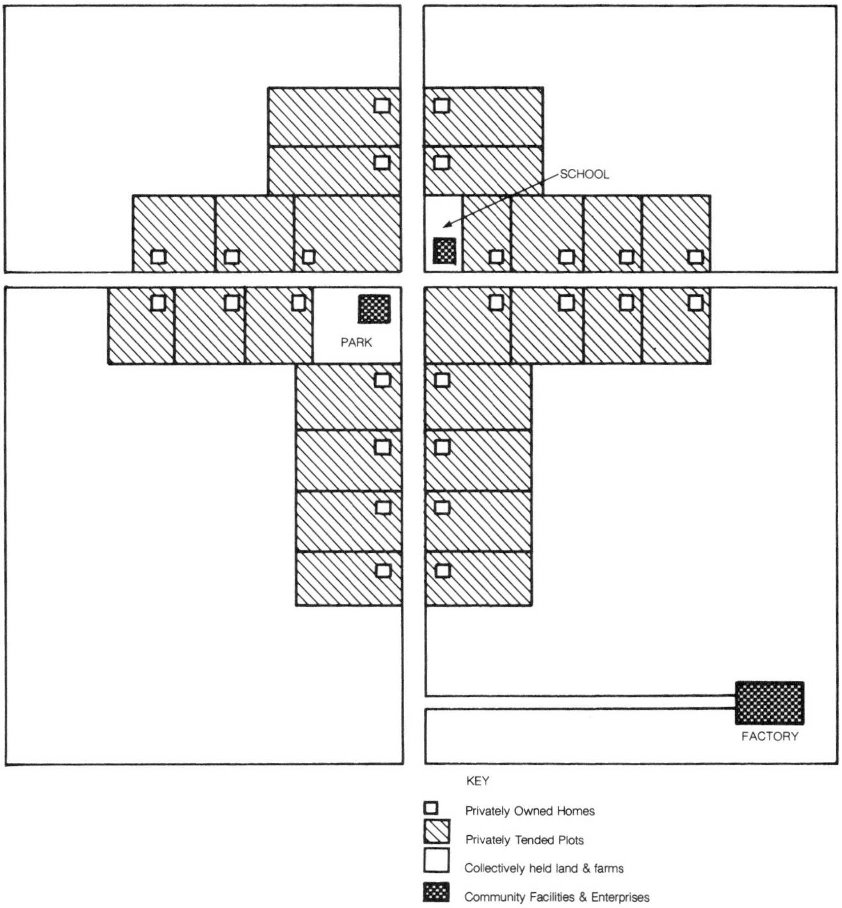

Figure 6
Schematic Plan for an Israeli Moshav

KEY

☐ Privately Owned Homes

▨ Privately Tended Plots

☐ Collectively held land & farms

▦ Community Facilities & Enterprises

dency and generating the need for additional gifts.

These were some of the ideas developed in 1967 and 1968 by the group in Exeter. But they came to fruition, and were adopted and changed as a result of the effort to implement them in southwest Georgia.

The second part of the story of NCI begins with Slater King, a man who was born in Albany, Georgia, attended Oberlin College, returned to help his father run a small grocery store, started his own business, and then became involved in the civil rights movement in the early 1960's. Over time, Slater King's training and instinct moved him to an ever increasing preoccupation

with the issues of economic justice and black cultural renaissance. In these efforts he was joined by Charles Sherrod, an ordained minister, who had moved to southwest Georgia in 1960, in the early days of the Student Nonviolent Coordinating Committee (SNCC), as a rural community organizer.

Primarily through the organizing efforts of Robert Swann, a member of the Exeter group, King, Sherrod, and several other black leaders from the South were given an opportunity to travel to Israel in the summer of 1968.

That's when it began happening. The travelers returned from Israel greatly moved by their experiences. Soon after their return they set up a meeting in Atlanta and established the nucleus of the organization that was to become NCI.

New Communities was incorporated in the fall of 1968 as a non-profit Georgia corporation. Its original board of directors included not only all those who had traveled to Israel, but also representatives of a broad spectrum of Southern civil rights organizations and community development agencies.

Slater King was killed in a tragic automobile accident in March, 1969. But prior to his death he was able to take an option, in behalf of NCI, on a 4,800-acre farm, some 20 miles to the north of Albany. Later that year, an adjacent tract containing 927 acres was added to the original acreage. In the meantime, New Communities met with success in its application for an initial $98,000 planning grant from the Office of Economic Opportunity, under Title I-D, to become a rural CDC.

The way it was

Ideals and goals are beautiful, but practice makes imperfect. The difficult reality that emerges from a chronic shortage of development capital, from the imperfections of people and limitations of knowledge, from political rivalries and bureaucratic stupidities can make the noblest of visions a source of incessant worry and recurrent trauma.

Probably most of the problems are unavoidable. How, for example, does one ask people to take risks who, because of their extreme poverty, cannot afford to risk? How does one gain the participation of the residents of a new town before there is a town? How does one avoid conforming to the dominant capitalist ethic of rewarding success and punishing failure? How does one select the first residents for a new town

with complete fairness? How does one reaffirm the principle of social equality, while creating a complex community that requires the recognition of specialized talents and the selection of legitimizing authority figures? Finally, to return to a theme raised earlier, how does one remain financially solvent and not sell out one's ideals to satisfy the demands of those who have granted support? Since that eventful day in early 1970 when the deed to the land was formally signed, NCI has survived, struggling from problem to problem and crisis to crisis. Some of the problems and crises include:

1. The annual payments on the land of over $100,000 have been an ever-present threat to economic survival. Contrary to plan, the cost of these payments has had to be borne by farm operations. Yet, to date, the farm has not had a single profit-making season.

2. NCI has often suffered from inexperienced management, as evidenced by inadequate economic planning, poor bookkeeping, unclear lines of authority, inadequate concern for public relations, and many other problems attributable to a lack of management skills.

3. The Title I-D planning grant from OEO was never followed up by additional OEO funds primarily, although not only, because of harsh political opposition on the local and state level.

4. For several years the annual harvest of vegetable crops was conducted by college student volunteers (a practice now discontinued). The institutional conflicts between local people and volunteers on the one hand, and the cultural conflicts between black and white college stu-

dents on the other, served as a major and dismaying source of disruption.

5. In 1974 a major confrontation developed between "management" and "workers." The workers on the farm began to seek affiliation with the United Farm Workers Union and to demand higher pay and better working conditions. Those in management positions and most board members countered with the argument that, in a community enterprise such as this, all are one: there is no place for labor-management distinctions in the traditional sense.

6. A social survey conducted in 1969 among a sampling of 92 rural black households in and near Lee County indicated that, more than anything else, these families hoped that NCI might be able to provide them with a better house (rather than a job, money, or social services). To date, NCI has been unable to move toward meeting this major popular demand.

7. The deep seated racism indigenous to the rural South has been a source of potential or real threat throughout the history of NCI. When fires broke out in the woodlands there was suspicion of arson. When commercial dealings with local merchants are undertaken, the prices offered are suspect. When a local ordinance is enforced or a permit sought, the exercise of racial bias is to be assumed.

8. In 1978, in response to the threat of creditors, the Board of NCI was forced to sell 1,350 acres of its land. The appreciation of land values over ten years accrued significantly to the benefit of NCI. Obviously, this sale was totally contrary to the principles and ideals of the CLT.

Despite these seemingly endless crises and perennial problems, and many others too embarrassing and too petty to mention, NCI continues to survive. *Problems and crises are not solved, they are outlived.*

The dilemmas of CDCs

A community development corporation (CDC) has been defined as "an organization created and controlled by the people living in impoverished areas for the purpose of planning, stimulating, financing, and when necessary, owning and operating businesses that will provide employment, income and a better life for the residents of these areas."[23] CDCs are business corporations with social objectives. As businesses, they need to remain economically solvent and, ideally, show a profit. In the service of their social goals, they must remain maximally democratic and responsive to the demands of their local constituencies.

Unfortunately, these two goals are frequently in conflict. For example, at NCI when the good, loyal, but only moderately competent farm manager had to be dismissed, it became a difficult, drawn out ordeal for the NCI leadership.

At one of the annual meetings, NCI members were invited by the chairman to give expression to their dreams for the future. One of the members rose and courageously suggested that, hopefully, one day a big factory, perhaps an automobile assembly plant might be established on NCI land. There would be jobs and prosperity for all. Many enthusiastic heads nodded in agreement. A beautiful dream, they thought. But, no, warned the much more cautious and experienced chairman. If NCI stands for anything, then it stands for self-determination and community control. Prosperity at the price of a return to slavery is the paradise of fools. The chairman won the day.

In the spring of 1975, a commercial farm management firm was engaged by some of the donor friends of NCI to conduct a comprehensive business evaluation of current conditions and future prospects. The summary of the firm's recommendations concludes with the following paragraph:[24]

> From our point of view, NCI defies all laws of economic survival. It should not be in existence because it is highly financed at 8½–9% interest; directed by committees, managed by a preacher and a former Extension agent, and operated by a group of poor individuals, some of whom are illiterate. There is no way such a combination can survive; but it has, it is, and it will survive because these people want it to succeed. . . .

Many issues and some answers

In the development of the first rural new town in Georgia, many issues have been confronted that are likely to be of relevance to similar developments elsewhere. Among these issues, which to date have only been partially resolved by NCI, eight are of special significance: land, organization, planning and the role of experts, housing, residents, economic development, and financing.

Land

Free federal lands are the only realistic and just solution to the settlement of economically uprooted families. There is no surer way to give poor people a new start toward economic independence than by granting them the basic resources that will enable them to build their own future. Grants of land for rural settlement are solidly within the American tradition. When the Pilgrims arrived on American shores, they were armed with charters from the King of England granting them large tracts of land for their colonization. Somewhat later in the history of New England, colonial legislatures were wont to make free grants of land to groups of individuals, ranging from 60 to 80 persons, for the purpose of establishing new townships.[25] Some 200 years later, when the United States government sought to extend its dominion over the western lands, it sold land to settlers at an average price of $2 an acre, and then later, under the Pre-emption Act of 1841 and the Homestead Act of 1862, it made land available free.

Of the nation's 2.2-billion acres, 755.3 million, or about one-third are owned by the federal government. Admittedly, much of this acreage is nearly uninhabitable, in deserts, mountains, or frozen tundra. But most military bases, many of which are surplus, (and most of which should be) are not so located and might be ideally suited for rural new towns. Such land grants would not cost the federal treasury one cent.[26]

The recipients of such federal land grants would be regional CLTs whose function it would be, within certain broad, legal constraints, to lease the land in accordance with plans and decisions reached by the incipient communities. Much of the land would remain in communal control. Individual tracts would be leased to residents on a 99-year basis, exclusively for their own use, not to be sold or subleased. Thus, the natural increase in land values would be denied to individual private speculators. This would substantially reduce the cost of development. It would help preserve equity among the residents, and make possible rational controls in physical growth.

The leasehold system here proposed is nothing new or unique. It has been used in such broad variety of places as Canberra, Australia, Israel, and the private, commercial new town development, Irvine, California. The reduction in development costs it can produce has been dramatically demonstrated by means of economic projections.[27]

Organizational structure

The organizational structure for the development and maintenance of a rural new town needs to be relatively complex. The southwest Georgia experience has shown that if different functions are not allocated to separate organizational bodies at an early stage, then confusion is likely to result.

During the first years at NCI, the entire board of directors was called upon to participate in decision-making concerning farm operations; this should more properly have been the function of a CDC. Later, problems importantly affecting the first residents were resolved by persons who did not live on the land and had only a casual knowledge of residents as individuals. Having recognized these problems, does not mean that NCI has been totally successful in resolving them. The full organizational structure outlined below has not yet evolved. At a minimum, a four-tiered structure appears to be required: a CLT, a local sponsor, a CDC, and a town corporation.

The *community land trust* serves as the benign trustee of the land. The rural new town would be limited and controlled by the trust only to the extent that the land may not be sold or subleased. The trust is the recipient of federal lands or of other land gifts, and guarantees that the land will be used to achieve the general social goals of rural new towns. The major active function

of the CLT is to identify, and if necessary, assist in organizing new local sponsors. It is suggested that CLTs operate on a regional basis, each trust serving a number of rural new towns. Individual trustees serve without compensation or other kinds of personal benefit.

The *local sponsor,* preferably a grassroots community organization with broad local representation, is the initial coordinator of rural new town development. In some cases it may be a local community action agency. The local sponsor first brings potential residents together, gains their involvement in decision-making, sets the basic guidelines for the community, and establishes the CDC. Perhaps after the CLT and the CDC are in place, the present Board of Directors of NCI will be viewed as the local sponsor.

Community development

The *community development corporation* largely performs a function which is analogous to that of a commercial developer. It operates in the manner of a business corporation, within the guidelines set by the local sponsor. It is cooperatively owned, functioning under the direction of a business manager. Its capital is derived both from the investments of its members, and from the issuance of non-voting stock to non-members. Membership is open to all residents and potential residents of the rural new town. Finally, it is likely to function most efficiently if it spins off a number of relatively independent subsidiaries in areas such as farming, housing construction, industrial development, and health care.

As suggested above, a degree of tension is to be anticipated between the local sponsor which has the primary goal of fulfilling communal purposes (such as making sure that new poor families are successfully integrated into the community) and the CDC which is responsible for the retention of economic viability (and, therefore, might give preference to attracting and retaining skilled workers).

The fourth element, the *town corporation,* will eventually be the government of the rural new town. In most states, special legislation needs to be enacted that will permit a local community to incorporate as an independent political entity at an early stage in its development, perhaps even before it has residents. The state of California permits the development of such "special districts."[28] Similarly the state of Kentucky has made legal provision for the establishment of "New Community Districts."[28] Such districts are more nearly able to control development within their own areas, reducing the potential of interference by county or other local governments. At least in its formative stage, the rural new town needs to be assured of this kind of maximal political autonomy in order that it may truly serve its intended ends, rather than being a tool, if not a victim, of external forces which have different designs and objectives. Only later, from a position of independence and strength, can it meaningfully build cooperative relationships with established local regional authorities.

The first officers of the town corporation will need to be appointed by the local sponsor, with due consideration given to existing political realities within the county and state. As the rural new town grows, the selection of the officers will shift to the residents.[29] At NCI a town corporation has not yet been established. This can be explained, in large part, by the fact that there is still no practical plan for the settlement of a sizeable number of families on the land.

Planning and the role of experts

To the extent that social planning has reference to the design of future reality, it has little relevance to what has occurred at NCI. At best, the plans and ideas projected by the Exeter group served to provide an initial source of inspiration. They specified an abstract communal idea which continues to serve as a symbolic rallying point, but rarely as a practical guide for decision or action.

But planning is more than designing; it is also doing. Social planning is not simply planning for, but rather planning with people, involving them maximally in every step of the action. In NCI this has been the explicit planning strategy from the beginning. Thus, all meetings of all groups and committees have been open to all interested individuals, and broad participation has been encouraged, often at a severe cost to efficiency and order.

The familiar, allegedly rational planning paradigm leading from problem definition to selection from among alternative solutions, to implementation, and then to the evaluation of results has rarely applied to NCI.[30] In large part, long range planning and careful decision making have been forced to give way to the frequently recurring need to respond to crises. Often there have been no real options, only imperatives which forced decisions. At other times, some of the most important decisions seemed to be made more in the light of faith than knowledge.

The author began his association with NCI with a view of himself as a moderately experienced social administrator, social planner, and community organizer. He somewhat naively produced endless pages of plans, organizational models, and programmatic suggestions, hoping that one or another of these might take root or serve as the stimulus for new ideas or alternative approaches. Perhaps in some small sense that has happened. Yet, over the years, he has learned to assume an ever less assertive role, volunteering only specific, circumscribed skills, such as in proposal writing or in public relations.

The short range effect of the social planning process has been to precariously keep NCI afloat, while providing exceptional opportunities for what Friedmann has called "mutual learning," benefiting a small number of rural people, black community leaders, and a few stray sheep (such as the author) within a unique experimental setting.[31]

Agents of radical social change have a choice among three primary modes of action: confrontation, infiltration, or people's advocacy. Each of these approaches is problematic. Confrontation tends to alienate precisely those whom the activist needs as allies.[32] Infiltration readily leads to cooptation and the abandonment of radical objectives. Advocacy is likely to be politically opportunist and ideologically noncommittal. It, too, readily lends itself to cooptation because the people demand quick, tangible results.[33]

At NCI we have attempted to steer an eclectic course which seeks to avoid each of these pitfalls. We have tried to learn how to work within, yet separate from the "system." Our aim has been to use the "system" against itself, as it were, to achieve our own, not its valued goals. When we have been in direct confrontation we have tried to confront nonviolently. We have identified as the target of our change efforts, not only the society and its institutions, but also ourselves. By struggling with a redefinition of the relationship between leaders and followers, between planners and residents, between those who think that they know and those who think that they don't know, we have attempted to sow the seeds of a "new world."

There has always been a generalized mistrust of experts and planners among the founders of NCI. It derives from an intuitive sense that experts, even when they are well intentioned, tend to exploit, and to misunderstand. Charles Sherrod, who throughout these years has been the primary leader of NCI, has consistently insisted upon a policy of radical self-determination. According to this view, the people must learn from doing, often from doing and failing and then trying again, with minimal interference and advice from the outside. Thus, if decisions are made by the Board and not acted upon, it is because there has been insufficient community readiness for action.

In addition, at NCI we have had the ever present problems of race. Within the context of the quasi-caste system which continues to characterize much of the rural South, the word of the "man" (i.e., the white man) is experienced by most poor blacks as the expression of an absolute. The "man's" word and the power that is implicit within it is experienced as a fact, rather than as an expression of opinion. The presence of the author, one of the few white persons on the board of directors of NCI, has inevitably been received in the light of this experience. The danger rests at both extremes, either to accept the word of the white man uncritically, or to reject it out of hand. In this setting, although all members of NCI have consistently behaved in relation to each other (though not to the external world) as if this cross-racial issue had been fully resolved, in effect, it remains only a few inches beneath the surface. For each individual, depending on his or her unique experiences, background, and personality, it continues as a different, unspoken problem.

Housing

The architects of the RNT will need to be given the freedom to develop innovative low-cost housing plans which meet not primarily the middle-class standards of FHA, but the needs and preferences of low-income rural families. An important experiment in this connection has been conducted by the Department of Agriculture of the Commonwealth of Puerto Rico, which to date has received little attention. It combines the mass production of stripped-down, concrete housing shells, with self-help methods.[34]

Once the cost of housing production has been reduced to a minimum, then the most significant area for saving is in the cost of money. To date, neither HUD, nor USDA loan funds have been available to the lowest income class of rural residents. The Farmers Home Administration has the best record in the low-cost housing field but it remains inadequate. As the cost of housing continues to rise at a rate greater than that of inflation there are more problems than solutions in this field.

The one advantage of housing is that it is tangible and visible. As such it readily lends itself to contemporary techniques of fund raising. The major problem is always finding enough cash for a down payment. Thus, charitable donations for initial down payments coupled with governmental loan guarantees are likely to be the best short-run solution for the development of housing in the RNT. In the longer term, the significant expansion of banking institutions such as the National Rural Development Finance Corporation, which is specifically oriented towards meeting the capital needs of rural poor families and CDCs offer a ray of hope.[35]

At NCI the failure to make significant progress in the construction of housing remains one of the major areas of disappointment. During these first ten years the emphasis has been placed on the farm program, jobs and the development of commercial and social institutions such as the farmers market and the pre-school program.

The planners of new towns of all types have to decide what to build first, housing or amenities.[36] In RNTs the additional question has to be asked, what comes first, jobs or residents. At NCI emphasis has been placed on the first. It is difficult to know, but perhaps this was a mistake. To date there are still fewer than ten families living on the land.

Residents

The most important single decision that is made by any authority in the development of a new town relates to the question of how the residents will be selected.[37] Shall they be rich or poor, white or black or racially mixed, young or old, employed or retired? Planning for a new town inevitably means planning for a specific population.

The RNT, as indicated, is primarily intended to meet the needs of rural poor families drawn from a designated geographic area. But if the community is to function with a reasonable degree of autonomy, it will also require persons with a broader variety of skills and backgrounds. On the other hand, if it is truly to serve its purpose by meeting the needs of the poor, then it cannot restrict itself exclusively to families headed by employable adults. Over half of the poor households in

America contain no potential wage earner; the reason for their poverty.[38] They are aged individuals or couples, single parent households with young children, or families headed by physically or emotionally handicapped adults. These, too, must be included in the rural new town.

There must be a crucial balance among family types chosen. But who shall make the decisions about families —the land trust, the local sponsor, the CDC, the first residents, or some outside authority? There are dangers in any one of these bodies making the decision unilaterally. It is the awareness of issues such as this, that contributed to the designation of the four-tiered organizational structure discussed above.

America is the land of "covenanted communities." Throughout the colonial period and beyond, individuals and families, brought together in the establishment of a village or township in the New World, devised and formally signed compacts, as it were, with each other in the presence of God, pledging mutual aid, support, and protection. Thus it is likely to occur with rural new towns as well. If these communities are to succeed, then they must be based, at least during their formative years, upon a bond greater than economic or political interdependence. Such a bond, drawing upon elements of religion, ethnicity, or ideology, while it may make the community exclusivist, if not provincial, is likely to be essential to its survival during its first, inevitably difficult years.[39]

Economic development

Planning for new towns in America has most commonly taken one of two forms: the improved suburbia model, or the company town. The first can be dismissed quickly since there is no way in which it can achieve the purposes of the rural new town. The second, the company town, is an anachronism, especially if its alleged purpose is to provide secure jobs for large numbers of non-technical, non-professional workers. It can only lead to the attraction of industries lured by the low-wage potential of the rural new town —a dubious, and at best a temporary advantage.

The RNT has a mixed agricultural, industrial, and commercial base. Since each family has its garden plot the community can reasonably aim toward maximum self sufficiency in food. The community based agricultural enterprise should emphasize labor intensive crops. The expanding organic food market offers a unique opportunity in this connection. By producing quality products for an increasingly nutrition-conscious consumer market, rural new town farmers may be able to directly compete with agribusiness.

In the industrial field, RNTs should concentrate on industries based on their agricultural production and/or relate to unique resources available to them. Priority should be given to industries that are not capital intensive and that can in part relate to local consumption. The development of a prefabricated housing industry would be an example of the latter.[40] There is, of course, the potential for private, public, as well as cooperative investment in the industries of rural new towns. Whether all three types of investment should be sought, needs to be carefully weighed by the CDC.

Service industries show special promise for rural new towns. They fall into three broad categories. Family-based services are those for which an individual family unit might contract with a governmental or private agency, such as for the home care of dependent children or adults. Especially now, with greater emphasis upon deinstitutionalization, such home-based services, buttressed by supporting services within the community at large, will be in increasing demand.[41]

Community-based services fall only partially into the category of services to dependent individuals. Ideally, each rural new town should function as the social, educational, and cultural hub of the agricultural region which surrounds it. Thus, the rural new town will benefit not only its own residents, but also the population of the much larger area of which it is a part.

When federal and state governments weigh the location of new public facilities, such as hospitals, universities, or special schools, preference should be given to the rural new towns. The presence of such an institution is likely to be invaluable in assuring the economic success of such a new community.

It may take a decade or two until a rural new town becomes economically self-sufficient. During its early years it will require special financial inputs in the form of tax abatements, low-cost loans, grants-in-aid, and special consideration in the location of public institutions. But such extraordinary costs might be contrasted on a cost-benefit basis with the expense of maintaining a large number of these families in poverty *and* on public assistance. The economic cost is calculable; the human cost is largely beyond calculation.

In order to assure the ultimate economic independence of the rural new town, early investments will need to be made in the social sector even more so than in the economic sector. Resettlement allowances, on-the-job training programs, and consumer education are some of the areas of support that will require early attention. It need be em-

phasized, however, that such programs should be developed under the auspices of either the local sponsor or the CDC. Social programs such as these, when they are designed and controlled at great distances from their roots, like some of the rural experiments of the 1930s, too easily degenerate into programs of social engineering.[42]

Financing rural new towns

Financing rural new towns will remain highly problematic as long as our society maintains its present social and economic priorities. At NCI we have mainly depended on large private charitable foundations. Relatively few governmental funds have been invested. We have been exceptionally sensitive to the principle of, "he who pays the piper calls the tune."

There will always be multiple approaches to satisfying the need for financial inputs. An attempt has been made to suggest some of these throughout this discussion. Land may come from one source, support for housing from another, and investment capital for industry from a third.[43]

The National Development Act was sponsored by Senator Proxmire and Congressman Sparkman in 1971. The Act envisaged the creation of a banking system which would have as its specific function the financing of socially desirable projects such as rural new towns. More recently, as a result of a law suit against the Community Services Administration, the National Rural Finance Corporation (NRDFC) was established.[44] This constitutes a small but reluctant beginning for serious federal involvement in the redevelopment of rural areas, but in no way does it signal the beginning of the turning of the tide.

The Institute for Community Economics has been mapping strategies for years with the aim of finding more adequate non-governmental support for CDCs.[45] Among other things, they have suggested and begun to experiment with the creation of a mutual fund which derives its investments from foundations, churches, and socially conscious individuals by investing in the non-voting shares of the CDCs. Such a mutual fund would probably take even higher risks than a governmental Development Bank. It would have a secondary advantage; through it, a national constituency might be developed in support of community development corporations and rural new towns.

After the town corporation has been established it will have the authority to issue tax exempt bonds, which is, within the context of present tax law, a major boon to the RNT as well as the investor.[46]

Conclusions

Probably the single most significant step that could be taken in the direction of implementing a policy of rural new towns for America is the revival of a federal land grants program that will specifically benefit small farmers. But such land grants can lead the way out of rural poverty only if they are accompanied by long-term, low-cost credit available for housing, and community-based industrial, agricultural, social, and commercial development.

That is what could happen, but it probably won't. It is our fate—those of us who are engaged in the "resettling" of America—to live simultaneously in two worlds: the world that is, and the world that could be. We certainly know the difference, but more importantly, we also have some ideas about how to get from the first to the second world. That is what this paper has been about.

No, we don't really expect that the federal government will establish an RNT policy within the discernible future. But we are not disillusioned because we understand that the task must begin with the people, not with the government.[47]

It might have been easier if the federal government had sold NCI some of its land at $2 an acre, much in the way that it granted land to white homesteaders in the 19th Century. It would have been easier if the government had a community development bank to make low-cost loans to small farmers and entrepreneurs. If, as a result, sufficient front-end capital had been realized, then a successful, self-liquidating housing program might have commenced at NCI years ago. If the USDA had a different approach to small farms and if it were institutionally less racist, then everything would have been easier—maybe.

But it did not happen, and it will not happen as long as most of the people in this country continue to overtly believe in inequality. For the present, even where public actions are taken to ostensibly assist those who are poor, usually the rich get richer and the powerful gain more power. That is why radical initiatives must primarily emanate from action that includes the people at the roots. Sadly, for the moment, many of the poor, too, share the belief in inequality. Only when we begin to see changes in this outlook, only when poor and unfree people begin to develop practical images of liberating institutional alternatives that meet the needs of their lives, can we, together with them and as a part of them, begin to consider how to faithfully restructure the entire society and build the world that could be.[48]

References

1. U.S. Bureau of the Census, *Statistical Abstract of the United States, 1978*, (Washington, D.C., Government Printing Office, 1979), pp. 14, 17, 682, and 685; also, U.S. Bureau of the Census, *Characteristics of the Population Below Poverty Level, 1977*, Current Population Reports, Series P-60, (Washington, D.C.: Government Printing Office, 1978), p. 7.

2. *Statistical Abstract of the United States*, pp. 14, 17.

3. Edward C. Banfield, *The Unheavenly City*, (Boston: Little, Brown & Co., 1970), p. 225 f.

4. *Washington Newsletter*, Friends Committee on National Legislation, no. 413, April 1979, p. 3; also, *The Changing Character and Structure of American Agriculture: An Overview*, General Accounting Office, (Washington, D.C.: Government Printing Office, 1978).

5. For a fuller discussion see, *The Family Farm Development Act*, Hunger, no. 17, Washington D.C., Interreligious Task Force on U.S. Food Policy, March, 1979. For a more theoretical perspective on these issues and an international perspective see, Dennis A. Rondinelli and Kenneth Ruddle, "Integrating Spacial Development," *Ekistics*, 43, no. 257 (April 1977): 184–194.

6. Ray Marshall and Allen Thompson, *Status and Prospects of Small Farmers in the South*, Atlanta, Southern Regional Council, 1976; also, "The Death of the American Farmer," *Win*, 8, no. 12 (July 1972), entire issue.

7. Page Smith, *As a City Upon a Hill*, (New York: Alfred A. Knopf, 1966).

8. *The Community Land Trust: A Guide to a New Model of Land Tenure in America*, (Ashby, Mass.: International Independence Institute, 1972); also, see, *Green Revolution*, 35, no. 2 (March 1978), a special issue on community land trusts. CDCs are discussed in greater detail in references below.

9. See, "Our Promised Land," *Southern Exposure*, 2, no. 213 (Fall 1974).

10. Ralph Borsodi, *Flight from the City*, (New York: Harper, 1935 reissued in 1973); see also Edward C. Banfield, *Government Project*, (Glencoe, Ill.: Free Press, 1951).

11. Peter Barnes, ed., *The People's Land*, (Emmaus Pa.: Rodale Press, 1975).

12. Daniel Patrick Moynihan, "Policy versus Program in the 70's," *The Public Interest*, no. 20 (Summer 1970): 91.

13. Melvin M. Webber, "The Post-City Age," *Daedalus*, (Fall 1968), pp. 1091–1110. Also see, Richard Dewey, "The Urban-Rural Continuum: Real but Relatively Unimportant," *American Journal of Sociology*, 65, no. 1 (1960), pp. 60–66.

14. Webber, "The Post-City Age," p. 1108.

15. Barry Commoner, Michael Corr, and Paul Stamler, The Causes of Pollution, *Environment Magazine*, 13, no. 3 (April 1971).

16. Marshall and Thompson, *Status and Prospects of Small Farmers*.

17. For a fuller discussion see, Shimon S. Gottschalk, *Communities and Alternatives: An Exploration of the Limits of Planning*, (New York: Halsted, 1975), p. 106 f.

18. Robert S. Browne, "The South," *The People's Land*, Peter Barnes, ed. pp. 40–43.

19. Henry George, *Progress and Poverty*, (New York: Random House, originally published in 1880).

20. M. K. Gandhi, *Non-Violent Resistance*, (New York: Schocken Books, 1951), p. 68.

21. The journal, *Working Papers for a New Society,* which published its first number in 1973, is representative of this trend; see also, *Self-Reliance,* published by the Institute for Local Self-Reliance, Washington, D.C.

22. Maxwell I. Klayman, *The Moshav in Israel: A Case Study in Institution Building for Agricultural Development,* (New York: Praeger, 1970); see also, Raanan Weitz, *From Peasant to Farmer: A Revolutionary Strategy for Development,* (New York: Columbia Books, 1971).

23. Geoffrey Faux, *CDC's: New Hope for the Inner City,* (New York: Twentieth Century Fund, 1971), p. 29.

24. Max W. Evans, Vice-President, Nortrust Farm Management Inc., Memphis, Tenn. Quoted from the cover letter to, *New Communities, Inc., Report,* February 13, 1975.

25. Public Land Law Review Commission, *The History of Public Land Law Development,* (Washington D.C.: Government Printing Office, 1968), pp. 43–44.

26. See, Recommendation No. 97, in, *One Third of a Nation,* Report to the President and to Congress of the Public Land Law Review Commission, (Washington, D.C.: Government Printing Office, June 1970), p. 226.

27. Edward M. Kirshner and James I. Morey, *Community Ownership in New Towns and Old Cities,* (New Brunswick, N.J.: Transaction Books, 1975).

28. *The New Community and Family Mobility Development System,* Interim Report, Urban Studies Center, Louisville, University of Louisville, June 1970, pp. 95–104.

29. Many of the issues regarding the establishment and coordination of local planning authorities to which this discussion alludes are examined in detail in, *Urban and Rural America,* Advisory Commission on Intergovernmental Relations, (Washington, D.C.: Government Printing Office, 1968), pp. 89–93.

30. Arnold Gurin and Robert Perlman, *Community Organization and Social Planning,* (New York: John Wiley & Sons, 1974), p. 62.

31. John Friedmann, *Retracking America: A Theory of Transactive Planning,* (New York: Doubleday & Co., 1973), p. 245.

32. Barrie Thorne, "Protest and the Problems of Creditability," *Social Problems,* 23, no. 2, (1975).

33. Lisa Peattie, "Reflections on Advocacy Planning," *Journal of the American Institute of Planners,* (March 1968), pp. 80–88; see also, Frances Piven, "Whom Does the Advocate Planner Serve?" *Social Policy,* 1, no. 1, 1970.

34. Emilia A. Davila, *Social Programs Administration,* Puerto Rico, Department of Agriculture, (July 1968). Mimeographed.

35. Susan Horn-Moo, NRFDC and its Proposed Program of Rural Development, *CCED Review,* Center for Community Economic Development, Cambridge, Mass., (Spring 1979), pp. 11–15.

36. This issue has been explored by the author in his studies of new towns in England, Germany, and Israel. Citizen Participation in the Planning of New Towns: A Cross-National View, *Social Service Review* 45, no. 2 (1971), pp. 194–204.

37. This is one of the main points made by Herbert J. Gans in, *The Levittowners,* (New York: Random House, 1967), p. 411 f.

38. U.S. Bureau of the Census *Characteristics of the Population.*

39. Rosabeth Moss Kantor, *Commitment and Community,* (Cambridge: Harvard Univ. Press, 1972), pp. 61–74.

40. E. F. Schumacher's concept of "intermediate technology" (more

recently called "appropriate technology") applies to RNT's. E. F. Schumacher, *Small is Beautiful: Economics as if People Mattered,* (New York: Harper & Row, 1973). Some of the ideas discussed in this section are currently being implemented among a variety of southern cooperatives. See, *Poor, Rural and Southern,* (New York: Ford Foundation Report, 1978), p. 9f.

41. The author has developed these ideas in greater detail. See "The Community Based Welfare System," *Journal of Applied Behavioral Sciences,* 9, no. 213 (1973): 233–242.

42. See, *Government Project,* pp. 234–6. This case study of a Resettlement Administration community in New Mexico established in 1935, contains important negative lessons for the developments of RNT's in the 1980s. See also Paul K. Conklin, *Tomorrow a New World,* (Ithaca, N.Y.: Cornell Univ. Press, 1959).

43. See, Leonard E. Smollen et al., *Sources of Capital for Community Economic Development,* (New Brunswick, N.J., Transactions Books, 1976). This is a practical manual, a guide for managers of CDC's, listing both govern-mental and non-governmental sources of capital.

44. See, *CCED Review.*

45. The Institute for Community Economics, 120 Boylston St., Boston, MA, 02116.

46. For a more complete discussion see, R. Bruce Ricks, "The Community Developer and the Public Sector," *Minnesota Experimental City II,* St. Paul, University of Minnesota, pp. 99–105. This is an example of the type of policy to which we raised objection above: it helps the poor by making the rich richer.

47. An analogous, though very different experience in community economic development is examined in detail by Stuart E. Perry, *Building A Model Black Community,* (New Brunswick, N.J., Transaction, 1978); also see, Paul Wellstone, *How the Rural Poor Got Power,* (Amherst: Univ. of Massachusetts Press, 1978).

48. In this instance the reference is not only to poor, rural blacks, but also to poor whites, Mexican–Americans, native Americans, women, and old people, indeed, to that true majority of our society which is, in effect, not yet free.

6 | Cerro Gordo
Future Residents Organize to Plan and Build an Ecological Village Community
Christopher Canfield

CERRO GORDO is a community of 100 families who are building a new town for themselves on 1,158 acres of evergreen forest and meadow—an entire valley on the north side of Dorena Lake, about 25 miles south of Eugene, Oregon. A thousand acres are preserved for common use: fir and oak forests, meadows, agricultural land, a whole mountain on the lakeside, town greens and plazas, and miles of trails (Figure 1).

The basic design concept of the community is the reintegration of village and natural environments. The natural limits of the landscape have been determined by an extensive ecological inventory, setting the maximum population at 2,500. The private automobile will be banned from the townsite, replaced by a trolley or minibus, bicycling, walking, and horseback—all made easier by a community delivery service. Thorough recycling will be a community function. Power will be supplied by sun, water, wind and bio-fuels as much as possible.

The village center, removed from its customary highway orientation and protected from automobiles, will be built to human scale on gently sloping forest and meadow land. Clustered townhouses, shops and community buildings will grow with the terrain, grouping themselves among public greens and plazas, big trees and streams. Wholesale commerce will be served by a railway transport connecting the town center with a loading dock on the highway.

A broad-based economy will include relocated small assembly and light manufacturing companies; an experimental college and growth center; writers, artists, and craftspeople; and agricultural production. These businesses will help support services within the community: shopkeeper, baker, teacher, carpenter, doctor, and so on. The honesty inherent in a face-to-face community will replace the mutual exploitation often found in large cities.

The Cerro Gordo Community is organized to facilitate planning, decision-making and self-funding by residents, future residents and community supporters. This is accomplished through town meetings, monthly meetings in several west coast cities, and regular community-wide gatherings.

The town's school will involve townspeople in the school's activities, and the town will open up its homes, businesses, and surrounding forest to the children. The entire town will become a learning environment as children and adolescents learn at first hand and adults exchange roles and apprentice part time at one anothers' jobs. Other community activities will include bringing in music, films, and speakers; volunteer work parties; and community gatherings and festivals.

Most importantly, we seek more meaningful and fulfilling ways of living. We want to make space for a deeper appreciation of people and nature. We want both the solitude of the forest and the warm life sense of the village. We enjoy the challenge of pioneering a new community and a new way of life. We want to reintegrate work and play. We're searching for ways to increase interpersonal contact and experimentation. We want the mutual concern and respect of real friendships; and we want to feel free to try new ways of relating and becoming who we are. We want to confront the social issues of racial equality, poverty and liberation from sex roles in a direct and personal manner. Our ethic is one of self-determination, freedom, cooperation, change, and personal growth.

Cerro Gordo is a community of future residents and supporters working together to plan and build an ecological village. We're a diverse group, but our project is guided by two sets of ideals that we believe belong together: ecology and community. We want to work with the natural cycles rather than fight them; we want to be part of a neighborly, self-reliant community.

We see some frightening trends across this country. Each year, over two million new homes are built with little regard for the long-term costs.

Figure 1
Surveying Cerro Gordo Ranch.
(Courtesy of Cerro Gordo)

This growing suburban sprawl covers over 1½ million acres of good farmland annually at a time when more farmland is needed to feed our growing population and less petroleum is available to maintain current agricultural yields. Very few of the new homes are built to conserve energy or trap solar heat, and sprawl itself dictates continuing high energy use for transportation, while it simultaneously stretches the fabric of community to the breaking point.

Cerro Gordo is an attempt to address these problems and others with simple, direct action. But we hope to do more than build a sensible lifestyle for ourselves; if we are successful, much of what we do will serve as a model for others to apply, in small towns and large.

We hope to show that ecological studies and careful land use planning can create a symbiosis of forest, farm and village; that sun, wind, water and biofuels can perpetually provide all the power we need to live comfortably in our homes; that we can do without the private automobile in our village and benefit from the elimination of its ecological and sociological costs; and that we can live happier, healthier, more fulfilling lives when we replace the standard-of-living rat race with a focus on people, nature, and quality of life.

The Cerro Gordo approach to community development involves future residents and community supporters in planning, financing, and building the community. We want to do more than build an ecological development; we want to create a living community. Our approach to creating community is to work together as a community from the very beginning to plan and build the town we envision.

Of course we recognize the relationship between physical development patterns and patterns of social inter-

action. For example, we expect community life to thrive much more readily in traditional mixed-use villages than in suburban sprawl, where homes have been cut off from commerce and culture. So we expect the physical design of our village to help foster the kind of community life we seek. But many new town developments have attempted to create new communities by putting people into well planned physical environments. The results have been mixed.

We believe that you can't create community *for* people. Community isn't a thing that can be packaged and sold. Community is something people do together. And so to create the community we want at Cerro Gordo, we're inviting other people who share our dreams to come create that community with us. By working together to plan and build the Cerro Gordo Community, we have found that we became a living community even before the first home was built on Cerro Gordo Ranch.

Cerro Gordo: Goals, progress, and processes
The land—goals and progress to date

The townsite selection criteria (see Table 1) were fulfilled beautifully when Cerro Gordo Ranch was found in spring, 1973, after an extensive two-year search. Located 20 miles south of Eugene, Oregon, and 5 miles east of Interstate Highway 5, the townsite has good access to a nearby urban center and to all forms of national transportation. And yet its 1,158 acres comprise the majority of a small valley in the foothills of the Cascade Mountains, bounded on three sides by government forest and on the south by Dorena Lake. With these natural boundaries,

Cerro Gordo will always have its own ecology, its own visual space, its own separate identity.

Cerro Gordo is a beautiful, varied place. Fir and cedar forests cover most of the property, but there are oaks and other hardwood trees, too, especially in the center of the valley. Three large meadows roll up the valley, covered in successive waves of purple, yellow, and white wildflowers during the summer; and many smaller meadows dot the valley and surrounding hillsides. The whole valley is oriented towards the lake and views of the Cascade foothills to the south and southeast. Several streams flow through the property. Cerro Gordo mountain rises 1,300 feet above the lake at its foot, commanding sweeping views in all directions. A rich wildlife community shares the valley with us. There are apple and pear orchards, some dating from a turn-of-the-century homestead. There are rugged wild areas, steep hillsides, and an Enchanted Valley at the north end of the property. With its varied places and many moods, you can hike Cerro Gordo Ranch again and again, and still have more to discover.

The western Oregon climate is wet. Annual precipitation averages 40 to 50 inches, with about half falling during four winter months and very little during four summer months. Winter temperatures range from the 20s to the 50s, with a few light snowfalls. Summer temperatures are generally in the 70s and 80s, usually cooling down to 50 to 60 at night.

Community planning
Goals

The basic design concept for Cerro Gordo is the reintegration of village and natural environments. Homes, businesses, and community facilities will be clustered together, creating a

Size:	1,000 acres or more.
Location:	Oregon, west of the Cascade mountains and northwestern California.
Terrain:	Mostly gentle and moderate. Buildable valleys and hillsides. Some rugged areas. Little or no river bottom agricultural soils. Maximum southern exposure. Site limited and defined by natural features.
Water:	Streams and ponds on the sites. A large river or lake nearby or adjacent. Ample water on site to support a population of 2,500.
Vegetation:	Fir forest, two-thirds to three-fourths wooded. Large and small fields and meadows.

Table 1
Townsite Selection Criteria

human-scaled village community and preserving the natural character of the landscape.

Basic land use categories designated in The Cerro Gordo Community Base Plan map (See Figure 2) are:

Village Center: the heart of the community, similar in concept to a traditional European village. Mixed use: community facilities, shops, offices, apartments above shops, townhouses, small workshops. High density: attached, multi-story buildings interspersed with courtyards, plazas and greens.

Residential: attached multi-story houses and detached single family houses in clusters. Most homes will have two orientations: a public side relating to access and adjacent homes, and a private side relating to private yards and community open space and views beyond.

Manufacturing: quarters near the Village Center for small, light manufactur-

Figure 2.
The Cerro Gordo Community Base Plan grew out of an extensive ecological inventory of the site that indicated appropriate land use categories. The guiding design concept is the idea of creating an economically viable, humanscaled village community while preserving the natural character of the landscape.
(Courtesy of Cerro Gordo)

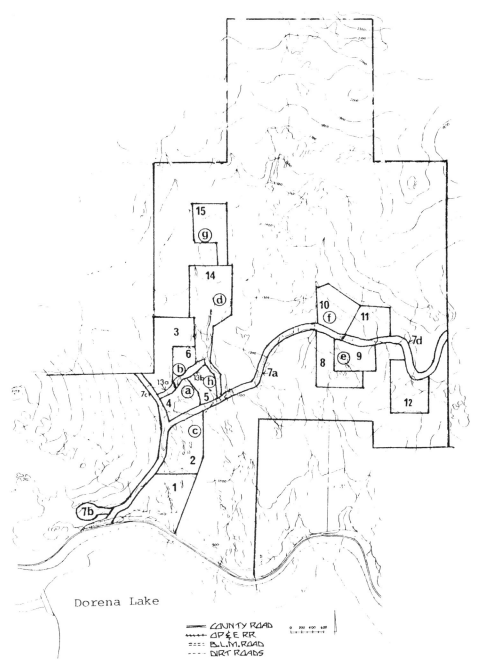

Dorena Lake

COUNTY ROAD
OP&E RR
B.L.M. ROAD
DIRT ROADS

0 200 400 600

ing and other business enterprises providing jobs for community residents.

Open Space: 1,000 acres of community-owned meadows and fir and oak for-

ests, a portion of which is reserved for intensive agriculture.

Emergency and major delivery access will be provided, but otherwise automobiles will be restricted to a parking area at the periphery of the property. There, a community motor pool could provide a variety of rental vehicles, in most cases eliminating the need for private automobile ownership. The Oregon Pacific & Eastern Railway now provides daily freight service along the southern boundary of Cerro Gordo Ranch. In the future, a box car trolley could serve as a mobile loading dock for wholesale commerce, connecting the Cerro Gordo Village Center and Manufacturing zone with Interstate Highway 5 and the Southern Pacific Railroad. Summer excursion steam trains now stop at Cerro Gordo when requested (Figure 3). In the future, a self-powered commuter car could provide hourly passenger service between Cerro Gordo and Cottage Grove and the Interstate.

Utilities will be designed to work in harmony with ecological systems. Water will be provided by wells and holding ponds on site, distributed by gravity and wind pumps as much as possible. Sewage and organic wastes will be recycled through natural digestion and composting processes, meeting health needs while augmenting and irrigating agricultural soils. Paper, metal, glass and other materials will be recycled through separate collection. Electricity will be provided at low costs by Lane Electric Cooperative, primarily from the northwest's hydroelectric generators. Pacific Northwest Bell will provide telephone service; and the community will provide coaxial cable for television, community video and other, more sophisticated communications possibilities, such as instant community-wide voting.

Agriculture at Cerro Gordo will make use of the small pockets of good soil and build up other soils over time for intensive gardening, orchards, and greenhouses. Home, cluster, neighborhood and community gardens could make the community self-sufficient in vegetables. Augmenting the current

Figure 3

Oregon Pacific and Eastern summer excursion steam train, which now stops at Cerro Gordo. The community's transportation system is designed to eliminate private automobiles within the town site, relacing them with a trolley or minibus system, a community delivery service, and trails for walkers, bicycles, and horses.

(Courtesy of Cerro Gordo)

orchards and planting trees in the Village Center and other neighborhoods will provide most of the community's fruits and nuts. Greenhouses could extend the growing season and provide other fruits and vegetables not otherwise suited to the Oregon climate. Poultry, eggs and other small livestock can be accommodated on the site. Forming a producer-consumer cooperative with nearby farmers and purchasing nearby farmland are possible means to approach agricultural self-sufficiency in other areas.

Progress to date

During 1973–74, an extensive ecological inventory of the Cerro Gordo townsite was conducted by the Corvallis planning firm, DeDeurwaerder Associates. Twenty-five environmental factors were studied and combined in various ways to show land use suitabilities from four different perspectives: the ecologist, the planner, the economist and a synthesis of all three. Soil, slope, and vegetation studies were analysed to determine hydrological carrying capacity of the site and tolerance to impervious cover on an acre-by-acre basis. Various community design concepts were explored.

All through 1975, Cerro Gordo planners worked closely with the 100 families who had joined at Cerro Gordo Community Association of future residents to develop The Cerro Gordo Community Base Plan. Committees of community members explored options for each aspect of the plan and published their reports in the monthly community newsletter. Feedback questionnaires were sent out and brainstorming sessions and discussion groups were held at several community-wide gatherings and ongoing monthly meetings in several west coast cities. Synthesizing the ecological studies and the desires of the future residents, the Community Base Plan shown in Figure 2 outlines the general character and form of the future town of Cerro Gordo, providing guidelines for both Phase I construction during the next few years and the detailed Comprehensive Community Plan that will be prepared by community members and planners during the Phase I development process.

In 1974, the Lane County Planning Commission denied our application for an Unzoned Area Development Permit for a village cluster of 46 homes on 5 acres, citing as reasons the lack of a regional plan and zoning to judge the impact of such a project and the County's then-current policy against privately operated sewage treatment facilities. In 1975 we instigated an alternate approach to getting construction started, securing septic approvals and creating parcels on which up to 5 homes could be built. In 1978 this approach yielded building permits for 15 homes and an industrial / community complex, but only 4 of these homes were built that year due to rapidly increasing construction costs and the difficulty in obtaining mortgage financing. In 1976–77, the Lane County Boundary Commission approved our applications for 14 connections for water service and cluster sewage systems. In 1977 the Row River-London Subarea Plan was adopted by the County, and in 1978 Cerro Gordo Ranch was zoned GR-10 (one house for each 10 acres), establishing a supportive climate for a 115-unit Phase I Planned Unit Development (PUD) application in 1979–80.

How we're proceeding

As far as we know, Cerro Gordo is the only new town project that is being planned and built by its future residents. The purpose is first to create a community of people and then an ecological village to house those people. The community planning process therefore strives to unite community values and goals and environmental suitabilities and limits into a Comprehensive Community Plan.

The planning process that started with the initial ecological studies and Community Base Plan will be continuing during the next few years with greater depth, breadth and resolution. The environmental studies are now being updated with more detailed information by community members, staff, planning interns and consultants. The first in a new series of values and goals questionnaires will draw from ongoing discussion meetings in several west coast cities and committee and staff reports in The Cerro Gordo News. Committees will be formed to enlist members' expertise, energy and interest in each planning area: community systems, housing, livelihood, agriculture, education, health, community life, and so on. Committees will be asked to explore options and feasibilities and report back through the newsletter for community response. Using this information and feedback, community planners will draft preliminary plans and system designs for community review, which will eventually lead to formal adoption of the Cerro Gordo Comprehensive Community Plan by the community members. All who participate in this planning process will help determine what Cerro Gordo will become.

The first 20 percent of Cerro Gordo (115 homes) can be built with current 10-acre zoning and a Planned Unit Development (PUD) approval, which we expect to obtain without serious difficulty in 1980. Proceeding beyond 115 homes to build the whole town for 2,500 people (about 600 homes) will require an amendment to the County's General Plan, designating Cerro Gordo as a New Development Center (NDC). Our community planners will apply for the NDC approval after the Comprehensive Community Plan is adopted by Cerro Gordo members.

Homebuilding
Goals

Just as in community planning, the central goal for homebuilding at Cerro Gordo is a synthesis of community values and environmental suitabilities. Community plans address this goal on a large scale; homebuilding addresses it in a more personal, immediate way. Instead of providing subdivided lots and model homes, the Cerro Gordo approach emphasizes participation in homesite and cluster planning and home design and construction. We believe this participatory approach is the key to maximizing the sensitivity and creativity only individuals and small groups can bring to the homebuilding / townbuilding process. With care and effort, homebuilders can come to know their site intimately, learn about its ecology and natural limits, and discover and design with its character and spirit. Working together to design home clusters, participants can clarify their personal housing / lifestyle preferences and share creative approaches while they're getting to know their future neighbors. There are many aids to facilitate participation, such as cluster planning services for community members, designers, and other consultants as needed, and owner-builder assistance programs by the community construction company. Participation to whatever extent possible in the homebuilding process is an important way to bring us together with a deeper understanding of and commitment to our environment and our community.

One of the desired results of participatory home and cluster design and construction is diversity in housing and lifestyles, as individuals and small groups pursue their personal goals within the context of the larger, supportive community. Housing types will vary from village apartments and townhouses to attached and detached residential clusters, to clusters in the Homesteading Neighborhood. Some people will design separate, self-sufficient homes; others will design boardinghouses or communal living arrangements.

The community will adopt certain energy conservation, aesthetic, and quality standards, but here again these goals will be addressed in a variety of ways.

Progress to date

After our application for a 46-unit village cluster was denied by the County in 1974, design work began on a smaller cluster of four attached townhouses, dubbed Howard House after our architect, Charles Howard. Unfortunately, we discovered that financing was not available at that time for attached townhouses in a rural area, and so these plans remain on the shelf. But designing Howard House helped us formulate a participatory cluster design process. The future residents of the cluster met with the architect weekly for several months to clarify their personal housing programs and take part in site planning and housing design. A number of new insights emerged out of this in-depth dialogue between future neighbors and architect. For example, at first participants indicated a desire for separate homes to provide

privacy; but after further clarification of what the participants meant by privacy, they adopted plans for attached townhouses with party walls of rock as a sound barrier. By meeting together regularly over a period of months, future residents got to know themselves and one another better, becoming friends and neighbors even in advance of residency. And by working together on site planning studies and architectural design (such as solar heating systems), they came to appreciate the rewards of building in harmony with the environment.

In 1976, several households began meeting to design the Nook Cluster, consisting of five custom-designed homes. Two are attached and three are detached, but closely clustered (Figure 4). The participants chose to include a cluster shop and laundry to be shared by all Nook residents; and a recycling center will be shared with the nearby Prolog Cluster. During the Nook planning process, one of the original families decided that they just didn't want to live so close to others; when they withdrew, another family joined to take their place. One of the Nook homes was finished and a second started in 1979 (Figure 5). Construction of the three others will have to wait for the PUD approval in 1980.

Construction of the Prolog Cluster was started in 1977 with the prototype Solar Duplex (Figure 6). These homes are designed to reduce space heating needs by 75 percent with extra insulation, insulating shutters, wood-framed, double-panel windows, air-lock entries and other conservation features. South-facing windows and skylights will provide much of the heat needed; one unit has a solar hot water heater and will store space heat in a basement full of gravel (Figures 7 and 8). A second duplex of similar design is planned near

(continued on p. 199)

Figure 4
Nook Cluster, a group of five homes that grew out of Cerro Gordo's participatory cluster design process.
(Courtesy of Cerro Gordo)

Figure 5
The first Nook home was completed in 1979.
(Courtesy of Cerro Gordo)

Figure 6
Construction of the Prolog Cluster was started in 1977 with the Prototype Solar Duplex, designed to reduce space heating needs through energy conservation and solar energy use.
(Courtesy of Cerro Gordo)

Figures 7 and 8
The Prototype Solar Duplex, the first units to be completed in the Prolog Cluster.
(Courtesy of Cerro Gordo)

7

8

Figures 9 and 10
To the west of the Solar Duplex is a large log home completed in 1978 by Cerro Gordo's first owner-builders.
(Courtesy of Cerro Gordo)

9

10

Figure 11
Built of timber milled from local trees, the Homestead Barn is framed by its future occupants.
(Courtesy of Cerro Gordo)

the first. To the west of the duplex a large log home was built in 1978 by Cerro Gordo's first owner-builders (Figures 9 and 10).

Plans for the Wellspring Cluster consist of five attached townhouses. Located at the edge of a large meadow, they have excellent lake views. The design is a second generation of the prototype Solar Duplex and has several energy conservation and solar heating features. Sizes range from 1,600 to 1,900 square feet, some with extra rental apartments. A cluster laundry, a workshop and a recycling center are planned. Construction of the Wellspring homes may be started in 1980.

The Homestead Neighborhood is a neighborhood of rural character, being planned and built by the people who intended to make their homes there (Figures 11 and 12). There philosophy is based upon the ideals of self-reliance, voluntary simplicity, providing their own organically grown food, planning and building their own homes and out-buildings, and cooperation among neighbors (Figure 13). Construction of the Homestead barn and workshop was started in 1978 using timbers milled on the property.

The first "new-age mobile home" was moved onto the site in 1978, and construction of the first permanent homes started in 1979.

During the next few years construction should begin on additional home clusters. Plans now being developed by various community members include a cluster for active retirees, a boarding-house, and an elegantly simple passive solar home cluster.

After the Phase I PUD approval is obtained, opportunities will be available to build homes in a variety of community plan zones and in a variety of natural environments.

Just as the Community Base Plan outlines general land use criteria, the Phase I Plan and Budget adopted by the Cerro Gordo Cooperative (the residents' association) outlines utilities phasing plans and budgets. Costs of residency set by the 1979 budget were a $500 Cooperative membership fee and $1,500 in Cooperative stock for each adult resident (whether renter or homeowner), and a $5,000 homesite fee and $15,000 in Cooperative stock per homesite. If these costs seem high, we can offer three encouraging comments: (1) total costs for clustered homesites at Cerro Gordo are about half what any one of us would have to pay to buy 10 acres in the area separately and provide minimal utilities; (2) several community members are cutting their homesite costs in half by combining their homes into a functional duplex on one homesite; and (3) these costs assume that all land, planning, and utilities costs have to be borne by only 115 homesites—but if the New Development Center approval is obtained from the County to build the entire town of Cerro Gordo, Phase I homesite owners will probably receive substantial rebates on their homesites as later homesites are sold.

How we're proceeding

People thinking about buying a home at Cerro Gordo are urged to first make sure they feel good about our community concept, our people, our site and our long range and phasing plans. We want them to feel confident that their personal goals can be realized within the context of the community. Once this is true for you, you're ready to join the Cerro Gordo Community Association of future residents ($35 per adult) and begin home planning, whether you want to build as soon as next year or not for some time.

Figure 12
Homestead barn and organic garden exemplify the ideal of self reliance.

(Courtesy of Cerro Gordo)

The best place to start your exploration of the community is the published history and ongoing newsletters, the Community Base Plan, the Phase I Plan and Budget and the periodic newsletter reports on Homebuilding Opportunities. There is information in these published materials that you need to know and that you can only learn by studying them. But as soon as possible you should get to know the community of people who are Cerro Gordo.

Cerro Gordo isn't a commune, but neither is it a land development. Cerro Gordo is face-to-face interpersonal community, the very nature of which requires its participants to examine themselves—their goals, their motivations and their expectations—and to work together with their future neighbors to assist one another in realizing both personal and community goals. The more meaningful the dialogue among future neighbors and the community at large about your personal goals and how they can be supported by and supportive of community goals, the greater chance personal plans will have to mature into a truly fulfilling way of life for the individual residents and the entire community of neighbors at Cerro Gordo.

The home planning and building process available to future residents begins with information on building opportunities, realities and procedures and a homebuilding questionnaire. Participants then prepare a personal program outlining their housing preferences and publish it in the community newsletter to contact other community members who have similar ideas. When they are ready to make a specific cluster proposal, they confer with community planners to coordinate the proposal with develoment realities and then submit a cluster concept proposal to the Design Committee of the Cerro Gordo Cooperative (the residents' association). With a concept approval they're ready to recruit additional participants through the newsletter and community meetings and begin the cluster design process. When the cluster is designed, the Design Committee reviews the plans and community planners seek the necessary government approvals to deed the homesites, at which time the participants join the Coop. Then they're ready for working drawings, building permits and construction, either as owner-builders or with construction services provided by the community construction company (or a combination of the two).

Livelihood
Goals

All communities are economies. The very existence of the town of Cerro Gordo is dependent upon securing adequate and desirable means of livelihood to support the townspeople. And growth to a well-rounded economic community—with full employment for townsfolk and all basic services provided within the town—is essential to the concept of a close, well integrated community at Cerro Gordo.

Beyond economic support there are several important basic considerations for the choice of community livelihood.

1. *Small scale.* Large businesses tend to become impersonal, bureaucratic, and unresponsive. Small businesses are more likely to be flexible and responsive to the needs of both the individual and the community. Workers have a greater sense of relatedness in small businesses—instead of a trivialized task on an assembly line, each person performs a significant portion of the process and has direct contact with the rest. A large business in a small town is susceptible to a neo-feudal "company town" syndrome. In contrast, an economy made up of many small businesses distributes wealth and economic power.

2. *Diversity.* A broad-based, diverse economy provides security: the economic well-being of the community doesn't depend upon the continued prosperity of any one business or industry. Economic diversity makes for a diverse town population, because a wide variety of job require-

ments allows and stimulates the presence of people with a wide variety of skills, backgrounds, interests, and goals.

3. *Affinity with community ideals.* We want work that is meaningful and fullfilling as well as employers willing to consider new approaches if they promise to be both rewarding for employees and viable economically. Products should be valuable in human terms as well as monetarily—they should be non-destructive and non-exploitative. The community concept of reintegrating work with other activities, and the town with the forest environment demands pleasant working conditions and processes that are essentially noise- and pollution-free.

Two basic types of economic activity in a community can be distinguished: (1) primary enterprises which export products or services out of the community, providing the basis of the town's economy by generating a flow of money into the community; and (2) secondary services provided to the community, providing additional jobs as the money eventually flows out of the community for goods produced elsewhere. An example of the first type is a company that manufactures electronic equipment for sale elsewhere. An example of the second type is the general store that retails goods produced elsewhere to townsfolk. It is easy to see that the economy of a very small community must be mostly primary production. But it is also clear that as the town grows, not only the number but the percentage of secondary service jobs increases, since the larger population supports services in both greater quantity and diversity. When the town eventually attains the optimum population of about 2,500, we can expect at least as many service

niches in the economy as there are primary production niches.

We anticipate that the economy of Cerro Gordo will include a wide spectrum of industries: light manufacturing and assembly, such as electronics, woodworking, furniture, ceramics, toys, clothing, scientific equipment, publishing and printing; remote services, such as research, design and mail order retail; education, such as a small experimental college, a growth center, retreat facilities and a research center; artists, writers and craftspeople, with perhaps an artisans' cooperative or craft school; agriculture and forestry; construction; and community services, such as a general store, a bakery, food and lodging, office services, teachers, doctor and dentist, etc. We also anticipate that along with the variety of economic activities there will be a wide spectrum of business ownership and management approaches, from individual enterprise to cooperatives.

Progress to date

A survey in the summer of 1978 revealed that the 60 adult community members living in the Cottage Grove area had found a variety of livelihoods, including the Cerro Gordo project offices; construction at Cerro Gordo and elsewhere; the Artisans Guild; graphic design; artist; writer-publisher; a health food store; health services and counseling; primary, secondary and college education, including the Cerro Gordo Center summer workshops; scientific consulting; bank teller; antique dealer; city public works manager; office services; and a woodworking business.

During the last few years we have experimented with various approaches to developing an economy for ourselves. One community member purchased a small woodworking business, moved it to the area and hired commu-

nity members. Another member purchased a local health food store. Others have started businesses of their own: graphic design, a publishing firm, scientific consulting, home remodeling and construction, an Artisans Guild and a dental office. In 1976, the Cerro Gordo Community Association sponsored a mailing to 1,500 small businesses on the west coast inviting them to relocate to Cerro Gordo; several businesses responded that they would be interested in moving to Cerro Gordo as community facilities are available for lease. This initial experimentation made it clear that it is certainly possible to develop an economy at Cerro Gordo. The obvious next step to that end is to provide commercial and industrial facilities on the townsite.

In 1978 building permits were obtained for an Industrial Cluster located at the northern end of the Community Base Plan Manufacturing Zone, adjacent to the future Village Center (Figure 14). The 4,000-square-foot office / meeting hall is planned for Cerro

Gordo project and other offices on the second floor and a community meeting hall and home for our Sun Dance School on the first floor. The 6,000-square-foot industrial building is planned for woodworking and other similar shop uses. The Cerro Gordo Cooperative (residents' association) plans to build these and other commercial and industrial facilities and lease the space to businesses. Conventional mortgage financing has been difficult to obtain for the Industrial Cluster at such an early stage in the community's development, so a community investment group may be needed to get construction started.

How we're proceeding

As a community of future residents, we have formulated a program to develop an economy at Cerro Gordo that will provide us with livelihood, thereby making the Cerro Gordo Community possible.

The community aspect of this pro-

Figure 13

Architect's drawing of proposed industrial Cluster.

(Courtesy of Cerro Gordo)

gram is economic planning, which will be an important part of the Comprehensive Community Planning process during the next few years. Through committees, newsletter reports, questionnaires and community discussions, we need to clarify our community economic values and goals, explore various approaches and systems, develop community economic models and phasing studies, and use these plans to guide our economic development efforts.

The individual aspect of this program is livelihood counseling for future residents. This starts with a questionnaire about skills, experience, interests and livelihood goals, and progresses with assistance in reality testing and creative solutions. This information helps determine community goals and guides economic development efforts. A referral service is planned, putting individuals seeking employment and employers seeking employees in contact with one another.

These same information gathering and networking services are available to future residents who want to gather people and resources to start new businesses or purchase existing businesses to relocate to Cerro Gordo. Such entrepreneurs are especially needed during the next few years to get the Cerro Gordo economy started and provide jobs within the community for the first residents.

Once community and individual members' economic goals have been clarified and resources gathered to provide commercial and industrial facilities at Cerro Gordo, a business recruitment program will be implemented. Trade magazine advertisements and direct mail will be targeted towards the types of businesses chosen by future residents. These business people will be invited to consider joining the Cerro Gordo Community and bringing their businesses with them. Those who respond will be sent information about our members who are interested in working in their field, about Cerro Gordo, and our Industrial Cluster.

Education

Goals

The central theme for education at Cerro Gordo is the integration of school and community, of learning and everyday life. The goal is to make the town and townsite the classroom, the community itself the school. One means to this end is to involve townspeople in school programs and activities; another is to open up homes, businesses, and the surrounding forest to the students; another is to make the school part of a larger community center, providing meeting spaces, a library, equipment and so forth to both the school and the community. This approach is meant to bring children and adults back together, to give them more opportunities for sharing experiences and perspectives and learning from one another. This approach is also meant to provide opportunities to learn at first hand, to learn by doing, to learn about everyday life, and to make learning part of everyday life.

Another important educational theme is respect for the unique needs, interests and abilities of each individual. This approach emphasizes learning rather than teaching, and offers meaningful choices to students with regard to curriculum and activities.

Continuing education is another important theme. Learning and growing are lifelong endeavors. Creating a community provides numerous opportunities to explore new fields and learn new skills, to learn from fellow community members and exchange roles and responsibilities.

Progress to date

In 1974 we started Sun Dance School, which operated preschool and elementary school programs for up to 15 children. Classes were held in a renovated shop building on a small farm one year and in a rented home another. The school was supported by tuitions, donations, teachers who worked for minimal salaries, and by parents and other community members who volunteered time and materials. Due to a current lack of suitable quarters, Sun Dance classes have been temporarily suspended, awaiting construction of the Industrial Cluster community building on Cerro Gordo Ranch. Sun Dance School is now seeking donations for its building fund for school furniture and equipment (donations are tax-deductible).

In 1977 the Cerro Gordo Center for Creative Community held its first eight-week summer workshop program in Ecosystemic Community Design. College students came from all over the country in 1977 and again in 1978 to camp at Cerro Gordo and pursue a variety of projects related to appropriate technology, organic agriculture, resource recycling, and planning and building the Cerro Gordo Community. These projects were supervised by several community members, experienced as college instructors or in their project areas. The workshops were supported by tuition from students and subsidies from Lane Community College, through which college credit was arranged. Through its educational, research and demonstration projects, the Center provides a means for its students to reintegrate the intellectual and experiential sides of their lives. At the same time, the Center provides a window for the Cerro Gordo Community, facilitating an exchange of ideas and experience between the community and the outside world. Within the next few years the Center hopes to begin construction of permanent facilities at Cerro Gordo, so it can eventually offer a year-round educational program, with classes and projects for community members as well as visiting students.

How we're proceeding

During the last few years, our community energies have been focused on getting construction started, so most of our community planning has emphasized "hardware": land use, utilities, transportation and housing. But the purpose of building at Cerro Gordo lies just as much with the community's "software" systems: economy, agriculture, education, health, governance and community life. It is these areas that deserve special attention in the upcoming Comprehensive Community Planning process, clarifying our values and goals, exploring our options, and developing realistic phasing plans. What kind of educational programs and activities do we want at Cerro Gordo for our children, for adults? What facilities and equipment? How will we as townspeople participate in these programs, and how will we finance them? What educational resources and opportunities are available in the area and within our membership? What are we going to do next year, and each year thereafter, to bring our plans into reality? These are the types of questions we need to address through values and goals questionnaires; committee explorations, newsletter reports, and community feedback; plan formulation, both long range and phasing; and then formal adoption and implementation of our plans.

Community life
Goals

Cerro Gordo intends to be a community of people who share a common desire for ecological living and a neighborly, face-to-face community, and people who have found ways to work together to achieve their common goals. Cerro Gordo is much more than just a housing development (even though we plan to build homes for ourselves) and much more than just an economic town where people live in the same area because that's where they have employment (even though we plan to secure livelihood for ourselves).

Beyond the shared beliefs in ecology and community, and the shared effort of making Cerro Gordo a reality, it's expected that the community will be diverse in ages, races, values and lifestyles. It's expected that a town of 2,500 people will be a community of communities with different opinions and approaches; but it is hoped that this diversity will not be divisive but strengthening and differences will be seen as complementary rather than contradictory. Beyond the community's support for a variety of lifestyles at Cerro Gordo, it is hoped that there will be a shared spirit of support and affirmation for each person in the community.

Governance of the ongoing community, like the community development effort, emphasizes community participation. Town hall meetings are envisioned, with citizen committees and elected boards assuming specific areas of responsibility and reporting back to the entire community. If the community chooses to incorporate as a municipality, thereby assuming law enforce-

ment responsibilities, the approaches discussed have been the British constable and the Native American concept of justice by reconciliation rather than retribution.

A community health center is envisioned which would emphasize preventive medicine and holistic health care and education. First aid and part time professional services could be provided fairly early in the growth of the town, and a town of 2,500 could support a doctor and dentist. Such a health center would complement nearby hospitals in Cottage Grove and Eugene.

A volunteer fire department is planned, supplementing a rural fire district station that will be built soon a few miles west of Cerro Gordo.

In addition to a town hall, other community facilities have been discussed, such as a library, a community recreation facility, and meeting rooms.

Community activities will include films, music, and, lectures. Community programs will emphasize both individual excellence and group participation in singing and dancing. Community holidays and festivals will be celebrated with special activities.

Progress to date

During the last six years, a strong and varied interpersonal community has grown out of the process of working together on building a new town. About 100 families are currently involved, some since the beginning of the project, others more recently. About half live in the Cottage Grove area near Cerro Gordo, most of the others up and down the west coast, and a few elsewhere. Our annual, week-long *Summer Gathering* brings most of the community together in Cerro Gordo Ranch. We keep in touch with

Figure 14
Summer gathering on the land; a strong and varied community has grown out of the process of working together to build a new town.
(Courtesy of Cerro Gordo)

one another through our monthly Cerro Gordo News, ongoing area group meetings and social events in several west coast cities, and bi-annual meetings and workshops in Seattle, San Francisco, and Los Angeles (Figure 15).

Here in Cottage Grove, the 60 adults and 20 children in the community get together often for all kinds of project meetings: community business meetings, committee meetings, planning sessions, mailing parties and work parties on the Ranch. There are also lots of other events, such as folk dancing, singing and music groups, a film club, potlucks, a food co-op, women's groups, discussion and interpersonal growth groups, meditation, political action groups, volleyball, and swimming and sailing at the lake. Even though we have yet to move onto the Ranch, we already have an active, well-rounded community.

At the same time we have gotten to know a lot of our neighbors in the area. When we first arrived in 1973–74, local people had a lot of questions and concerns about who we were and what we planned to do, and a lot of colorful and creative rumors were circulated about the hippie developers. Now that people have gotten to know us personally, we have more support and little or no vocal opposition, and people have expressed respect for our members, our plans, our perseverance and our quality solar homes.

How we're proceeding

We have gathered together as a community to build ourselves an ecological village.

We have organized supporting membership and future residency programs to bring us together to get to know one another, to clarify our community values and goals, to explore alternate approaches and to implement community action to achieve our common objectives. Working together to build ourselves a town is helping us become the community we want to be.

So far this community process has involved about 100 families who have concentrated most of their efforts on getting ideas together, people organized, land purchased and construction started. These initial pioneers have blazed a trail to prove that we can survive crises, obtain permits, secure financing and build houses. Now the way stands clear to build a Phase I of 115 homes and supporting services — the first 20 percent of the future village of Cerro Gordo.

In order to proceed we must double or triple our strength as a community to be able to achieve this large task; and we must clarify our goals and strategies in a whole new way to keep this large endeavor on target and responsive to our desires. New supporting membership and investment programs are designed to recruit an extended Cerro Gordo Community of future residents and supporters with whose help we can follow through on our Phase I plans. At the same time, the participatory Comprehensive Community Planning process will help clarify community values and strategies in all areas: community systems, housing, livelihood, agriculture, education, health and community life.

Creating community

Community isn't a thing. It's something you do. We yearn for community. How can we achieve it? Feeling our need, we fantasize our ideal community. Communicating our ideals, we find others with similar goals. Shared goals give us direction; shared effort makes our progress manifest. Through communication, cooperation and commitment along the way, we create a growing interpersonal relationship. Working together we create community. Once on the path, we find we have arrived.

The evolution of the Cerro Gordo process

During its first nine years (1970–1979), the goal of an ecological village planned and built by its future residents has been addressed in three different ways. Each approach was pursued for about three years, and can be characterized by the organization that carried the initiative: the Town Forum (1970–73), the Cerro Gordo Community Association (1973–76), and the Cerro Gordo Cooperative (1976–79). In 1979, Cerro Gordo came full circle with a membership vote to return to the original Town Forum approaches to community development.

The Town Forum

Cerro Gordo was started in 1970, when Christopher and Sherry Canfield began a series of discussion groups to collect ideas for the community. Two years of open meetings and interviews of people working with environmental and community projects evolved a *Town Prospectus* outlining the proposal to build an ecological village. The nonprofit, educational Town Forum was organized, and about 100,000 brochures were sent out to members of environmental and community organizations and periodical subscribers. The brochures described the proposed community and invited people to send for the *Town Prospectus* and take part in planning the new community. By the spring of 1973 about 2500 people had subscribed to the Town Forum publications. About ten percent of these subscribers joined a Special Program to explore following through on the *Town Prospectus* proposal; most of these people visited Cerro Gordo Ranch during the summer of 1973, many pledging financial support for the purchase of the ranch and the environmental studies.

While the Town Forum community planning discussions and the Special Program meetings were open to anyone who made a small donation ($5 per year for the Town Forum publications, $25 for the Special Program), it was felt that a more serious commitment was needed to participate in the purchase of Cerro Gordo Ranch and the long term, complicated business of site development. By the end of 1973, forty Special Program households had contributed $54,000 for 15-year-term limited partnership shares in Canfield Associates, Oreg. Ltd., with Christopher Canfield as general partner. This partnership purchased Cerro Gordo Ranch in January of 1974 for $50,000 down and a mortgage for $262,000 with provisions to release acreage free and clear for development as needed. The limited partnership's role was to conduct the site development business separate from the future residents' association for the sake of business efficiency, but subject to a limited return on investment, and approval of development plans by the future residents. Future residents were to have a major role in formulating and approving community development plans, but the business of fulfilling those plans was to be left to the general partner and a small group of experienced consultants.

The Community Association

Monthly meetings in several West Coast cities and a community-wide Thanksgiving Gathering in the fall of 1973 led to the publication of a monthly newsletter beginning in January of 1974, and the formation of the Cerro Gordo Community Association with eight elected leaders at the Easter Gathering that spring. An outgrowth of the Town Forum's Special Program, the Community Association was the non-profit organization of future residents of Cerro Gordo, with a dispersed membership of 100 households living in various cities up and down the West Coast and across the country.

Immediately, the role of the Canfield limited partnership became the subject of debate. Some of the community members (most of whom had supported the limited partnership the previous fall) felt that the Community Association should not only plan the community but manage the site development business as well. In addition to the predictable testing of direction and leadership of the new project, there were strong opinions about organizing the project in a way that "felt right." After several months of re-examining alternative organizational and financial approaches, it became clear that there were two distinct philosophies held by community members: some felt that authority had to be vested in the group as a whole, which would authorize individual actions on its behalf; and others felt that authority would naturally flow to the individuals who assumed responsibility for making the project work, regardless of the stated formal procedures. When a membership vote was taken in September of 1974, the limited partnership approach was confirmed by a four-to-one margin, but with widespread emotional reservations.

During 1975 the Community Association formulated the Cerro Gordo Community Base Plan. Volunteer committees explored various approaches for each aspect of the community plan such as transportation, utilities, housing, and agriculture. Committee reports were published in the monthly newsletter, discussed at monthly area meetings in several West Coast cities, and feedback questionnaires tallied from the members. Committee presentations and group discussions and brainstorming sessions took place at three community-wide gatherings; each drew over 100 participants. In February of 1976, the 100 Community Association members voted to adopt the Base Plan with only one dissenting vote.

The Cooperative

By early 1976 working drawings were being prepared for the first cluster of homes at Cerro Gordo, and it was time to make provisions for residents to assume ownership and management of community open space, utilities, and other community facilities. Although a large minority of Community Association members had opposed a distinction between residents and future residents in 1974, by 1976 the members authorized (with only one dissenting vote) the formation of the Cerro Gordo Cooperative, Inc. as the separate residents' organization. Members of the Cooperative had to be residents of Cerro Gordo and all residents had to be members of the Cooperative. The Cooperative was designed to function as a private town government; in addition to owning and managing community land, utilities and facilities, Cooperative members had the authority to enact rules for use of community property and to sponsor other community activities.

When the Cooperative was organized in June of 1976, a Community Development Agreement was simultaneously adopted which divided the development responsibilities among all three organizations: the Community Association, the Cooperative and the limited partnership. In addition to community planning, the Community Association assumed responsibility for economic development and membership recruitment. The Cooperative assumed responsibility for approving site development plans and budgets and for financing site development and the purchase of Cerro Gordo Ranch. The partnership sold Cerro Gordo Ranch to the Cooperative and continued with a reduced role of providing community planning and site development services to the Cooperative.

Although it appeared in 1976 that there was a sufficient number of committed and capable community members to assume overall responsibility for the project, the Cooperative was slow to provide leadership. Consequently, much of the initiative came from a few staff people and the partnership. Problems in securing bank financing delayed the start of construction until August of 1977. Then the Oregon Corporation Commissioner ruled that Cooperative memberships were securities that had to be registered with the state. This ruling was reversed in August of 1978, but by then the 1978 construction plans were hamstrung by the lack of utilities financing. By the fall of 1978 the Cooperative was threatened with foreclosure on both Cerro Gordo Ranch and the Prototype Solar Duplex. The Cooperative had expanded by then to over 40 members, but many had only tentative plans to move onto Cerro Gordo Ranch. Added to this wide range of commitment level was a diversity of economic philosophies. Various divergent approaches were proposed to address the Cooperative's financial problems, but none could generate sufficient support to be effective. On top of it all, future residents in the Community Association felt unable to fulfill their development responsibilities with such a dispersed membership, and they felt disenfranchised from the important Cooperative financial decisions, so they were pressing to have the Community Association dissolved and future residents admitted as members of the Cooperative. In time of crisis, the Cooperative's group process just couldn't cope with the difficult financial problems.

The Town Forum

Fortunately the members recognized their inability to agree on solutions to the pressing financial problems, and they did the next best thing: they supported a few key staff members as they did whatever they could to resolve the difficulties. The threatened foreclosures were averted, after which community members voted to approve a major project reorganization. Management of the site development business was transferred to the few people who have a long term commitment to wrestling with the related complexities and problems. This step freed community members to focus on what they really *wanted* to do (as opposed to what they had felt they *ought* to do): building a home or developing a neighborhood, starting a business or school, working on community plans or organizing community activities. Membership in the Cooperative is now limited to actual Cerro Gordo residents, who review and approve community plan amendments and construction projects. Future residents and community sup-

porters now take part in planning and building the community through programs sponsored by the non-profit Town Forum, Inc., which is organizing the Cerro Gordo Community Development Trust to assume the community planning, financing and construction responsibilities of the limited partnership, which will then be discontinued. (The Community Association has already been dissolved.) Somewhat older and wiser, Cerro Gordo has returned to its original approaches to bringing people together as a community to plan and build an ecological village.

The Cerro Gordo process

Planning magazine described Cerro Gordo as "a new town with something new," referring to our approach of recruiting future townsfolk to plan, finance and build the new town. Although we have barely started construction, we believe we have learned some important lessons about the dangers and the rewards of this approach.

It is certainly clear why commercial developers don't seek future resident involvement. Just the business of planning, financing, securing approvals for and constructing any major development is difficult enough as it is, fraught with problems, delays, and risks. Involving future residents in planning decisions compounds these difficulties. Involving future residents in the site development business makes it nearly impossible to function. Community development requires many pieces to come together (and fit) at just the right time. Too many people involved in too many aspects of a project tend to tear it apart with their different goals, philosophies and perceptions.

These kinds of problems plagued

Cerro Gordo most when we organized around our rhetoric rather than our realities. Most community members have been former suburbanites who yearn for "community" but have little experience with community living. Some members with strong dreams have found it hard to accept an approximation of those dreams in reality. With those strong dreams, it has been difficult for some members to trust other community members to do what's right. There has been a tendency to view different dreams as contradictory rather than complementary. Initiative has been met with defensiveness more often than affirmation. One common definition of "community" that the members supported can be characterized as "everybody does everything." This approach addressed members' needs for personal and community control, but the result was a large disparity between the responsibilities the members told themselves they ought to be carrying and the responsibilities they really could or even wanted to carry. Further, when "everybody does everything," it's a rare event when the group can muster both the authorization and the energy to get anything done.

These problems were lessened when we adopted a different definition of community, in which community is viewed as a differentiated organism. When we decided to let individuals do what they can do, and perhaps more importantly, what they *want* to do, we released a tremendous amount of positive energy. Things got done. Of course, there still remained the need for community coordination, both of long term goals and of project business affairs. Long term plans are still submitted to community vote, but the formulation is left to community members who really want to work on those plans. And fortunately the community has several members who really want to wrestle with the day-to-day realities of the site development business; this work is now done in a way that encourages membership participation, which is different than requiring membership participation by placing the burden of responsibility on every member's shoulders. The "everybody does everything" community model made unrealistic demands upon Cerro Gordo community members. The differentiated organism model, by focusing on individuals and the evolving arrangements they work out among themselves, encourages people to *be* the community while they help it grow. Cerro Cordo has been most successful

when we have focused on individuals and what they really want to do. More gets done more joyously with this approach.

The future of Cerro Gordo

We expect to obtain the Phase I Planned Unit Development approval in 1980 for the first 20 percent of Cerro Gordo (about 115 homes). Most of these homes should be built during the first half of the 1980s, as well as the businesses that will provide employment for most of these residents. As Phase I is being built, planning and approvals will be pursued for the entire town of 2,500 people. If the New Development Center approval is ob-

tained, construction of the entire village could be completed some time in the 1990s.

We expect the community building process to continue to evolve as the village grows. Exactly where this adventure will lead is hard to foresee. We have our ideals, like stars, to guide us. But the center of activity is down to earth, as we struggle to pioneer a new lifestyle, with only shorter or longer sections of the path ahead visible as we move through the valleys and over the promontories. Fortunately, planning and building the village of Cerro Gordo has already created a community as real and rewarding in the present as the future evolved community promises to be in the future.

Urban Decentralization

THE VERY IDEA of civilization, both historically and etymologically, is tied to the existence of the city. For the past 5,000 years, civilization has been energized by the dialectical tension between the opposites of city and wilderness, the center and the periphery. But now, in the sunset age of industrialism, this polarity of opposites is approaching the point of maximum tension. If the urban wasteland continues to spread into every corner of the globe, destroying all other ways of life and patterns of human settlement through the corrosive influence of its consumptive ethos, industrial civilization will explode and collapse into a new dark age of totalitarian control and terrorist revolt. Yet even in places where industrialism is still only a distant dream, the gleaming glass and steel towers of the modern city already exist, in Theodore Roszak's words, as the "ritual centerpiece of a worldwide cargo cult that waits for capital and know-how to arrive from distant lands of enchanted affluence."[1]

But for the tens of millions of peasants who hover around the edges of these beacons of opportunity, the city is a mocking symbol of their highest hopes. Like their black, Puerto Rican, and Mexican-American counterparts in American cities, the urban peasants of the third world are trapped by a vicious cycle of chronic unemployment, hazardous housing, often violent crime, and declining (if any) services. For the majority of humankind, the inexorable expansion of the empire of cities has brought only a growing gap between expectation and reality.

But, until recently, this has in no way affected the growth of urban areas anywhere in the world. It is estimated that by the end of this century, 60 percent of the U.S. population will be living within three massive conurbations. A T-shaped area extending east from Chicago to Boston and south to Washington, D.C. will have a population of 117 million people. A band stretching west from Sacramento to San Francisco and south to

San Diego, California will support 34 million inhabitants. Between Jacksonville and Miami, Florida there will be 13 million inhabitants. The remainder of the U.S. population, 80 percent of which is already classified as urban, will be gathered together in metropolitan areas only slightly less concentrated.[2]

Such unprecedented levels of population concentration are, unfortunately, not unique to this country. Whereas there was only one city in the world, London, with a population of one million in 1820, by 1985 there will be 273 cities of one million or more, 147 of them in less developed countries. But the city of one million is already being replaced by the city of ten million. London and New York reached ten million in 1950, but, by 1985 there will be 17 of these "cities," 10 of them in developing countries.[3]

This enormous increase in the size and extent of urban areas creates a qualitative change in the nature and meaning of the city. Until the rise of megalopolis, the city had always existed as a spatially defined entity within a rural and wilderness context. Even ancient Rome, with a million inhabitants, was clearly articulated from, and in close relationship with, the surrounding countryside. A person could easily walk from the dense center to the rural area just beyond the boundary of the city. Today, the gargantuan size and formless sprawl of megalopolis drives the constantly receding countryside always just beyond the reach of its ever advancing system of inefficient, high speed, energy-intensive transportation.

Such unreasonable size is only matched by an equally irrational pattern of organization of work and residence. The typical industrial city in America can be conceptualized as a series of concentric rings. The inner core is made up largely of a high concentration of business headquarters, providing employment for the highly educated white collar workers in the knowledge and managerial professions who live in the suburban and exurban rings which encircle the ring of inner city ghettoes around the center-city. The less skilled workers who live in these deteriorating center-city housing areas are increasingly unable to find work in the manufacturing sector as industries automate or leave the city for parts of the U.S. and world where the costs of land and labor and the tax advantages are more favorable. The result is a divorce between work and home which is only compensated for by a massive daily migration of commuters, most of whom spend two to four hours a day alone behind the wheel of a car just to get to and from work (a radical monopoly in Ivan Illich's terms).

It is clear that this creates enormous inefficiencies in energy use, a pattern of consumption which is becoming increasingly difficult for individuals or the society as a whole to afford. However, the spatially reinforced segregation of urban population into age, income, ethnic and racial groups that is also created by this wasteful organization of urban function points up the greatest irony and failure of megalopolis.

The historical role and unique value of the preindustrial city (at its best) was to dissolve the suspicion, fear, and hatred of the stranger which has always been the dark side of life in the small town, hamlet, and rural village. This was accomplished by bringing diverse cultural, ethnic and ideological groups into direct face-to-face contact within the close confines of the city, forcing people to confront the facticity of "otherness." Out of this confrontation of opposites, the narrow parochialism of the rural base of a society was transformed into a new, more universal brotherhood based on the shared space and common purpose of the urban community.

But the modern metropolis, in Murray Bookchin's words, "assimilates rural parochialism as a permanent and festering urban condition. No longer are the elements of the city cemented by mutual aid, a shared culture, and a sense of community; rather, they are cemented by a social dynamite that threatens to explode the urban tradition into its antithesis."[4] Rather than providing a means of dissolving the barriers which stand in the way of a more universal human community, the modern city segregates the "other" into inner city, suburban, and exurban ghettoes of mutual fear and misunderstanding, where the only exchange of values, ideas and culture occurs across the windshield of a car and the viewing screen of a television sitcom. Conspicuous consumption, fueled by the greed and envy inculcated by the mass media, has replaced the unity through diversity that the urban community has traditionally provided.

In another enantiodromia of history, where a movement in one direction ends in a place opposite to its origin, the urbanization of the earth has led to the demise of truly urban values. While Karl Marx could speak with some justification in the last century of the "idiocy of rural life," we might equally speak today of the "idiocy of urban life."

To recover the city as a place which nourishes free inquiry, creative experimentation, and the development of universalizing forces and cosmopolitan values, we must, paradoxically, dissolve and then imaginatively restructure megalopolis into a network of richer, more compact, human scaled, and clearly defined urban areas. To once again have cities, we must discover how to limit their formless sprawl across the landscape.

Whenever a movement reaches its limit, there is always the beginning of a movement in the opposite direction. In the case of the city this has already begun. If megalopolis is the end product of a process characterized by positive feedback between energy consumption and growth, the emerging age of scarcity of fossil fuels and mineral resources has begun to introduce negative feedback into the process of urban growth. In other terms, the internal contradictions of megalopolis are already beginning to limit its further expansion.

These limits are most clearly evident in the old industrial cities of the northeast and upper midwest, where, in the 1970s, for the first time since the 1930s, more people left the cities than arrived. Typically, those who left (and continue to leave) are predominantly young, white, and relatively affluent. Those who remain behind—the old, the poor, the black—confront the second major problem facing the major metropolitan areas in these regions, that is, the loss of manufacturing jobs. New York City alone, from 1953 to 1973, lost 38 percent of its manufacturing employment, largely to the sun belt cities in the south and southwest.[5] And, while jobs in the services increased over the same period, there was still a net decline in employment opportunities. Moreover, since the residents of the inner city are less likely to be eligible for service sector jobs than manufacturing jobs, the result of this pattern has been to increase unemployment among the poor while increasing the net energy consumption of the city as a whole, as people from the growing exurban fringe commute from ever-increasing distances to the center city for the newly created knowledge-industry positions.

As people leave the city for the suburbs (where most of the outmigration has ended up) or other cities in other parts of the country, the tax base of the city declines. However, the cost of maintaining basic services (most of which are fixed costs such as fire protection, sewers, streets, etc.) does not decline even though finances for providing them do. This creates a Catch-22 situation where the city has one of three choices: (1) to increase taxes to maintain services, (2) to decrease services, (3) to borrow money to maintain services. All three choices only contribute to the further exacerbation of the problem. If taxes increase, the competitive edge of the city suffers, leading to a further outmigration of the relatively affluent sector of the population able to move. This further erodes the tax base, leading to increased pressures to curtail basic services. If, instead of increasing taxes, the city chooses to decrease services, the result is a decline in the quality of living which, again, leads to a loss of population and a further exaggeration of the gap between basic services and the city's ability to pay for them. If the city chooses to keep taxes and services at existing levels by borrowing money, the basic dilemma is made worse at some point in the future, since the cost of debt service increases to the point where the city begins to lose access to further credit. At this point the city is unable to meet its increased financial commitments to maintain even a reduced level of services.

This somewhat simplified presentation of the plight of the industrial city reads, of course, like the recent history of New York City. But New York is far from being the irresponsible black sheep that its critics claim. Recent studies of the fiscal strength of major U.S. cities suggest that the other northeastern cities are in equal or worse condition.[6] Moreover, as the costs of energy continue to increase, the cities in the south and southwest, which have recently benefited from the interregional shift in population, jobs and political power, are likely to experience equally serious problems of the same kind. In fact their problems may be worse, since the pattern of growth in these cities will more nearly approximate the sprawl of Los Angeles rather than the more energy efficient pattern of those older cities currently in decline. It is only a matter of time before the plight of New York becomes the fate of all our major cities.

Nor is this problem limited to the United States:

The sickness of the city is not confined to America, but is endemic to all of industrial culture. Some Canadian cities are in decline. Across the Atlantic, the city of Glasgow, built on a now-exhausted coal seam, is in a state of advanced and apparently irreversible deterioration. London is shrinking at an annual rate of 50,000 people, and its inner city is now reduced to two-thirds of its 1939 population. In 1973 the population of Paris declined for the first time in recorded history. On the other side of the industrialized world, ten Japanese cities have declared bankruptcy. Tokyo—the largest city on earth, and capital of the most urbanized nation on earth—is losing population at the rate of 170,000 per year and stands at the brink of default. Even in the partially industrialized U.S.S.R., hastily erected cities are aging rapidly, portending an era of physical decline. It seems fair to conclude that the decline of the city is a general phenomenon throughout industrial civilization.[7]

The industrial megalopolis, like every other institution and activity which has been created by cheap energy, must now expect a period of rapid and fundamental change if it is to survive during the coming age of energy and resource scarcity. We must restructure the human habitat in such a way that it does not depend for its existence upon large-scale machinery, constantly increasing flows of concentrated non-renewable energy sources and raw materials, and the long distance transportation of goods to mass markets.

What kinds of changes are implied by this? Before attempting to answer this question let us look first at some of the principles that must guide the great cultural transformation ahead.

If we are to create a sustainable form of culture out of the crisis of industrialism, we must, at the very least, learn how to live within the limits imposed by the ecosystems that sustain us. That is the essential message of the dilemma of ecological scarcity.

Our aim must be to create a symbiosis between nature and culture. To achieve this goal, human culture must come to emulate in its functioning, as far as possible, the dynamic equilibrium characteristic of a mature ecosystem.

If that is to be our goal, then perhaps this period of cultural transformation can be likened to the transition from a pioneer or juvenile ecosystem to a mature or climax ecology.

We observe dog-eat-dog competition every time new vegetation colonizes a bare field where the immediate survival premium is first placed on rapid expansion to cover the available energy receiving surfaces. The early growth ecosystems put out weeds of poor structure and quality, which are wasteful in their energy-capturing efficiencies, but effective in getting growth even though the structures are not long lasting. Most recently modern communities of man have been in 200 years of colonizing growth, expanding to new energy sources such as fossil fuels, agricultural lands and other special energy sources.[8]

While ruthless competition, rapid growth, high birth rates, and uncontrolled exploitation of natural resources may be advantageous in a "pioneer society," it is clear that such tactics reveal their destructive tendencies when a saturation level is reached.

> Whenever an ecosystem reaches its steady state after periods of succession, the rapid net growth specialists are replaced by a new team of higher diversity, higher quality, longer living, better controlled and stable components. Collectively through division of labor and specialization, the climax team gets more energy out of the steady flow of available source energy than those specialized in fast growth could.[9]

Thus, in the shift to a steady state, mature human ecosystem based on the efficient use of renewable energy sources, it is necessary to replace ruthless competition with symbiosis, to replace high birth rates with birth control, and resource exploitation with resource recycling and conservation. If we are to escape the crashes which often characterize shifts from growth to steady state in nature, we must assume responsibility for the design of culture. Our aim must be to create a human ecology that embodies the basic principles of steady state ecosystems: stability, diversity, symbiosis, metabolic efficiency, and nutrient and resource recycling.

As biologist John Todd has said, "If we created a culture in the image of the biosphere, it would bring about a revolutionary change in the way in which people live on earth. It would have an impact as great as the introduction of agriculture some ten thousand years ago. Biological consciousness would fundamentally alter our sense of what human communities might be."[10]

The characteristics of mature ecosystems provide guidelines for assessing whether or not changes are headed in the right direction. (See Table 1.) Perhaps the most generalizable principle for the design of ecological cities is the idea of changing the linear through-put of energy, food, water, minerals and other raw materials into a circular pattern based on the recycling of resources and the local production and consumption of renewable energy sources. Like a mature ecosystem, the goal of an ecological city is to achieve as large and diverse a physical, social and economic structure as possible within the limits set by available energy inputs and the prevailing physical conditions of existence (soil, water, climate, and so on). The creation of stable, high quality and sustainable habitats and healthy, self-reliant and meaningfully employed people is the goal. Such ecological cities would indeed represent a new symbiosis between humanly managed habitats and naturally-occurring ecosystems.

What David Morris has done, in the first paper in this section, is to translate this somewhat abstract model of a mature ecosystem in nature into a new paradigm for the reconstruction of the urban political economy. Rather than thinking of municipal governments merely as "real estate developers and social welfare dispensers," Morris argues persuasively

Pioneer State (Industrial Cities)	Climax State (Ecological Cities)	
Few species with one or few dominant species (simplicity)	Many species with relative equality among species (diversity)	
Quantitative growth	Qualitative growth	
Competition among species, with few symbioses	Cooperation among species, with many symbioses	
Short, simple life cycles	Long, complex life cycles	
Mineral and nutrient cycles relatively open, rapid and linear	Mineral and nutrient cycles circular and slow	
Detritus relatively unimportant in nutrient regeneration	Detritus relatively important in nutrient regeneration	
Rapid growth	Growth controlled and limited by complex feedback circuits	
Relatively inefficient use of energy	Efficient use of energy	
Energy flows linear (in large increments through simple channels)	Energy flows circular (in small increments through multiple channels)	
Low degree of structure and order (high entropy)	High degree of structure and order (low entropy)	
Low stability to external perturbation	High stability to external perturbation	

Table 1

Contrasting characteristics of pioneer and climax ecosystems as an analogue of industrial versus ecological cities.

for a new approach which sees the city as a "nation" seeking economic independence through a strategy aimed at achieving local self-reliance in the areas of energy, food, shelter, employment, and other basic needs. Thus, municipal government in the future would, like the self-reliant free city states of the Medieval era, assume full responsibility for planning and coordinating economic development within its borders in order to keep resources within the local economy, reduce imports and expand exports. Like the nutrient and resource flows within a steady-state, mature ecosystem, such an urban economy would become a more efficient, balanced and stable closed-loop system, capable of making the maximum use of available energy, raw (and recycled) materials, land and labor. Morris presents an urban model ideally suited to providing a high quality of life within the emerging age of energy, capital and resource scarcity.

As Morris illustrates through numerous examples, this approach to urban revitalization is made possible by recent developments in technology, such as low cost, high speed computers, which make it possible, for example, for a city with economic as well as political authority to map the movement of capital through its borders, inventory the content and flow rate of the solid waste stream, identify existing and needed skills, chart existing and alternate (i.e. renewable) energy flows, and estimate the costs of a wide range of development alternatives.

The concept of the "city as nation" is also an imaginative and appropriate response to the current plight of the industrial city—the loss of manufacturing jobs, the rising costs of bureaucratically administered services, and the declining economic base and quality of life. In addition to the ability to inventory and understand how it operates as a political, economic and ecological system, the city as nation now has access to a wide variety of new, smaller scale, more energy efficient and less capital intensive technologies capable of turning current urban problems into resources for stable economic development. For example, new industries, as in the past, would want to be located near both raw materials supply and concentrated markets for the sale of finished goods. By building new small scale production plants within the city, which could be supplied by mining the vast resources of the urban solid waste stream (now a major pollution problem), it would become possible to create new jobs for the poor and unskilled, and generate local tax revenue, thereby placing a bottom line on the decline in basic services. Rather than importing vast amounts of increasingly costly and scarce raw materials (which undermines local economies), such an approach would, by converting a linear flow of resources into a circular one, convert an environmental and economic problem into an opportunity for ecologically sound economic redevelopment.

Similarly, programs aimed at energy conservation and solar retrofitting of existing commercial and residential areas would not only rehabilitate existing building stock, but would also increase local employment, thereby decreasing welfare and unemployment costs, while simultaneously reducing the outflow of local capital for increasingly costly and expensive fossil fuels.

These and the many other possibilities for rebuilding the political economy of existing cities, described by David Morris, make it clear that the crisis of megalopolis holds the potential for creating more compact, energy efficient, and locally controlled communities. But the key to this strategy is adherence to the principle of community economic development. Clearly, the growing movement toward local self-reliance is redefining our cities, neighborhoods, and households as self-managing producers of wealth rather than merely dependent and helpless consumers of wealth produced by large scale, centralized corporations. Thus, Morris presents the central issue of the 1980s and beyond as a question of whether we shall have a single global village under corporate management or a globe of economically self-reliant villages exchanging information, culture and values (rather than raw materials and finished goods) within a bioregionally based, equitable world order. Ultimately, a stable world order depends on a stable local order.

That is why the growing movement toward neighborhood revitalization and community economic development is so crucial to the transformation of industrial civilization. The next two articles, by Michael Freedberg and by Daniel Goldrich et al., describe in some detail how self-reliant cities are beginning to come into existence through grass roots action aimed at restoring local control over the basic necessities. While their focus is on the case study description of similar efforts in two different cities, they portray an approach to urban redevelopment that can provide a model for resolving some of the most pressing problems that are likely to confront the entire nation in the years ahead.

Emerging energy and resource scarcities will generate two conflicting tendencies for future urban development. One set of forces will accelerate the process of "gentrification" (the colonization by wealthier classes of neighborhoods occupied by the poor), as middle and upper middle income whites rediscover and reinhabit the inner city residential areas in an attempt to reduce the burdens created by long-distance commuting. This process will tend to drive up urban land values, with the result that the largely black, Puerto Rican and Mexican-American communities will be pressured to abandon their homes and neighborhoods. However, the urban poor are not likely to easily succumb to this renewed drive for their removal, and will respond by demanding not only that their neighborhoods be saved but that increasingly scarce economic resources be used for their revitalization. Thus, the stage will be set for a major confrontation between socioeconomic classes and racial groups. Once again, our cities will become the battleground for the resolution of fundamental issues of equity and social justice which Americans have never fully faced or accepted, even during the age of economic growth and expansion.

This time, however, the realities of increasing costs and declining resources will make it impossible for us to sidestep the demands of the poor and disenfranchised for distributive justice. No longer will it be possible to subsidize the rich and powerful in order to encourage economic growth in the false but convenient belief that the benefits will "trickle down" to those at the bottom of the socioeconomic ladder. The pernicious intent and effect of such a substitution of economics for politics will be clear to all involved.

As we attempt to do more with less, we shall have to devise ways to more equitably share smaller pies. In short, we shall have to rediscover the art of politics, which has always been, until the era of cheap energy, the way societies have settled questions of how to distribute scarce resources. For a nation whose major institutions and dominant ideologies are premised on the conscious avoidance of such difficult political decisions, this could prove to be no small problem.

From the narrow perspective of resource consumption, the process of gentrification will be welcomed. It will not only save energy and allow for a more efficient and rational organization of habitat and services, but it will also increase the cities' sagging tax base. By diverting urban growth away from the exurban fringe, prime agricultural land adjacent to major population centers will be saved, thereby making it possible to restore a more energy efficient system of food production and distribution. For all of these reasons the return of suburbanites to the city will be seen by a broad coalition of interest groups as both a necessary and desirable response to the fiscal crisis of the cities and the energy and resource crisis of the nation.

However, the experience of the East 11th Street project, described in the paper by Michael Freedberg, convincingly demonstrates that gentrification is not the only economically valid way for cities to rebuild their decaying inner cores. Through a coordinated program of community-based economic development which included sweat equity housing rehabilitation, the use of on-site renewable energy systems (solar heated domestic hot water and wind generated electricity), the development of open space (parks and community gardens), and the development of youth programs and educational opportunities for people of all ages, the East 11th Street Movement has been able to save a neighborhood many had defined as beyond hope. Freedberg's paper provides a concrete example of how the goals of *equity and justice can be achieved by, not instead of,* the revitalization of existing urban neighborhoods.

While it is clear that the limited and carefully planned provision of some new, in-town, mixed income, and mixed use development will also have to be a part of any comprehensive rebuilding of our cities (e.g. the proposed Marin Solar Village described in the paper by Peter Calthorpe), the great majority of urban change must be modeled on the pioneering efforts of the East 11th Street project. We shall have neither the physical nor social capital necessary to simply start from scratch. Rather than writing off poorer neighborhoods through a program of "planned shrinkage," as has been proposed by some, an urban policy for the future must facilitate the self-help efforts of the people who already live in our decaying urban neighborhoods.

The reasons for this approach, if not already obvious, are made so by the case study described by Freedberg. For one thing, we have run out of places to dump the poor. (Unless we create reservations for their progressive removal as we did in the case of the Native Americans who happened to live where we wanted to be.) Why not provide them with the resources they need to stay where they are and make a decent life for themselves? Not only is this the most humane, just, and straightforward approach, but it is the most cost-effective, both for the poor and for society. As Freedberg points out, the East 11th Street project has clearly demonstrated that self-help and neighborhood-based development can provide basic services at a fraction of the cost of bureaucratically administered programs. Not only were the actual construction costs of rehabilitating abandoned tenements significantly less than either new construction or the use of conventional contractors for rehabilitation, but the participants, many of whom were previously unemployed, developed marketable skills and a way to support themselves and their families after the completion of their new cooperatively owned apartments. The results of this project —

the decrease in unemployment and welfare costs, the increase in property values and tax revenues, and the reduction of demand for police and fire protection—have all contributed to the solution of New York's fiscal crisis.

However, the real benefits of the project cannot be easily quantified. Rather than a slum beset with crime, physical decay, and despair, the entire 11th Street area is gradually being transformed into an economically and socially viable community, with all that implies. People feel good about themselves again. They are more inclined to help each other. Vacant lots that once provided hangouts for drug pushers and addicts are now beautiful and productive fruit and vegetable gardens and parks for children to play in. (With the help of the Trust for Public Land, the community has purchased the five vacant lots used for the community gardens and placed them in a community land trust to be used in perpetuity as a site for local food production.) Rather than being at the mercy of escalating energy costs and large impersonal institutions, the use of heavy insulation and solar energy has provided a permanent hedge against inflation and a source of local community pride. Rather than having a sense of powerlessness, people are beginning to see themselves as active agents of change, capable not only of helping themselves to change, but also capable of helping other neighborhoods to change themselves.

As a result, the 11th Street Movement, which began as an effort to rehabilitate and cooperatively own one abandoned tenement in one New York neighborhood, has now become a part of a neighborhood wide revitalization effort on the Lower East Side and a source of inspiration for neighborhoods throughout the city (and nation). Technical assistance, for example, was provided to Cuando, a local Spanish youth group that had taken over an abandoned church for use as a meeting and recreation center, to build the city's first passive solar wall with a grant from the National Center for Appropriate Technology. Other groups, such as the People's Development Corporation in the South Bronx, have built on the experience of the East 11th Street Movement to begin a process of community-controlled development aimed at realizing a vision of the neighborhood as a self-managing urban village, a "family of 10,000," committed to local economic, social, cultural and physical development based on self-help and mutual aid.

While all of these efforts and other related projects are not free of often serious problems, the enduring value of the East 11th Street project is that it has conclusively demonstrated the viability and desirability of an approach to neighborhood revitalization that flies in the face of conventional economic analysis and bureaucratic planning theory. Needed now is a national commitment to the principles embodied in this pioneering experiment and the development of a comprehensive policy framework to encourage similar efforts throughout the country. Failure to do so in the emerging age of ecological scarcity is likely to lead to a series of events that will make the urban riots of the 1960s appear tame by comparison. A grassroots, community-based approach to urban decentralization and revitalization is our best, and perhaps only, long-term solution to the conflicts created by the multiple crises of resource scarcity, urban decay and social and economic injustice.

Daniel Goldrich and his co-authors Maureen Good, Steve Greenwood, and Jim McCoy describe their work in another poor urban neighboorhood, the Whiteaker neighborhood in Eugene, Oregon. This project is the most comprehensive effort to date to create an integral urban neighborhood through a process of locally controlled economic development. Like David Morris, they see this effort within the context of the historically crucial conflict which is now coming to a head as energy and resource scarcities and other environmental limitations begin to force us to "share smaller pies." The central issue is whether we shall have a radical democratization and decentralization of society or a continued centralization of economic and political power on behalf of the largest corporations. Unable to expand total wealth through the progressive application of more large scale technology and the consumption of increasing quanta of energy, the global corporations are moving to depoliticize the public arena while demanding that government divert public funds toward their own subsidization. However, at the same time, the energy and resource crisis facing industrial economies is focusing more attention on the national condition John Kenneth Galbraith has described as "private wealth and public squalor." This is leading toward increased demands that government provide more effectively for the public good through increased expenditures for social welfare. Clearly, we can no longer even pretend to do both in the emerging era of ecological scarcity and economic crisis.

In energy terms, this issue translates into the choice between what Amory Lovins has called the hard and soft energy paths. While the soft path, which relies on energy conservation and decentralized renewable energy systems, would tend to lead toward a more decentralized and democratic society, the hard path, with its heavy emphasis on the rapid expansion of centralized, capital and energy-intensive high technologies, would in Lovins's words lead to "a world of subsidies, $100-billion bailouts, oligopolies, regulations, nationalization, eminent domain, corporate statism."[11]

Clearly, the momentum of existing forces is in the direction of hard path technologies and centralized corporate statism, since our entire political economy has evolved to regulate and promote a conflict-free environment for the growth and development of large scale corporations. If this trend is to be reversed, there must be a widespread, informed and vigorous grassroots movement toward local economic control and community development through environmentally appropriate technologies.

The Whiteaker neighborhood in Eugene, Oregon, like the East 11th Street community in New York, is at the forefront of this counterforce.

Like many other neighborhood movements, Whiteaker first became self conscious as a community by struggling to fend off the threat of a proposed freeway. However, unlike most neighborhoods, which tend to demobilize once the immediate threat to well-being is removed, Whiteaker has continued its evolution to the point where it has now mobilized to implement a broad-based program of community controlled economic development and environmental enhancement, dictated by and responsive to local needs and preferences.

The key innovation adopted by Whiteaker is the idea that development should be a public process of community stock-taking, planning, and action—a notion described in the first paper by David Morris and illustrated in the case study described by Michael Freedberg. Through the vehicle of a Community Development Corporation and a one-of-a-kind grant from the National Center for Appropriate Technology, Whiteaker has committed itself to a "more self-reliant, economically democratic and environmentally sound future." This Urban Integrated Community Demonstration project was focused around the coordinated development of programs in energy conservation and solar energy utilization, local organic food production and distribution, housing rehabilitation and cooperatives, and a neighborhood-based system of health care.

Since the rate of inflation for basic necessities has been roughly twice the rate of overall inflation, the Whiteaker effort is of great relevance for a wide range of American communities. Should this courageous prototype of a future created and controlled by a local community succeed (as it is likely to do), it would clearly demonstrate that a political economy based on environmentally appropriate technologies and an emphasis on local control is a real, workable, and desirable alternative to a present and past which has been shaped by unresponsive institutions, exploitative technologies and undemocratic development processes. Should we decide to make it so, the history of the Whiteaker neighborhood could become the future history of many neighborhoods in a restructured urban America.

The papers by Morris, Freedberg, and Goldrich et al. make it clear that existing urban areas can not only be spared from the vicious cycle of decline and collapse which threatens many American cities, but that they can be reshaped to meet our material and spiritual needs in ways that enhance our deepest values and democratic ideals. The de-structuring of megalopolis into a multi-nucleated pattern of compact, socially viable neighborhoods, towns, and cities can thus be seen as both necessary and possible.

As mentioned earlier, while the reconstruction of existing "gray areas" by the urban poor must be a vital and necessary part of the process of transforming urban America, it is not sufficient. There is still the problem of the outmigration of young, white and affluent residents (which undermines the economic base of the city) and the logistical nightmare of transporting people from the growing suburban and exurban fringe to the central commercial business district where they work. Since the relatively low-cost, portable liquid fuels upon which this spatial distribution is based are in shortest supply, the recolonization of the city must soon come to replace the suburbanization of the earth as the dominant trend for urban growth and development.

As Peter Calthorpe argues, not only is suburbanization the cause of many of the social, economic, ecological and political problems of the city, but it is more energy-, land-, and resource-intense than any other form of human settlement. Solar suburbs would be an ironic and mocking "solution" to the crisis of the industrial city.

This suggests two kinds of changes. First, existing suburban areas must become more densely inhabited and more socioeconomically and racially diverse through the introduction of a wider range and larger number of sources of employment. (Perhaps the most likely and valuable contribution the suburbs could make to a renewable-energy-based society would be through urban agriculture—the labor- and skill-intensive production of herbs, fruits and vegetables, fish and poultry products). Rather than creating more problems to be solved in this way in the future, however, growth should be aimed at urban in-fill for families that work in the city.

Developments such as the proposed Marin Solar Village (to be built on an abandoned air force base in Marin County, California) would ensure that existing urban infrastructure (such as mass transit, utilities, markets, and roads) is more effectively utilized. By also ensuring that new in-town development is ecologically designed to operate on renewable energy sources, recycle organic and non-organic "wastes," provide for substantial levels of organic local food production, and make widespread use of walking, bicycling and public transit (instead of automobiles), projects such as the Marin Solar Village point the way toward a viable urban pattern of the future. While the fate of this particular case study is still in doubt, it is only a matter of time before the logic of necessity forces every American city to begin the process of recolonizing, integrating and diversifying in the direction of sustainability and equity.

Such efficient use of urban and suburban land will also make it possible to create a new pattern of food production in and around existing urban areas. Every civilization is ultimately a reflection of its agricultural base. Megalopolis is the counterpart of a system of agriculture which has progressively substituted energy and machines for people. If, as has been argued, the era of cheap and abundant energy and mineral resources is rapidly drawing to a close, then it is clear that both industrial agriculture and the industrial city must be radically changed.

Already the subsidization of agriculture by fossil fuels is becoming more and more economically infeasible. It is likely to become more so in the near future. If a relatively conservative fivefold energy price increase were to occur in the next two decades (the rate of increase in the recent past has been more than twice this amount), the price of food would increase 7.5 times (again, based on recent trends). Biologist W. Jackson Davis has traced the implications of this scenario as follows:

It is instructive to explore the consequences of a 7.5-fold food price increase for the average American family. In 1973, the intermediate budget for a family of four people included $2,532 for the food bill, 23% of its median income of $10,971. If food costs 7.5 times as much in the year 2000, the same family will incur a food bill of $18,990. Between 1951 and 1971, median U.S. incomes increased linearly. Linear extrapolation of the curve to the year 2000 yields a projected median income of $19,000, against a projected food bill of $18,990. In other words, after buying the groceries the U.S. family of four would have exactly $10.00 with which to purchase the remaining necessities of life, including housing, clothing, medicine, transportation, education and recreation.[12]

While it is obvious that such a scenario could not occur because its approach would precipitate fundamental changes in how food is produced, distributed, and consumed, the extrapolation of current trends certainly makes an effective argument for the necessity of radical change. Actually, since real income is likely to fall in a period of declining net energy, the situation could become much worse much sooner. Moreover, the multiple problems of industrial agriculture—massive erosion of topsoil, depletion of groundwater, destruction of soil structure through compaction (from large scale machinery), and salinization through excessive amounts of irrigation, and so on—suggest that there will be many other factors besides economics that will come into play to force the transition to a more rational and sustainable agriculture. While the production of grain alcohol could mitigate some of the effects of the escalating costs of operating farm equipment (thereby tempering the inflation of food costs), the entire food production / distribution system is so completely dependent upon concentrated energy inputs, from natural gas for nitrogen fertilizers to fossil fuels for the processing, packaging, and transportation of produce, that the mere substitution of on-farm liquid fuels will not substantially alter the total picture. In fact, since organically derived liquid fuels must also be used to supply the expected shortfall of conventional liquid fossil fuels in the transportation sector, the costs of these substitutes will also tend to increase substantially due to the economics of supply and demand. In short, our present system of energy-intensive agribusiness is inherently unsustainable.

Major changes are required in what is produced (eating less energy-intense foods, lower on the food chain), how it is produced (organic agriculture on more ecologically balanced, diversified and labor-intense farms), where it is produced (food must be grown nearer to where it is consumed), and how it is prepared, packaged, and distributed (bulk packaging and local distribution). All of these changes point toward the development of a new pattern of truck farms and urban agriculture along the lines described by William and Helga Olkowski and Gary Garber in this section (Figure 1).

Like the economic and industrial possibilities described by David

Figure 1
A contemporary exam-
ple of the use of urban
agriculture to achieve a
degree of economic in-
dependence, energy
self-sufficiency and a
chemically free source
of food so necessary in
augmenting the existing
patterns of agricultural
dependency in the
United States.

Morris, all these changes are made possible by recently developed information, techniques, and technologies. For example, using the French Intensive / Bio-dynamic method of horticulture invented by Alan Chadwick
and developed further by John Jeavons at Ecology Action in Palo Alto,
California, it has been estimated that an entire balanced diet can be grown
on as little as 2,500 square feet per person in a six-month growing season.
(In the U.S., commercial agricultural techniques require at least 10,000
square feet to produce similar diets.) Not only are yields per unit area from
two to five times higher than national averages for all crops (including
vegetables as well as soybeans and wheat) but the method requires only $1/4$
to $1/31$ the water, $1/4$ to $1/16$ the purchased nitrogen fertilizer (often this
can be entirely met by locally composted organic wastes), and $1/100$-or-
less human and mechanical energy per pound of vegetable produced, once
the soil content and structure has been brought up to standards.[13]

Jeavons estimates that a backyard gardener could grow a year's supply
of vegetables and fruits (322 pounds) on as little as 100 square feet in a six-
month growing season, making the gardener's time worth over $4 per
hour at current prices for food. (This assumes 10 minutes a day). The economics of this operationally simple but biologically sophisticated method
of intensive cultivation suggest the possibility of creating a new class of
"mini-farmers" who, it is estimated, could earn up to $20,000 per year
working 40 hours per week on $1/10$ of an acre.[14] It is important to note that
these projections are derived from actual experimental test results from a
$3\frac{3}{4}$ acre plot of (initially) thick clay soil. These possibilities, then, are real.

William and Helga Olkowski, who have pioneered many similar
methods of intensive food production argue that urban agriculture is a

necessary part of the transition to a solar society. They project a pattern of more clearly defined cities surrounded by green belts of intermediate scaled, intensive and ecologically balanced farms, complemented by the intensive in-town cultivation of food in backyards, empty lots, parks, and on rooftops, porches, and solar greenhouses. This "greening" of the city would reduce transportation costs for food delivery, increase freshness and nutritional quality and variety, allow the recycling of urban organic wastes through composting, and in general, reduce the energy and resource requirements across the entire food system. In addition, such an urban agriculture would create new opportunities for employment close to areas where people live, thereby strengthening the economic structure and declining tax base characteristic of many existing cities.

Their argument is made even more persuasive by the several case studies they describe, ranging from the system of food production at the Integral Urban House they helped to create in Berkeley, California (where bees, fish, poultry, rabbits, herbs, fruits and vegetables are grown in a typical urban yard) to experiments in rooftop gardening in the warehouse district of San Francisco (which involved the composting of organic wastes from area restaurants and the construction of planter boxes from scrap lumber). These projects can be seen as the first steps toward the eventual creation of an entire food production / distribution system which would include local markets, small scale seed, nursery, and germ plasm centers as well as community scale composting operations (e.g. the one already run by the Berkeley municipal government) and community solar greenhouses.

Along these lines, Gary Garber describes the Cheyenne Community Solar Greenhouse, a 5,000 sq. ft. structure built by volunteer labor and operated by low income senior citizens as a year round source of low cost, nutritious herbs and vegetables (Figure 2). As energy and resource costs continue to escalate, solar greenhouses (first for those on fixed incomes, perhaps, but later for the entire community), are likely to become a feature of every neighborhood, home and community.

The production of food is certainly an important part of this approach. However the sense of community which is generated by working side by side with friends and neighbors is, in many respects, of equal or greater importance. The community solar greenhouse is an idea and technology which is relevant to many other institutions and contexts. Inspired in part by the Cheyenne example, the University for Man (UFM), a highly successful free university community education program in Manhattan, Kansas, has recently completed construction of a facility comprised of a community solar greenhouse (for use by elderly and handicapped citizens), a community shop and tool lending library, and a resource library and community design center (Figures 3 through 8). In conjunction with students and faculty from the College of Architecture and Design and the Department of Horticulture and other departments at Kansas State University,

Figure 2
Working in the Cheyenne Community Solar Greenhouse, as described by Gary Garber in this section. As well as providing self-sufficiency, community gardening efforts produce the physical enjoyment and peace of mind lacking in a trip to the supermarket.

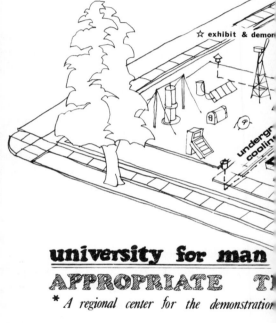

☆ exhibit & demon

undergr
coolin

university for man

APPROPRIATE   TI

* *A regional center for the demonstration*

the UFM Appropriate Technology Program is using this facility as a base for demonstration, research, education and outreach design services to the more than 40 similar community education programs in small towns throughout Kansas.[15]

It is possible to imagine many other combinations, such as a neighborhood based food cooperative, community greenhouse, laundry and day care center, or an extended care facility or senior center combined with an

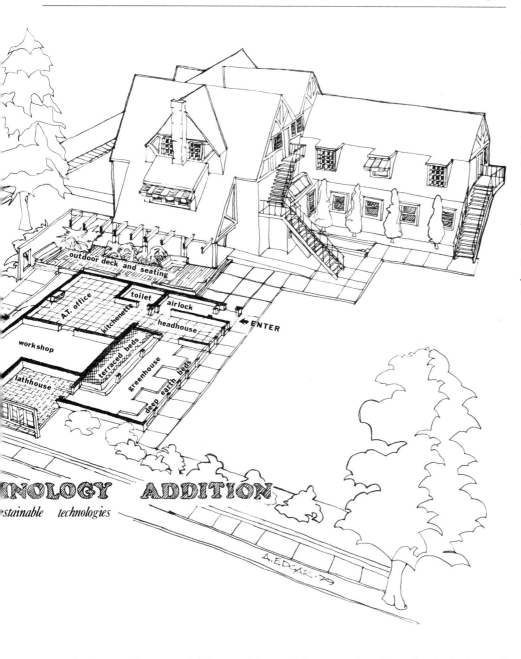

Figure 3
A drawing of the interior space plan for the Appropriate Technology *addition to the* University for Man *building in Manhattan, Kansas, designed in conjunction with the students and faculty at Kansas State University. This facility is used by the UFM as a planning and teaching center servicing more than 40 similar community education programs in the state of Kansas.*

attached greenhouse which would provide space heating, fresh fruits and vegetables, and valuable and pleasant horticultural therapy. As shown by these examples and the Cheyenne Community Greenhouse, the transition to local food systems provides many opportunities for enriching the quality of life as well as the quality of the food we eat.

The final two papers in this section on Urban Decentralization address the question of how to rebuild existing small towns and regional cities into

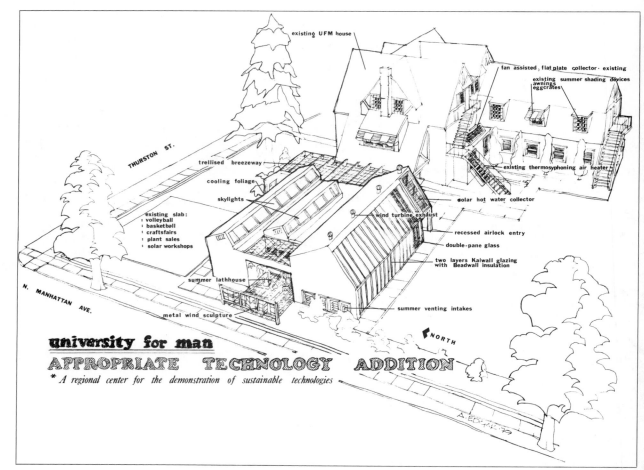

existing UFM house

fan assisted, flat plate collector · existing

existing summer shading devices
existing awnings
eggcrates

THURSTON ST.

trellised breezeway

cooling foliage

skylights

existing thermosyphoning air heater

solar hot water collector

wind turbine exhaust

recessed airlock entry

double-pane glass

two layers Kalwall glazing
with Beadwall insulation

existing slab:
: volleyball
: basketball
: craftsfairs
: plant sales
: solar workshops

summer lathhouse

N. MANHATTAN AVE.

metal wind sculpture

summer venting intakes

NORTH

university for man
APPROPRIATE TECHNOLOGY ADDITION
* A regional center for the demonstration of sustainable technologies

Figure 4
The exterior drawing for the finished Appropriate Technology *addition showing mechanical and technological elements in the design of the addition and solar retro-fitting of the existing UFM center.*

locally controlled, energy self-reliant communities. Marshall Hunt and David Bainbridge describe the steps the city of Davis, California has taken to monitor, understand and then limit the amount of community energy consumption. The key tool in their effort has been an energy conservation building code and zoning ordinances aimed at achieving a minimum reduction in energy use in new residential construction of 50 percent. The remarkable thing is that these changes in codes and ordinances have involved only minor increases in the cost of housing. For example, added cost for the first 46 homes built to code specification was only $35.10. The reason is most of the changes involve making the right decisions about orientation, shape, color, and the location and size of glazing rather than the addition of exotic technologies. Even the process of code enforcement, which many people feared would be an administrative nightmare, was made remarkably simple and routine.

Like the building codes, the zoning ordinance changes have achieved significant results with almost no additional costs. In fact, in some cases, such as the requirement to reduce street widths in order to reduce summer

Figure 5
*Through heavy resist-
ance insulation, exten-
sive south glazing and
movable insulation
(hinged skylight shut-
ters, thermal shades
and the beadwall sys-
tem shown being used
for shading), the UFM
addition is expected to
meet 80% of its annual
space heating needs
from the sun. An ac-
tive solar hot water
system provides 100%
of the building's needs
while sun-shades,
earth/air tubes and cross
ventilation provide
comfort in the summer.*
(Photo: Alan Edgar)

Figure 6
*Volunteers from the
Retired Senior Volun-
teer Program grow food
year-round in the
UFM community solar
greenhouse, demonstrat-
ing that urban agricul-
ture and solar energy
can improve the quality
of life as well as save
energy.*
(Photo: Gary Coates)

overheating of the urban microclimate, costs for the city and developers
have been reduced. Other city–wide energy savings have been achieved by
the expansion and enhancement of the already exemplary Davis bikeway
system, the encouragement of mixed use development (i.e., home businesses), the installation of clotheslines (now required in rental housing),
and the planting of deciduous trees on streets and parking lots.

Perhaps the most heartening effect of these modest changes at the community level has been the increased energy consciousness and action they
have stimulated at every scale of environment, from the retrofit of existing
housing to new construction. Village Homes, a 70-acre subdivision which
was started about the same time as the code studies, is now the nation's
most successful passive solar development. Not only is this project pioneering new methods of dwelling design, but it has also become a social
innovator as well. The community has extensive bike and pedestrian
paths, commonly owned and managed greenbelt areas, and a 13-acre community farm of orchards, vineyards, and vegetable fields. Village Homes
is demonstrating that energy conservation and passive solar energy use can

Figure 7
The solar heated Community Workshop and Tool-Lending Library provides an important resource for increasing local self-reliance.
(Photo: Doug Walter)

Figure 8
An edible landscape, including fruit and nut trees, solar cold-frames and food driers, a fish pond, herb garden, berry patch, French Intensive Biodynamic vegetable garden, and native edible wild plants landscape will complete the UFM community solar addition.
(Photo: Alan Edgar)

help to convert the anomie of modern society into a vital sense of community.[16]

Since 1973, household energy use in Davis has declined by 18 percent, whereas it has increased in surrounding communities and elsewhere in the nation. Moreover, the sense of community energy consciousness which has been created makes it possible for more substantial changes to occur in the future, such as the development of integrated community energy systems from renewable energy sources. Perhaps the most important lesson of the Davis experience is the demonstration that local communities can achieve significant levels of energy conservation through their own action.

Needed next is a demonstration of how an entire town could achieve energy self-reliance through changes it initiates itself. While no existing community in America has put together all the changes discussed in the preceding papers, Dennis Holloway and his students at the University of Minnesota have mapped out such a scenario for the transformation of Winona, Minnesota, a river town of approximately 30,000 residents. This remarkable article, profusely illustrated with visual images of the process of change and its results, shows how the retrofitting of individual dwellings and neighborhoods could lead to the creation of "ecological, energy-conserving, self-managing communities." Based on the success of the many case studies described in this section on Urban Decentralization, it should only be a matter of time before the vision presented in this last paper becomes a reality in many towns and cities throughout America.

Taken as a whole, the articles in this section make it clear that the process of destructuring and rebuilding urban America has already begun. The direction of change is toward local self-reliance in all areas of life—from energy and shelter to food, education, health care, police, and governance. Over the next 25 to 50 years such efforts will become more widespread, comprehensive, and carefully integrated, as the escalating costs of energy and mineral resources force us to reconsider the organization of everyday life and our presently unsustainable pattern of settlements. All the changes implied, from programs of energy conservation and solar retrofitting in existing areas to the development of new "solar villages" within metropolitan areas, will have the effect of increasing local employment, strengthening and diversifying local economies, and creating a renewed sense of community based on the daily experience of interdependence.

Over the longer run (the next 50 years and beyond) these changes must be complemented by and coordinated with a bioregionally based (see next section) shift in the location of population and the allocation of employment. We must repopulate our rural areas as we restructure our urban habitat, if we are to achieve the overall goal of meeting basic human needs from renewable resources. This implies the development of policies for the conversion of nonviable megalopolitan areas to productive uses (e.g., urban agriculture), the construction of rural new towns (such as those described earlier in this book) and the reconstruction of more viable communities in existing regional cities and small towns.

The overall effect of these changes will be the transformation of industrial civilization into a low-energy, yet technologically sophisticated meta-industrial society within a world order of relatively self-reliant bioregional economies. If the first steps in this direction are any indication, we are likely to find that the world we shall create is more satisfying than the one we must leave behind!

References

1. Theodore Roszak, *Person/Planet: The Creative Disintegration of Industrial Society,* (Garden City, N.Y. Anchor Press / Doubleday & Co., 1978), p. 241.

2. Ibid, p. 248. Population percentages are taken from a study by James Sundquist, *Dispersing Population: What America Can Learn From Europe,* (Washington, D.C.: Brookings Institute, 1975).

3. See Barbara Ward, *The Home of Man,* (New York: W. W. Norton and Co., 1976), p. 4.

4. Murray Bookchin, *The Limits of the City,* (New York: Harper & Row, 1974), p. 76.

5. W. Jackson Davis, *The Seventh Year: Industrial Civilization in Transition,* (New York: W. W. Norton and Co., 1979), p. 239. I am also indebted to Davis's discussion of the plight of the city.

6. Ibid., p. 244. This conclusion concerning the economic vulnerability of major U.S. cities is drawn from a study by T. N. Clark, T. S. Rubin, L. C. Pettler, and E. Zimmerman, "How many New Yorks? The New York fiscal crisis in comparative perspective," Research Report No. 72 of the Comparative Study of Community Decision Making, which is available from T. N. Clark at the Department of Sociology, University of Chicago, IL 60637.

7. Davis, *The Seventh Year,* p. 245.

8. Howard T. Odum, "Energy, Ecology, and Economics," in Lane de Moll and Gigi Coe, (eds.), *Stepping Stones: Appropriate Technology and Beyond,* (New York: Schocken Books, 1978), p. 20.

9. Ibid., p. 21.

10. John Todd and Nancy Jack Todd, *Tomorrow Is Our Permanent Address,* (New York: Harper & Row, 1980), p. 56.

11. Amory Lovins, *Soft Energy Paths: Toward a Durable Peace,* (New York: Harper & Row, 1979), p. 55.

12. Davis, *The Seventh Year,* p. 201.

13. John Jeavons, "Mini-Farming," Available from Ecology Action, 2225 El Camino Real, Palo Alto, CA 94306. A book describing the basic techniques of Biodynamic / French Intensive Horticulture, *How To Grow More Vegetables,* is also available from the same address.

14. Ibid.

15. For a more detailed discussion of the University for Man (UFM) and the idea of community education, as well as a description of the participatory process by which the UFM Solar Addition was designed, see, Gary J. Coates, W. Mike Martin, and Alan Edgar, "Community Education and Participatory Design: A Case Study of the Use of Scenario Modeling in the Design of a Solar Greenhouse," in John Hayes and Rachel Snyder, (eds.), *Proceedings of the Fifth National Passive Solar Design Conference,* (Newark, DE:

Publication Office of the American Section of the International Solar Energy Society, Inc., 1980), pp. 81–85. More detailed information on the design features of this passive solar building and related demonstration / education projects can be obtained by writing Gary J. Coates, Director, UFM Appropriate Technology Program, 1221 Thurston Avenue, Manhattan, KS. 66502.

16. See David Bainbridge, Judy Corbett, and John Hofacre, *Village Homes' Solar House Designs,* (Emmaus, PA.: Rodale Press, 1979).

7 | Self-Reliant Cities: *The Rise of the New City-States**

David Morris

A new way of thinking

For business purposes the boundaries that separate one nation from another are no more real than the equator. They are merely convenient demarcations of ethnic, linguistic, and cultural entities . . . The world outside the home country is no longer viewed as [a] series of disconnected customers and prospects for its products, but as an extension of a single market.

President of the IBM World Trade Corporation

THE SIGNS ARE THERE, harbingers of a new way of thinking. From the hills of Seattle to the arid flatlands of Davis, from the industrial city of Hartford to the university town of Madison, cities are beginning to redefine their role in our society. Long viewed as little more than real estate developers and social welfare dispensers, municipal governments are asserting a more important function, that of overall planning and development. Buffeted by natural resource crises beyond their control, cities are looking to ways that they can encourage local self-reliance in energy, food, and materials. Finding themselves vulnerable to plant closings, cities have begun to evaluate whether they could generate development internally, relying on hundreds of small businesses, rather than one or two large corporations.

In this planning process, local self-reliance is the goal. The city is treated as a nation. City officials are trying to keep resources within the local economy by reducing imports and expanding exports. New data collection techniques and increasingly sophisticated input / output methodologies combined with low-cost computers allow cities to map their resources. Cities are beginning to track the movement of capital through their borders, to analyze the composition of their solid waste stream, to evaluate the cost of new development, the amount of energy their buildings use, and the skill levels of their unemployed.

By expanding their authority over local development, cities blur the traditional distinction between public and private sectors. In viewing themselves as nations, they undermine continental free trade, one of the principal tenets of our federal constitution. Finding that free trade may not, in fact, provide the greatest benefit to their citizens, cities have begun to map strategies for optimum use of their resources.

The energy crisis is the catalyst for many of these developments. The 1,500 percent increase in the price of crude oil between 1973 and 1980 undermined traditional economic development practices.

---

* "Self-Reliant Cities: The Rise of the New City-States" by David Morris is copyrighted by the Institute for Local Self-Reliance and appears with the author's permission.

There is irony in the sudden change. Our public schools still extol the benefits of a shrinking globe. Textbooks acclaim the increasing speed of transportation, from the clipper ships to the steamers, to the airplanes, to the jet planes, that permit us to reap the benefits of expanded trade and interdependence. We still learn that a global division of labor makes it efficient for us to build a house with glue imported from one continent, fixtures from another, wood from another, and nails from still another, rather than produce these materials locally.

Yet even as this lesson is taught, rapid changes in energy prices undermine its validity. It is increasingly uneconomical to raise a tomato in California, transport it by refrigerated truck to New York, place it an open freezer in a supermarket to wait for the consumer to drive a two ton, steel bodied, internal combustion engine car half a mile to buy it. Small scale steel mills (the industry calls them mini mills, or neighborhood mills) can now compete with mills ten times as large because they use locally available scrap metal, avoiding high transportation costs. Small brick factories that closed down in the 1950s and 1960s when declining energy prices encouraged capital-intensive, highly centralized production units are reviving. Energy prices now comprise the single most important variable in total production costs. One British study found that a ten mile increase in the delivery radius of the brick industry would require an additional consumption of ten million gallons of diesel fuel.[1]

As energy prices increase, so does the value of used materials. It requires eight times the amount of energy to make an aluminum can out of bauxite, as to recycle an aluminum can. Similar energy savings can be found in recycling paper or glass.

The energy crisis may be considered part of a larger materials crisis. Petroleum, coal, natural gas, and uranium are scarce, but so are many of our widely used construction and fabrication materials. As the shortages become more widespread, the marketplace finds recycled materials more attractive.

Until the mid 1970s cities considered their garbage a giant headache. One survey of city officials found that solid waste was their number one problem. Land for dumps was running out, and more rigorous application of air pollution ordinances were closing down incinerators. Out of desperation cities began to seek alternatives. Some, like Ames, Iowa, and Hempstead, New York, began to burn their wastes, using the energy for their municipal buildings. Others, such as Seattle, Washington, and Modesto, California, in more systematic fashion, separated the waste stream into its component raw materials, and processed these into intermediate, and final products. In Fresno, California, the county collects newspapers, and sells them to a community development corporation which shreds the papers, adds fire retardant chemicals, and produces high quality insulation materials. These are used in energy conservation programs. Thus, what was once a problem is turned into a resource. Instead of paying people to dispose of newspapers, the city converts them into a valuable product. Jobs are generated locally, as is local revenue. The end product, insulation, can be used in conservation programs which also reduces the amount of money exported to pay for imported energy.

A city the size of San Francisco generates about 1,500 tons of solid waste per day. Broken down into component materials, assuming 100 percent collection, San Francisco produces as much

The conception of the city as a cooperative for the improvement and development of the capabilities and lives of its inhabitants is at odds with the doctrine of laissez faire and a national capitalism that has turned local citizens into consumers and so many free floating factors of production to be assembled and disassembled by the forces of the national market. The older conception of the walled city as a shared common enterprise has been weakened by the breaching of its walls and its transformation into an open economy.

Norton E. Long,
The Unwalled City

aluminum as a medium-sized bauxite mine, as much copper as a small-sized copper mine, as much paper as a good-sized timber stand. The city itself is a mine. Its waste stream becomes the basis for new industries.

Manufacturing of recycled materials has another feature that makes it attractive for local production. Manufacturing firms usually locate near their raw material supplies. Steel mills locate near iron ore deposits. Paper companies locate near forests. If our cities become mines for recycled material, we can expect that industries will locate near the source of supply. Moreover, factories that rely on recycled materials require less capital, and can be smaller than comparable factories using virgin ore. An aluminum plant using recycled aluminum requires about 10 percent the capital as one using virgin bauxite. Steel mills using scrap metal can be built with much less capital than conventional mills. The same holds true for paper mills using recycled material. Plants are cheaper, they use less energy (and less water, and are less polluting) and can serve nearby markets.

Rising energy prices also encourage decentralized energy generation. From 1900 to 1975 there has been an extraordinary centralization of energy generation. Power plants have grown larger, while corporate ownership patterns have become more concentrated. Giant nuclear reactors serve markets hundreds of miles away. New England obtains its heating oil from Saudi Arabia. Maryland gets its natural gas from Algeria.

In the age of political uncertainty, these long distribution lines have made our communities vulnerable. Social upheaval in Iran brings gas lines to Toledo. The city of Davis has coal particulate matter blown in the faces of its citizens because surrounding counties want more electricity. Grand Forks,

North Dakota must wait to see whether Canada will cut off its natural gas supply.

Cities have begun to react to this dependent condition by moving toward energy self-reliance. San Diego County now mandates solar hot water heating in new homes. The city of Springfield, Vermont is constructing a small hydroelectric facility. By 1981, Springfield will be exporting electricity to the same central utility from which it had been purchasing electricity for almost 30 years. Clayton, New Mexico now gets 15 percent of its electricity from a windmill.

Yet local self-reliance means little unless there is also local ownership of resources. Absentee ownership of businesses and land presents a basic conflict between the city's desire to maximize social benefit and the absentee investor's desire to maximize his return on investment. This is especially true in housing, where whole neighborhoods are evicted because federal tax laws, and private greed, combine to make speculation a profitable investment.

For many urban officials, unfortunately, the objective of the municipal corporation is similar to that of private, profit-making corporations. The bottom line is what counts. Thus cities try to reduce their low-income population because the poor contribute less to the property tax base, and have larger families or more demand for social services which burden the city's budget. These cities want to increase the portion of middle and upper income families consisting of one or two professionals, and no children. Urban renewal, upzoning, and commercialization of residential neighborhoods are their basic planning techniques. The tax base is the bottom line, not human resource development or community stability.

Other cities have begun to view their residents as citizens and stockholders.

The city becomes, as the Greeks first envisioned it, a means to realize the good life. Since a majority of many city residents are renters, such an attitude would lead the municipal corporation to protect the stability of neighborhoods faced with rent increases or condominium conversions.

In Madison, Wisconsin, landlords seeking to significantly raise rents must file a statement to describe the impact such an increase will have on tenants. In the same city tenants can be certified as collective bargaining agents by the city Rental Accomodations Board. In Davis, California, no one can buy a single family dwelling unless he or she is willing to live in it as the principal place of residence for at least a year. In the District of Columbia a graduated capital gains tax penalizes the speculator who buys and sells property quickly.

Cities whose bureaucracies have traditionally been fragmented under the prevailing belief that discrete, separate functions characterized the city, now realize that there is a synergy to municipal development. The new awareness is that the city is an integral system; any planning must take into account many factors which previously had been considered outside the province of the municipal corporation. Cities which once actively encouraged private development, now find themselves investing and operating quasi-public entities to comprehensively develop sections of the local economy. In doing so, these cities find themselves redefining the role of the private sector and the marketplace.

A brief history of the city as state: Medieval burgs

It is ironic that contemporary cities should become the leaders in a movement to redefine the nature of modern economics. For the revival of cities in the middle ages was part of the economic transition from feudalism to capitalism, and the marketplace was both their foundation and their reason for being. Cities fought with kings and bishops and landed gentry to gain acceptance of the basic requirement of any commercial enterprise: the sanctity of the contract.

The proliferation of free cities, given the primitive nature of communications, was astonishing.

> With a unanimity which seems almost incomprehensible . . . the urban agglomerations, down to the smallest burgs, began to shake off the yoke of their worldly and clerical lords. The fortified village rose against the lord's castle, defied it first, attacked it next, and finally destroyed it. The movement spread from spot to spot, involving every town on the surface of Europe, and in less than a hundred years free cities came into existence on the coast of the Mediterranean, the North Sea, the Baltic, the Atlantic Ocean, down to the fjords of Scandinavia, at the feet of the Appenines, the Alps, the Black Forest, the Grampians and the Carpathians; in the plains of Russia, Hungary, France and Spain.[2]

The struggle for autonomy was a long one. Cambrai made its first revolution in 907, and three or four more before it finally obtained a charter in 1076. The charter was repealed twice, and twice won again. The total struggle for independence took 223 years.[3]

But there was a fraternity of liberation. Cities shared their newfound wisdom. Constitutional advances developed by one town would quickly be passed on to hundreds of others. The charter of Beaumont became the model for over 500 towns and cities in Belgium and France. Cities held labor conventions. They made alliances, and trade agreements.

The city and the corporation were at

first synonymous. Only later, when the merchants became a class apart from the craftspeople, and the city fathers became the wealthy, did the division between public and private corporation occur. Cities had economic might as well as political authority. They often bought in bulk for their inhabitants, and set prices and wages. As one writer comments, "The city was a positive instrument of the public welfare, for it could not only proscribe, but also promote."[4]

Although by the 17th Century the free cities of Europe had fallen into ruin, torn by internal dissensions and external rebellions, a good deal of this tradition of extended municipal authority carried over to the New World. The Albany charter of 1686 illustrates the wide range of accepted municipal powers. In addition to the usual public safety functions, it had a monopoly on trade with the Indian tribes. It owned all vacant land within its boundaries and the council alone had the power to allow an individual to practice a trade or craft.

The city as tenant: Nineteenth Century America

After the revolution, American cities were subordinated to the states. To presidents like Thomas Jefferson, who viewed an agrarian society as the basis for social harmony, cities were a source of problems, not benefits. Ralph Waldo Emerson summed up the 19th Century attitude toward cities, "Whenever I enter a city I lose faith." As long as there was little concentration of population, there was little interest in and little need for municipal authority. The 1840 census showed only twelve cities with 25,000 residents or more, and only three which contained populations greater than that of Florence in the 14th Century (90,000), one of the great city states of that period.[5]

But rapid urbanization lay just ahead.

> Between 1830 and 1840 railroad mileage increased from 28 to 2,818. The first telegraph message was sent in 1844. In 1852 Otis invented the passenger elevator and the first Bessemer converter was put into operation a year before the end of the Civil War. Centralized business services became possible in 1867 when the first practical typewriter was developed. The telephone was invented in 1876 . . . The 1880's were boom times in building, as skyscraper frame construction was introduced.[6]

By 1880 there were 77 cities with populations greater than 25,000 and 20 cities over 100,000. Philosophically, institutionally, and physically, the nation was largely unprepared for what Adna Weber termed "the most significant social phenomenon of the century — urbanization."[7] Social reformers had one all-encompassing term for the problems of the cities of the 1890s: congestion. In New York's Tenth Ward (Lower East Side) the density reached 900 persons per acre, over 500,000 people per square mile, possibly the highest residential density achieved anywhere in the world in recent times (the current density of Manhattan is 120 people per acre). The rapid growth in population, and extensive immigration and internal migration, as well as rapid industrialization, coupled with "the great and novel experiment of the day, namely, universal manhood suffrage" alarmed and threatened local elites.

Cities had no existing authority to deal with the social turmoil resulting from those rapid changes. State legislatures repeatedly intervened in local affairs. The Tennessee legislature withdrew the Memphis city charter in 1879.

The Pennsylvania legislature authorized the Governor to replace elected local officials with state appointees in 1901. New York, Maryland, Illinois, Michigan, and Missouri abolished the local police departments of their largest cities and established state boards in their place. Legislatures created new city positions, ordered salary raises, and mandated pension hikes; they passed bills relating to the smallest minutiae of city life, such as the naming of streets and closing alleys. Massachusetts enacted 400 special laws dealing solely with the city of Boston between 1885 and 1907. New York's legislature passed 390 acts for New York City between 1880 and 1890.

The courts upheld any and all intervention by the state. In the eyes of the courts, cities were "mere creatures of their state legislatures." In 1868 Judge John Foster Dillon, in a case involving the city of Clinton's challenge to a state statute granting the railroad the right to seize, without compensation, as much of the city's streets as the railroad deemed necessary, set down the legal doctrine of the time:

> Municipal corporations owe their origins to, and derive their rights wholly from the legislature. It breathes into them the breath of life, without which they cannot exist. As it creates, so it may destroy. If it may destroy, it may abridge and control . . . They are, so to phrase it, mere tenants at the will of the legislature.[8]

In 1907 Supreme Court Justice William H. Moody agreed, "The power is in the State, and those who legislate for the State are alone responsible for any unjust or oppressive exercise of it."[9]

The distinction between the municipal corporation and the private corporation was illustrative of the different standards by which public and private sectors were evaluated. By the 1880s, the private corporation had been cloaked in the constitutional privileges of any person, unfettered, with few controls. One contemporary legal observer has noted that the new-style corporate status judged that the only social relevance of corporate status was as a means of promoting business. The counterpart to this conclusion was that business activity regulation was not a proper function of corporate law. In other words, corporation law exists to help businessmen to act rather than to police their actions.

Yet this same period gave birth to a strong movement for municipal autonomy. In 1875, the delegates to the Missouri Convention for the first time gave local governments the constitutional right to frame and adopt a charter with a governmental structure tailored to meet their own needs, and with at least some powers to act without specific legislative authorization. By 1925, 14 states had home rule provisions either in statutes or the constitution. Cities were rarely given as much authority as they desired, but on the whole these constitutional changes gave somewhat more autonomy to local officials.

From the city beautiful to the city as entrepreneur

The internal problems of the cities were at least as much a barrier to local self-reliance as were outside interventions. There was very little data available on the city's housing stock, and demographics. City accounting systems were disorganized, and it was the rare municipality that could compare its own performance to that of other cities because their record keeping and budgeting systems were usually incompatible. The first city planning commission was established in Hartford, Connecticut, in 1907. Massachusetts, in 1913, required all cities with populations over 10,000 to create official planning boards. By 1922, 185 cities had done so. New York City was the first to adopt a comprehensive zoning ordinance, which involved the city directly in land use planning. By 1926, when the U.S. Supreme Court upheld their constitutionality, there were 564 cities with such ordinances, and on the eve of the depression there were 800.[10]

Yet planning was not a full-time function. By 1926 only 46 cities had planning budgets greater than $5,000.[11] City planning was restricted to planning for aesthetics. To a society which saw little role for the public sector, comprehensive planning was viewed as an unwise intervention by government.

One English writer at the time aptly observed:

> In America it is the fear of restricting or injuring free and open competition that has made it so difficult for cities to exercise proper and efficient control over their development. The tendency therefore has been to promote those forms of civic improvement which can be carried out without interfering with vested interests. To impose severe sanitary restrictions, to limit the height and density of dwellings, or to prevent the destruction of amenities on privately owned land, may all help to reduce the profits of the speculator—hence, if he has any influence over the local governing bodies, he will secure that nothing but what is absolutely necessary and legal shall be done in these directions. But to purchase large public parks and to develop civic centers adds to the value of the privately owned land and buildings in the city . . . [12]

The Depression effected a revolution both in the role that government played in our society and in the relationship of cities to the federal government. Harrassed by the twin problems of rising relief expenditures and growing tax delinquencies, urban leaders were exposed earlier than the nation's governors to the need for massive action to reverse the deflationary trend. City halls around the country became the targets of protests by armies of the unemployed. City officials initially turned to state capitals for assistance, but rural dominated legislatures and budget minded governors opposed loosening the purse strings to assist "profligate" cities. Rebuffed at the state level, municipal politicians turned to Washington for help. A new organization, the United State Conference of Mayors, was established to lobby for federal aid to localities. In 1937 the Federal Housing Act made formal the new relationship between the federal government and the cities.

The influence of the New Deal went further than direct aid. The new philosophy of government as an active force in the economy encouraged city planners to redefine their own horizons. The Urbanism Committee, of Roosevelt's Natural Resource Committee, concluded:

> In fact, the entire scope and conception of local urban planning needs broadening. While the influence of the physical environment upon the economic and social structure of the community is everywhere in evidence, planning agencies and planners have been slow to recognize and give proper emphasis to the social and economic objectives and aspects of planning and zoning. Studies of the economic base of the community, its soundness, deficiencies and its prospects, and the need for a selective program of industrial development have been almost wholly overlooked. The pressing problems of housing have not received the attention from planning agencies it deserves.[13]

In 1940, the first housing census took place, providing city planners with their first real data base. In 1954 the Housing Act provided funds through its Section 701 planning provision.

The capacity of local governments increased dramatically in the years between 1950 and 1975. In that period the federal budget expanded by 700 percent; state and local government budgets increased by 1,500 percent. Between 1950 and 1978 the federal civilian payroll rose by 33 percent; state and local payrolls tripled.

However, with expanded budgets came increased dependence on state and federal agencies. The difference in fiscal autonomy between pre-World War I and Vietnam War era cities can best be illustrated by the following statistics: In 1913 nearly 80 percent of combined state-local revenues came from local sources. By 1970, 80 percent came from state sources. In the period from 1920 to 1955 nearly three quarters of local revenue came from local sources, principally the property tax. By 1971–72, state transfers accounted for more than 30 percent of total local revenue, and direct federal aid brought the total close to 45 percent. In 1967, federal aid to the largest cities amounted to nine cents for every dollar of locally generated revenue. By 1978, federal aid constituted 50 cents for every dollar that the big cities raised. In 1976 the nation's largest cities received more money from Washington than they did from their own state governments.[14]

Federal aid, until the 1960s, was primarily used to complement and expand local and state planning efforts. Since federal aid was part of a formal partnership, there were often matching requirements.

The riots of the early and mid 1960s, however, illuminated the impact of the migration of the white middle class populations especially from the older mid-Western and Eastern cities. The federal government provided money, not as a complement to local planning efforts, but as a means to attain national social objectives, in many cases over the objections of local governments. Thus funds were, for the first time, given directly to community organizations, and to low income groups, thereby bypassing the city. Civil rights, and later, environmental criteria, were imposed on localities desiring part of the federal largesse. In return for compliance, the federal government began to give 100 percent grants, with no matching requirement.

Categorical and project-related grant programs proliferated, developing a crazy quilt arrangement. By the early 1970s there were more than 400 grant programs. Each city competed for a piece of the pie. There could be little long range planning because no city knew beforehand whether it would be awarded the contract, or if its grant would be renewed.

Under Richard Nixon dozens of categorical grant programs were combined into block grants. The Comprehensive Employment and Training Act, the Community Development Block Grant program, and the General Revenue Sharing program were established. Block grants represented almost 50 percent of total direct money from the federal government to the cities. There were few strings attached to these allocations. They were distributed on the basis of formula, so that cities knew beforehand the amount they would receive. Although these programs were renewed every five years, and their regulations were often radically changed, they did provide a more secure planning base for local governments.

Development:
The cost of growth

During this era cities were addicted to growth. Yet they began to gather data on the costs of growth as well. Money from the Department of Commerce established economic development planning departments in more than 50 cities. Environmental legislation forced cities to estimate the impact of growth. Increasingly sophisticated computer models permitted cities to monitor the flow of resources through their borders.

What they found was profoundly disquieting. One suburb of San Francisco, Fairfield, found to its surprise and dismay that total tax revenues from a proposed new subdivision would pay only half of the required new police services and nothing for other services. A 1974 study of Madison, Wisconsin, estimated the cost of a new acre of development was $16,500 for installing sanitary sewers, storm drainage, water mains, and local streets. The figure did not include the acre's pro-rated share of the cost of new schools, fire stations, arterial streets, wells, landfills, etc.[15] Hartford, Connecticut discovered that three out of every five city jobs were held by suburban residents, and that 70 percent of the total wages paid by the city left the city. In Oakland, California, 72 percent of city contracts went to businesses located outside the city.

In 1980, Washington, D.C., excluding the federal government, found that it paid $500 million for energy. Only 15 cents on the energy dollar returned to benefit the local economy.

A study of an older ethnic neighborhood in Chicago revealed that its residents had deposited $33 million in a local savings and loan association, but had received back only $120,000 in loans. A Washington, D.C. neighborhood found that, of $750,000 in annual income to a local MacDonald's, approximately 65 percent was exported from the community.

A new term entered the urban vocabulary: leakage. Cities began to examine the flow of resources through their borders. They came to understand that the "balance of payments" and "balance of trade" mattered almost as much to local governments as to national governments.

As cities gained sophistication in the planning process they began to evaluate the traditional practice of courting big corporations to locate branch plants in their community. As one observer noted, this type of development often was accompanied by negative impact also.

> When new industries are attracted from outside, they bring the well-advertised benefits of new jobs, orders for local suppliers, and a fresh infusion of money into a community. But there can be severe drawbacks. A firm with highly specialized labor requirements may bring its most highly paid workers with it. The jobs left for local residents may be few, menial or both. But local taxpayers will have to pay for new schools, roads, and other services for the newcomers. Capital investments to attract new firms have virtually bankrupted some communities —and even then they face the possibility that a big multinational firm may later decide there's even cheaper labor in Mexico or Taiwan and desert the area as rapidly as it came.[16]

The mating dance between cities and giant corporations had become too one-sided. One business magazine described the situation as a "rising spiral of government subsidies as companies play off city against city and state against state for the most advantageous terms."[17] Atlanta advertises its wares on Cleveland television programs, and has opened an industry recruitment office in New York. In tiny Bossier City, Louisiana, the chamber of commerce encourages schoolchildren to write more than 900 letters to corporate executives telling them of the city's need for jobs, and its abundance of assets, such as clean air.[18]

Cities often used their right to seize land to put together a site large enough to lure a corporation and then, at its own expense, to install the physical infrastructure necessary to service the industry, and finally, borrow money in order to provide low interest loans to the business, while writing off local taxes for ten or twenty years as a further enticement. When a city tries to negotiate with a giant corporation, it is a nerve-wracking experience, for it is a seller's market. The Detroit suburb of Trenton, population 24,000, gambled by refusing to give Chrysler Corporation the $36 million in tax breaks it had demanded in return for expanding its 4,400-employee engine plant. The City Council offered only $24 million because it felt the city needed the money for the school system. Edward M. Heffinger, mayor pro-tem of Trenton, nervously commented, "Our overriding concern was—what if we had guessed wrong here." Officials from Indiana, New York, and Ohio were waiting in the wings, wooing Chrysler. Finally, Governor Milliken of Michigan stepped into the fray, persuading the federal government to put up a long term, low-interest loan. In this instance, as with most, the final resolution turned more on one's political contacts with the federal government, than with anything the local government could do.

Yet attracting outside investment, ironically, may well increase economic instability. Absentee-owned businesses tend not to be good neighbors. They cut back employment during down cycles and recessions more than lo-

cally-based companies. They are less likely to purchase local services and products, such as legal assistance, financial consulting, capital borrowing and factor inputs.

The balance sheet of conglomerates is chillingly objective. Subsidiaries can be closed, not because they are losing money, but because they are not making enough. Says Joseph Danzansky, Chairman of Giant Foods, "But let's face it. Many stores are closed not because they operate at a loss, but because they are marginal and the capital can be more advantageously invested elsewhere." When Uniroyal closed its inner tube plant in Indianapolis, the Wall Street Journal noted, "Uniroyal could have kept the plant operating profitably if it wanted to, but under pressure from the securities markets, management decided to concentrate its energy on higher growth chemical lines . . . Many companies have grown too big to look at the small market."

Global corporations vs. municipal government: The rise of economic development planning

Cities, caught in this vicious cycle, end up courting fewer and fewer companies. In 1971, there were 12.4 million business enterprises of all sizes and kinds in America, including 3.3 million farms. Of that 12.4 million, over half (6.4 million) had gross sales of less than $10,000. Another 3.4 million failed to reach $50,000 in sales, and still another 1 million had $100,000 in yearly sales. Thus, nearly 11 million of the nation's 12.4 million firms, or 87.2 percent, had sales of less than $100,000 in that year.[19]

On the other hand, less than 1 percent of the service firms had multistore operations. Of the 275,000 manufacturing companies in the United States about 10 percent had more than 99 employees.[20] Three companies sold 80 percent of the cold breakfast cereal in 1975. Three companies sold 80 percent of the home insulation in that year. Four sold 70 percent of the dairy products. One sold 90 percent of the canned soups.[21] Fewer than 30 giants owned over 20 percent of the cropland. Eight oil companies controlled 64 percent of proven oil reserves, 44 percent of uranium reserves, 40 percent of coal under private lease, and 40 percent of copper deposits.[22]

Yet it turns out that small businesses, not the giant corporations, are the backbone of local economies. A massive study of 5.6-million firms (representing 82 percent of the nation's private jobs) was conducted by David Birch. He tracked these firms over a 7-year period, from 1971 to 1978, and concluded that the country's biggest job producer was small firms. Two-thirds of all new jobs were created in companies employing fewer than 20 people. The top 1,000 firms on the *Fortune* list generated only 75,000 jobs, or just a little more than 1 percent of all new jobs created between 1970 and 1976.[23] Birch found that most jobs came from the start-up of new firms, and the expansion of existing small businesses, destroying the myth that economic development is created by plant relocations and expansion by big corporations.

These figures gave an ironic twist to the frenzied competition among cities for giant plant locations. Cities, built on a foundation of thousands of small businesses, often found themselves in the position of forcing out small firms in order to make room for a branch of a larger corporation.

By the end of the 1970s, cities were beginning to understand the nature of

their dilemma. Simultaneously, a new generation was coming to power in our city councils, mayor's offices and small business sectors. Maturing in the activist 60s, this generation considered it natural for the government to be a facilitator, and a catalyst for social and economic development. It accepted the right of the community to impose conditions on private capital in the name of equal rights, environmentalism and equity. Paul Soglin in Madison, Gus Newport in Berkeley, Bob Black in Davis, Nick Carbone in Hartford, Marion Barry in Washington, D.C. were some of the new era of municipal leaders who combined expertise with social commitment.

These and other cities have begun to directly involve themselves in economic developments. In 1974 the Housing and Community Development Act provided Community Development Block Grants, lump sum payments to cities which enabled them to coordinate community development and economic development planning. The 1977 Amendments to this Act expanded the economic development activities permitted under the CDBG program.

These increased funds and authority gave rise to dozens of local economic development corporations, with the power to acquire land, lease land, construct buildings, and provide short and long term financing to businesses. Dayton's City Wide Development Corporation was established in 1972. The Baltimore Economic Development Corporation was set up around the same time. Chicago's Economic Development Commission was formed in 1977.

Cities directly control vast human, physical and financial resources. The budget of Memphis is over half a billion dollars. Cincinnati's is nearly as large. The bonding capacity of cities is often much larger than their budgets, giving them the ability to develop long-term construction projects, and provide low interest loans for economic development purposes.

In 1978 Chicago floated a $100-million bond issue for low interest mortgages to Chicago residents. This placed the city in direct competition with local financial institutions. "How would you feel if you were offering loans at 9.75 percent and the place up the street started advertising 8 percent?" asked a trade association official when interviewed by a local reporter.

Detroit has 21,000 municipal employees. Memphis and Boston have 25,000. There are at least seven counties or cities in California that have over $100 million in public pension funds. The city of Washington, D.C. owns over 4,000 buildings, and hundreds of acres of land.

Cities have an important lever in encouraging local small business development: government purchasing. The dollar volume of state and local government purchasing has grown dramatically in the past decade, and it now exceeds that of the federal government. In 1963, the federal government spent approximately two-thirds of all money spent by all levels of government for goods and services. In 1973, state and local governments spent $75.7 billion on purchases of goods and services, some 50 percent more than the federal government.

This abundance of resources is now combined with expanded municipal authority. The judicial system has accepted the right of cities to interrupt interstate commerce. Several local governments favor local suppliers. Detroit and Livermore, California have purchasing provisions awarding contracts to local suppliers even if they bid up to

5 percent higher. The state legislature in Maine mandates that state institutions such as penal institutions, vocational and technical schools, and state hospitals purchase food locally, even if it is 5 percent higher in price. In Washington, D.C. the city government is required to purchase 25 percent of all its goods and services from local, minority-owned firms.

Newark and other New Jersey cities require public employees to live inside city limits. Bowie, Maryland, and Oberlin, Ohio, have enacted legislation which imposes an economic penalty on the sale of non-returnable bottles. An early court decision upheld the right of a city to impose a uniform weight ordinance for bread. It might be possible to impose an ordinance requiring uniform container sizes. If such were the case, it would become much easier to establish reusable-bottle-washing factories.

Programs moved from simple business promotion to targeted intervention in the local economy based on economic research and planning. The city has moved beyond traditional service functions to more entrepreneurial investments. Sometimes the city itself operates a business. Cities since the turn of the century have owned and operated energy, water, sewage and transportation utilities.

Cities have been involved in other business enterprises, but the courts have not always upheld the city's determination of what constituted a "public purpose." The Arizona and Oklahoma constitutions specifically grant municipal corporations the right to engage in business. Relatively new undertakings such as low-rent housing, airports, off-street parking facilities, have gained public acceptance as public purposes by the courts. Less generally, approval has been given to such commercial undertakings as hotels, restaurants, and liquor stores. Cities in Ohio have been permitted to own a railroad that operates outside municipal limits. Ten cities own their own cable television systems.

However, the new generation of city leaders tends to believe less in direct municipal ownership than they do in the city as an overall economic planner, the mechanism that establishes the rules for private investment and channels resources into those areas of the local economy that would most effectively benefit large segments of the local population. Thus, the economic development authority of Dayton provides funds to cooperatives. In Madison, the city development corporation provides funds to worker self-managed businesses. In Eugene the city uses money to establish a neighborhood-owned, community land trust.

The boundary line between public and private is a fuzzy one, and evolves as the society changes. One Minnesota high court noted, "the need for local power grows with the complexity of modern life and the population."[24] A Court of Appeals wrote, "as a commonwealth develops politically, economically, and socially, the police power likewise develops within reason to meet the changed and changing conditions."[25] Still another judge noted, "economic and industrial conditions are not stable. Times change. Many municipal activities, the propriety of which are not now questioned, were at one time thought, and rightly enough so, of a private character."[26]

The interplay of the private and public sector is nowhere more evident than in the land use restrictions which state and local governments have imposed on private development. Perhaps the most revealing set of restrictions is the Vermont Land Use and Development Law enacted in 1970. Nine district en-

vironmental councils oversee a population about that of a small-sized city. The Chittenden Environmental Council denied a permit to a regional shopping mall containing 80 stores, and 440,000 square feet of commercial space, in the town of Williston. The reason was that the store would reduce tax revenues of the city of Burlington, causing the state to compensate it for some of the lost tax revenues which would have supported the educational system. This development was denied because it would draw away commerce from neighboring towns, reducing the tax base for the local government.

The municipal corporation, in short, is an evolving creature. Once viewed as nothing more than a "mere creature of the state legislature," a "mere tenant," cities now possess immense economic and political authority. They are still subordinate to the state legislatures. But in an increasing number of states, the burden of proof that they can exercise power is no longer on the cities, but on the states to prove they can't. Forty-one states had home rule provisions by 1975, either as part of their constitutions, or by statute. Some, such as Maryland, Alaska, and New York, used language such as in the Tenth Amendment to the U.S. Constitution. Before home rule, cities could exercise no powers that were not explicitly given them by the state legislatures. Under many home rule provisions cities can exercise any powers which are not explicitly denied them.

Armed with the knowledge that small business is the catalytic force in the local economy, understanding their resource flows better than at any other time in history, imbued with the determination of a generation matured during difficult social times, our municipal corporations are now beginning to tackle their problems with increasing initiative and innovation. The energy crisis, which has confronted cities with the potential for rationing, shortages, serious economic dislocation, and reduced budgets, reinforces the need to operate more efficiently and productively. As we enter the 1980's, one central issue remains. How far can our cities go toward achieving self-reliance? Can we realistically conceive of the city as a nation, producing a significant amount of its goods and services?

The city as nation: Inventorying the resource base

What would be the resource base of our self-reliant city? Perhaps the easiest way to conceptualize the problem would be to imagine what the city would do if it were suddenly cut off from the rest of the world by wartime conditions, a national truckers strike, or gasoline shortage. What types of human, natural, financial, and physical resources might be available?

Most cities do not view their rooftops as a resource. Yet one study of Washington, D.C. discovered it has more than 330-million square feet of rooftop space, about 20 percent of the land area of the city. Moreover, many of these rooftops were either flat or tilted in the southern direction, making them ideal for solar technologies. At current conversion efficiencies, that study concluded that 75 percent of all non-transportation energy, electric as well as thermal, could be generated, after economical conservation, by covering rooftops with solar arrays.

What about vacant land? The prevailing attitude is that the modern city looks like Manhattan. However, no city matches the density of New York. In 1970, only 50 percent of America lived in areas with more than 10,000 people. Of these, half lived in cities

with over 100,000 inhabitants, and a third of these, in turn, lived in cities with more than 1 million people.

The average density of cities with more than 100,000 people is less than seven people per acre. As Daniel Eleazar wrote ten years ago, "many of these American style city dwellers—in every socioeconomic bracket—actually live on plots of land that would look large to a Chinese or Indian farmer."[27] One study done in the early 1970s found that among a sample of 86 cities with populations over 100,000 the average amount of vacant land available per capita was 2,279 square feet.[28] This ranged from a high of 6,279 square feet in the West South Central states, to 360 square feet in the Mid-Atlantic region. Of this sample, it was found that Beaumont had 68 percent of its land vacant, and about half of San Diego and Phoenix at that time consisted of vacant land. Another study involving 38 cities in Oregon found that those with populations between 10,000 and 50,000 had about 30 percent of their land area vacant.[29] This enormous land reserve could be available for agriculture. Current American per capita annual consumption of food requires about an acre of land. According to one study:[30]

a conservative estimate of the numbers of people that can be fed on a vegetarian diet with or without dairy products is about four per acre . . . This figure does not include lengthening the growing season with greenhouses. A diet including fish or meat two or three times a week would increase the amount of land needed by at least 25–50 percent.

According to John Jeavons and Michael Shepard, based on three years' growing experience, a full balanced diet may eventually be grown on as little as 2,500 square feet per person in a six-month growing season.[31]

W. Jackson Davis took the data which formed the basis for the study of 86 cities noted above, and estimated the amount of open space in the cities on which food could, in principle, be grown.[32] He then chose as his benchmark the highly efficient, non-industrial agriculture of the Chinese, in which about 18 persons per acre can gain subsistence diets. He found that the percentage of subsistence level diets that could be reached ranges from 16 percent in Detroit to almost 60 percent in New York City.

Obviously, when we examine food production, we must also take into account the availability of water and fertilizers. The city, fortunately, is a giant nutrient machine, spewing out organic and human wastes. These can be used as fertilizers, and, in fact, municipal composting operations and sewage composting operations are increasingly commonplace around the country. One study, of the Omaha–Council Bluffs, Nebraska area found that from sludge alone "more nutrients are available . . . than the average supplied by Nebraska farmers." It concludes, "By the year 2000, with increasing waste volume and rising fertilizer prices, benefits to the region's farmers in terms of supplying crop nutrients could exceed $1 million annually."[33]

It is quite possible that cities would want to use the land surrounding the city as a giant green belt, much as Davis, California and a number of other cities are planning. Given cooperation among metropolitan authorities, or annexation power by the municipality, the land area involved could be extended greatly, and one can explore still other possibilities for home grown raw material production.

In 1949, Egon Glesinger wrote his classic, *The Coming Age of Wood,* forcefully arguing for an industrial civiliza-

tion based on wood.[34] Noting that an acre of forest could yield annually several times as much fiber as cotton, and as much sugar as the same soil planted in sugar beets, he concluded,

> It can be readily demonstrated that the renewable biomass on our planet is quantitatively sufficient to supply the needs of the current world population. It can also be shown that we possess the needed chemical technology for the production from biomass of many of the commodities that we now produce from fossil fuels, such as fuel oil, gasoline, and synthetic polymers.

Timber yields have greatly increased since Glesinger wrote that paragraph. Presently, the new annual growth of U.S. forests is 38 cubic feet per acre per year. The average American uses about 75 cubic feet of wood products for all purposes. Thus, two acres would be required to supply the wood needs of an average American.[35,36]

However, the major portion of wood products, outside structural and veneer uses, is for packaging, and most of this packaging is unnecessary. Paper made from wood is easily recycled. We might see our consumption of wood being reduced for these uses as it is expanded to produce pharmaceuticals or synthetics.

It is possible, however, to use other woody plants instead of timber. Just before World War I the Department of Agriculture investigated the advantages of hemp, which had been a source of paper before the chemical pulping process was introduced in the middle of the 19th Century. The study concluded that hemp could produce four times the pulp per acre as wood, that paper made from it lasted much longer, and that it had the unique advantage of growing to maturation in a single season. The tragedy of forest fires that wipe out 40 years of growth would be minimized.

There are now bagasse factories, bamboo factories, straw factories. One of the most promising plants appears to be kenaf, which yields 3.7 to 12.4 tons per acre, some 5 to 8 times more than wood. Thus it appears that one could reduce the current land area required per American to about one half acre per person, making it conceivable that a greenbelt surrounding our cities could produce almost all the raw materials necessary for our industrial civilization.[37]

What other resources are available to our "wartime," isolated city? A city the size of Dayton has more than 50,000 students in its public school system. If the city has a city university or a community college, there may be several thousand more. It has thousands of teachers, with a wide range of skills. It has laboratory space, computers, machine tool shops through its vocational training centers. It is always astonishing that we can treat our students as consumers of knowledge during their tenure in our educational system, rather than producers of wealth. There is no reason a student cannot learn trigonometry while sizing a solar collector as well as by doing abstract exercises in the back of a textbook. A student can learn chemistry by analyzing soil to be used to raise vegetables, or by analyzing the nutritional content of those vegetables, as well as he or she can by doing lab exercises. The ancient aphorism, "I hear and I forget. I see and I remember. I do and I understand," still holds true. Our schools should be able to contribute greatly to our community needs. One school system in Hazen, North Dakota grinds its own wheat, and buys its own beef from local rangers and dairy producers. "Why should we only be turning out welders?", Superintendent Joe Crawford asks, "Why not meat cutters?" In late 1978, Hazen became the only school in North Dakota to get a federal custom permit to operate an inspected meat plant. The next step is to become a fully licensed custom meat plant so students can sell meat to other schools and customers. Students also process whole frozen chickens.

In Hartford, Connecticut, the "workplace" program links up school systems to local businesses. Students earn money while working in the businesses in fields that they are studying in school. Hartford has gone one step further, setting up an auto mechanic business where students earn while they learn, providing a top quality service to the community while gaining credit toward a degree that will help them in later life.

Cities have the resource base to move toward local self-reliance. Not self-sufficiency, for even nations are not self-sufficient. But independence—looking inward instead of outward, building on their scientific and technical knowledge to design systems that maximize the benefit to the city as a whole.

As cities look to retain as much economic value within their borders as possible, they will inevitably turn their attention toward manufacturing and processing. We are taught that manufacturing facilities must be larger. We think of the automobile assembly lines in Detroit, or the Gary, Indiana steel mills. Yet the further we investigate, the more we can see that manufacturing facilities can be designed to fit within our emerging self-reliant city. There appears to be an almost infinite number of tradeoffs between capital and labor, between energy and labor.

The city as factory:
Making it at home

Joe Bain, in a classic study of economies of scale in manufacturing, concluded, ". . . after a century and a half of rapid industrial expansion, of extraordinary technical progress, and of generalized belief in the virtues of size, it still remains that the average factory in the United States or Great Britain employs only two or three score people. . ."[38]

Researchers have since come to a similar conclusion—most of the things we find necessary in our society could be manufactured within our larger urban areas. One such study found that, if automobiles and petroleum products were excluded from the total, 58 percent of total final goods consumption, by value, of a population of one million could be produced locally in small plants. Sixteen percent of the consumption needs could be produced by plants for a market population of 200,000.[39] Other researchers found that even when the plant was smaller than optimum, the resulting increase in the cost per unit produced was quite small.[40] A shoe factory which produces for a city of 100,000, instead of a region of 500,000, may have production costs only 5 to 10 percent higher. Since production costs only represent a small fraction of the selling price, such increases could be made up through middleman profits, or transportation expenses. Or, as we have seen above, cities could, in their taxing or procurement policies, value locally produced items higher than those which are imported.

Most of these studies of plant sizes look at existing technologies. John Blair, the late economist, describes a more recent phenomenon, the rise of what he dubs "centrifugal technologies."[41]

With plastics, fibreglass, and high performance composites providing high strength and easily processed materials suitable for an infinite variety of applications; with energy provided by such simple and efficient devices as high energy batteries, fuel cells, turbine engines, and rotary piston engines; with computers providing a means of instantaneously retrieving, sorting and aggregating vast bodies of information; and with other new electronic devices harnessing the flow of electrons for other uses, there appears to be aborning a second industrial revolution which, among its other features, contains within itself the seeds of destruction for concentrated industrial structures.

For example, one plastics executive compared the costs in the late 1960s between plastic molds. "A thermoforming mold made of epoxy costs approximately one to two percent of an equivalent steel stamping die, and we have yet to find out how many pieces can be run from a mold." Plastic bodied cars can be produced at much less cost than a steel bodied vehicle. One observer notes, "The outside availability of power train components and the use of plastic bodies should reduce his capital costs markedly below what is currently required to enter the industry at any given level of output."[42] The close tolerances required of piston engines are not necessary for electric vehicles, reducing the need for both capital and labor. One British car manufacturer described the electric car as a "far less complex vehicle than the existing motor car and contains about one fifth of the parts that are in present-day cars." The tooling required to produce a plastic bodied car in the late 1960s was about $1.5 million, compared to the $500 million then required to initiate production of conventional steel bodied piston engine cars.

The idea that there might be a variety of capital and labor tradeoffs in manufacturing was proved most dramatically by Ernst Schumacher and his organization, Intermediate Technology Development Group. While visiting Zambia at the invitation of President Kenneth Kaunda in 1972, he discovered a serious economic crisis. The farmers could not get their eggs to market because of a labor strike at the egg carton factory. When Schumacher inquired as to the location of the factory he was surprised to learn it was in the Netherlands. After returning to Europe he sought out the President of the company, and asked him whether it might be feasible to design a factory to meet only the needs of the small market of Zambia, which required but one-million egg cartons a year. The president, speaking from 30-years' experience, answered that his factory was designed to be most efficient, and that if any factory were to produce egg cartons at less than the rate of one million a month it would have to produce them at a higher cost.

Undaunted, Schumacher set his team to work. Eighteen months later an egg carton manufacturing plant was operational in Zambia. It produced, not one million egg cartons a year, but only a third of a million, for there were three distinct egg market areas in the country, and three factories were needed. The plant produced egg cartons at the same unit cost, were more labor intensive, and used local materials. When industrial engineers were asked why they never designed a factory like that before, their answer was, "Because no one asked us to."

In Chile, a Schumacher colleague was asked if he could find them a supplier of glass jam jars because they were importing jam jars from Britain to put their jam in. The researcher recalled, "The mind boggles at the thought of a boatload of empty jam jars being transported there to be filled

with jam, and then exported back again to the Western World. I thought that was basically crazy." He found that glass was made primarily from sand, limestone, soda ash, and a few trace elements like arsenic. Soda ash could be replaced with seaweed, but the glass would be slightly green. Arsenic could be eliminated, but there would be tiny bubbles in the glass. A furnace normally cost about 25,000 English pounds because it required highly sophisticated refractory materials. The reason why these materials were used was that the furnace was expected to last for ten years. But if there were local refractory clay, and the people were prepared to reline every six months with refractory bricks, the proposed plant could produce one thousand jars an hour with local raw products for a modest investment.

This last example holds important lessons. We may find that in stressing local self-reliance we must choose between various tradeoffs. We might be able to produce a functionally equivalent product in a variety of ways, depending on how much we want to substitute indigenous resources for imported resources.

The service sector: Concentric circles of responsibility

Local self-reliance means concentric circles of responsibility. This is as true in the service sector as it is in the materials goods manufacturing sector. The guiding principle of subsidiarity is that the larger entity should not be assigned a function that can be done more efficiently by a smaller one. What the family can do, the community should not do. What the community can do, the city should not do. What the city can do, the state should not do.

In health care delivery systems, most diseases can be prevented by cleaning up the environment, and by public education. The school system would teach us about medical care as a primary course. The workers would have more control over the environment of the workplace. The next line of defense against disease would be neighborhood clinics, staffed by paraprofessionals, and neighborhood laboratories for testing. Finally, there would be a central hospital, under the supervision of the city, where there would be capital intensive equipment, and professional supervision for the 5 percent of the cases which require such care.

In the area of criminal justice, we find that most crimes occur within a neighborhood. Most murders occur within the family or among close relatives. Neighborhood courts could "try" these cases, and mete out punishment on the basis of restitution. The guilty would have to perform acts of restitution to the victims and the community. In cases of higher crimes, central courts would take over. In Dayton, Ohio neighborhood patrols are trained by the police force. They do not make arrests, and do not carry arms. But they handle 80 percent of the work load because they act as diffusers of violence and tension. When the eyes and ears of a neighborhood are supportive, crime drops.

Whether we are dealing with sanitation, health care, energy generation, or other sectors, the same consideration of scale is crucial. How do we involve the most people in the effort? What is least costly? What systems are most flexible so that we do not inhibit future choices by the actions that we take today?

Localism and globalism: The struggle between small and big

Local self-reliance is a positive concept. It strengthens the local economy, it builds self-confidence and skills at the local level. But those who are attracted to the ideas presented in this chapter should consider several major problem areas. For instance, balkanization can mean parochialism, and rivalry.

One may wonder how much more parochial and competitive we can be, with cities fighting with cities to attract scarce corporations, to be awarded scarce federal contracts, to be allocated scarce petroleum. Cities are stealing about anything they can from their neighbors, including sports teams.

Parochialism can be combatted only by a massive dose of information. Currently the mass media tell us what the corporate and national leadership are doing, and thinking, and wearing. Stories about cities with similar problems to ours, or small businesses with similar products, or neighborhoods with similar situations are delegated to human interest spots on network news, if they make it into the news at all. Local self-reliance can provide a basis for a dramatic increase in city-to-city, and neighborhood-to-neighborhood information exchange. With over 10,000 cities and counties, such an exchange could effect a significant transfer of innovations.

Another problem of local self-reliance is the potential that it will slip into what our British friends call "local self-sufficiency." America is enormously rich in money, technology, and natural resources. We must realize that for most of the world, our crises would be luxuries. Waiting in a gasoline line would be a fantasy much sought by most of the world, which burns dung for fuel, or harvests increasingly scarce wood, and rides donkeys to market.

Yet local self-reliance can help us to reach out to these developing countries, and share information of a practical nature. As we learn to design our cities so that they live within their resource budget, we will be developing systems that can teach, and learn from those in other nations. Just as city-to-city exchanges in this country might be one result of local self-reliance, such exchanges on an international level might be another result.

There will be hard choices involved in deciding what we will do with our resources. Questions of equity, scale, and environment will all arise: yet that, above all, is the role of the political process. Politics only recently has been a process by which we vote for people. Originally it was a process by which we actively participated in allocating resources. As Alexis De Tocqueville wrote, "Town meetings are to liberty what primary schools are to science. They bring it within the people's reach. A nation may establish a free government, but without municipal institutions it cannot have the spirit of liberty."

And, of course, there is the problem of confronting those centralizing forces that are so powerful today. The 1980s will be a period of social turmoil. Those who want to use local self-reliance as an excuse to drop out of society will find it impossible. Although local self-reliance, recycling, small scale production, solar energy, preventive rather than treatment systems, may make more sense, we have to confront institutions built in another era, when resources were plentiful, growth was the objective, and affluence was a never-ending spiral. We are cursed with giant central power plants, interlocking directorates between big banks, big factories, and big government, production systems far removed from their markets, bloated bureaucracies which are on the whole unproductive, if not downright destructive, and hierarchical organizational structures which remove the top policymakers from the impact of their decisions. We must not expect an easy time.

Still, we cannot avoid the choice. We are at a turning point in history. Under any scenario, the future will look very much different from the past. We can seize the opportunity and potential that comes from a period of rapid social change, and design a society in which we, and our children, would want to live. So far, to be sure, the signs are few. Yet they point the way to a new vision, a new context, . . . and a new way of thinking.

References

1. Rein Peterson, *Small Business: Building a Balanced Economy,* (Ontario: Press Porcepic, 1979), p. 42.

2. Petr Kropotkin, *Mutual Aid,* (Boston: Extending Horizon Books, 1955), pp. 162–163.

3. Ibid. p. 200.

4. W. I. Goodman and E. C. Freund, *Principles and Practices of Urban Planning,* (Washington, D.C., ICMA, 1968), p. 13.

5. Ibid.

6. Ibid., p. 16.

7. Adna Weber, *The Growth of Cities in the Nineteenth Century,* (New York: Columbia Univ. Press, 1963).

8. "City of Clinton vs. The Cedar Rapids and Missouri River Railroad," 24 Iowa Law Review 455 (1868).

9. Hunter vs. Pittsburgh, 207 United States 161, 178(1907).

10. Goodman and Freund, *Urban Planning,* p. 23.

11. Ibid.

12. John Nolen, *New Ideals in the Planning of Cities, Towns, and Villages,* (Boston: Marshall Jones Company, 1927), pp. 133–134.

13. Goodman and Freund, *Urban Planning,* p. 26.

14. John Shannon and John Ross, "Cities: Their Increasing Dependence on State and Federal Aid," in Harrington J. Bryce, *Small Cities in Transition: The Dynamics of Growth and Decline,* (Cambridge: Ballinger Publishing Co., 1977), p. 189.

15. Elizabeth Carswell, *Less is More,* (Madison, Wis. 1974).

16. Neil Pierce, "Smokestack Chasers Who Miss the Point," *Washington Post,* 30 May 1977.

17. *Business Week,* 21 June 1976.

18. *Wall Street Journal,* 22 March 1978.

19. Charles Mueller, testifying in hearings on "The Future of Small Business in America," Report to the Committee on Antitrust, Consumers and Employment of the Committee on Small Business, U.S. House of Representatives 95th Congress, 1978.

20. Barry Stein and Mark Hodax, *Economics of Scale in Manufacturing: The Case of Consumer Goods,* (Cambridge: Center for Community Economic Development, 1977).

21. Representative Morris Udall, *National Journal,* 30 July 1977.

22. Jeremy Rifkin and Ted Howard, *Who Shall Play God?,* (New York: Dell Publishing Co., 1977), p. 105.

23. David Birch, *The Job Generation Process,* (Cambridge, MIT Press, 1979).

24. City of St. Paul vs. Dalfin, Minnesota

25. 89 Cal Rpts at 905, citing Miller vs. Board of Public Works, 234 P. 2d 381 at 383

26. Central Lumber Co. vs. Waseca 1922, 152 Minn 201, 1888.

27. Daniel Eleazar, "Are We a Nation of Cities?", p. 95.

28. Ray M. Northern, *Vacant Urban Land in the American City,* (Corvalis: Oregon State University, 1971).

29. Bureau of Municipal Research and Service, Planning Bulletin no. 2,

(Eugene: University of Oregon, 1961).

30. Michael Connor, staff paper, Washington, D.C. Institute for Local Self-Reliance, 1975.

31. John Jeavons, "1972–1975 Research Report Summary on the Biodynamic French Intensive Method," (Palo Alto: Ecology Action, 1976).

32. W. Jackson Davis, *The Seventh Year: Industrial Civilization in Transition,* (New York: W. W. Norton & Co., 1979), p. 232, citing C. Abrams, "The Uses of Land in Cities," *Scientific American,* 213 (1965): 150–162.

33. Roger Blobaum, *"The Use of Sewage and Solid Wastes in Metropolitan Omaha,"* (Washington, D.C.: Roger Blobaum and Associates, 1979.)

34. Egon Glesinger, *The Coming Age of Wood,* (New York: Simon & Schuster, 1949).

35. Stephen A. Spurr, Henry J. Vaux, "Timber: Biological and Economic Potential," *Science,* 20 February 1976.

36. Statistical Abstract of the United States, 1976, "Per Capita Consumption of Timber Products," 1950–1975, p. 681.

37. Joseph E. Atchison, "Agricultural Residues and Other Nonwood Plant Fibers, *Science* 20 February 1975.

38. Joe S. Bain, *Barriers to New Competition,* (Cambridge: Harvard Univ. Press, 1956).

39. Barry Stein and Mark Hodax, *Economics of Scale.*

40. See, for example, F. M. Scherer, "Economies of Scale and Industrial Concentration," in Harvey J. Goldschmid, H. Michael Mann, J. Fred Weston (editors), *Industrial Concentration: The New Learning,* (Boston: Little, Brown & Co., 1974).

41. John Blair, *Economic Concentration,* (New York: Harcourt Brace Jovanovich, 1972), p. 151.

42. Data taken from Hearings on

Economic Concentration, Part 5, Subcommittee on Antitrust and Monopoly, 1967.

Selected Bibliography

ALCALY, ROGER E. and DAVID MARMELSTEIN, ed., *The Fiscal Crisis of American Cities,* New York: Vintage Books / Random House, 1976.

ANTIEAU, CHESTER J., *Local Government Law,* Washington, D.C.: Georgetown Univ. Law Center, 1974.

BACH, EVE, et al. *The Cities' Wealth,* Oakland: Community Ownership Organizing Project, 1976.

BERRY, WENDELL, *The Unsettling of America:* New York: Avon Books, 1978.

BLAIR, JOHN, *Economic Concentration,* New York: Harcourt Brace Jovanovich, 1972.

BLOCK, A. HARVEY, *Impact Analysis and Local Area Planning: An Input / Output Study,* Cambridge: Center for Community Economic Development, 1977.

BRADLEY, RICHARD C., *The Costs of Urban Growth: Observations and Judgements,* Colorado Springs: Pikes Peak Area Council of Governments, 1973.

BRAVERMAN, HARRY, *Labor and Monopoly Capital,* New York: Monthly Review Press, 1974.

BURNS, SCOTT, *Home, Inc.,* Garden City, N.Y.: Doubleday & Co., 1975.

CARLSON, RICHARD J. *The End of Medicine,* New York: Wiley Interscience, 1975.

CONLEY, GARY N., "How to Attract Private Investments into the Inner City Through the Use of Development Subsidies," Washington, D.C.: National Council for Urban Economic Development, 1977.

DE TOCQUEVILLE, ALEXIS, *Democracy in America,* New York: Washington Square Press, 1968.

Economic Practices Manual, Sacramento: Office of Planning and Research, 1978.

FOX, KENNETH, *Better City Government,* Philadelphia, Temple Univ. Press, 1977.

GALAMBOS, EVA C., *Making Sense Out of Dollars: Economic Analysis for Local Government,* Washington, D.C. National League of Cities, 1978.

GOLDSCHMID, HARVEY J., et al. (ed), *Industrial Concentration: The New Learning,* Boston: Little, Brown & Co., 1974.

GOODMAN, W. I. and E. C. FREUND, *Principles and Practices in Urban Planning,* Washington, D.C.: International City Managers Association, 1968.

HARVEY, DAVID, *Society, the City and the Space: Economics of Urbanism,* Washington, D.C.: Association of American Geographers, 1972.

HENDERSON, HAZEL, *Creating Alternative Futures; The End of Economics,* New York: Berkley Publishing Corp., 1978.

HILL, MELVIN B., *State Laws Governing Local Government Structure and Administration,* Institute of Government, Atlanta, Univ. of Georgia, 1978.

HINDS, DUDLEY, NEIL G. CARN, NICHOLAS ORDWAY, *Winning at Zoning,* New York: McGraw-Hill Book Co., 1979.

HUBBELL, L. KENNETH (ed), *Fiscal Crisis in American Cities: The Federal Response,* Ballinger Publishing Col., Cambridge, 1979.

JACOBS, JANE, *The Economy of Cities,* New York: Vintage, 1970.

JEQUIER, NICHOLAS, *Appropriate Technology: Problems and Promises,* Paris: Organization for Economic Co-operation and Development, 1976.

KAPLAN, SAMUEL, *The Dream Deferred,*

New York: Vintage Books / Random House, 1977.

KIRSCHNER, EDWARD M., and JAMES L. MOREY, *Community Ownership in New Towns and Old Cities,* Cambridge: Center for Community Economic Development, 1975.

KOHR, LEOPOLD, *The Breakdown of Nations,* New York: E. P. Dutton, 1978.

KOTLER, MILTON, *Neighborhood Government,* New York: Bobbs-Merrill Co., 1970.

KROPOTKIN, PETR, *Mutual Aid,* Boston: Extending Horizons Book, 1955.

LOVELL, CATHERINE, et al., *Federal and State Mandating on Local Governments and Exploration of Impacts and Issues,* Riverside, Ca.: Graduate School of Administration, Univ. of California, 1979.

LOVINS, AMORY B., *Soft Energy Paths,* New York: Harper & Row, 1979.

MERRILL, RICHARD, ed., *Radical Agriculture,* New York: Harper Colophon Edition, 1976.

METSNER, ARNOLD J., *The Politics of City Planning,* Berkeley: Univ. of California Press, 1974.

MORRIS, DAVID, *Planning for Energy Self-Reliance: A Case Study of the District of Columbia, Washington, D.C.:* Institute for Local Self-Reliance, 1979.

MORRIS, DAVID and KARL HESS, *Neighborhood Power: The New Localism,* Boston: Beacon Press, 1975.

MORRIS, RICHARD S. *Bum Rap on American Cities,* Englewood Cliffs, N.J. Prentice-Hall, 1978.

MUMFORD, LEWIS, *The Culture of Cities,* New York: Harcourt Brace Jovanovich, 1970.

OKAGAKI, ALAN, *County Energy Plan Guidebook: Creating a Renewable Energy Plan,* Fairfax, Virginia: Institute for Ecological Policies, 1979.

OSTROM, ELINOR, et al., *Community Organization and the Provision of Police Services,* Beverly Hills: Sage Publications, 1973.

PETERSON, REIN, *Small Business: Building a Balanced Economy,* Ontario: Press Porcepic, 1977.

PRATTEN, C. F., *Economies of Scale in Manufacturing,* Cambridge, England: Cambridge Univ. Press, 1975.

QUARLES, JOHN, "Federal Regulations of New Industrial Plants," Washington D.C., self-published, 1979.

Rainbook: Resources for Appropriate Technology, New York: Schocken Books, 1977.

RIDGEWAY, JAMES, *Energy Efficient Community Planning,* Emmaus, P.A.: The JG Press, 1979.

RIFKIN, JEREMY and RANDY BARBER, *The North Will Rise Again,* Boston: Beacon Press, 1970.

SCHERER, F. M., et al., *The Economics of Multi-Plant Operation: An International Comparison Study,* Cambridge: Harvard Economic Studies, 1975.

STEIN, BARRY A., *Size, Efficiency and Community Enterprise,* Cambridge: Center for Community Economic Development, 1975.

STEIN, BARRY A. and MARK B. HODAX, *Competitive Scale in Manufacturing: The Case of Consumer Goods,* Cambridge: Center for Community Economic Development, 1976.

STOCKS, ANTHONY H., *Considerations of Scale on Providing State and Local Public Goods,* West Virginia Univ., Center for Appalachian Studies and Development, 1968.

VERNON, RAYMOND, *The Changing Economic Function of the Central City,* New York: CED, 1959.

ZWERDLING, DANIEL, *Democracy at Work: A Guide to Workplace Ownership, Participation and Self-management Experiments in the U.S. and Europe,* Washington, D.C.: Association for Self-Management, 1978.

8 | Self-Help Housing and the Cities
*Sweat Equity in New York City**
Michael Freedberg

AMERICAN CITIES enter the next decade profoundly changed by the political forces of the 70s. The past ten years have seen the emergence of a new urban politics, based in the neighborhoods. Unlike earlier community initiatives, neighborhood organizations have combined accountability to community residents with the delivery of social and human services to become powerful advocates for their constituents' needs. In the process, they have developed fundamentally different approaches to urban revitalization than those advocated by the planners, city administrators, and policy makers of the sixties.

The shift to community-scale renewal programs utilizing existing resources has not come without presenting a whole new set of problems and difficulties, nor has it become an integral part of government policy. The federal government's programs, which largely determine the state and local agenda, reflect a peculiar kind of

schizophrenia—in an effort to satisfy downtown development interests on the one hand, and neighborhood demands on the other. For the former, the Urban Development Action Grant (UDAG) program supplies one half a billion dollars a year largely to the "private sector" for large scale hotel and other projects; for the latter, a $15 million Self Help Development Grant program for small grants to community groups. Thus, President Carter visits the South Bronx, and the first project that emerges is the familiar new construction at Charlotte Street—a peculiar beginning to rebuilding a neighborhood with thousands of abandoned buildings suitable for rehabilitation.

While the Miami riots provide a timely reminder that the urban crisis is not over, nor restricted to one particular region, it is the older northeastern cities that have undergone the most dramatic—and traumatic—changes. With the flight to the suburbs, the shift of capital to the Sunbelt, and the influx of new waves of Black and Hispanic migrants into these cities, city government resources have been hard pressed to maintain services with the available

* Portions of this paper appeared in "Rebuilding the City: 519 East 11th Street, New York," by Michael Freedberg, in *Communities,* No. 26, May/June 1977.

revenues. Cleveland went bankrupt, New York City almost did.

The cities are barely emerging from a period which provoked profound questions about their future. The old questions—Are they manageable? Can they be "governed?"—have been replaced with new ones—Can they survive? and if so, For whom? Urban policy in the sixties and early seventies was based on a belief that the solutions lay in the hands of government: decentralized bureaucracies, improved welfare systems, and better services. This is no longer the case.

Meeting low-income housing needs

Nowhere is the failure of the sixties' solutions clearer than in the cities' efforts to preserve the housing stock for low-income families, whose loss of housing has become a major national problem. Inflation has forced up the cost of housing by some 61.5 percent in the past five years. More than 3.5 million low-income renters are forced to pay over 50 percent of their income for housing. Other factors putting the squeeze on low-income families include:

- The massive losses in rental housing due to increasing numbers of condominium conversions for middle- and upper-middle-income homeowners —as many as 48,000 per year in Chicago alone.
- The displacement of large numbers of low-income families—particularly those on fixed incomes—as a result of the growing "back-to-the-city" movement in many cities. Increased property values are forcing both renters and homeowners out of their neighborhoods.
- The reduction in federal subsidies for low-income housing. Subsidies

for an estimated 60,000 fewer housing units are projected for the 1980 budget over the 1979 fiscal year.

- The abandonment of hundreds of thousands of housing units in the inner city neighborhoods of the older cities of the Northeast and Midwest. In a survey conducted by the Comptroller General of the United States, 113 of 149 cities reported an abandonment problem of some kind.

In June 1977, Detroit reported some 12,000 abandoned buildings, while Philadelphia had an abandonment rate of 4.3 percent, or over 21,000 buildings.

Nowhere has abandonment been greater, however, than in New York City, where the city itself has acquired large numbers of multifamily abandoned buildings through an aggressive tax foreclosure policy. By some estimates, the city will own over 250,000 units abandoned by their previous owners by 1981. As many as three million units could be acquired by local governments nationwide through such tax foreclosures.

The massive abandonment (some 30,000 apartments a year) in New York—in the South Bronx, East Harlem, and Ocean Hill/Brownsville— has left huge areas of the city devastated: urban wastelands of smoldering buildings, empty lots and deserted streets.

Multifamily abandonment is a slow, complex, and painful process, occurring primarily in older, deteriorating tenement buildings. With rents remaining constant or decreasing, and without mortgages to refinance their investments, landlords find it increasingly unprofitable to maintain their buildings. With fuel and maintenance costs going up, the owner first cuts back on basic repairs, stops paying utility bills, stops paying property taxes (while usually still collecting rents)— and ultimately walks away from the building. The tenants who remain are left without heat, hot water and other basic services. In some cases, the building is fire-gutted, allowing the landlord to collect fire insurance—the last source of profit from an otherwise wasted resource. Traditional city responses have ranged from re-selling these properties to the highest bidder through scavenger or sheriff's sales; demolishing the structures as unsafe, to be replaced eventually with new construction; or doing nothing at all. Some planners have proposed a "planned shrinkage" approach, which would involve writing off areas of abandonment as too costly for local governments to maintain as municipal revenues decrease in an age of "scarce resources."

Organizing for neighborhood change on East 11th Street

The lower East Side of Manhattan is, in many ways, a typical, deteriorating low-income New York neighborhood. But at the same time, it is a community with a unique history of successive groups of immigrants since the turn of the century—the gateway to America after Ellis Island. In addition, unlike other low-income areas in the South Bronx or Brooklyn, the Lower East Side is located in the heart of downtown Manhattan, close to Madison Avenue and Wall Street. Therefore, it is potentially valuable real estate.

One block in the heart of this neighborhood—11th Street between Avenues A and B—has organized itself to turn around the seemingly endless process of abandonment, fires, demolition and decay. With courage, commitment, motivation and plain hard work, a neighborhood once filled with despair has begun to show signs of hope. A wide range of diverse resources— both government and private—were mobilized by the community to achieve its goals, an early example of hundreds of similar groups working in the city's low-income neighborhoods, loosely connected to form a powerful

Figure 1
11th Street, between Avenues A and B, in the lower East Side of Manhattan, is the site of a major experiment in sweat-equity housing rehabilitation and neighborhood-based community development.

(Photo by Gibby Edwards)

voice for the solutions to their neighborhoods' and therefore the city's problems.

The 11th Street experience is not a complete success story. Because of external and internal forces, it has not yet managed to create a sustainable economic base that would provide jobs and income without long-term government support. The conditions which the 11th Street residents began to fight—and are still fighting—still exist. And now there is a new threat—the return of the middle class, who have rediscovered the neighborhood's desirable location, close to Wall Street and midtown Manhattan. This could undo much of the positive accomplishments of present neighborhood residents, unless the gentrification process is carefully controlled.

At the same time, 11th Street presents a model of how housing, job training, and community development goals can be combined to take on intractable urban problems which local governments have refused to deal with. It provides a case study of how housing programs involving their users, combined with a commitment to the goals of homeownership for neighborhood residents, can spark a dramatic transformation in political, land, environmental, and economic relationships.

East 11th Street was a typical abandoned city block until a group of block residents initiated negotiations with the city's Housing and Preservation Department for a loan to begin rebuilding one of the vacant burned-out buildings, 519 East 11th Street. The negotiations lasted over one year, based on the need to convince a skeptical bureacracy that untrained, unemployed local residents could renovate and successfully manage a building in this condition, and of this size. The structure was owned by one of the large slumlords in

the neighborhoods, and was one of the first to be burned: thirteen fires had broken out in a three week period when the tenants had begun organizing against him. The building had been taken over by the city through its tax foreclosure program—and was scheduled for demolition, as were ten other buildings on the block.

The city's response would traditionally have been to demolish the structures, even though it had no plans or resources to build on the site in the future. Faced with the virtual disappearance of the physical housing stock, the residents proposed an alternative: that they purchase the building at 519 East 11th Street for a nominal sum ($1) and renovate it with their "sweat equity" and a rehabilitation loan from the city's (now defunct) Municipal Loan Program. In addition to reducing the cost of construction, it was argued that the sweat equity contribution would allow them to acquire title to the property without cash equity of their own. The city agreed to sell the building for $1,800 ($100 for each existing apartment) and make the loan. The tenants paid themselves $3 an hour out of the city loan for 32 hours a week; the remaining eight hours became their equity in the cooperative. After eighteen months of work by the tenants, the building was ready for occupancy. All the work, including the mechanical trades—electrical, plumbing and heating systems—was done by the tenants themselves, with professional supervision. Over 300 burned beams were replaced, and a building given up for lost was transformed into a non-profit, cooperatively owned building, housing eleven low-income tenants in two and three bedroom apartments.

As a result of the 519 success, other neighborhood and block residents expressed interest in renovating additional buildings. Soon, two additional buildings were under construction, producing 50 more units of sweat equity construction, this time using CETA job training funds. The projects were sponsored by a neighborhood-wide housing group, Interfaith Adopt-a-Building, and a block organization which was formed to coordinate the wide range of resources which were now being directed at 11th Street—the 11th Street Movement. The block organization developed a comprehensive community development plan, including housing, job training, energy conservation / alternative energy resources, education and youth development, open space development and community gardening. In addition to these efforts, sweat equity "homesteading" programs began in other neighborhoods of the city—East Harlem, the South Bronx, Ocean Hill / Brownsville in Brooklyn and other neighborhoods.

The low-income housing movement in New York (as well as many other cities) is now based on a belief that tenant ownership (in particular, nonprofit cooperative ownership) and self-management is the key to long-term preservation of the neighborhoods. Rather than seeing the expansion of government bureaucracy as a solution to the problems of the cities, there is a growing belief that the neighborhood groups—the people who have historically been the backbone of the cities' development—probably hold the key to the future.

How homesteading works

The 11th Street group, and others like it, have shown that sweat equity—urban homesteading focussing on nonprofit cooperative ownership—can be an innovative and successful way of increasing the housing supply for

Figure 2
Tenants, under professional supervision, completely rehabilitated 519 East 11th Street, a tenement that had been abandoned after a major fire had gutted it.

low- and moderate-income families in inner city neighborhoods. It utilizes a dramatically underutilized housing resource—abandoned multifamily buildings—which would otherwise be demolished or auctioned off in the private market. It encourages rehabilitation and recycling of these structures at a cost far lower than conventional programs, and minimizes the commitment of costly rent subsidies by the federal government. Perhaps most importantly, urban homesteading encourages "self help" involvement by the homeowners. In many cases, the sweat equity contribution of the homesteaders provides the only means for affordable, low-income housing in deteriorating urban neighborhoods.

At the same time, the self-help process is not a simple one. If anything, it is more complex and presents difficulties which conventional developers do not face. In New York, neighborhood-based sweat equity sponsors have put together a sophisticated package of financing and support mechanisms. In combination, they produce startlingly low rents (or carrying charges) for the homesteaders. The self-help approach costs approximately half the construction costs of conventionally financed and rehabilitated buildings, and one quarter of the cost of new construction. Among the devices used to achieve these savings are the following:

Self-help construction and maintenance. By managing and operating the buildings themselves after construction is completed, the tenants save themselves management fees, superintendent and accounting fees normally incurred. They are also able to undertake much of the repair work themselves.

Elimination of contractor overhead and profits. This saves some 10 to 20 percent of costs normally incurred.

Below market rate interest mortgages, either Section 312, 3 percent-20 year financing, or low-interest loans supplied through Community Development Block Grant programs.

Nominal purchase price of abandoned buildings.

Reduced professional fees. Many homesteading groups have managed to acquire professional architectural, engineering and other services at lower costs.

Supplemental job training funds. The use of CETA or LEAA job training funds reduces mortgageable costs and additionally provides job training for local residents.

Non-profit cooperative ownership. This automatically reduces ongoing operating costs by eliminating profits normally included in rental charges. In addition, return on equity, liquidity, tax shelters, financial leverage, cash flow surpluses, and other investment considerations are not included in homesteading projects.

Reduced vacancy rates. Because of the commitment of time and energy, and the ownership achieved, vacancy rates in homesteaded buildings are reduced significantly.

Tax abatements and exemptions. Use of tax abatements and exemptions based on the extent of improvements in the building has reduced the tax burden on homesteading buildings —a proper use of such tax relief instruments.

Energy conservation measures. As the developers, the homesteaders have a stake in insuring low energy costs. Substantial energy conservation measures, including the use of solar, wind and other attractive renewable energy sources, have contributed to lowered maintenance and operating costs.

Beyond the actual cost savings achieved, sweat equity has three other important effects. First, it achieves a shift from private absentee landlord ownership to tenant cooperative ownership. The by-laws of the cooperatives guarantee that the properties will remain off the speculative real estate market for the life of the mortgages. Second, it provides the basis for long-term community economic development, by incorporating housing reha-bilitation, which stems abandonment and reverses building deterioration, with job training, which provides job skills and improves employment op-portunities. In addition, energy conser-vation measures adopted in the build-ings insure the long-term survival of the buildings by reducing on-going fuel costs, and the small businesses which can be established with the learned skills can provide long-term jobs, and generate new neighborhood capital. Each building thus not only meets specific housing needs, but can begin to meet the larger economic needs of the neighborhood as well. A third possible effect of these efforts is to prevent "displacement" of low-in-come residents when the neighbor-hood becomes more attractive to young, middle income "professionals" —the "urban pioneers" who are re-turning to the inner cities. By remov-ing properties from the speculative market, by giving residents a stake in their neighborhoods, and providing home ownership options previously only available to middle income fami-lies, urban homesteading can establish low-income "anchors" in communities which would otherwise bear the full force of the gentrification process.

Since the first pioneering projects, the sweat equity approach has been ad-versely affected by rampant inflation. As a result, it is increasingly difficult for very low-income homesteaders to produce affordable housing without additional subsidies. However, while sweat equity is not the whole solution to the problem of low-income hous-ing, the multiple advantages (which in-clude lower costs) of this approach should make it the cornerstone of any effective housing policy.

Energy applications

The most significant step taken by the 11th Street tenants after acquiring 519 East 11th Street was the installation of conservation, solar, and wind en-ergy systems—the first of their kind in an urban setting. The huge investment made by the tenants of 519 needed pro-tection. The tenants had taken on a large loan commitment from the city of New York. Unless steps were taken to conserve on-going maintenance and

Figure 3
Installing insulation at
519 East 11th Street.
(Photo by Energy Task Force)

operating costs, the long-term survival of the building would be threatened. Increased fuel costs played a part in the building's abandonment in the first place, and were continuing to escalate at an alarming rate. In the fall of 1974, when the construction at 519 began, home heating oil was priced at 40¢ a gallon; by the time the building was ready for occupancy, oil costs had risen 30 percent. It has increased even more since that time.

The City's Housing Department originally allocated $300 for building insulation—barely enough to weatherize the roof. With a grant from the Community Services Administration, the building was "superinsulated" to increase energy savings. A double layer of insulation was installed throughout the building, in addition to low-cost storm windows and other basic conservation measures. The tenants went a

step further, however, by installing New York's first solar system on the building's roof, for domestic hot water heating. This active solar system uses some 600 square feet of flat plate solar water collectors installed on racks on the building's roof, facing more or less in a southerly direction. A small backup oil burner was installed in the building's basement, along with a well-insulated 500-gallon storage tank. The storage tank both stores the heat collected on the roof, and contains a heat exchanger which transfers this heat to the building's hot water system.

In addition to drawing widespread attention to the project, and to the relevance of solar energy in a low-income, multifamily urban residential setting, the solar system has provided real savings to the 519 cooperative of some 65 percent of the building's hot water costs. The solar system, combined with conservation measures, reduced the building's total energy consumption by more than 70 percent. In the summer months, 99 percent of the demand for hot water can be met by the solar system. In the winter months, the solar fraction typically drops to the 55-percent level. In the first year of operation, the tenants paid some $2,600 for their annual heating needs, as compared with more than $7,000 for a normal tenement building without the conservation measures.

The 519 tenants did not stop there, however. As a result of a long-standing billing dispute with the local utility, Consolidated Edison, the building's electricity was shut off in mid-summer, shortly after the solar system had begun operating. The shutoff affected the solar circulating pumps required to circulate the heated water in the collectors to the storage tank in the basement. The system threatened to explode, as the temperature in the

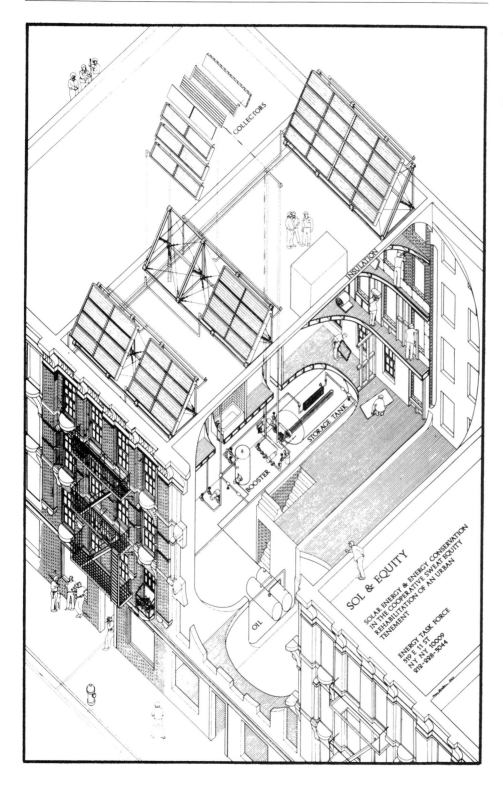

Figure 5
Solar energy and energy conservation in the cooperative sweat equity rehabilitation of an urban tenement.

Figure 6
The Empire State
Building as seen from
behind wind generator.
(Photo by Gibby Edwards.)

Figure 7
Pulling up the 2 kW
wind generator.
(Photo by Energy Task
Force)

collectors rose above the 200°F mark. The tenants managed to drain the system themselves and avert a disaster. But the shutoff showed the tenants their vulnerability. It was clear that the solar, sweat equity and other innovative measures they had taken had not given them the "self-reliance" they imagined they had achieved. With the help of volunteer students (who later formed the Energy Task Force), they began installing a 40-foot tower with a 2-kilowatt recycled Jacobs wind generator on the building to supply the lighting in the hallways and the basement. Instead of using car batteries to store the direct current they used a "synchronous inverter," which allowed them to use the Consolidated Edison utility grid as their storage base for excess electricity—converted from DC to AC current. Then, 519 demanded that Consolidated Edison pay them for this extra electricity, since the utility was selling this power to other consumers.

Consolidated Edison balked. They argued that the 2-kilowatt wind electric generator represented a danger to their workers, was against the tariff to produce electricity on the other side of their meter and the electricity was not "synchronized" enough with their own. After lengthy, contentious (and well-publicized) negotiations, the state's Public Service Commission ruled that the tenants had the right to produce their own power, to pump excess electricity into the grid, and furthermore, that the utility was required to pay the tenants for this new power. As one of the tenants said: "There are three utilities in New York—Con Ed, Brooklyn Union Gas, and 519 East 11th Street."

The 519 victories, however, did not come without accompanying difficulties. The wind generator, it turned out,

Figure 8
*Consolidated Edison in
the background of the
East 11th Street wind
generator.*
(Photo by Gibby Edwards)

had to contend with insufficient wind, despite the proximity of the East River and cost effectiveness was brought into question. An additional cost effectiveness problem was the monthly "demand charge" by the utility to cover its overhead in order to be available to supply 100 percent of the building's needs, if necessary. And, the vibrations of the wind generator blades created possible structural problems. Despite these issues however, the project became an important precedent for wind power projects in New York and elsewhere in the country. (As a result of this breakthrough, for example, a new 20 Kilowatt machine was installed on the banks of the Harlem River in the South Bronx by a community-based group now using it for commercial purposes).

The solar system also ran into difficulties because it had been built prior to inclusion of solar references in the city's building code. The wood support structure was found to be in violation and the tenants were required to rebuild the system with metal racks to conform to the code.

Open space development

The alternative energy applications in 519 developed a new consciousness among the neighborhood residents about the potential of appropriate technologies in a variety of uses. One of the first areas to receive the attention of the 519 tenants was vacant land. Building abandonment was a major neighborhood blight, but the land vacated when structures were demolished was more

of a problem when it became large neighborhood dumps. The homesteaders first converted a vacant lot adjacent to their building to a "pocket park" complete with garden and basketball court. Then they built a community garden with block residents on the next street, 12th Street, on a large, five-lot empty space. Utilizing the burned beams from the sweat equity buildings, they constructed raised beds for French intensive/biodynamic gardening. They literally had to make their own soil, with a combination of elephant manure from Ringling Brothers' stationed a few blocks north in Madison Square Garden, compost and leaf mulch from Long Island. Block residents called the garden "El Sol Brillante"—the shining sun. Many residents unable to participate in building rehabilitation or uninterested in housing activities became avid gardeners (in one case,

growing the first Lower-East-Side peanuts, later sent to the White House).

The gardeners, who formed a self-contained group to manage and administer their garden, experimented with simple cold frames to extend the growing season. Their activities and the Puerto Rican rural and agricultural tradition played a strong part in generating interest in this effort. An important connection was made when the garden began receiving assistance from the Trust for Public Land, a nonprofit San Francisco-based organization, to purchase the vacant lots, owned by the city through tax foreclosures. Normally the land would have been sold at private auction. But the tenants were able to work out a negotiated sale with the city and purchase the garden at a nominal sum for perpetual urban agricultural use. A community land trust was established, made up of gardeners and

Figure 11
Community garden mural behind wild-flowers growing on landscaped mounds of rubble.
(Photo by Gibby Edwards)

representatives of neighborhood groups, to take title and manage the garden (the first such trust in New York City), creating an important precedent for similar community-based purchases elsewhere in the city. The Trust for Public Land is now working with a variety of community groups on the East Coast on similar projects.

In addition to the community garden and the pocket park, the 11th Street residents began to convert a vacant lot, adjacent to another sweat equity project, into a playground. The project involved neighborhood children themselves in the design and construction of the playground, once again using recycled materials discarded during building renovations.

Job training

But these changes, and the new ownership of property that neighborhood residents are achieving, have little value if each owner has no means of economic survival. The majority of residents were unemployed; neighborhood residents were the first to feel the impact of cutbacks in city hiring practices during the 1975 "fiscal crisis." Median income, at that time, was under $5,000. The neighborhood groups sponsoring the housing rehab projects recognized that a direct attack on unemployment would be needed as an integral part of the housing effort. Partially funded by the City's Department of Employment with CETA monies, a job training program was set up to operate on each sweat equity site.

Figure 12
An important benefit of the sweat equity approach to building rehabilitation is the job training tenants receive.

Thus, at the end of the construction period, each individual acquires an apartment through his/her sweat equity contribution, and also acquires valuable skills in the construction and renovation trades.

No one would suggest that the CETA combination with housing rehab was ideal. An inherent conflict between the "production" oriented nature of housing rehab, with its requirements for meeting construction deadlines, and the training aspects of a CETA contract developed. Some of the projects which followed preferred to eliminate CETA entirely, while others developed the "sweat-contractor sweat" concept, which involved bringing in professional contractors for the more difficult mechanical trades and skilled work.

Where CETA is now being used, qualified union journeymen are hired in supervisory positions to provide training. In some projects, a good "placement" record has been achieved by program graduates—either in union apprentice programs, locally-managed construction and maintenance companies, or in building management and maintenance services for the city. Thus the earning power of the homesteaders has been increased, and, along with improved employment opportunities, there is an increased ability to meet the debt service on the rehabilitation loan. (A study by the Urban Homesteading Assistance Board shows that the income of all homesteaders increased during the building rehabilitation period).

Education

A range of support educational services was also instituted along with the job training initiatives. A minimum of a high school diploma is required for placement in union apprenticeship programs, and most of the homesteaders had not progressed beyond ninth grade. Many of them spoke only Spanish. A local high school was contracted to provide high school equivalency English courses. Some homesteaders received their diplomas within months of beginning courses. In addition, classes were held in blueprint reading, architectural drafting and a wide range of trade-related skills.

As important, perhaps, were the range of educational programs begun for younger community residents—elementary, junior high and high school students. Through a local youth organization, an after school center was set up on 11th Street run by high school tutors. A vocational training program for neighborhood youth was established as an adjunct to the adult training program.

Taking charge: A neighborhood based approach to community development

At least 750,000 families in New York City live in substandard housing. Over 250,000 apartments are abandoned. The sweat equity approach contrasts strongly with traditional "slum clearance," urban renewal, or other large-scale development efforts. Involving billions of dollars, these programs achieved very little in alleviating the conditions in the low-income neighborhoods. The self-help alternative now being developed on 11th Street and elsewhere in the city involves a neighborhood by neighborhood approach by community groups who have learned the skills and developed the expertise necessary to function more effectively than have the municipal bureaucracies. A typical city block houses some 2,000 residents.

Figure 13
"Pito," a 519 resident,
at a community festival.
(Photo by Energy Task
Force)

These are people who identify with that block and feel a sense of community. They may have grown up there or belong to its social clubs. They define the block as their neighborhood. In the community, neighborhood residents begin to feel that they can have some influence on their city environment. It was this kind of climate that nurtured the 11th Street effort.

Only a few years ago most properties on the 11th Street block were privately owned. Today, the largest number of buildings are tenant owned or tenant managed. In the New York City context, where there are strong pressures toward individualism and isolation, cooperation has been a basic requirement for the success of the community development effort. Both during the construction period and after each building is occupied, the sweat equity group is intimately involved in decisions regarding design, apartment layouts, construction scheduling, financing, loan processing etc. In order for these decisions to be made effectively, working and personal relationships must be established. The process is thus an intensely personal one—the reason why housing administrators and developers feel it is unworkable.

This doesn't mean that each group has no organization. The corporation established by each building has a traditional board structure, even though most of the decision-making is done at group tenant association meetings.

The shift towards cooperative ownership has created new attitudes on the part of the homesteaders towards their community as a whole. There is still a long way to go. There are clear limits to the control which any group, particularly made up of low-income families, has over its immediate environment. But there is, at least, a sense of being in charge. The new sense has spread to other community groups, and has strengthened the community's relationships with government agencies. In each building, there is a move towards community control—of educational, health and daycare services,—involving hundreds of neighborhood residents.

Changing economics

By involving people in the housing renewal and community revitalization process, a way has been found to deliver basic services without the administrative and bureaucratic costs (and red tape) usually associated with city services. Actual savings in housing rehabilitation costs are significant. The 11th Street homesteaders borrowed $177,000 to renovate their building—$189,000 less than it would have cost if they had used a conventional contractor. Demolition costs of $10,000 were saved. The buildings are put back on the city's tax rolls; the monies expended in maintaining the building are spent in the neighborhood at local suppliers, or in hiring local repair services. But perhaps most significantly, the homesteaders are contributing federal, state, and city taxes. So the advantages to the local government are clear: a reversal in income flow has taken place—instead of into the neighborhood with welfare and unemployment payments, monies are now flowing out.

The critical next step is to translate the changed economics into economic development. To a real extent community groups are dependent on government financing for the variety of programs now being administered. A shift in emphasis must now begin if true self-reliance is to be established. The potential on 11th Street is there. With the growth of the self-help housing effort, a significant purchasing power has developed in the neighborhood, and, with it, the skills to meet the demand in the neighborhood itself. Until now the neighborhood has been dependent on outside contractors to maintain, repair, and renovate its buildings; now for the first time there is a community work force capable of providing the same services.

In the energy area particularly, the new skills being learned are an important first step for the community to tap the huge market represented by solar and conservation. The hope is that neighborhood-based energy and construction companies can be established, which will not only provide jobs, but, perhaps, over time, can generate capital which can be turned back into the neighborhood for such purposes as small home improvement loans.

Postscript

Since the beginning of the East 11th Street project, the neighborhood movement, New York, 11th Street and urban policy have changed significantly. The author, after five years of housing development work on the Lower East Side, has left the neighborhood. However, the 11th Street Movement is continuing a range of appropriate technology and community development projects, including the first rooftop passive solar system on one of the sweat equity buildings, an aquaculture system in one of the basements, breeding the first urban fish in New York City, and a range of housing activities.

Shortly after 519 was completed, the neighborhood (along with an area of the South Bronx) was declared an Urban Homesteading Demonstration Neighborhood by the Department of Housing and Urban Development, which committed federal low-interest loans to replace the defunct Municipal Loan Program. Two more buildings, with a total of 50 housing units, were rehabilitated and converted to sweat equity housing co-ops.

The 11th Street Movement has also developed a neighborhood-wide coalition, the Lower East Side Environmental Action Coalition (LEAC), with two neighborhood youth groups, which received a grant from the National Center for Appropriate Technology for a wide range of alternative energy projects—including an urban "passive solar wall," window greenhouses, a neighborhood recycling center and further community gardening initiatives.

City-wide, the 11th Street Movement was instrumental in the formation of the Appropriate Technology Action Coalition (ATAC), which now produces New York's appropriate technology newsletter, *Alternate Currents;* and, in addition, helped form the Energy Task Force, which supplies technical assistance to neighborhood groups in the areas of solar energy, energy audits and conservation implementation.

Nationally, the homesteading movement has gone country-wide. Sponsored by the Department of Housing and Urban Development, technical assistance is now being provided by the Urban Homesteading Assistance Board to homesteading sweat equity projects in six cities—Boston and Springfield, Massachusetts; Chicago; Hartford, Conn; Oakland, California; and Cleveland, Ohio. These programs do not differ substantially from the early 519 model.

But, despite these successes, the Lower East Side has not been "turned around." Abandonment has remained a widespread phenomenon, and the rate of abandonment has certainly exceeded the rate at which neighborhood groups have rehabilitated the buildings. There has been an increase in the number of occupied buildings which the city has acquired title to and which are turned over to tenant management. But by and large the "sweat equity alternative" still remains that—an alternative peripheral to basic city housing policy.

There are a number of reasons for the continued step-sister role for sweat equity. One is the city's continued reluctance to process loans speedily and commit itself to self-help housing. The time-consuming process of loan packaging and building rehabilitation thus remains a deterrent to all but the most determined homesteaders. On the Lower East Side, unexpected problems arose between the 11th Street Movement and the neighborhood sponsor, Interfaith Adopt-a-Building. The sponsor felt that the resources should be centralized, whereas the 11th Street residents felt that they should be managed on a block level. The "centralist" argument won out, with the result that some of the ownership involvement was lost. A division also developed between the centrally-managed CETA job training program, and the building-managed construction loan effort.

As a result, building residents lost the sense that the building they were working on was "theirs." They came to see the neighborhood sponsor as their employer, or the city's representative. These difficulties translated themselves into management problems on the succeeding sweat equity sites, problems which delayed construction and eventually brought some of the buildings to a halt.

A key problem, not generic to the Lower East Side, was that the early sweat equity neighborhood sponsoring groups came to rely too heavily on CETA job trainees for their on-going program operations. This was true for both Adopt-a-Building and the People's Development Corporation in the South Bronx, which achieved spectacular success after President Carter visited their sweat equity/solar site in 1978. Both grew at a dramatic rate, and, to some extent, were not able to fully involve community residents and, at the same time, develop an adequate management structure.

What is important, however, is the fact that tenant self-help and self-management has become an important part of the city's response to the vastly expanded ownership role assumed by the city of landlord-abandoned buildings. The city is turning many of these buildings over to tenant groups for "interim" management, and eventual cooperative sale. Some of the programs include:

- *Community Management Program.* Through this, the oldest of the alternative management programs, the city contracts with community-based, non-profit housing groups to manage and upgrade city-owned, occupied buildings in which there are active tenant associations. Rents are used to pay maintenance and operating costs, while CDBG monies cover extraordinary repairs, operating deficits, administrative staff salaries, and, in some cases, moderate rehabilitation. The rehab is undertaken by the community group, providing job training for local residents in the process. After two or three years the aim is to sell the buildings to the tenants as co-ops, for $250 an apartment. If the tenants are not interested in buying, the building can be purchased by the community group.

A variation of the Program is the *Management in Partnership Program,* which is aimed at smaller, less experienced and newer community groups. In this case, the city contracts with a sophisticated management company to train and assist the community organization in administering the buildings.

• *Tenant Interim Lease (TIL) Program.* Under TIL, organized tenant groups living in city-owned buildings sign an 11-month, renewable lease with the city, which allows them to manage and maintain their buildings from the rent roll. The interim lease gives the tenant group general control of the basic management and maintenance of the building, but the city's permission is required to evict tenants, or to restructure rents. Small amounts of CDBG funds can be used to supplement the buildings' rents for major repairs, emergencies, and systems replacement. Through the Urban Homesteading Assistance Board (UHAB), a city-wide non-profit technical assistance group, tenants are required to participate in a bookkeeping and management training program. The buildings are city-owned and the tenants therefore are not burdened by full costs of property management during an "interim" period. They are exempt from property taxes and fire insurance (held by the city), providing a temporary "cushion" from the marginal economics of maintaining rental property. The intention is to sell the buildings eventually to the tenant association as a cooperative: after the eleven-month period, the tenants are given the first option to purchase, at $250 per apartment. Surveys of the buildings show rent collection levels of 95 percent in TIL buildings—as against 35 percent in those managed directly by the city.

Thus, ironically, the sweat equity concept lives on in slightly modified form in these "community management" buildings, and also in a successful national program—where the city governments are more committed to these efforts. (For more information contact the Urban Homesteading Assistance Board, 1047 Amsterdam Avenue, New York, NY 10025.)

9 | Community-Controlled Economic Development and Environmental Enhancement:
The Case of the Whiteaker Neighborhood, Eugene, Oregon *

Daniel Goldrich,
Maureen Good,
Steve Greenwood,
and Jim McCoy

THIS IS AN ACCOUNT of an urban neighborhood community's effort to gain substantial control over its future economic development and environmental enhancement. The context for that effort lies in the deterioration of an environmentally destructive and, in important respects, dehumanizing political economy, and in the emergence of a movement for community-based political, economic, and environmental reconstruction. Accordingly, we will set the context first, followed by an inquiry into the Whiteaker venture in Eugene, Oregon.

The political economic context

A juncture seems to have emerged where a choice will be made between radical democratization and decentralization of society or radical centralization of power on behalf of the largest corporations. Alan Wolfe has described the historical arrangement between capital and democracy as a tradeoff which admits more and more of the populace into the political arena, provided that decisions affecting capital accumulation are preserved primarily for private determination.[1] Now, however, this historical tradeoff has become subject to renewed, heightened conflict. According to James O'Connor, a fiscal crisis has developed, with the monopoly sector (essentially, the global corporations) requiring increasingly heavy subsidization by the state, while demands for a wide variety of social welfare expenditures have also increased.[2] A conflict results between the major state functions of promoting

* During the preparation of this article, Daniel Goldrich was supported by a Public Service Science Residency from the National Science Foundation. The views are those of the authors and do not necessarily reflect those of NSF.

capital accumulation and legitimacy. This in turn has led to an establishment campaign to depoliticize the public arena and depress expectations of government while emphasizing to politicians the necessity to restore conditions conducive to profitability and heightened investment. The crisis is heightened by the resource scarcities and environmental limitations that make the accustomed economic growth so hard to restore. Until now, it has been growth which has allowed us to escape high conflict over competing demands in the post-World War II period.[3]

The energy crisis dramatically reflects and represents the juncture, a drama raised to the level of the spectacular by the collapse of the imperial attempt to hold the line in Iran. The choice is between what Amory Lovins calls hard and soft energy paths, with their opposed consequences concerning (among others, such as cost, resource renewability versus exploitation, and employment intensity) centralized versus decentralized decision-making.[4] (Hard paths, based on nuclear plants and far-flung electricity grids, also require a virtually militarized security apparatus, which further reinforces centralization.) The current administration effort to telescope the process of nuclear plant siting and licensing— right in the face of the Three Mile Island event—reflects the pressure to restructure the political rules of the game to reduce public policy input; while the emerging commitment to a synthetic fuels program involving a heavy public subsidy for the huge energy corporations also dramatizes this and O'Connor's theory of fiscal crisis.

Capitalist development has given rise to the predominant role of global corporations, which in turn has generated a large-scale expansion of the federal administration to regulate them, meet their social costs, and promote a rationalized environment for their continued growth. This trend toward domination of our society by large scale institutions (both public and private) has received new impetus, given developing resource scarcities and other problems of capital accumulation referred to earlier. National planning seems on the horizon, most likely through institutions representing the global corporations. Such centralized planning will be difficult to hold publicly accountable, and will be mystified and presented to the public as properly in the realm of removed expertise. This would accentuate the long-term trend toward the diminishing role of the political institutions traditionally representative of more localized interests.

The very scale of these institutions renders their functioning incomprehensible to the public or even their own labor force. Incomprehensibility precludes accountability or control. Furthermore, the vast bureaucratic organization and high degree of standardization of work required of these large institutions reduces the scope of responsibility of employees in a way that severely diminishes their humanity and capacity as citizens for confronting major societal crises such as the environmental crisis.

The simplification of the economy, with power accumulating in the management of the global corporations, also results in the relegation of local communities to the status of commodities, to be used insofar as they can contribute to the desired level of growth of corporate profits. The community is subject to environmental pollution and abrupt plant dislocation, the latter trend most obvious regionally in the Gray Belt—the old traditionally industrial regions of the Middle West and Northeast—as unaccountable corporate headquarters seek low wage / low tax, nonpoliticized locations within this country and under highly coercive conditions abroad.[5]

At this juncture, the movement toward decentralized political economic democracy offers the prospect of a rebalanced reorganization of society based on a locally and regionally integrated, more self-reliant and self-managed political economy. The reduction of scale of key institutions would promote comprehensibility and therefore local control, an essential requirement for democracy. A community-based economic development strategy requires a conscious public process of economic planning focused directly on community needs and goals. Such processes could generate a corps of citizens at the community level with experience and self-confidence in economic planning, giving the society more capacity for a locally-based system of national planning. Without such a strategy, a highly centralized, elite-dominated system of planning seems inevitable.

Sources of movement toward community-controlled economic development

Catastrophic events often produce pioneer communities. The abrupt closure of the Campbell Works of Youngstown Sheet and Tube seems to have mobilized a broad coalition—workers, unions, churches, business, officials—in that Ohio steel city to propose a joint community-worker-owned enterprise to buy out the closed plant. Distress over the devastating loss of jobs was reinforced by the reported discovery that the absentee-corporate new owner bought out the local firm and drained it financially to acquire other holdings, depriving it of resources necessary for investment in new technology and pollution control equipment. This finding reportedly generated an angry energy disposed toward a solution emphasizing local control.[6] Regardless of whether the Youngstown community enterprise eventuates or not (and it now seems unlikely because of the withholding of key federal loans and other assistance), it is reasonable to expect more and more such cases of rapid community mobilization, since the dislocations are increasing and a community control perspective is developing on a widespread basis.[7]

Another major current in the movement is institutional innovations at the neighborhood level, designed for the acquisition of greater control over decisions significantly affecting the life of the community. There tends to be a typical history to such community-building processes, though development often ceases after successfully warding off a threat. The history passes through the following stages: (1) mobilization against a specific perceived threat (often related to a freeway impact or the incursion of a powerful outside institution such as an urban renewal agency, or a fiscal crisis-induced economy measure such as the closure of a neighborhood school); (2) a more comprehensive effort to protect the integrity of the neighborhood; (3) the emergence of a recognition of the values inherent in the neighborhood as a place, and a disposition to go beyond protection to enhancement of that environment; (4) the creation of new institutions such as a neighborhood newspaper and a community organization that strengthen local identity and generate visions of a desirable future; and (5) fortification of the community organization and development of its capacities through incorporation, and

successful acquisition of paid staffing.

After a certain amount of struggle against powerful institutions through which a sufficient core of activists has been recruited from among the residents, a structural understanding of the neighborhood and its problems emerges; that is, a perception that problems occur not by chance but as a consequence of the normal functioning of the political economy. Where there is this sort of local history, some set of local citizens comes to realize that they have at least temporarily saved the neighborhood from deterioration and have created a support system for it. They are likely to feel some confidence, competence, and fulfillment, and a sense of rising political influence. At this point, community awareness may have developed to the point where the idea of community control has motivating power, and interest may be directed to the economic base—a forbidding but crucial level. One of the most significant and flexible institutions for gaining leverage over economic development is the Community Development Corporation, owned and controlled by the local residents through an elected board of directors.[8]

CDCs were devised for bootstrap operations in impoverished communities during War on Poverty years, and their record has produced many substantial successes. Any community can create one to produce directly or to promote subsidiary enterprises for whatever goods or services might meet local needs. The principle of democratic control can be extended to include the workers involved in the decision-making process, for a dual form of community- and worker-controlled enterprise.

Such community-based economic development ventures are ambitious undertakings, because of the lack of investment capital for nontraditional enterprise, the relative unavailability or undermobilization among local residents of the range of business skills, especially those required for cooperative or community enterprise, the lack of self-confidence and the amount of mystification surrounding the realm of the financial and economic, and the length of time and amount of energy necessary to create and sustain such enterprises.

The opportunity for increased public support of such efforts in the recession-ridden late 20th Century lies in the fact that an overwhelming proportion of new jobs created in this country derive from new or expanded small business, not global corporations, as noted by David Morris in the first paper in this section. With rising energy costs, the economy of scale in production shifts toward local production for local use. To the degree that inflation derives from oligopolistic control of production, decentralized production offers part of the strategy against inflation, toward full employment, and the meeting of human needs, especially if it is based on environmentally appropriate technology (as in the examples of health care and energy given by David Morris in his article in this book).

A community-based strategy contrasts dramatically with the traditional community development strategy. Increasingly, communities of widely varying economic character find themselves vulnerable to destabilizing external forces, as mentioned previously. The traditional and continuing local strategy for dealing with a precarious economy is to redouble efforts to attract new branches of major corporations, though that means competing against virtually every other locality in the country for the scarce new plants.[9]

Despite verbal commitment to "clean" new industry and enthusiastic projections of the general benefits to come with a successful campaign, the tendency is for a growth coalition to: minimize consideration of adverse environmental impact; conceal the tax burden involved in site preparation and service extension; avoid the issue of how much employment would be created of what duration of time for whom (local residents or outsiders), and; ignore the likely possibility that the recipient community would be gaining the plant at the expense of an unfortunate counterpart that lost it. The most serious aspect of the situation is the covert, closed nature of the process, discouraging the perception and articulation of fundamental public-interest questions. The response to the specter of public review is, that in a competition so keen, none can afford a negative, conflictual, "political" image.

A major justification for a community-based economic development strategy is that it requires a conscious, public process of community stock-taking, planning and action. The focus is directly on community needs, goals, and control. The process leads to an awareness about traditionally mystified fundamental issues that politicizes and moves a community to action. The scale of the prospective enterprises is comprehensible and therefore more amenable to democratic control. The base in local place makes it much more likely (but doesn't insure) that environmental enhancement will become a principle of economic planning, along with associated principles such as community-costing (assessing ventures according to costs and benefits to the community), and life-cycle costing (assessing costs and benefits over the life span of technology, facility, etc.).

The strategy of community controlled economic development can be implemented experimentally wherever local communities mobilize the resources to try it. Such communities then serve as prototypes for a reorganized environmentally sound political economy, amid the gathering failure of the global corporate-based one. The presence of such prototypes is a crucial political resource at any crisis point where major economic reorganization must take place on an emergency basis.

Neighborhood overview

This neighborhood of about 7,000 people is one of Eugene's poorest and most problem-beset. At the same time, its diverse patterns of life, its natural setting near the city center, surrounding a picturesque butte and park, bordered by the Willamette River, and the concentration of Eugene's relatively few, historically relevent structures within its borders, provide many existing and potential amenities for a rich urban life. Given the low population density, the proximity to the city center, the relatively low land values, and the general scarcity of land in an extremely rapidly growing small metropolis, Whiteaker is under irresistible pressure for development. The Whiteaker Community Council, a nonprofit corporation officially recognized by the City of Eugene as the neighborhood association, has been trying to gain some substantial control over the character of that development.

Whiteaker has been the most consistently active of Eugene's neighborhood associations. The WCC has committed scarce volunteer energy, funds, and staff time to exploration, formulation, and implementation of a strategy for community-controlled economic development and environmental enhancement to achieve a future guided by local preferences. The key institution here is a nonprofit community development corporation.

Recently, Whiteaker people organized a wide range of local groups committed to a more self-reliant, economically democratic and environmentally sound future to apply for a one-of-a-kind major grant from the National Center for Appropriate Technology. This mobilization of human resources was successful, so that Whiteaker is now the site of an Urban Integrated Community Demonstration (UICD). This is a planning project focused on the integrated development of activities in energy conservation, food production, waste recycling, housing rehabilitation and cooperatives, and health care, based on environmentally appropriate technologies.

The following seem to us to be some of the major points of significance about the Whiteaker neighborhood, from the standpoint of the political, economic, and environmental situation of American communities.

Whiteaker development strategy hinges on its attempt to gain control over its economic base—a highly ambitious goal given the widespread and growing dependency of American communities on political–economic decisions made elsewhere, by people locally unaccountable. Rather than accepting the traditional and exploitive dichotomy between a healthy economy and a healthy environment, Whiteaker's economic development strategy is based on a long-run perspective that emphasizes environmental enhancement. Thus one of the early economic planning projects focuses on an integrated network of environmentally sound activities and employment in the production of food, energy, housing and health—areas of basic necessity.

An emphasis on the basic necessities is of particular significance for the last decades of the 20th Century, because of the high and increasing inflation in these very same areas. Recent studies have shown that about 80 percent of American households spend about 70 percent of their income in these areas, and that the cost of living for these basic necessities has been inflating at roughly twice the rate of overall inflation.[10] Hence, to the degree that Whiteaker can make any headway on increasing the access to and control over these necessities of life, on a range of scales from single blocks to clusters of blocks to the entire neighborhood, it would become one of a crucial set of demonstration models for a wide range of American communities. So in a context where the prevailing political economy is resource and generally environmentally exploitive, and appropriate technology has been starved for funds and legitimacy and made to appear the province of the bizarre or esoteric, Whiteaker has an opportunity through NCAT to play a significant role in the development of a political economic program based on husbandry of resources and an emphasis on renewability.

Another point of significance is the range of participants in one or another part of the program, including: primary school children learning to raise food and teen-agers developing new occupational opportunities; a severely underserved neighborhood population developing a potentially appropriately structured health care program, and; a host of nonprofit, cooperative, and governmental organizations working together in the NCAT and related endeavors.

Whiteaker has developed a continuity of leadership comprised of both elected representatives and paid staff, while expanding the numbers of active citizens. This continuity is crucial to the neighborhood's capacity for achieving its objectives. Given the relatively low pay, economic insecurity, and high stress in community organizing positions, it is significant to note that one aspect of the NCAT grant is an inquiry into the possibility of providing a prepaid health plan for neighborhood employees. If successful, this would provide an important fringe benefit that could facilitate organizers being able to make longer-term commitments to their work.

We will focus on the following dimensions of the Whiteaker situation: its demography and city context, a history of the neighborhood organization, and Whiteaker's community-based economic development strategy and process, including, prominently, the part played by the NCAT grant. The last sections of the paper treat major problems faced by the neighborhood, its resources, and its prospects.

Intermittently, the reader will encounter our attempt to include information about particular events, meetings, or conflicts that might appear mundane, trivial, or out of place. We include them because we think they alert the reader to real political factors in the course of community development, such as the failure to communicate because of exhaustion and the consequences of that, or the appearance of renewed opposition at an unexpected point, threatening to burn out neighborhood activists, or the occurrence of some form of support for the neighborhood endeavor. We think taking such points of community vulnerability into account should prepare others better to confront inevitable conflicts and stresses and find resources to transcend them.

Demography

Whiteaker tends to have a concentration of young adult and elderly people, and many single-parent households, with relatively fewer two-parent nuclear families. The census tracts comprising the area are the city's lowest in income. A 1976 county-sponsored social services survey found 23 percent of the neighborhood's households living in poverty; a total of two-thirds of the households surveyed were considered low-income by HUD standards (below 80 percent of the Eugene-area median income); and 35 percent of the households were paying more than 35 percent of their income for rent. Census data reflect disproportionately high unemployment, blue collar and service occupations, and a high incidence of substandard dwellings and other buildings. About three-fourths of the people are renters, compared to less than half in the city as a whole. Much of the property is absentee-owned. Associated with this socially rather problematic image is an extremely high transiency rate, which makes neighborhood organization a very difficult task.

There is an extremely varied pattern of land use. There are light and heavy industrial areas, a booming border zone of commerce and public facilities as well as a quite marginal traditional commercial strip, major highways and arterials, one of which bisects the neighborhood one way while the Southern Pacific Railroad bisects it the other, and several different residential zones. These include some old single-family dwellings, a small area of historic homes, one area of smaller single-family homes near the river undergoing very rapid escalation in value, plus areas of substantially deteriorated single-family housing planned for higher density. Given present zoning policy, these last-mentioned will inevitably be developed poorly from the standpoint of neighborhood goals concerning the stabilization of residency —especially as they relate to low-to-moderate income families and self-reliance, since public spaces for food-raising would be extremely limited, and it is hard to arrange for energy conservation in rental units. (More will be presented about these problem / opportunity areas subsequently.)

In addition to this general demographic profile, we can provide some information about those who have been active participants in the Whiteaker Community Council. The following description is based on a spring 1978 interview survey of those who had attended at least one WCC meeting in the previous six months. A high percentage of such "attenders" still present in the neighborhood at the time of the study were interviewed. Demographically, and in other respects, this profile corresponds closely with our observations as participants.

Women and men are equally represented. They are predominantly young —about four-fifths are between 25 and 34 years old. They are of low-income and highly educated. Half owned their own homes, a considerably higher percentage than in the neighborhood generally, but an even higher percentage reported some period of unemployment within the two years preceding the survey. In this highly transient neighborhood, the active participants were overwhelmingly new residents (less than 3 years' residence).

This is an unusual profile. The facts of youthfulness, high education, low income, unemployment experience, and active neighborhood involvement despite recency of residence suggest the presence of a communitarian motivation and an orientation toward political economic alternatives. Further evidence of this can be seen in their highest preferences among six types of organization in which to work—an enterprise owned cooperatively by the employees, one's own business, and an enterprise owned and controlled by the neighborhood. Small, privately owned business and publicly owned enterprise were ranked lower, and fully 86 percent ranked "a branch of a multinational corporation" last. These data form a profile similar to what would be expected of the young people Kenneth Keniston described around 1970 in "Youth, a New Stage of Life," if that characterization were projected into the late 1970s. This social sector is a likely source of initiators of a neighborhood movement toward community-controlled economic development and the formation of CDCs, because such institutions tend to meet their personal needs to make a commitment to society and to vocation and for socially significant and challenging work, without sacrificing their sense of self or personal integrity.[11] This is in contrast to so much of the available employment today, which occurs within large-scale bureaucratic institutions, private or public. These institutions tend to deny responsibility to all but a handful of high-level employees, to reduce individual effort to the aspect of replaceable cogs in a machine, and to constitute a large part of prevailing political economic and environmental problems.

It is clear that this active set of neighborhood citizens is demographically quite different from other important elements of the neighborhood population. Thus an obvious problem (for later inquiry in this paper) is the degree to which the neighborhood leadership is linked to the middle-aged and elderly

and those more locked into poverty or near proverty. However, this set of activists has been crucial to the articulation and mobilization of possibilities for neighborhood development.

History

Community mobilization in Whiteaker began about 1970 over the issue of a proposed freeway destined to have much adverse local impact. The experience generated a campaign to amend the city charter to require a plebiscite on any proposed arterial highways. Over the objection of most city officials, two-thirds of the electorate ratified the initiative. Since then the neighborhood has gone through many stages of action, now common in many American communities (formation of an association, protection of the neighborhood school under threat of closure because of declining enrollment, community school program, community garden plots, outreach work of several types). Together with city planning staff, local people developed a neighborhood land-use refinement plan officially adopted in 1978 by the city council, so that a major step has been completed in delimiting neighborhood development according to the preferences of neighborhood residents as well as city-wide planning objectives.

Whiteaker residents also went to work on historic research in the early-settled East Butte area, work that led in 1978 to the city council's designation of that area as Eugene's only Historic District. Since then, there has been a continuing controversy over the area, with a small group of neighbors fighting the city to make housing development in the area subject to rules requiring compatibility with its historic character.

The County-sponsored social services survey of 1976 provided critical

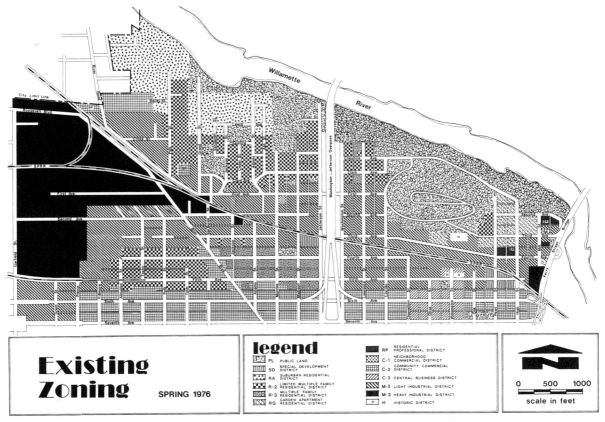

Existing Zoning

SPRING 1976

legend

PL	PUBLIC LAND
SD	SPECIAL DEVELOPMENT DISTRICT
RA	SUBURBAN RESIDENTIAL DISTRICT
R-2	LIMITED MULTIPLE FAMILY RESIDENTIAL DISTRICT
R-3	MULTIPLE FAMILY RESIDENTIAL DISTRICT
RG	GARDEN APARTMENT RESIDENTIAL DISTRICT
RP	RESIDENTIAL PROFESSIONAL DISTRICT
C-1	NEIGHBORHOOD COMMERCIAL DISTRICT
C-2	COMMUNITY COMMERCIAL DISTRICT
C-3	CENTRAL BUSINESS DISTRICT
M-2	LIGHT INDUSTRIAL DISTRICT
M-3	HEAVY INDUSTRIAL DISTRICT
H	HISTORIC DISTRICT

0   500   1000
scale in feet

information about the social character of the neighborhood, the extent and qualities of being poor, the composition of households, and the sense of the residents about major social needs. This became an important base for planning for the 1977–1980 allocation of Community Development Block Grant funds.

Eugene has had a progressive neighborhood recognition policy since 1974. This policy facilitates neighborhood organization, provides some crucial funding (for example, for the production and distribution of newsletters, a highly significant medium in the development of consciousness of community-in-place), requires formal charter conditions protective of democratic practice, and promotes the referring of locally and regionally relevant issues to

organized neighborhoods as a key source of citizen input. The city government has also allocated a substantial proportion of its CDBG monies to Neighborhood Improvement Programs targeted to the central area. This has certainly helped to avoid the kind of blight characteristic of many major cities. Together with the facilitation of neighborhood organization, the city has promoted organized, grass-roots constituencies to formulate allocations of large funds for local improvements (a very different matter from organizing a citizen committee from the top that is broadly representative but lacking in real accountability to organized groups, which are conscious of their own needs). Other cities have used CDBG dollars principally to benefit upper income residents, and with

Figure 1

General Land Use Pattern. Together with the city planning staff, local people developed a neighborhood land-use refinement plan officially adopted in 1978 by the City Council. This was a major step in guiding neighborhood development according to the preferences of residents as well as city-wide planning objectives.

Figure 2
Front page, Whiteaker
Neighborhood News,
August 1979, Cheryl
Hawkins, Editor.

Energy Surveys Awaiting Return

The energy component of our NCAT grant (National Center for Appropriate Technology) is in full swing. Sam Sadler and Don Corson of Oregon Appropriate Technology (OAT) are coordinating the energy programs with help from volunteers John Jennings and Jan Schroeder. Sandy Pitler, Whiteaker outreach worker, is the community's liaison with the energy component.

NEDCO: Preparing for Whiteaker's Future

On June 27, the WCC held a special meeting to ratify the proposed by-laws and Articles of Incorporation for Whiteaker's newest branch: NEDCO, or the Neighborhood Economic Development Corporation. This is a non-profit corporation formed to facilitate the planning, funding, and implementation of economic activities in Whiteaker. This is a big step: it allows for a new range of ac-

Also at the meeting, a Board of Directors for the NEDCO was nominated. By-laws call for a board of 5 to 15 members. Considering the complexity and diversity of NEDCO's proposed economic activities, (a housing co op, commercial property acquisition, neighborhood-owned businesses), an attempt was made to recruit a board that would be well-versed in these diverse areas.

much less citizen involvement in the process.[12]

In Whiteaker's case, the funds have been allocated to low-interest housing rehabilitation programs, building a community center, hiring outreach workers as key neighborhood staff, supporting day-care facilities, and providing organizational and financial support for the Community Health and Education Center, and Project Self-Reliance—a program of energy conservation and alternative technology projects, emphasizing community education and locally provided technical assistance. For 1979–1980, a major part of the funds were allocated to economic development, which will be discussed in more detail later in this paper.

CETA funds were acquired for staffing economic development feasibility studies, beginning a teen program, mobilizing neighbors for a rape and crime prevention program, and for the organization of a highly successful neighborhood fair as part of an outreach effort.

Economic development

Why the turn toward community-based economic development here? There is the objective fact of a predominantly low-income population needing more economic opportunity. There is also a substantial nucleus of young adults who have become oriented away from the dominant large-scale political economic institutions and toward more communitarian, cooperative alternatives, largely as the result of the long, diffuse, formal and mostly informal educational experience with the national controversies of the 1960s and 1970s. Many have had substantial cooperative and collective experience as well. The foregoing recent history of the neighborhood reflects the gathering sense of and commitment to place on the part of a growing set of active citizens. These major antecedents seem to account for the way in which the neighborhood responded to the opportunity provided by the community development funds allocated to it by the city.

The Neighborhood Advisory Group (NAG) that met to plan the CDBG allocation in the fall of 1977 included several people who had either formal educational or alternative community experience involving an active critique of the impact of the prevailing political economy on the local community. Accordingly, they allocated funds for staff to do background research on: cooperative housing, as one of the few good housing solutions for low-income people, a solar greenhouse demonstration project, and the formation of a Community Development Corporation for the neighborhood. Just at the end of 1977, Whiteaker's application for CETA positions in economic development (and other areas) was accepted. In the winter of 1978, a community forum series on alternative economic development strategies was organized and co-sponsored by a wide range of neighborhood associations and community organizations. It was well attended, with a consistently large delegation from the Whiteaker neighborhood. This series helped further to prepare a climate for consideration of community-based economic development.

In spring 1978, a Whiteaker Committee on Economic Development was formed to work out priorities in the area. Lane County's Housing and Community Development Department made a staff person available on a part-time basis to assist the Committee. The members sponsored a survey of residents' perspectives on and potential involvement in a local economic development program. The Committee wanted such information both for its own sake and as a way of generating information about its activities among the residents—in other words, it was an effort in democratic accountability. The survey, done by a set of students

from a Community Politics class, had two parts. One part was based on interviews with people active in the WCC (referred to earlier regarding background information on neighborhood activists). An experimental part was also attempted by distributing a questionnaire to a substantial set of households, as an insert into the neighborhood monthly newspaper, which also contained an article about the survey and the need of the committee for citizen input. Inasmuch as very few people in Eugene had been confronted with thinking about concerns such as community economic control, the survey must be assumed to have appeared irrelevantly time-consuming to many people. Furthermore, we had no way of knowing at that time how many people took the neighborhood newspaper seriously enough to scan, let alone read it in depth. In any event, about 10 percent of the distributed questionnaires were collected, in no way allowing any assumption of representativeness, and probably tapping those particularly alert to economic politics. So two sets of data became available, one small in number but drawn from a substantial proportion of active attenders of the association meetings, and the other, somewhat larger, but not permitting much of an assessment about representativeness.

The activists seemed to be highly disposed politically to these ideas. Almost everyone thought it makes sense for the neighborhood to try to create enterprises for needed employment, goods, or services. Over 80 percent disagreed that "big corporations help to make strong local communities," and agreed that "local communities have too little control over their own economic situation." They were evenly divided as to whether the environment should have the highest or equal priority with job creation and a better economic base in local planning, and none preferred a lower priority for either goal.

The activists expressed a very high degree of support for proposals about community economic control and development. They were virtually unanimous that a CDC would be a good idea, a substantial majority considered it a high priority for the neighborhood and almost none considered it a low priority; three-fifths indicated they would buy a share in one, the rest being more undecided than opposed. Very high proportions supported the idea of employees as well as community representatives on the governing board. Such other proposals as cooperative housing, the solar greenhouse, a community development credit union, land banking, and setting up a nonprofit housing rehabilitation corporation were endorsed by percentages ranging from 74 to 89. Four-fifths took the trouble to indicate some way in which these ideas applied to their personal situation. Three-fourths indicated a dispostion to open a savings account in a proposed credit union. All but one-fifth said they had talked with family, friends, or neighbors about these ideas in the past few months; even more indicated an interest in learning more, and over half said they wanted to become more involved in activities of this sort.

The residents responding to the questionnaire survey inserted in the newspaper were also supportive, though by less extreme majorities, the differences being more in incidence of uncertainty than in outright rejection of the ideas. It seems significant that in a low-income community that has suffered through bad economic times in the seventies, these residents were as concerned as the activists with giving

the environment high priority in local economic planning. This is at least one case where decentralization is associated with environmentalism under some rather unfavorable conditions.

Despite the limitations of the survey, the overwhelming degree of expressed support for community economic control and development proposals provided the Committee and the NAG a stimulus to move ahead to the next stage.

A reconstituted NAG of 11 members was elected in early fall 1978, with representation from each area and some at-large. From September through December, they met once a week (with some subcommittee meetings in between), usually for three hours and often more. Early in the process they agreed that the great bulk of the $330,000 should be allocated for activities that built-in the principle of leveraging—that is, that CD funds should be used in such a way as attract other funds. Ultimately, most funds were allocated to economic development, for cooperative housing, and for the general purpose of property acquisition and development, and for staffing of these projects on a two-year basis, probably coordinated through a Community Development Corporation, and for continued outreach workers to inform people about and involve them in the economic development projects. Much smaller sums went to an appropriate technology demonstration, Project Self-Reliance. Citizen involvement had been sought by regular coverage in the Whiteaker newspaper, including previewing crucial decision dates, leading off in the fall with a brain-storming session at a WCC meeting, and holding both a mid-term progress assessment and a final approval session at a WCC meeting.

Four major decision points remained. The city's citizens advisory committee on block grant allocations had to meet with the NAG on its proposal and then later pass on that modified proposal, as did the city council, and finally the regional office of HUD. The committee had never before been called on to deal with community-based economic development ideas. Although periodic background reports on development proposals had been sent to the committee and to relevant departments of city government, there seemed to be a tendency to deal superficially and skeptically with these until meeting directly with the NAG. At that meeting, several issues arose, reflecting the committee's inexperience with these ideas, some quite legitimate committee concerns, and the fact that neighborhood staff and volunteers were learning about this step-by-step (for which the neighborhood tended to be regarded as "flaky," rather than appreciated for its hard and pioneering work). It became clear that the neighborhood participants were so exhausted by their own process that they failed to explain adequately what they were thinking and doing to the committee members and city administrators on a person-to-person basis.

At this point, additional work was done to meet some committee concerns (for example, the need for fail-safe points and staged funding), and more effort was made to communicate. A vist to the neighborhood by Stewart Perry, the country's foremost authority on community-based economic development, was extremely useful in identifying issues requiring more communication and in eliciting a surprising degree of underlying agreement.

A city staff report expressing serious concern and advocating major shifts in the neighborhood program was introduced just before the final committee

Figure 3
Project Self-Reliance
poster by Larry Parker

meeting without opportunity for neighborhood deliberation. By that point, however, sufficient agreement had been reached so that the committee and, a week later, the city council, approved the neighborhood proposal;[13] the HUD office, also inexperienced with this economic strategy, followed suit some months later.

Two economic development tasks ensued immediately. One was to convene a wide variety of community organizations interested in appropriate technology, self-reliance and environmentally sound enterprise to decide whether to apply for a major grant from the National Center for Appropriate Technology, and then to work up the formidable proposal.

The other was to deliberate the desirability and form of a Community Development Corporation. Concerns were raised that a separate organization might fragment community effort, be less accountable, and drain energy needed for a range of endeavors. In the end, the people decided to form a separate CDC, in order that sufficient time and attention could be given to complex new enterprise issues, but the membership requirements were made as open as those for the WCC (residency, work within, or serious involvement in the neighborhood). In addition, the first set of directors was to be elected at a well-publicized WCC meeting, and the CDC was expected to report regularly to the WCC and in the Whiteaker newspaper.

There are some important issues of scale concerning the Whiteaker CDC. Though many observers have questioned whether a neighborhood of 7,000 could appropriately support such an institution, from a political standpoint, the small scale promotes its comprehensibility by the citizens and their capacity to control its direction. In the history of CDCs in the United States, while many have been substantially successful at economic development, by virtue of their large size they have been much less successful in promoting control by the community. Another scale consideration has been that Whiteaker residents have had to pioneer while being conscious of the fact that appropriate scale for some enterprises within this community-based strategy might have to be city-wide as soon as sufficient political support has been mobilized to organize actively at that level. The CDC has accordingly been structured to allow for Whiteaker's participation in neighborhoods-wide or city-wide enterprise.[14]

A number of important supports have been acquired for the economic development effort, each of which has provided needed technical support. Lane County Legal Aid accepted Whiteaker's application for ongoing legal counsel. This represents LCLA's first shift in policy away from a sole concern for individual low-income people's cases and toward a collective focus on economic development as a way of aiding low-income people structurally. Through Legal Aid, the neighborhood now has access to a local law firm's donated advice on property acquisition, taxation, etc. plus access to two key backup research and assistance centers of the National Legal Services Corporation—the National Economic Development Law Project and the National Housing Law Project.

University of Oregon architecture professors Michael Pease and Christie Coffin successfully applied for a University Year in Action grant to recruit a set of students and establish a design studio in the neighborhood. They have been working on the locally determined priority of the Blair area redevelopment. (This crucial problem / opportunity area is discussed more thoroughly below.)

Through the local CETA administration, an economic development trainee was hired with particularly appropriate background. She is a woman with years of business experience, an informal leader in the Blair commercial area, and an active supporter of the neighborhood economic development effort.

Stewart E. Perry, a national authority on community-based economic development, has been brought in twice through county Housing and Community Development funds to consult on a range of economic control and development issues.

Based on an unsuccessful but well

developed neighborhood grant proposal, the HUD Office of Neighborhood Development invited two Whiteaker representatives to an OND briefing of a set of western region neighborhoods, and then selected Whiteaker to receive technical assistance, in an innovatively decentralized program, from an advanced neighborhood. The latter, the Tri-Cities Union for Progress, Newark, New Jersey, has sent two representatives with 12 years of organizing experience, especially in cooperative housing and community health services, to advise a range of Whiteaker staff and residents.

Finally, Whiteaker was awarded NCAT's first-of-its-kind $150,000 Urban Integrated Community Demonstration (UICD) planning grant, to be supplemented by technical assistance from NCAT for fund-raising and implementation of the planned activities.

The urban integrated community demonstration

The UICD was a planning process designed to enable the residents to become more self-reliant in the areas of food, energy, housing, health, and recycling, on an integrated basis and in a way providing good employment. Several local appropriate technology organizations worked to plan applications of their innovative approaches or technologies to an entire low-income neighborhood.

Administration. An experienced Whiteaker outreach worker and resident was hired to coordinate the grant program; a staff was hired whose commitment was reflected in the considerable number of hours of unpaid pre-grant planning, and a neighborhood advisory committee was elected. Offices were rented and renovated by volunteers in

an old garage structure, key to neighborhood planning for the revitalization of the Blair commercial area. If the neighborhood proceeds to acquire the buildings, as is a good possibility, the rent will have assisted the acquisition.

Food. This program had three components—neighborhood farming, developing the fruit and nut tree potential, and school gardens. The aim of promoting cooperative farming on a substantial basis at the neighborhood level proved overly ambitious; though several block farms were identified, organized, or supported by project resources, and may serve as models in the neighborhood over time. Surveys showed the existence of considerable fruit and nut trees, the harvest from which could be expanded. While a neighborhood tree maintenance enterprise did not seem feasible, some "extension" type of effort might lead to greater development of the resource. A curriculum for elementary and preschool children in food-raising has been prepared and put into effect at Whiteaker school and two local daycare centers.

Energy. The energy component was wide-ranging. Given the fact that about 70 percent of Whiteaker residents are tenants, as are about half Eugene's residents, the most impactful route to reducing energy costs would be a mandated weatherization program at the city level, the financial mechanism for which would not unfairly burden tenants or homeowners. Working with people from the local public utility and from city government, the energy group developed a proposed city ordinance that would require weatherization within six years, during the first part of which a concerted public educational effort would be made. The cheapest mode of financing would be the sale of bonds to create a relatively low-cost loan fund from which people could borrow to weatherize. The city, or its utility, could reinvest those bond monies not in use at the particular time, the earnings on which could further reduce the cost of the program. Loans could be repaid through a surcharge on one's utility bill or be built into the cost of property at the point of resale. A well-attended city-wide town meeting sponsored by Whiteaker generated support for this proposal, which is currently under consideration by a city government task force charged with developing a local weatherization plan. Since there is considerable impetus behind this effort in Eugene, it seems likely that the city council and community will be presented with a plan in the relatively near future.

Another part of the energy conservation planning effort concerned land-use guidelines. These include clustering, landscaping, maximizing solar access, and reduction of paved areas. These guidelines have been incorporated into the planning efforts focusing on Blair area redevelopment, described below.

The energy group studied the criteria Whiteaker has considered important in its economic development effort (for example, environmental enhancement, job creation, community enterprise) to determine how best to incorporate these in energy business planning. There was considerable interest in creating a community-oriented enterprise under Whiteaker's Community Development Corporation (the Neighborhood Economic Development Corporation, NEDCO) to take advantage of some of the economic activity generated by energy conservation, as well as concern about the high cost of establishing a new business and NEDCO's lack of experience. A plan was made to set up an energy services company that would begin by taking orders from residents for weatherization work, which would then be subcontracted to an existing firm at a substantial discount. As activity and experience grew, the firm would begin to do the work with its own employees, shift from just weatherization to the installation of alternative energy facilities, and expand toward a wider-ranging retailing of components and systems. NEDCO incorporated Whiteaker Energy (WE), which began operation in spring, 1980. Its board structure envisions one-third representation each from NEDCO, investors, and WE workers.

Recycling. By tapping the solid waste stream, low-income people especially can gain access to inexpensive resources as well as needed employment. The primary planning activities in this area concerned the feasibility of a full-range recycling center in the neighborhood serving a substantial sector of the metropolitan area, providing crucial support to existing recycling enterprises, and assessing the feasibility of an organic reclamation and composting business.

A major study was done on the feasibility of a recycling center, that provides a strong base for future recycling planning. Three necessary conditions were specified: a coalition of recyclers to provide sufficient materials for economic operation, grants or donations to acquire an industrial site and basic equipment, and sufficient budget for a publicity and marketing program. While none of these conditions yet exist, the study provided a base for an effort to seek funds to acquire a highly desirable site in the neighborhood. A subsidiary study was done on the feasibility of a composting enterprise. Appropriate siting and technology were identified, but the key uncertainty is the market, the specification of which remains to be done before further effort would be worthwhile.

The recycling planning gave some crucial support to a promising but struggling recycling cooperative, Garbagio's, in the form of a study of legal and organizational structural issues and assistance with an organizational development plan. Implementation of these efforts has helped to provide direction and staff support so that Garbagio's is more equipped to accomplish needed growth.

Housing. Much of the local housing stock is owned by absentees, charging high rents and letting stock deteriorate. Individual renters can do little about this, but collectively, the neighborhood has been working toward housing programs to reverse the situation. As previously described, Whiteaker has been planning a cooperative housing demonstration. NEDCO has acquired one particularly good site for new construction, and is in the acquisition process for a set of dwellings and sites in the Blair area for rehabilitation and conversion to a co-op.

Through cooperatives, low-income renters can become owners. Their key facilitating characteristics have been summarized in the work of Community Economics, Inc., as follows: (a) only a single mortgage is involved, held by the cooperative, each unit of which is represented by one shareholder; (b) the cooperative can be totally financed, so that little capital is needed by the shareholders—the equivalent of a down payment is the cost of a share (it can be approximately equal to one monthly payment); (c) since equity does not accrue to the individual share-holder, turn-over in housing units need not be refinanced, avoiding a major source of housing inflation; (d) share-holders benefit by being owners, since owners as opposed to renters can deduct property taxes and mortgage interest payments from their state and federal taxes, and also benefit by state property tax exemptions for those of low-income or the elderly; and (e) low-income share-holders are considered renters for purposes of benefiting from federal rent subsidy programs.[15] The community gains a supply of decent, cheap housing, protected from speculation, and a set of people experienced in democratic decision-making and collective problem-solving concerning the meeting of basic needs and the development of a place, all within a conscious, community context. All the other A. T. activities have had and will continue to have a special focus on co-op housing as a particularly favorable point of integration.

Health. The Whiteaker social services survey identified health care as the first priority need. In response, the WCC has been assisting in the development of the Community Health and Education Center (CHEC), a neighborhood-based clinic emphasizing prevention. This preventive emphasis has led to a three-point program to take CHEC further toward neighborhood self-reliance. A medical self-help program has been geared to community education in prevention and home health care techniques. Study has been made of the feasibility of a Health Maintenance Organization (HMO) model for Whiteaker. This is tied to the first stage of a complex, federally-required process to develop a prepaid health plan through CHEC. If ultimately applied to neighborhood employees, it could be an important component of a benefits package. Of course, tough legal, financial, and administrative problems will have to be worked through over a lengthy period before such a plan can be realized. Fi-

Figure 4
The Blair area: (a) de-
teriorating commercial
buildings; (b) the barn
—a distinctive structure
anchoring the area; (c)
vacant lot, auto-park-
ing-dominated apart-
ment buildings, and
residential street zoned
for density. NCAT
grant and economic de-
velopment offices
located in rehabilitated
old store shown in (a).
(Photos by Action for
Whiteaker, University of
Oregon Design Studio.)

nally, a Whiteaker Health Action Council, composed two-thirds of residents and one-third of health care providers, has been organized as a regular part of the WCC to develop neighborhood health activities, provide feedback and advice to health agencies, and to promote their accountability to the neighborhood.

Evaluation. The intensity of an eight-month planning grant put a strain on neighborhood resources, but produced results that will have an impact for years to come, as should have been indicated in the previous account. The following are several observations on the experience. (1) The very nature of a short-term grant program creates difficulty regarding community accountability. The grant advisory committee had to be organized quickly, and was put into the position of advising on an inherited activity, since many members were not involved in developing the program. They had to work without having time for adequate training in such important matters as neighborhood history and group process. Alternatively, an existing representative body of the neighborhood could have been assigned the task. But such groups tend to have a full agenda, and there is a continuing preference for recruitment of additional residents

into responsible positions. (2) The grant announcement called for, and Whiteaker's proposal responded with, a breadth of focus that, in retrospect, was hard to carry through in a short period on a limited budget. Despite underbudgeting coordination and other staff time, much was produced because people worked far more than they were paid for. This, however, had the effect of draining people of their energy and enthusiasm, an effect that is hard to assess in the short run. (3) The simultaneous development of the NCAT project and NEDCO, which were not simply overlapping in personnel or focus, made coordination difficult. For example, NEDCO staff and board were working on basic organization and planning at the time when several of them were also involved with other Whiteaker staff in a major short-term planning / research effort. This made full communication and conflict resolution difficult. (4) A decision was made to hire local, somewhat experienced people for the project insofar as possible as opposed to previously uninvolved people with greater expertise available in the region. This put some such people through a painful learning process; but regarding the long-run effort, community people would have had to learn these skills

anyway. Short-run efficiency in this sense was perhaps sacrificed to long-run gain.

The economic development agenda, in summary

The new board of directors of the Whiteaker community development corporation (Neighborhood Economic Development Corporation, NEDCO) inherits the following workload, a considerable one for volunteer directors: oversight of the NCAT enterprise projects in recycling and energy services, development of the cooperative housing project, and assessing the value and feasibility of property acquisition to gain leverage over the revitalization of the Blair area. The economic development goals which each effort promotes are the following: (1) The NCAT enterprises would increase the capacity of the neighborhood for self-reliance and lower the cost of living, especially relevant to the inflation-beset situation of those of low-income; (2) Jobs would be created in environmentally sound, locally-controlled enterprises; (3) Cooperative housing would give residents more control over and lower the cost of a basic necessity, and should prove an especially strategic focus for the integration of

the other appropriate technology processes.

How does Blair revitalization fit? The Blair effort needs to be seen as part of an overall endeavor to redevelop Blair as a neighborhood, from its current condition of an old, deteriorated commercial strip adjacent to an area with a substantial amount of poor quality housing. The Blair area awaits, in an utterly dependent stance, a shift in private market conditions that may generate renewed development by absentee investors. The University Year in Action (UYA) studio group has done crucial work in clarifying the interconnected problems and opportunities there. Redevelopment of the commercial sector is necessary to provide for the needs of Blair area residents without reliance on automobiles. The redevelopment of Blair as a higher density residential area is necessary to the support of the commercial sector (as well as meeting city objectives for more close-in housing). The NEDCO is accordingly working toward the acquisition of a strategic and historically significant commercial property that would give the community some control over the redevelopment effort—so that facilities and amenities preferred by the neighbors are created there. And, as noted, NEDCO's first housing coop

Figure 5
Block Planning, *a poster for neighborhood revitalization and a sample of several posters prepared by the* University Year in Action Design Studio *to facilitate the community planning process.*
(Copyright by Michael Pease and Christie Coffin)

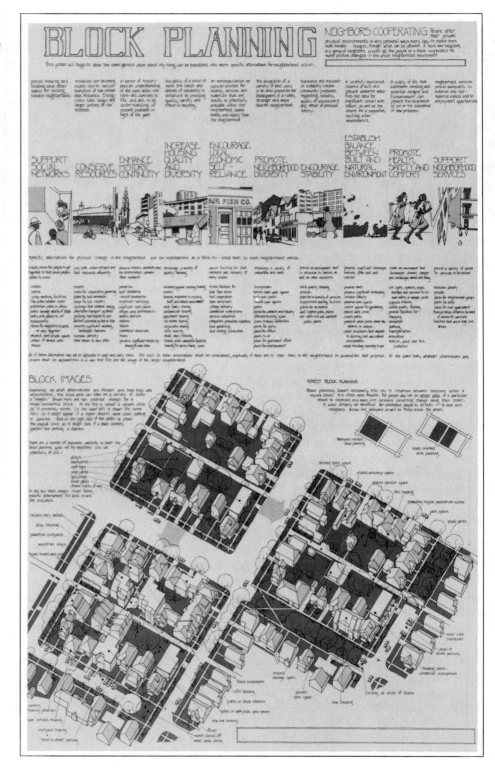

is being developed in Blair to promote good low-cost and community-oriented housing there, and to serve as a demonstration of integrated environmentally appropriate ways of living regarding food-raising, health care, and energy conservation. If neighborhood preferences are to be implemented, however, a host of difficult issues must be creatively confronted.

This leads us to the consideration of a series of problems currently facing the Whiteaker neighborhood, foremost of which is displacement.

Broader political structural problems—Displacement

Whiteaker is a prime candidate in the Eugene area for heavy displacement or gentrification (replacement of low-income renters by upper-income renters or buyers). The NCAT grant program and the whole economic development thrust has as a key goal the improvement of environmentally appropriate economic opportunity for the low-income population. These goals will be meaningless unless low-income people continue to be able to reside in the neighborhood.

The vacancy rate for both rental and sale housing in Eugene has always been critically low and it is projected to be so for the foreseeable future. Eugene has had a less than 1-percent vacancy rate recently; it may be slightly better now but way under the 5-percent level denoting a housing crisis. Inasmuch as Eugene is a highly desirable area and is growing rapidly, housing costs have been escalating dramatically. Whiteaker is a prime candidate for severe displacement because of the following factors: low population density, proximity to the city center, high rentership, relatively low land values, substantial areas zoned for higher density,

the general scarcity of land in the metropolitan area, and natural amenities such as the bordering Willamette River and a large, picturesque butte and park.

Despite this situation, there has been little work done on the displacement problem in Eugene, aside from some good but very limited city programs such as the one which provides rent supplements to those low-income renters whose landlords rehabilitate the dwelling, thus requiring or justifying a higher rent. Since the main problem is that caused by the pattern of private investment and development, no government agency is compelled to take on the problem. In the winter of 1979–1980, however, the immediate threat of condominium conversion of two central area apartment buildings comprising a significant amount of such rental units available to elderly citizens has led to a public outcry, and the city council is working on an ordinance to control condominium conversion.

There are two major kinds of housing problems in Whiteaker. In areas of single-family homes, prices have risen very rapidly and substantially. There are other areas with old, generally quite deteriorated homes, with a high degree of absentee ownership, designated both by the neighborhood refinement plan and city plans for higher density development. The issue here is the appropriateness of new development.

As we try to devise a policy tool kit to prevent displacement throughout the neighborhood and to promote desirable housing development in the areas just mentioned, we have two valuable guidelines in the neighborhood refinement plan and the state land use law. The neighborhood plan seeks a broad and stable mix of residents, conservation of housing, and diversity of housing in type of structure, cost, and density. The state land use law's housing goal calls for each unit of government acting to "encourage the availability of adequate numbers of housing units at price ranges and rents which are commensurate with the financial capabilities of Oregon households . . ."

Based on other communities' experience, it seems the case that no one tool can be effective with such a complex problem. (By itself, for example, rent control leads to condominium conversion and reduction of needed apartment rental units, especially for those of low-to-moderate income; policies putting limits on private developers may prevent bad development, but do nothing to meet the need for additional housing units). Thus, an integrated set of policy tools needs to be carefully crafted to the particular local situation. Another principle is to try to force those creating displacement to bear the costs, as opposed (in the case of private developers) to merely profiting from it.

Regarding the general problem, the following are some tools tried and proposed in various communities that, taken together, should have substantial impact: an anti-speculation tax; federally supported programs through which low-income renters may become owners; a municipal housing development bonding program to underwrite low interest and low down payment for low-income buyers; constraints on condominium conversion (requiring developers to make available to elderly tenants extended or lifetime leases at current rates modified by a cost-of-living escalator, a requirement of mandatory consent by a minimum proportion—usually 35 to 50 percent of existing tenants, special financing assistance for low-to-moderate income purchasers, or even total prohibition of such conversion when the vacancy rate

for rental housing falls below a certain percentage); limiting single-family dwelling buyers to those who will live there at least one year; denial of demolition permits (where low-rent units are involved) if the private redeveloper fails to provide an equal amount of replacement housing for any low-rent units destroyed.[16,17]

In areas such as Blair and West Butte, architects Pease, Coffin, and their student associates have found that the kind of apartment building most likely to be built under existing zoning (numerous recent examples have been the very tangible basis for their ideas) are highly unlikely to produce either the traditional housing amenities and values or a range of values articulated by the neighborhood plan and other programs. For example, because such apartments leave little common space for either recreation, playground, or greenery (the small amount of common space is used for parking), and afford minimal living space, families are unlikely to want to stay there any longer than necessary. Yet an increase in stable family residence has been declared a priority. Energy conservation is another high priority of the neighborhood, especially for low-income people, yet presently there is little incentive for developers to provide it. Another aspect of the integrated NCAT approach is increasing local self-reliance in food. Under present circumstances, Blair and West Butte residents will be precluded from participating in such an advantageous program, because of the extreme lack of gardening space in the apartment areas. Hence the Action studio is proposing a special Urban Community District (UCD) to promote desirable directions. This district would use a point system to evaluate proposed development by its capacity to provide energy conservation, require a reduction of street space for cars, an increase for public recreation and gardens, and a concentration of house siting for these common purposes and for energy conservation (instead of the present arrangement of apartment buildings separated by 10 useless feet of setback space). Additional units might be awarded as an incentive to a developer who met a certain range of objectives. In the interim, prior to more focussed public and official consideration of these proposals, the WCC was able to gain a rezoning of part of the East Blair area to limit the most damaging kind of apartment development.

However, it is important to realize that presently in Eugene, as generally in the United States, little investment is being made in apartment building, especially for low-to-moderate income tenants. The package of policy tools described above would further discourage such investment by constraining profitability. Hence it would be probably crucial to include additional policy tools to generate the funds for needed new housing. One such tool would be the creation of a tax increment district in the neighborhood to channel some of the rising property values into a nonprofit, neighborhood housing services corporation. (The essence of the tax increment district is that bonds are sold for housing construction purposes, based on future neighborhood property tax assessments. The city would freeze the level of its revenue from property taxes and the increase in value of the neighborhood then accrues to the tax increment district to pay off the bonds.)[18] The corporation could then build and manage cooperative and rental housing for low-to-moderate income people, carefully developing types of units according to gravest need.

The Urban Community District, tax increment district, and bonding program are flexible tools. They could be experimented with in Blair, for example, and then if effective, shifted or expanded to other needy city areas for given periods. Priorities guiding the districts could be modified over time as needs change. But the most compelling aspect of this range of policies is the power to deter undesirable development and to promote development, preferred according to democratically adopted, socially equitable local, municipal (though the goals are less clear at this level), and state plans.

In order to promote further public consideration of and support for such policies, some Whiteaker representatives worked in late 1979 with counterparts from four other central area neighborhoods containing a substantial amount of low-to-moderate income housing to incorporate a non-profit Neighborhoods Housing Resource Center. Its goals are: (1) promoting and coordinating a comprehensive anti-displacement strategy regarding residents of low-to-moderate income; (2) promoting infill, new construction, and conversion housing which provides shelter at a range of cost and for a range of household types; and (3) promoting and implementing design solutions to achieve neighborhood and citywide goals. This is one of the first instances in Eugene where neighborhoods facing common problems have tried to mobilize common resources to deal with them.

However, we do not want to leave the impression that all Whiteaker's housing problems have a solution in city policy. The WCC's efforts to provide amenities for some of its more deprived residents has generated the neighborhood's first major internal dispute. The Council has been seeking to acquire a site for a much needed and supported park in the Blair area to serve the needs especially of nearby apartment renters, many of whom are low-income. Contested by the owner, a long-term, elderly resident, the city has condemned the site for public acquisition. Many neighbors, particularly elderly home-owners, reject the coercive action. Yet in an area of increasing cramped apartments with extremely limited recreational space, the park would be a significant amenity. So redevelopment efforts have already led to a difficult social conflict, primarily between owners and renters within the neighborhood.

Broader political structural problems—Generating external support for community-based economic development

Since Whiteaker is the first Eugene neighborhood (first in Oregon as well) to seek decentralized community-controlled economic development, and since it has an increasingly informed program and an alert, mobilized corps of activists, the neighborhood has acquired a radical, feisty image. Simultaneously, city officials and administrators have been pushed from another direction by a business sector seeking traditional incentives to economic growth (attracting new industry, for example). The city administration has, at this point, only limited commitment to and limited knowledge of the broad range of community-based economic development policy innovations occurring in other American cities, such as those David Morris writes about in the first paper in this section.

Consequently, in at least these early stages, the neighborhood has had to take on all the risks of community-based economic development without skilled assistance from within city government. With its scarce resources, Whiteaker now has to provide virtually all its own economic development planning, often receiving criticism for inevitable (and temporary) inadequacies, a frustrating double bind.

The city council on the whole seems open to a variety of not necessarily mutually exclusive economic development approaches, and has recently formed its own economic development commission for policy advice. It will be important whether the new economic development commision develops a decision-making structure and set of policies that actively facilitate, allow for, or discourage neighborhood-based economic development. Despite the pressure of daily work that must still be done, Whiteaker people must find the time and energy to communicate and develop common purpose with other interested neighborhood associations, community organizations, and the city council and staff. The same must be attempted at the county level, where there is currently a highly skeptical, conservative majority on the commission. It is important to take the time and energy to explain wherever possible what is actually being done in the neighborhood, how decentralization may be cutting long-run costs of and pressure for bigger government at the local level, and so on.

The abovementioned problems reflect the neighborhood's need for finding the energy and strategy to build citywide coalitions to support environmental and economic policies appropriate to the 1980s and beyond. Connections need to be made between the large numbers of environmentally-oriented citizens dispersed through the community and neighborhood groups such as Whiteaker, and the city council and administration. Another connection that must be made is that between Whiteaker, as a low-to-moderate income neighborhood, and organized labor, since there are many common potential interests, but also potential conflicts. For example, although major unions such as the UAW have sponsored Community Development Corporations in areas such as Watts, there has been little effort to deal with issues which can arise between fledgling community enterprises and labor unions regarding wage standards, and training low-income youth and heads of families caught in dead-end jobs.

But this has been a critical limit of neighborhood organizing all across the country to date—the difficulty of organizing politically for mutual aid even in the same city, let alone statewide or nationwide.[19] The strength and appeal of the neighborhood movement (sense of place, intimate sphere of social action, grassroots democracy) are also weaknesses, in that extreme localism defies the need to organize for facilitative policy at the various levels of government. To do this requires, first of all, that neighborhood leaders and staff build such tasks into the organizational effort and recruit the extra people necessary to carry them out. Secondly, it is important to find funds to maintain staff who can do the research and development to undergird these efforts. Otherwise, staff and activists committed to other crucial work burn out trying to cover all fronts.

Intra-neighborhood problems—Extending and intensifying organizational links into the community

A major neighborhood-level problem is the need to mobilize the relatively less involved sectors of the community, such as seniors, blue collar families, and the various sections of the poor. Some are linked to neighborhood programs through such social services as those aimed at seniors, daycare, and the community school. However, they have not become significantly enough involved in the ongoing political decision-making processes, nor the more basic structural efforts, such as community-controlled economic development.

The NCAT grant poses an additional challenge and opportunity through its intent to build a cooperative, communitarian way of life against ingrained values and customs, in the absence of an abrupt, overwhelming crisis. (The reference here is not so much to the abstract level of values about cooperation, but to the more mundane and ultimately crucial level of taking personal time to participate in weeding the block farm or doing one's stint of cooperative food-drying, or taking part in a home health care educational program that ultimately would reduce reliance on expensive professional medical services, a trade-off necessary to the success of any neighborhood health plan.)

The outreach workers are the critical element here, and the key strategy is to locate likely blocks in each of the four areas of the neighborhood and work with the residents to develop these as demonstration blocks. Starting with economic development, through cutting their cost of living and gaining some control over basic necessities (for example, in food-raising, health care), residents of such blocks might also be linked through active outreach to participation in community enterprise creation through source-separation recycling and contracting locally for weatherization, and through the recruitment of un- or underemployed residents for jobs in these enterprises.

Charles Hampden-Turner pioneered the idea of *social marketing,* the advertising of community enterprise-produced goods and services in terms of the social values furthered in their production and consumption.[20] Here, Whiteaker would try to take the process a crucial step further by building in demonstration blocks from whose experience other residents might more readily learn than from educational efforts in the abstract. Outreach and education at this stage could point concretely to neighbors who have collectively saved dollars, promoted their own health, produced good and satisfying food, and acquired jobs with a future that enhance the worker both through democratic organization of the work and through the significance to the community of that work (part of the solution, as opposed to part of the problem). Such pioneers can describe how they've broken through their own resistance to cooperation and what the gains and costs have been in concrete personal terms—how they feel about going to work in the morning, how they felt at first about separating garbage (and how much time it would take) and later came to feel about creating wealth with it, how they've felt about and dealt with conflict with neighbors who shirked their responsibilities, and so on.

Intra-neighborhood problems—Internal organizational development

Given the long-term nature of the community-based economic development process and community-building in general, it is extremely important to sustain long-term commitment among community organizers / staff people.[21] The workload tends to be overwhelming—long hours, innumerable meetings, insufficient and insecure external support, and the sheer difficulty of the pioneer tasks (creating and maintaining small business has been an extremely tough task in recent decades as the economy shifts in favor of global corporations; how much tougher it is to create democratically accountable community enterprise with multiple objectives). Material support tends to be extremely inadequate—low pay, insecure tenure, and few basic fringe benefits. In the face of these conditions, the American experience is that most organizers "burn out" or otherwise leave their work by the age of thirty. This seems to be the critical age because it is at about that point that young adults have the compelling personal need to establish enduring intimate relationships and raise children. Obviously the making of relationships during a time of enormous social change requires a lot of time and commitment, which brings the needs of personal life and community-building directly into conflict in the life of the organizer or staff person. Getting agreement on a decent level of recompense (including basic benefits such as a health plan, especially important as one makes the transition from unencumbered youth to young adult with family responsibilities), is a crucial community task.

In Whiteaker, visits by community organizers from other cities have been very valuable in creating perspective on this issue. For example, Ed Andrade, an organizer/staff person from a very poor, ghetto area of Newark, consulting (through the Office of Neighborhood Development program) with the "whiter," less impoverished Whiteaker neighborhood, has made it clear that staff salaries in his community are much higher than in Whiteaker—high enough to provide an incentive for continued commitment. It is significant that Ed Andrade and his co-worker Becky Andrade have been organizers in their neighborhood for 12 years, into their forties, thereby providing much needed continuity and accumulation of experience to their community's effort.

As the neighborhood develops new programs and attains the resources to implement them, some problems arise concerning organizational complexity, democratic functioning, and community control. There are inevitable tensions between staff and volunteers over differential access to information, hiring, pay levels, accountability, the degree to which elected office-holders do their homework, allowing them to make the decisions needed by staff to get on with projects, and so on. Furthermore, there are internal staff problems that arise from the short-tenured basis of many staff positions (the NCAT grant period was for 8 months; CETA positions vary but are often for less than 12 months) and the pressure to carry through a task. Both these kinds of problems put a premium on developing an organizational culture of problem-solving which includes agreements and rules for processing conflict, and methods for the efficient democratic management of meetings and the orientation of new staff members and volunteer participants.

Developing support structures and problem-solving agreements and practices among staff, and among staff and their families, and staff and volunteers is as important and appropriate a (social) technology in a self-reliant community effort as any other tool or task that can be imagined. Despite their manifold benefits, however, many community organizations forego the effort of creating them. To a substantial degree, despite the presence of several people skilled in these areas, this characterizes the Whiteaker effort as well. One of the major reasons seems to be the belief that while things are going well, one doesn't really need them, and when things have deteriorated, one doesn't have the time or energy to divert to their construction. But if community-building is considered on the basis of experience to date, those involved should come to recognize that the effort is a very long, arduous one, and that sustenance for that long-haul effort needs to be provided. Support groups and problem-solving agreements are a key part of that sustenance.

Resources and prospects

In the course of this account, we have referred to a wide range of public agencies at all levels, community organizations, Whiteaker residents and others who have contributed to the development of the neighborhood program. It seems highly significant that the more basic the program thrust, the more participation has been generated in the community. Thus, we have some reason to expect that further development of the economic effort, reinforced by the NCAT resources and direction, will elicit growing support from Whiteaker citizens.

At a time of growing cynicism about and delegitimation of government among the public (at least in part for reasons laid out in our introduction), the developing relations with agencies facilitative of community control, decentralized democracy, and self-reliant institutions have been heartening to those involved in the Whiteaker venture and have given legitimacy to their efforts. By facilitative, we refer not only to much needed capital, and the prospect of assistance in finding funds to implement planned programs, but equally the flexibility of NCAT in administering the grant by meeting Whiteaker preferences and needs as opposed to forcing the neighborhood to fit rigid bureaucratic standards.

We refer as well to the way in which the NCAT project has brought together the range of community organizations and community-oriented individuals whose work together seems to have provided a source of personal satisfaction, mutual support, and stimulation. We refer also to ONDs making available direct consultation by highly professional community organizers from a more established neighborhood enterprise.

The neighborhood and its larger community are moving toward self-reliance in another respect. In recent years, people working in Whiteaker have participated in the programs of the New School for Democratic Management in Eugene and other cities. In fall 1979, a set of representatives of community organizations also working with the neighborhood held the first session of a Eugene Community Enterprise School. From now on, it may be possible to provide local education in community enterprise management, organizational development (such as problem-solving, conflict resolution, avoidance of burn-out), focused specifically on local needs at a particular stage. In view of some of the neighborhood organizational problems described earlier, this new local resource seems especially important.

We have presented a series of problems facing the Whiteaker neighborhood. Difficult as these are, our perspective is that the more we move into crisis in this country, the clearer it is that we have to choose our problems. One choice is to try for a technical fix, a wartime-like emergency basis for the acquisition of scarce energy and other resources, and an increasing concentration of power in huge federal and global corporate bureaucracies, as the principal institutional means to these ends. The problems Whiteaker has chosen to address derive from an attempt to create institutions of a more democratic and environmentally enhancing character. There is at least a chance that a community reconstructed in this manner will, with all of its problems, enhance people.[22]

References

1. Alan Wolfe, *The Limits of Legitimacy* (New York: Free Press, 1977); *see also* Wolfe, "Capitalism Shows Its Face," *Nation,* 29 November 1975, pp. 557–63.

2. James O'Connor, *The Fiscal Crisis of the State* (New York: St. Martin's Press, 1973).

3. A mark of the conflict is the intensifying phenomenon of taxpayer rebellion, limiting the state budget and forcing the choice between capital accumulation and legitimacy.

4. Amory Lovins, "Energy Strategy: The Road Not Taken," *Foreign Affairs,* 55 (October, 1976): 65–96.

5. Such dislocations are described in Jeremy Rifkin and Randy Barber, *The North Will Rise Again; Pensions, Politics and Power in the 1980s* (Boston: Beacon Press, 1978). For some creative responses, see chap. 20.

6. Paula L. Cizmar, "Steelyard Blues," *Mother Jones,* April 1978, pp. 36–42, 52; Ron Chernow, "Nectar or Lemons?" ibid., pp. 45–52; and Deborah Baldwin, "Youngstown: Picking Up the Pieces," *Environmental Action* 9 (February 1978): 4–7.

7. David Moberg, "Shuttered Factories, Shattered Communities," *In These Times,* June 27–July 3, 1979, pp.

11–14.

8. Basic information about CDCs is available through the publications of the Center for Community Economic Development, Cambridge, Mass. Two CCED pamphlets describe CDCs and forms of organization of them; see "Community Development Corporations" and "Alternative Models for CDCs," 1975. The history of the first generation of CDCs may be obtained from Stewart E. Perry, "Federal Support for CDCs; Some of the History and Issues of Community Control," Center for Community Economic Development, 1973.

9. Harvey Molotch analyzes this strategy and the constellation of interests promoting it in "The City as a Growth Machine: Toward a Political Economy of Place," *American Journal of Sociology,* 82 (September, 1976): 309–32. John H. Mollenkopf describes the structure of the urban growth coalition, in "The Crisis of the Public Sector in America's Cities," in *The Fiscal Crisis of American Cities,* ed. by Roger E. Alcaly and David Mermelstein (New York: Vintage, 1977), pp. 113–31. The intensity of the competition between Ohio and Pennsylvania for the Volkswagen plant is described in Ron Chernow, "The Rabbit That Ate Pennsylvania," *Mother Jones,* January, 1978. A careful local case study of an attempt to lure an electronics firm to Eugene, Oregon is available in Alean Kirnak and Jack Condliffe, "The Cone/Breeden Controversy; a Case Study in Land Use and Economic Development," Survival Center, Univ. of Oregon, 1977.

10. Leslie E. Nulty, *Understanding the New Inflation: The Importance of the Basic Necessities* (Washington, D.C.: Exploratory Project for Economic Alternatives, 1977). For updates indicating the growing severity of the problem, see Ann Crittenden, "Inflation Balloons Prices for Basics at Double Rate" (*New York Times* Service), *The Oregonian,* 13 November 1978, and "Nader Urges Consumer Strike to Protest Growing Inflation," *Eugene Register-Guard,* 28 June 1979.

11. Kenneth Keniston, *Youth and Dissent* (New York: Harcourt Brace Jovanovich, 1971), "Prologue: Youth as a Stage of Life," pp. 3–21; Richard Flacks, "Making History vs. Making Life," *Working Papers,* II (Summer 1974), pp. 56–71; Robert J. Lifton, *The Life of the Self: Toward a New Psychology* (New York: Simon & Schuster, 1976), chap. 6, "Forms of Revitalization," pp. 139–46; Fred Block, "The New Left Grows Up," *Working Papers* VI, no. 5 (September/October 1978): 41–49; and Daniel Goldrich, "Community Organizers as Institutional Innovators: A Developmental Perspective," paper for meeting of the International Society of Political Psychology, Washington, D.C., May 1979.

12. Richard Kazis, "A Beginner's Guide to Block Grants," *Self-Reliance,* March–April 1977, pp. 10–12.

13. Having received approval of its formulation of the program, the neighborhood agreed to negotiate subsidiary differences with city staff.

14. This has been a double bind for the neighborhood, in that observers have articulated their skepticism or hostility in terms of the neighborhood's *presumed* interest in self-*sufficiency* and their doubts about whether this small neighborhood could effectively organize and operate an enterprise. At the same time, they have opposed a community-based economic development strategy on a broader, city-wide basis. Thus the neighborhood residents have had to undertake all the risk in such a strategy, if they want to try to move ahead at all.

15. The work of Community Eco-

nomics, Inc. (then, the Community Ownership Organizing Project) on co-operative housing is described in the following reports, published in Oakland: Edward Kirshner and Eve Bach, "Low-to-Moderate Income Housing: A Proposal for Local Communities," 1974; Kirshner and Chester McGuire, "Savo Island Financial Feasibility Study," 1975; Kirshner and Joel Rubenzahl, "Pilgrim Terrace Feasibility Study," 1977; and Kirshner and Rubenzahl, "Cooperative Housing Feasibility Study: Davis, California," 1977.

16. Chester Hartman, "Displacement: A Not So New Problem," *Social Policy,* March / April, 1979, pp. 22–26. See also "Condominiums Force Low-Income Renters out in Cold," *The Oregonian,* 23 July 1979 and Karen McCowan, "Conversions to Condominiums Multiply in Area," *The Sunday Oregonian,* 1 July 1979.

17. Hartman, "Displacement . . ." p. 24.

18. These ideas are taken from the work of David Morris, of the Institute for Local Self-Reliance, Washington, D.C., personal correspondence.

19. See David Moberg, "Experimenting with the Future: Alternative Institutions and American Socialism," in John Case and Rosemary Taylor, eds., *Co-ops, Communes and Collectives* (New York: Pantheon Books, 1979), pp. 274–311.

20. Charles Hampden-Turner, *From Poverty to Dignity* (Garden City, N.Y.: Anchor Books / Doubleday & Co., 1975), especially chap. 6, "Social Marketing and the Organized Poor," pp. 193–228, and chap. 7, "Orchestrating Social Movements," pp. 229–54.

21. Goldrich, "Community Organizers . . ."

22. The following organizations and their publications provide information especially relevant to community controlled economic development and environmental reconstruction:

Self Reliance
Institute for Local Self-Reliance
1717 18th St., N.W.
Washington, D.C. 20009

Center for Community Economic Development Review
Center for Community Economic Development
639 Massachusetts Ave., Suite 316
Cambridge, MA 02139

Ways and Means
Conference on Alternative State and Local Public Policies
1901 Q St., N.W.
Washington, D.C. 20009
(See also their *Public Policies for the '80s,* citing extensive resources.)

NAN Bulletin
National Association of Neighborhoods
1612 20th St., N.W.
Washington, D.C. 20009
(See also their *Neighborhood Economic Enterprises* by N. Kotler.)

Economic Development Law Project Report
National Economic Development Law Project
2150 Shattuck Ave.
Berkeley, CA 94704

The Public Works
Comunity Enterprise, Inc.
6529 Telegraph Ave.
Oakland, CA 94609

A Guide to Cooperative Alternatives
Communities
P.O. Box 426
Louisa, VA 23093

Institute for New Enterprise Development
17 Dunster St.
Cambridge, MA 02138

10 | Beyond Solar: *Design for Sustainable Communities**

Peter Calthorpe
with Susan Benson

SOLAR ENERGY is quickly becoming a false panacea for our energy ills, the Holy Grail of soft technology. The danger now is that this bright technology may cast a long shadow over the broader issues of the patterns of growth and development and their effects on resources, the environment, and people's lives. Quite simply, adding passive solar systems to American homes does save energy inside but does not take into consideration the accompanying land use, infrastructure costs, and transportation demands. In truth, the form and density of housing, the land use patterns, and the resulting transportation systems have a much greater potential for energy savings than any solar applications. If our community-scale development were rational, residential solar applications would need to provide little more than marginal improvements. "Small-scale" may need to be larger than the single-family dwelling, and the "soft path" may have to include more than alternative fuel sources and technological fixes.

Symptomatic treatment of our energy ills belies an understanding of their causes. If a significant reduction in energy consumption is to be achieved, the energy use inside a building cannot be separated from the energy use dictated by its location and its interrelationships with other buildings. A building is tied to energy use not only by its structural and mechanical design, but by its implicit infrastructure (the amount of pipes, roads, and utility wires it demands), and by its connections to employment areas and community services.

Since the Second World War, the predominate symbols of our development—moreover, our progress—have been the growth of suburbia, freeways, and high-rise office buildings. These developments create an infrastructure and a development pattern which must be rethought at the same time that alternate energy solutions are developed. If they are not, there is a danger that solar and other alternate energy sources may become a mechanism to perpetuate these inefficient patterns rather than

---

* Portions of this paper appeared in the article "The Solar Shadow: A Look at Issues Eclipsed," *New Age,* March 1979.

a means to achieve a more environmentally sound culture.

The present emphasis of solar development assumes the continuing expansion of suburbia and focuses on the single-family dwelling. It has been estimated that if all the homes built between now and 1990 employed passive solar heating and cooling systems, as much oil would be saved as is expected to be recovered from the Alaskan North Slope. However, these estimates are based on fuel reductions for heating and cooling alone; not taken into consideration is the Siamese twin of the single-family dwelling—the automobile. If the increased number of automobile trips resulting from the growth between now and 1990 were figured into a net energy analysis, the savings produced by passive solar would be greatly overshadowed.

Single family suburban development demands large amounts of yet another resource in short supply: land. Zoning restrictions and development patterns generally require the single family dwelling to "float" on its site, surrounded by minimum setbacks from the street and neighboring lots. These requirements make suburban development extremely land-inefficient. As available land is demanded by agriculture and industry, in addition to housing, the price inevitably goes up, so that the privacy and space afforded by the single-family home is no longer within the reach of many low- and even middle-income families. Land, like energy, is being squandered.

The potential energy savings that solar heating and cooling of buildings could provide is also undercut by the inherent inefficiency of our common housing forms. Without solar and with a more severe climate, Sweden requires approximately 50 percent less energy use per capita than the United States.

There are many ways that we could greatly reduce the energy demands of new housing. Unless community-scale issues are addressed comprehensively, solar could become a kind of chemotherapy for irrational development.

The cost of sprawl

A thorough investigation of the resource and environmental cost of new developments was made in 1975 by the Real Estate Research Corporation, in the study "The Costs of Sprawl." RERC assessed six model community types most likely to occur on undeveloped land adjacent to existing metropolitan areas. (In the past decade 70 percent of the growth in this country occurred in such areas.) Each community type used in the study contains the same amount of land, 6,000 acres, has 10,000 dwelling units, and a population of 33,000. The communities are made up of detached single-family homes, clustered single-family homes, townhouses, two-story walk-up apartments, six-story apartment buildings, and a combination of all the above.

Land use diagrams for various housing types (Figure 1) clearly illustrate the relative environmental costs of the different development patterns, showing a 200 percent difference in land-consumption between the higher- and lower-density housing projects. In terms of capital costs of construction (which reflect resources consumed in building and to some degree the amount of pollution produced in the process), the comparison yields an identical contrast (Figure 2). The energy consumption of each housing scheme is determined primarily by the amount of automobile use within the development area, combined with the residential heating and cooling consumption. Even though the study does

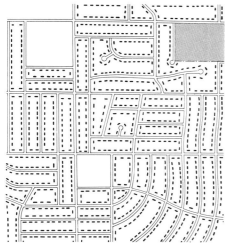

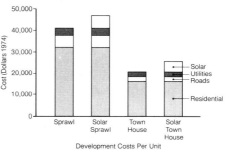

not include the effects of the development's location with respect to job or town centers, the resulting energy consumption difference between the high- and low–density models is nearly 100 percent (Figure 3). In all the issues contrasted, high-density planned developments had a more benign environmental impact than low–density sprawl.

Let us assume that a solar installation, either passive or active, can reduce the energy consumption of each dwelling for heating, cooling, and hot water by 50 percent on a national average. This 50 percent reduction would produce a new graph, in which the average energy consumption for each solar single-family dwelling would still exceed the consumption of the nonsolar, climatically unresponsive, higher-density dwelling by 30 percent! Moreover, this solar application would not significantly affect the water and pollution, transit, or land use comparisons. It would, however, raise the capital costs for the low-density model significantly, fueling the argument that only a financial elite can afford such an environmentally responsive future.

Clearly, the question of how to heat and cool suburban houses may not be as important as the *type* of housing to be heated. Soft technology addresses the issue of keeping technologies in scale with their end uses, but as far as housing is concerned, the end use itself

Figure 1
Land use comparisons of sprawl versus townhouse models: the sprawl model consumes 500 acres, whereas the townhouse model consumes only 200.

Figure 2
Development costs per unit. Energy consumption is also reflected in building costs: materials and labor. The number of linear feet of roads and utilities is 50 percent less for townhouses than for the sprawl model.

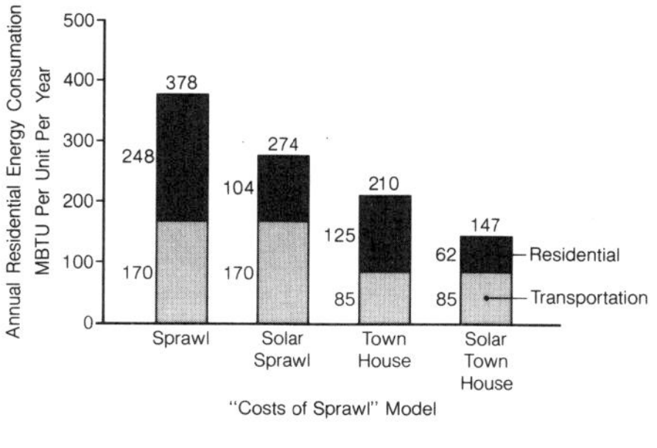

Figure 3
Costs of sprawl model. Most residential models of energy consumption look only at energy consumed for heating, cooling, lighting, and appliances. Implicit in residential energy consumption is energy consumed for transportation. Standard townhouses consume 30 percent less than the sprawl model, while townhouses with solar achieve an even greater energy savings.

has not yet been sufficiently questioned.

Transit

Transportation is the largest nonindustrial energy consumer in this country, accounting for 25 percent of the national energy consumption. In this realm, as in the domain of solar design, conservation ought to precede the implementation of alternative fuel sources. The simplest technique for reducing transportation is to minimize the distance between home and work, commerce, and school. The largest potential for energy conservation lies in mixed-use zoning. Care must be taken to create an environment receptive to pedestrians, bicycle transportation, and local mass transit. These concerns can, in turn, help to support the kind of human-scale urban amenities, (such as cafés, neighborhood parks, and local shops) that generally make higher-density communities more livable.

Overall densities, the pattern of daily activities, and the alternate transit systems available are the issues critical to reducing total auto miles traveled for individuals. Distribution of employment sites (decentralizing downtown employment concentrations), decentralization of commercial site location (the presence of local neighborhood stores and services), and diversification of transit networks (bus, trains, trolleys, bicycles, pedestrian paths) become the significant variables. Many studies of land use and transit energy consumption have reached identical conclusions: Higher-density, mixed-use environments in all cases required less transit per capita.

There is much comparative, empirical information on actual gasoline consumption in different types of cities that supports these conclusions. In their report "Metropolitan Development and Energy Consumption" D. Keyes and G. Peterson analyzed data from 134 cities, correlating gasoline consumption to population, proportion of high-density housing, proportion of jobs located in central districts, miles of four-lane highway, miles of mass transit, household income, and retail price of gas. Their conclusions: "A gasoline-efficient city is small, has a large proportion of its population living in high-density areas, and has a relatively uniform distribution of jobs and population."

Residents of the average single-family household in Portland, Oregon, travel 12,200 miles per year, an equivalent of 136 MBTUs. The typical family living outside the city limits travels 23 percent more miles per year (approximately 35 MBTUs) than the city-dweller. This figure represents the same amount of energy necessary to heat an average low-rise condominium in town for one year. Thus, the urban dweller could heat a home with the energy saved by his / her reduced transit.

The reduction of the national average of 13,000 miles traveled per capita per year not only would be environmentally responsible, in reducing our pollution, but might provide a higher quality of life. The distance that we cover daily and the speed at which we travel clearly affect the integrity of our communities. The automobile has clearly remolded our built environment in scale and function, to the detriment of the human psyche, as well as to resource conservation. Rapid transit speed inversely affects the richness, complexity, and variety of our buildings. Thus far, high speed has been paralleled by the development of larger-scale, abstract, and monolithic buildings, while historically, slower speeds have corresponded with buildings of greater subtlety, articulation, diversity, and depth.

In *Tools for Conviviality* Ivan Illich proposes a culture in which transit speed would be limited to 15 miles per hour. The impact of such a "slow-down" would not only create a greater potential for human interaction, under-standing, and community, it would of necessity implement a reintegration of housing, commerce, and employment. Such a measure might seem extreme, but clearly we must begin to reconsider transit in a broader context encom-passing community scale, cultural concerns, and resource management. Mixed-use planning, transit networks and speeds, and building density and scale are integral aspects of a more eco-logical lifestyle, whereas, solar applica-tions are limited in their ability to change the way we live.

Form, density, and scale

The question of optimum building massing, size, and orientation has been studied extensively. Several empirical studies have shown that the energy de-mand of a multiple-family dwelling can be one-half that of a single-family dwelling—or less. The old row house, with proper orientation, massing, and, most important, its common walls (which typically represent 40 percent of the building's exterior), can achieve thermodynamic results comparable to those of underground houses—today the symbol of energy-conserving, well-insulated, environmentally re-sponsive design. It may be true that burying 40 percent of the single-family dwelling would achieve nearly the same thermodynamic results as the common walls used in multiple-family dwellings, but at what cost? Even though the insulation might be "dirt-cheap," the excavation, special struc-

ture, and waterproofing necessary to use it are not. Thus, perhaps the best argument in favor of underground de-sign concerns not energy conservation but sound insulation and "aesthetic conservation."

The use of appropriate glass orienta-tion, thermal mass, shading and passive solar systems can significantly improve the performance of *all* housing forms, although the single-family dwelling demands more extensive and therefore more expensive modification to pro-vide for its consistantly higher energy requirements. So far many excellent passive designs for single-family resi-dences have been devised, but very few for multiple-family applications. The reason for this lack is not that passive solar is inappropriate for these building types (in fact the reduced loads tend to make this application more cost-effec-tive): lack of development is due both to common preconceptions and gov-ernment policy concerning passive solar feasibility.

With higher-density housing, solar access for each building does become an issue, but, with the increased effi-ciency of the units, proper orientation, and shading setbacks, solar require-ments for severe climates can easily be met. Figure 4 shows a planned cooper-ative housing project in northern Cali-fornia. With ten apartments clustered around a common atrium, the apparent surface area of the building is reduced. The atrium acts as a solar collector as well as an entry vestibule and common space. This project allows thirty-two units per acre, a large area for parking (as required by the city), and some pri-vate space.

An example of a more classical townhouse adapted for passive solar heating is Villa Florence, a low-cost, farmworker housing project planned in Watsonville, California (Figure 5). In

Figure 4
Santa Rosa Creek Co-op, a thirty-two-unit passive-solar, cooperative apartment building to be built in Santa Rosa, California. The atrium serves as both a solar collector and a common entry.

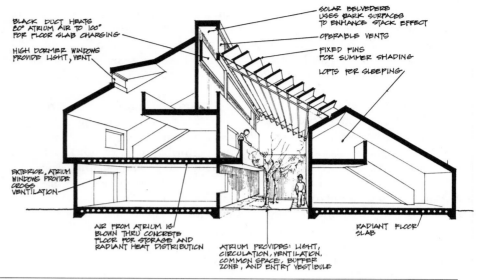

Figure 5
Passive solar townhouses at low-cost farm-worker housing project planned in Watsonville, Cal. This system needs half the greenhouse area and thermal mass of a passive single-family home here.

("Techo." Developers: Environmental Community Housing Organization. Architects: Van der Ryn, Calthorpe, and Ptrs.)

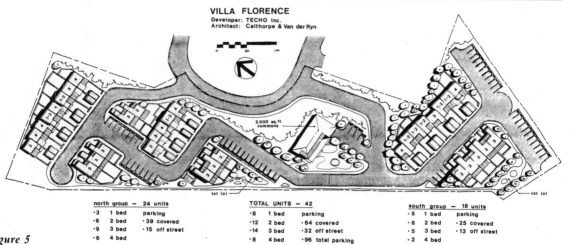

north group — 24 units		south group — 18 units	
•3 1 bed	parking	•5 1 bed	parking
•6 2 bed	• 39 covered	•6 2 bed	• 25 covered
•9 3 bed	• 15 off street	•5 3 bed	• 13 off street
•6 4 bed		•2 4 bed	

TOTAL UNITS — 42	
•8 1 bed	parking
•12 2 bed	• 64 covered
•14 3 bed	• 32 off street
•8 4 bed	• 96 total parking

this case the cement-block common walls, useful for sound insulation and fire safety, are also used for thermal mass. Because of the reduced heating requirements, the passive solar system needs only about one-half the greenhouse area and one-half the thermal mass required for a passive single-family home in the same climate (Figure 6).

In larger-scale buildings for commercial, civic, and other uses, the thermodynamics shift from loads generated by heat loss or gain through the building's exterior to internal loads generated by lighting, equipment, and people. Many of the larger office buildings actually are heating their perimeters at the same time they are cooling their interiors. Since lighting and cooling are often more important at this scale than heating, a new emphasis on natural light and ventilation is necessary. Window shading, building orientation, daylighting, thermal mass, and buffer zones all can reduce energy consumption significantly. "Site One," a new office building for the State of California which employs many of these techniques (Figure 7), has a projected energy consumption of 24,000 BTU per square foot per year, whereas the office tower across the street, built in 1960, consumes close to 150,000.

What is significant in all this is that there appears to be a range of optimum building forms and scales, dependent on use but uniformly human-scaled, walkable, dense, and varied. In housing, these optimums not only are most

of buildings represent, in themselves, a strong indictment of the unholy alliance of office tower, freeway, and suburban tract.

Process and development

The continuous dichotomy through the history of development strategies —ranging from the utopian communities of the nineteenth century through garden cities to the urban highrise, the federal highway subsidy, and the re-

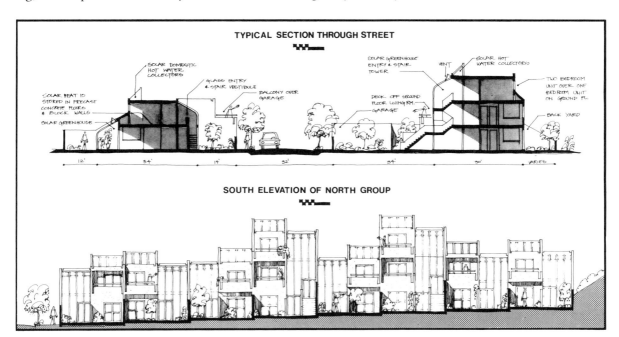

cost-effective with the application of solar but seem to coincide with the optimal energy and transit systems for higher-density developments. In addition, low-rise, high-density housing forms are more suitable for district heating and use of the waste heat produced by electrical generation—that is, co-generation. (In Sweden 19 percent of residential heat is supplied by a district-scale hot water system that uses waste heat from electrical generators.) The heat-loss thermodynamics

sulting growth of suburbia—has been perceived as being a case of centralized planning versus decentralized, autonomous action. This interpretation is a misconception, however: development is nearly *always* planned, no matter how scattered and irrational the outcome may appear. The true distinction involves the goals and concerns of the planning—the long-term versus the short-term view.

The solar home—promoted as a decentralized, do-it-yourself, small-scale

Figure 6

Sectional drawings showing typical section through street and south elevation of North Group, Villa Florence.

Figure 7
*"Site One," a 250,000
sq. ft. energy-
efficient office building
for the State of Cal-
ifornia, recently com-
pleted in Sacramento.*

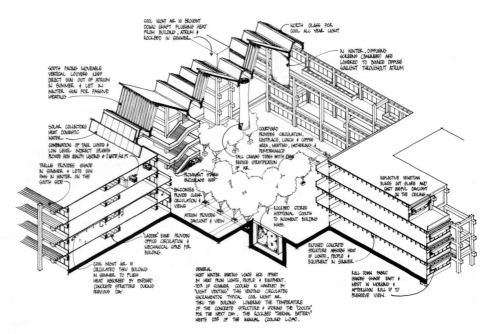

alternative to massive technologies—reinforces the notion of living autonomously and therefore diminishes the sense of interdependence necessary for comprehensive solutions to interactive environmental problems. Suburbia has always been an escape—an escape from cities, from communities, from neighbors, from poverty. The danger inherent in the current image of a solar suburbia, as a soft path to a sane culture, is not just that it overlooks important environmental issues but that it advances the technology of escapism.

Today there is a tendency to take a safe, save-the-wilderness-in-my-back-yard approach in preference to tackling thornier inner city problems. The vision of a self-sufficient suburban future has distracted many solar advocates from the pressing social problems of urban decay; yet, ironically the solution to those urban problems may hold more potential for energy-efficiency than do short-term, single family-oriented solar solutions. Climate-responsive design—including solar sys-

tems where applicable—can have its greatest impact in urban centers.

A classic example of ecologically sound urban pattern capable of supporting a strong, centered community can be found in the courtyard house of Peking, which offers privacy, solar access, and a cultural fabric of great richness and diversity. Each court is surrounded by the dwellings of four to five families (comprising up to thirty individuals) and a common work space, usually located on the south side of the court. Significantly, the courtyard house is the basic political grouping from which a representative is elected to the neighborhood committee. Thus, family, social, political, and cultural patterns are expressed in this fine-grained, human-scaled environment.

Some recent development plans have begun to focus more on creating humane and vital town centers than on energy or resource conservation per se (though they do contain ecological features). A plan for the village of Aptos, a

Figure 8
Capitol area plan, a mixed use, low-rise, high-density plan to allow state workers to walk to work.
(Van der Ryn, Calthorpe and Partners.)

small town near Santa Cruz, calls for a mixed-use village center made up of commercial sites, offices, and townhouses all located in the same zone. This mix is woven together with a network of internal pedestrian paths and a system of bicycle pathways connecting the village to surrounding areas. Similarly, the recently adopted Capitol Area Plan for downtown Sacramento (Figure 8) calls for mixed, low-rise residential and commercial development in a zone dominated by office buildings which, until now, has been essentially evacuated every day at 5:00 P.M. Interestingly, although the plan calls for energy-conserving features in buildings, and will in fact reduce transit, infrastructure, distribution, heating, and cooling requirements, conservation was not a major rationale: concentrated land use and community coherence played a larger role.

The problem with planned development is that, viewed simplistically, it can seem oppressive, conjuring up images of a totalitarian, Kafkaesque, bureaucratic labyrinth. Solar designs, on the other hand, offer up visions of total self-sufficiency, a quality much prized by those seeking alternatives today, whether in terms of schooling, health technologies, or communities. The autonomous house is advanced as not only an energy-conserving residence, but a complete ecosystem. Models such as the Integral Urban House of the Farallones Institute and the New Alchemy Ark on Prince Edward Island, although working toward complex ends, inevitably tend to reinforce the image of single-family independence. This fascination with autonomy has led to a bizarre marriage of appropriate technology advocates and private sector developers; together they threaten to colonize rural land and curtail already limited open space.

In failing to demand the organization of community-scale efforts, many sectors of the appropriate technology movement tacitly condone speculative, land-exploitive suburban development. The alternative to single-family,

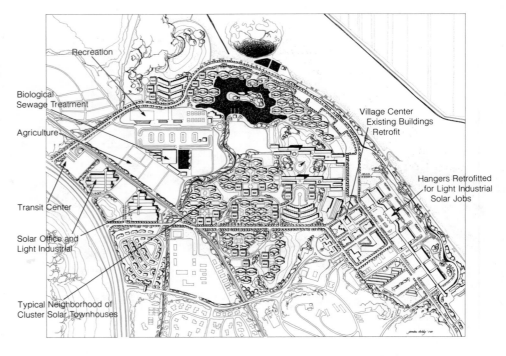

detached homes need not be leisure condominiums or government high-rise housing projects. Community groups could—and should—play a major planning role in the development of their own neighborhoods, along with local planners and builders. Residential cooperatives, for example, offer an opportunity for groups of individuals to participate in designing complexes—a task normally left to developers. Whole towns could be created in which open space and individual privacy are provided—towns whose housing designs incorporate the environmental options of a rational transit system, clustered utilities and services at a lower cost, and small-scale agricultural projects. That individual expression is still possible in a planned high-density context is demonstrated by the residential areas of many older cities, where architectural diversity, visual complexity, and personal uses exist side by side.

Marin Solar Village: A plan for a sustainable community

Perhaps the most ambitious energy-conserving community plan to date is a current proposal to transform the 1,271-acre site of Hamilton Air Force Base in Marin County, California, into a model of energy-conserving strategies and integrated systems on the town scale. The air force base, now excess property, has been offered by G.S.A. to the County of Marin for civilian activities. Amidst a flurry of proposals, including a shopping center and regional airport, Van der Ryn, Calthorpe & Partners and the office of Gordon Ashby have sketched a development plan which integrates economic and social issues with the regional and national environmental concerns of sprawl and energy (Figure 9).

Jane Jacobs, long an advocate of diverse and supportive urban neighborhoods, should find a potent weapon in the energy crisis. Energy-conserving

planning strategies will inevitably re-direct growth back to the cities where density, mixed use, and mass transit potential combine to reduce fuel con-sumption. In the East this force no doubt will have the positive effect of spurring inner city redevelopment and infill. In the Sunbelt growth zones, the resource shift will find a different ex-pression. The Marin proposal, as a model, would substitute coherent, re-source-sufficient, satellite communities for sprawling bedroom communities. The plan proposes a growth pattern with lowered demands on national re-sources as well as on the local infra-structure (roads, power, sewer) and its debilitating capital costs.

The strategies employed in the plan principally involve existing technolo-gies and design practice. Foremost is the mixed-use plan and low-rise, high-density housing (Figure 10). Approx-imately 1900 new townhouse and apartment-type dwellings would be built over a ten-year period in five distinct neighborhoods, giving an over-all density of approximately four units per acre. All dwellings are planned with private gardens and terraces as well as passive solar heating and natural ventilation. But the solar component merely augments the efficiencies of party walls and floors for reducing residential energy demands.

There are no through streets in any neighborhood. Each neighborhood is bounded by a loop road. Cars are parked under buildings or in peripheral surface lots. No home is more than 400 feet from the car. Neighborhoods are connected by pedestrian and bicycle lanes that are accessible to special ser-vice vehicles.

By clustering the housing with a vil-lage center and light industry park within walking distance, the standard transit component of new suburbs is greatly reduced. On average, 40 per-cent of a family's transit is for the type of services and recreation located cen-trally in the proposed solar village (Fig-ure 11). The expectation is for up to 50 percent of the population to work on site (Figure 12). The existing airplane hangers will be renovated for 650,000 sq. ft. of commercial space in addition to a new corporate center. As growth has been limited throughout the Bay by environmental and transit con-straints, the Marin Village plan has be-come an attractive option for many local firms for a new expansion site that will overcome the county's con-straints with a positive concept.

A more ambitious proposal is the re-

(Continued on page 327)

Figure 9-b

Site model of Marin Solar Village showing: commercial agriculture center with solar green-houses and Solar Aquacell System for ecological waste treat-ment and methane energy production (left center); lakefront resi-dential area (upper left); village center and adjacent neighborhoods (right center); corporate center and transit center (lower center); light in-dustrial zone (upper right).

Figure 10
*Four typical passive
solar attached housing
types configured to
allow 100 percent solar
access, private yards,
shared open space, and
up to 80 percent solar
heating. (a) Town-
house cluster of up to 14
units around a shared
plaza employing a com-
bination of greenhouse,
direct gain, and Trombe
wall passive solar sys-
tems; (b) Atrium
apartments of 10 units
sharing a solar atrium
as entry and heat source;
(c) South terrace hous-
ing of stacked town-
houses on the site's south
slopes. Each unit has
private entry and south-
facing decks; (d) Solar
rowhouses define a
pedestrian street. Direct
gain and Trombe wall
solar systems are
employed.*

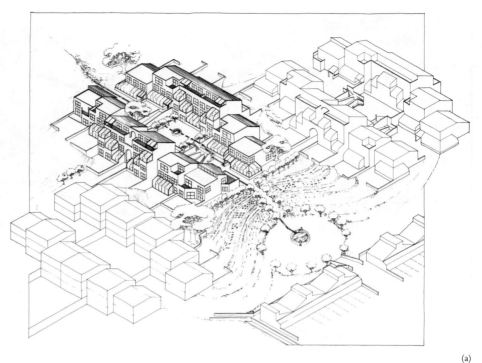

(a)

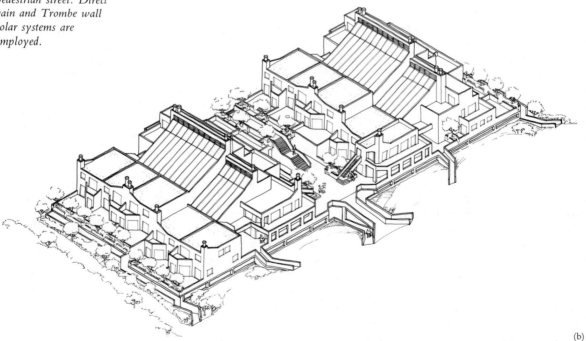

(b)

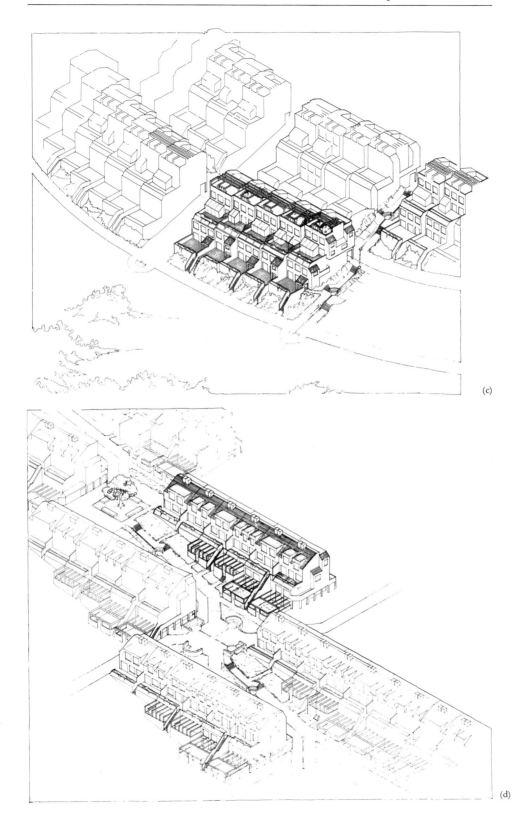

(c)

(d)

Figure 11
Recreation center converted from an Air Force hanger— swords into plowshares.

Figure 12
New office space provides on-site jobs in energy efficient structures. Atrium buffer zones, day lighting, and night ventilation reduce energy consumption by 70 percent.

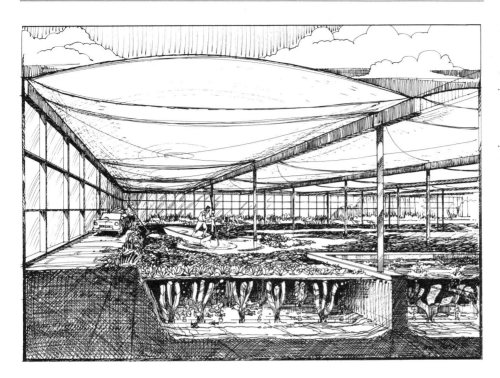

Figure 13

Biological sewage treatment plant employs solar ponds under inflated greenhouse to accelerate the nutrient cycle. The system produces biomass methane, fertilizer, and feed from sewage.

(Continued from page 323)

duction of autos in the Village and residential core. Currently, 30 to 50 percent of our urban and suburban land area is dedicated to the auto. Reducing automobile access will create inconvenience but will make possible a more compact, human-scaled community. It will also reduce road area, pollution levels, energy consumption, capital costs, drainage systems, water table depletion, and the higher microclimate temperatures caused by black top "collectors." From a proposed transit center, an abandoned railroad spur will be activated, linking commuters to the Ferry and San Francisco.

On-site electrical power generation to manage peak power demands is proposed. Such community-scaled systems allow the waste heat of generation to be used in district heating systems for commercial greenhouses, residential and some light process industry purposes. Once again, the density and

compactness of the community is critical. Such district heating systems are common in Europe, with Sweden providing for 19 percent of its residential demands with the waste heat of power plants. In the United States, 68.8 percent of the energy used in electrical power generation is wasted, while in Sweden 47 percent is wasted, with 24 percent supplying heat to district and industrial systems.

The proposal matches its power, transit, and building program with ecologically-sound, biological support systems. Rather than a standard chemical process sewage plant, the plan calls for a total biological treatment process (Figure 13). This system, developed by Solar AquaSystems, San Diego, introduces the "waste" back into the nutrient cycle, producing hyacinths (commonly "water lillies") for biomass or feed, edible shrimp, fresh potable water, and recreational ponds. Such a system is now being constructed for the city of Hercules, California.

As the cost of transit rises, the economics of food production will shift. Truck farms around New York are making a comeback. Biomass and water from the sewage system will be used in on-site farming operations and community gardens at Marin Solar Village. Wherever possible, edible plants and trees will be employed as landscaping within the Village. Fish farming will be a major industry. Much of the site which is currently diked and pumped will be returned to the Bay or managed for a combination of salt water, brackish water, and freshwater food production. An employment base is created, a fuel efficient, nutritional food source is supplied—it takes 1.5 pounds of feed to produce one pound of fish, as compared to 15 pounds of feed for each pound of beef produced— and land is returned to its natural state.

What of the social and economic structure of such an environmental Utopia? As a replacement for the monoculture of suburbia, with its economic segregation, Marin would be a clear improvement. By renovating some 130 existing housing units, lower income groups and the elderly will be accommodated. The range of employment and social services planned should nourish a diverse community. The development economics appear to be strong, with the efficiency of high-density housing and the reduced infrastructure requirements creating a potential for lower costs. As federal policy shifts away from highway subsidies, as utility capital costs soar, power generation is constrained and more agricultural land is consumed, local governments will begin to suffer the economic burden of energy inefficient growth patterns. This will inevitably

lead to zoning and government subsidies conducive to developments such as the Marin proposal.

Clearly, the idea of Marin Village is not new. Ebenezer Howard's "Garden City" and Wright's "Broadacre" are both Utopian models of environmentally-integrated communities. Each in its own way was a visionary response to the pressures of urban growth. Each had political and social underpinnings; Howard's a socialist structure for the worker, Wright's a Jeffersonian concept of independent and self-sufficient families. Marin Solar Village, however close in appearance to the new towns and garden cities, is responding to a different set of pressures. Rather than urban overcrowding and alienation, it responds to the inefficiencies of sprawl, the false economies of subsidized fuel, the exploitation of land and resources, and the environmental impact of a consumer society. It is an attempt to reurbanize growth in the United States to move towards the vitality, diversity and integration that cities can offer. As the economic results of the energy crisis crystalize, it may become difficult to discern if the Marin plan is visionary or mandatory, Utopian or merely expedient.

It is clear that development of any alternative technology must be seen in a comprehensive social, political, and environmental framework. Alternative technologies must be used as tools for new settlement patterns, rather than as compensations for the old. Clearly, the belief that a technology alone can significantly change our culture, or sufficiently alter our patterns of energy consumption, is erroneous. Solar energy must be considered in conjunction with the more vital concerns of integrated development, town planning, land preservation, and resource management.

11 | Urban Agriculture
A Strategy for Transition to a Solar Society
William and Helga Olkowski

TODAY AGRICULTURE IS essentially the business of producing food, while in the past it was also a way of life upon which all else depended. The small garden or plot is still the primary source of food in many parts of the world, but agribusiness, the large scale, highly mechanized food and fiber production system common all over North America, is the primary food source for the "developed" industrialized nations. Although this food system is touted as being more advanced, thus better than the back-breaking agriculture of old, it has many important problems that augur the need for future changes. Among the more critical problems are the high fossil fuel subsidies that are driving the costs of food production upward, through increasing costs of fuels, fertilizers, labor, pesticides and machinery for the producer. (A comparison of the fossil energy costs of production for major agribusiness crops is presented in Table 1.) Other major problems that influence the economics and social workings of modern agriculture include urban encroachment, increasing mechanization, and the loss of native plant and animal

germ plasm potentially useful in biological control and breeding programs.

Urban agriculture addresses all these problems and provides a direction for humanity to evolve a new cultural path. This article explores various aspects of this emerging decentralizing cultural force in agriculture.

The food-fuel equation
The solar income

Calories are the universal measure of fuel. A "small" calorie (c) is the amount of heat needed to raise the temperature of one gram of water one degree centigrade. It is also called the gram calorie. The calorie of the weight watcher, abbreviated "C" is a large calorie or kilocalorie equal to 1,000 small calories. A gallon of gasoline can provide 31,500,000 small calories. A resting 150-lb. adult uses nearly 3,000 small (gram) calories per minute, or about 3,000 large calories per day.

But humans cannot eat gasoline. Food is the fuel of humanity. A hundred grams of hard red spring wheat contains approximately 160,000 small calories. Both gasoline and wheat calo-

Table 1
Fossil energy usage of major U.S. crops

Crop	Fossil Energy Flux★ (MCAL/ACRE/DAY)
Tobacco (flue cured)	125
Vegetables and fruit (average)	56
Rice	34
Pasture (fertilized, irrigated)	23
Peanuts	18
Corn silage	17
Corn grain	17
Sorghum grain	16
Cotton	14
Sugar beets	11
Sugar cane	9
Barley	6
Alfalfa	6
Soybeans	5
Wheat (spring)	5
Oats	4
Pasture (fertilized)	2
Range	0.03

Source: G. H. Heichel, "Energy Resources and Forage Production," Symposium on food production and energy, present status and future alternatives, American Association for the Advancement of Science, February, 1978.
★ MCAL/ACRE/DAY = million kilocalories per acre per day

ries are derived from the sun. The gasoline is the stored and concentrated energy of the sun, accumulated by plants from the sunlight falling over a large area over a long period of time. In the same sense, coal is concentrated solar energy. By comparison with gasoline or coal, the daily incoming sunlight is dilute, providing approximately 76,000 gram calories per square foot every hour on a sunny June midday at the latitude of San Francisco.[1]

Coal and gasoline, the fossil fuels, have provided the energy capital for the concentration of modern human populations into the huge, centralized living and working networks we recognize as the 20th Century metropolitan areas. But our finite supply of fossil solar capital is rapidly being depleted. We must turn from living on our capital (fossil fuels) to living on our income (daily and seasonal flows of solar energy).

A funny thing happened to the human fuel production system on the way to the last quarter of the 20th Century. After a millennium of supporting our species on dilute solar income we evolved modern agribusiness, heavily dependent on a fossil fuel subsidy. It has been estimated that in a number of U.S. crops, 10 calories of fossil fuel are consumed to produce 1 calorie of human food. This calculation takes into consideration only the fuel for the agricultural machinery and chemicals (pesticides and fertilizers); if the energy needed to package, promote and distribute the food to our present centralized populations is included, the ratio is even higher. Of course, a hundred years ago, New Yorkers did not expect fresh Mexican tomatoes in January, nor could one find frozen South African lobster tails in Butte, Montana in any season. Delicacies aside, however, what will we do when the solar capital is no longer abundantly and cheaply available to truck our food to the city, or to drive to the local supermarket to pick it up?

In the U.S., more than 70 percent of the people now live in over 7,000 communities considered urban (over 25,000 people). But that statement, developed from U.S. Bureau of Census data, does not provide a sufficiently insightful picture. Urban communities are not the towns of yesteryear, surrounded with nearby farmland and much of the water and mineral resources needed to support them. Rather, many are parts of what are referred to as "standard metropolitan statistical areas" (SMSAs). These SMSAs with their population concentrations and concommitant concentrations of calorie need, are characterized by the centralization of services.

Centralized water treatment, waste management, fire and police protection, public landscaping, even centralized school and information systems, are examples of common urban life support systems that have spawned the huge bureaucracies with which most of us are familiar. Together with the complex of large corporations that bring us such amenities as the identical fried-chicken, canned goods, cosmetics, vehicles, clothing and appliances from coast to coast, these centralized systems help to promote a sense of victimization in each of us individually. Control over our lives seems to be in the hands of a very few who are relatively unapproachable except by those representing special interests backed by large financial resources.

In response, in varying degrees, many urban dwellers are now crying out for increased control over their own lives. Though occasionally expressed in the form of self-defeating efforts, such as measures that reduce the local tax base and thus shift control away from local government to State or Federal government, the longing for greater autonomy is unmistakable. This may take the form of yearning for the real or fancied self-reliance of rural and small town life.

Rural / urban lifestyles

The mass media, federal efforts to stabilize farm income, a college education, and corporate farming are some of the diverse factors that have helped to convert a large number of farm inhabitants to urban lifestyles. Rural dress, home furnishings, and landscaping, food and entertainment preferences are modeled after those in TV-land and cannot be distinguished from their big city counterparts. Nevertheless, the ideal of smaller more comprehensible and controllable living units not only remains in the U.S. consciousness but has taken on a special urgency with the growing perception of the coming scarcity of solar capital, or fossil fuels, and the "energy crunch."

It is interesting to compare some of

the advantages of the ideal of classical rural life with the glamour of the urban environment that originally lured large populations to the cities.

characteristics than the rest of the world. About 80 percent of the total arable land (400-million acres, or MA) is under cultivation. In addition, about

Classical (Ideal) Rural Advantages	Classical (Ideal) Urban Advantages
1. Close to the soil and food production	Escape from low-status, dirty agricultural work
2. Clean air, water, soil, food	Variety of food choices and manufactured, human-created landscapes
3. Work matched with seasons and personal rhythms	Cash rewards for work in a wide variety of settings
4. Close to wild plants and animals—in touch with nature	Close to other people
5. Regular physical exercise	Relief from physically strenuous work settings
6. Quiet, away from city noise, close to the sounds of nature	Proximity to diverse cultural, educational, and entertainment sources
7. Being one's own boss, wresting one's life support from nature	Job security within human networks which provide a buffer against the uncertainties of weather and other natural forces

Even from such a simplistic comparison some things are evident. Implicit in a number of the "advantages" of urban life is the concentrated calories or energy consumption, the dependence on solar capital we spoke of earlier. How is it possible to have the best of both worlds? Urban agriculture is one way, and knowing about the changes in land use patterns helps one understand the scope and magnitude of the forces that are already altering the patterns of the urban and rural settlements.

Urbanization destroys agricultural land

Only 11 percent of the earth's land surface is arable, or usable, for crop production. In the U.S., 25 percent of about 470-million acres is naturally suitable for agriculture. Thus, the U.S. has on the average better land and soil

780 MA are in pasture and rangeland and 470 MA are in forest. About 75 MA could be drained, irrigated, graded or otherwise converted to agricultural production if the money and energy were available for such expensive schemes, and if this could be pursued without pressure from conservationists.

A recent study of non-Federal land use changes by USDA's Soil Conservation Service (SCS) indicates that the loss of cropland is occurring faster than previously thought—about 10 MA per year have gone out of cropland since 1967, reducing agricultural land by 79.2 MA for the period 1967–1975.[2] During the same period, 48.7 MA have been converted to cropland— roughly 6 MA per year. Over this period, the net loss of cropland has been 30.5 MA, or almost 4 MA per year.

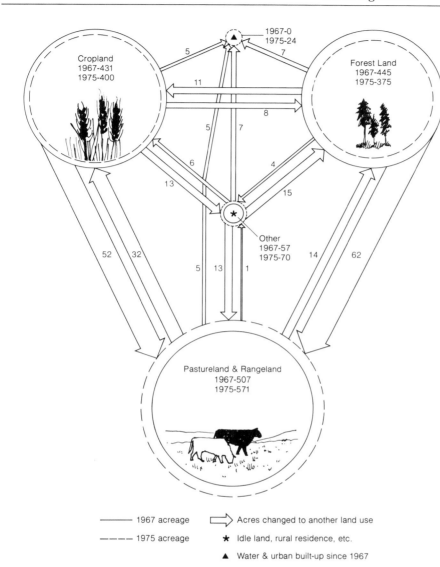

Figure 1

Land use conversions between 1967 and 1975 (million acres)

Source: Potential Cropland Study, *U.S.D.A. Soil Conservation Service, Statistical Bulletin, no. 578 (1977)*

The actual SCS measurements of net changes in the different land use categories are indicated in Figure 1. Of the 24 MA indicated as converted to urban or inundated by water, 17 MA were converted to urban, and other build-up areas (often with Federal assistance—about 2.1 MA per year). During the period covered by this study, approximately 30 percent of the land converted to urban areas came directly from cropland, about 0.6 MA per year.

About 60 percent of this land, and 40 percent of the 7 MA converted to water, were in the highest cropping quality land classification (I to III). Thus, not only is urbanization occurring in food-producing areas, but it is often doing so on the highest quality soils. Further, the rate of conversion to urban land use is occurring faster than previously estimated; a total of 24 MA is being held for eventual urban development. The conversion of these prime production soils to asphalt, concrete, buildings, etc., is an irreversible process representing a loss not only to U.S. populations but, because the U.S. exports a great deal of food, it represents a loss to the world community.

Insofar as this agricultural land is not replaced by new, intensive forms of food and fiber production or by solar collectors for generating electricity, heating water and buildings, it represents a loss of solar income. In addition, it includes the loss of:

- The esthetic value of open space
- Water collection sites for replenishment of ground water and catchment for surface waters
- Protection of environmentally sensitive areas like wetlands and flood plains
- Wildlife habitat, e.g., deer, grouse, quail, pheasant, rabbit
- Waste treatment areas—both a depository for sludge and as a place where particulates and other air pollutants are filtered out

Table 2
Conversion to urban and built-up areas and water between 1967 and 1975, by farm production region [thousand acres]

Region	Urban	Water
Northeast	1,318	110
Lake states	1,231	140
Corn Belt	2,149	575
Northern Plains	867	289
Appalachian	2,183	269
Southeast	2,615	3,275
Delta states	800	144
Southern Plains	1,170	1,321
Mountain	1,242	82
Pacific	1,318	110
AK, HI, PR, VI	263	26

Source: *Potential Cropland Study,* U.S.D.A. Soil Conservation Service Statistical Bulletin, no. 528 (1977)

At least the following factors contribute to the loss of agricultural land.

1. *Historical patterns:* In this country, urban centers developed close to agricultural production areas for purposes of trade and to supply manufactured goods to a still largely rural population. At first little prime land was used and the loss was insignificant and tolerable. As the urban population grew, these centers expanded "naturally" along rivers, harbors, and on the deep, rich, well-drained soils of their adjacent former agricultural resources base.

The same characteristics that make an area viable for agriculture make it attractive for construction of roads and buildings: level topography, and availability of water and deep soils which are easy to manipulate (compared with rocky or steep areas).

2. *Government assistance projects:* Grants for sewers, waste treatment facilities, dams, water distribution systems, highways and Federal buildings and other facilities frequently take place without regard for or recognition of the fact that farmlands are finite resources of high public value. Private lending institutions also have a hand in this process.

3. *Economic pressures on farmers:* As urban areas expand, the cost and value of the land begins to rise, often pushed by speculation. As the adjacent land increases in value, so do property taxes, and estate and inheritance taxes. Soon the value of the land for urban development outweighs what the farmer can make from production. The farmer, therefore, has great incentives to sell.

4. *Urban encroachment:* The expanding urban areas bring vandalism. Air pollution reduces crop yield. Increased traffic makes it difficult and dangerous to drive farm machinery on the road. Complaints from urban neighbors arise over manure, fertilizer, and pesti-

cide applications. As political power shifts, ordinances that restrict bees, chickens, goats, and other animals become more common.

5. *The farmer's view of the future:* As farmers become convinced that their land will eventually be urbanized, they stop investing in improvements that can be passed on to future generations —an "impermanent" syndrome sets in. This change in thought process can precede the actual change in land use but it becomes a self-fulfilling prophecy. Many farmers, certain that the urban area will take their farm, merely wait for it to happen and sell to the highest bidder when they are ready to retire.

Regardless of the mechanism for increasing the size of urban areas, what is clear is that the best land for food production is being covered by urban areas. Thus, we will be forced to produce food on these spaces if an adequate supply of calories is to be available. Calories, however, are not the only limits to the growth of living systems. Minerals necessary for life support can also be limiting.

Mineral resources as a limiting factor

Traditionally, urban areas have represented a halfway-house for mineral resources, extracted in the countryside and on their way to the dump, or "sanitary" landfill. Yet, as our solar capital in the form of fossil fuels becomes scarce, the minerals extracted using this capital will become a limiting factor upon our society. How the flow of minerals, as well as energy and money, is controlled must ultimately determine the productivity of a region. Reuse and recycling of mineral resources must inevitably become sufficiently attractive to influence the shift of established subsidies away from new to secondary materials.

The potential for local recycling of materials, the growth of urban areas upon agricultural soils, the ideal of self-reliance and the appreciation of nature, and the dilute nature of solar income, all have implications for urban food production as a decentralizing mechanism and a strategy for transition to a solar society.

The shift to a solar society
Biosolar collectors

Plants are solar powered mineral extraction systems, or geosolar engines. Microbes also can be used to release minerals from rock sources, once extracted from the soil-water solution. The arrangement of these minerals in plants, their chemical composition and variation, is the basis for all animal life. These chemical configurations are thus the raw material of human civilization.

The solar income to a specific spot of earth changes little when houses, apartments, factories, and stores replace the farmer's crops. Perhaps air pollution does cause some modification of calorie production potential, but basically the sun continues to shine daily upon asphalt, cement and shingle as ever it did before on productive forests or fields. To observe this daily income of energy come and go, unharnessed by geosolar engines, is like watching oil leak away from an uncapped well. But unlike oil, the solar energy income is dispersed, and its collection must also of necessity be dispersed, or "decentralized."

The challenge before us is to learn how to use this dispersed incoming solar energy and other, indirect, solar processes (such as wind, water and biological action) to make or extract most of the products we now make primarily from and / or with the aid of fossil fuels: fertilizers, fuels, oils, medicines, paints, dyes, preservatives, soaps, pesticides, clothing, utensils, building materials, and so on. Of course, in many, if not most cases, it is fueling the manufacturing and distribution or transportation processes themselves that will be the most difficult problem to solve.

The social changes required to shift to a society based on solar income are quite substantial. New aggregations of people will form around the new solar production units, markets, and services. The rising cost of transportation will inevitably mean a return to a more dispersed population with more decentralized life support systems. "Solar sense," a comon sense informed of the solar facts of life, would suggest that the green belts of urban centers be composed of intermediate-scaled, highly intensive and / or specialty farms. The farms themselves will inevitably become centers for the production of goods and human foods rather than merely raw materials for processing elsewhere into saleable products. To the age-old production of fiber will be added that of fuel and oil. What could the urban areas produce?

Why urban agriculture?

It is easy to look ahead and see that the reduction of fuel and mineral supplies will change most current social activities and patterns. A basic question for each of us is whether these changes will be thrust upon us or whether we will deliberately create the world we want. Urban agriculture is one constructive way to encourage and provide for a more even transition to the solar society and the changes in group consciousness.

By urban agriculture, or urbagriculture, we mean the small-scale, intensive production of food close to living areas, in backyards, empty lots and parks, on rooftops and porches and indoors. In the United States, urban food production, including some small animal raising, was common during the depression and in "victory gardens" during World War II, and, during the last decade, has once again become popular. Since current food production systems use fossil fuels at many points, the price of certain foods has tended to rise as fast or faster than the fuels. This has added economic incentives to a movement that was originally motivated more by interest in developing personal self-reliance and getting back in touch with nature.

When large numbers of urban individuals and families produce some of their own food a number of simultaneous changes can occur:

1. *People, with their own labor, produce some part of their life support directly:* This, in turn, provides tax free, direct economic support, saving money partially in proportion to how much effort is expended. Community gardens and greenhouses can become the support supplement for those without land of their own. Through personal direct energy investment and wise selection of crops, those foods that command a relatively high price in the market become available through small or no cash investment, for example, when saving and swapping of seeds or plants takes place (herbs are a good example).

The direct production of even a small amount of one's own life support, with the sense of self-reliance that it engenders, provides mental and physical health benefits that may be difficult to quantify but seem already to be generally well-recognized. A nation of people that in a single decade can become joggers and runners and modify its fat intake (with a related dramatic drop in mortality from heart disease) should recognize the health and economic benefits from growing their own food.

2. *Fossil fuel energy is conserved:* The foods that are most likely to be grown in intensive urban outdoor and solar greenhouse settings are the very ones that consume the most fossil fuel energy in proportion to consumable calories when produced on the farm: tomatoes, lettuce, and other salad greens, and strawberries are good common examples. In the large scale production of these foods, fossil fuel is expended in plowing, herbiciding, fertilizing, pesticiding, cultivating, harvesting, sorting, cooling, transporting, distributing and storing. By comparison, a crop such as wheat is relatively less energy intensive to produce, store and distribute on a mass scale. Its cultivation lends itself to large-scale mechanized settings. At the same time, small-scale intensive production of vegetable crops substitutes hand labor for mechanized work, uses recycled organic matter and applies different standards of appearance and uniformity, (see items 3 and 6) with an overall reduction in fossil fuel demand.

Simply moving the production of some foods closer to the consumption point, and reducing cooling and storage needs through use of solar greenhouses to extend the seasons, has the potential of saving fossil fuel.

3. *Food is available with fewer pesticide residues:* Intensive small-scale food production can be accomplished with less pesticide use because hand and other labor intensive alternatives are viable; problems may be less severe through a diversity of plantings; and losses to pests are most tolerable, particularly cosmetic losses, since the products don't have to compete in the market place, they are consumed even if subject to some slight insect damage. Harvest wastes can be recycled faster and easier.

4. *Nutritional improvements are possible:* Growing food close to the home means there is less time between harvest and consumption, and that it can be picked and consumed at peak ripeness, when vitamin levels are highest. With many vegetables both factors can be important in obtaining optimal quality. Some can be eaten raw, fresh from the plant, often the most nutritious way of all (but they should be washed because of lead dust due to fallout from automobile exhaust and other air pollutants).

5. *Greater variety of vegetable foods becomes available:* In home and community gardens and greenhouses it is possible to raise varieties of common vegetables too succulent or fragile to withstand the rigors of mechanical harvesting or treatment during transportation and market distribution common in commercial operations. Exotic or ethnic foods can be raised that are often high priced and / or hard to find in standard markets because of low demand. A number of smaller U.S. seed nurseries now specialize in vegetable varieties that have only regional interest or old-time favorites that for various reasons (not flavor, nutrition or beauty, but mainly the mechanization of agriculture), are now no longer available from farms.

6. *Recycling technologies gain acceptability:* Composting organic kitchen wastes and garden debris has experienced both a gardening and municipal revival in the U.S. during the last decade. As more people realize that nitrogen is one of the main limiting factors for plant growth, they will begin to appreciate the value of their own urine and feces. Wastes that were once refuse will become "acceptable." This will encourage the adoption of safe ways of handling these resources locally and this in turn will conserve, and reduce

the need to produce, synthetic fertilizers.

7. *Agricultural policy, land use and nutrition become more comprehensible to urbanites:* As large numbers of urban people begin to understand the basics of plant, animal and soil care, the need to protect and nurture the country's agricultural base will become obvious.

8. *Some agricultural land may be freed for production of fuel, export, and other products that do not serve the home table directly:* "Solar sense" directs the marketplace, that is, it is used more frequently to determine what crops agricultural land is selected to produce, rather than depending on tradition alone or artificially-based subsidies.

9. *Urban food production facilities become part of urban planning and design:* Roofs, parks, housing projects, etc., will be designed to provide space for family and community gardens and greenhouses. The "ecotect," ecologist-architect-urban planner, will become a key professional in the solar society. Just as today our houses, apartments, office buildings, stores and warehouses are expected to meet certain standards in terms of foundations, electrical wiring, water conveyance, and so on, eventually people will expect that their basic design and construction provide spaces and facilities for collecting solar energy, through food plants and other means, as well as ways to recycle mineral resources within the system itself, or collect them for community recycling. A flat roof or deck too weak to support containers of food plants? A porch without a section closed with glass to provide greenhouse or cold frame space? A hospital, military installation, or library grounds with expanses of unused grass instead of community food gardens? A south-facing wall or roof without a collector? That's like walking into City Hall and finding

a dusty dirt floor and a smelly outhouse in back. It is not only outmoded, it offends the "solar sense!"

Fire and police protection, street sweeping, libraries, schools, public transportation and preventive health clinics are now regarded as minimal facilities that should be provided through the multitude of formal cooperative arrangements among people represented by municipal governments and associated private institutions. In the same way, parks providing indoor and outdoor community food growing spaces must be expected, and demanded (also constructed, and maintained), as an integral part of the urban areas of the near future.

10. *Children are educated in school on the many possible ways of harnessing the dilute solar income:* Constructing a collector for heating household hot water is technologically simple, but a child isn't born knowing how to build one; so, too, raising food intensively, while not difficult, must be learned. Such skills are as necessary to individual and family survival in the solar society as knowing how to read, use a calculator, or turn the knobs on the TV, and certainly must become part of every child's elementary education.

Some examples
An integral urban house

1. *The Ideal:* Ideals are goals that may never be reached. They function to inspire and motivate. The integral urban house is such an ideal. The concept is that of a human habitat that goes beyond the functions of the typical home.

In the usual sense the house protects against the extremes of regional climate and daily weather. It buffers against the cold and heat, wind, sunlight, dust, and rain. By moving food preparation and storage, water and waste conveyance and power distribution into the house, what was primarily a climate buffer becomes a complex system for processing basic life support resources. Add to this the telephone, radio, television, stereo and computers, and services and information exchanges, it becomes possible to go well beyond primary physiological needs. The occupants of the home have become connected not only to their local community but to humanity at large, both geographically through global media, and historically in terms of the arts of civilization.

But for all that, if the development of the home ends there, the house remains a parasite upon the land and a total burden upon its maintainers. The typical home now largely wastes both the solar income it daily receives and the mineral resources that pass through it. It takes from the forests for its structure, furnishings, reading materials, and fuel as well. The typical home also takes from the often fragile ecosystems of estuary, swamp, desert and prairie for its food and fiber. It also uses the waterways and mineral riches for its power and the products of the marketplace. The house shelters its occupants, but to the larger community it gives "wastes." These latter emerge unappreciated and consequently unsorted: the metals with the glass, organic, paper, and plastic all jumbled together; the toxic mixed with the benign.

Because the home is such a total parasite, as are its neighboring urban habitats, it is not surprising that the occupants experience themselves as victims or, at best, ineffectual ciphers in a large, impersonal, centralized system.

Each technological process, whether its goal is heating water, or producing bricks, solar collectors, and windmills or manufacturing cars, has a scale of operation most suitable to the requirements of the resource base, work force, and end-product consumers. The best known persuasive argument for a reexamination of technology from this perspective is the book *Small is Beautiful* by the late British economist E. F. Schumacher. As we suggested earlier, some foods, such as tomatoes, from a "solar sense" perspective are best produced in small-scale systems close to consumption; in containers, greenhouses and gardens. Others, such as wheat and cotton, are best grown in large-scale settings. The concept of the integral urban house arose in part out of the answers to the question, What life support processes can best be undertaken at the household, apartment, housing project or neighborhood scale? How can we transform the house from parasite to producer?

2. An Existing Integral Urban House: A group of six of us founded the Farallones Institute in 1974. The authors of this article presented our concept of what an integral urban house might be to the rest of the group very early in the development of the institution. The argument originally brought up by certain members of this group against investing our limited resources and energies into an urban habitat expressed the gamut of negative attitudes towards urban areas that one might expect to encounter almost anywhere. They ranged from skepticism over whether it would work, to distaste for the pollution and constraints of the city as compared with the attractions of beginning a new ecologically harmonious community in a more pristine rural setting. Because we were vociferous and persistent, it was finally agreed that some support could be spared to test the concept. Because it has worked, and continues to do so, it is worth describing here (Figure 2).

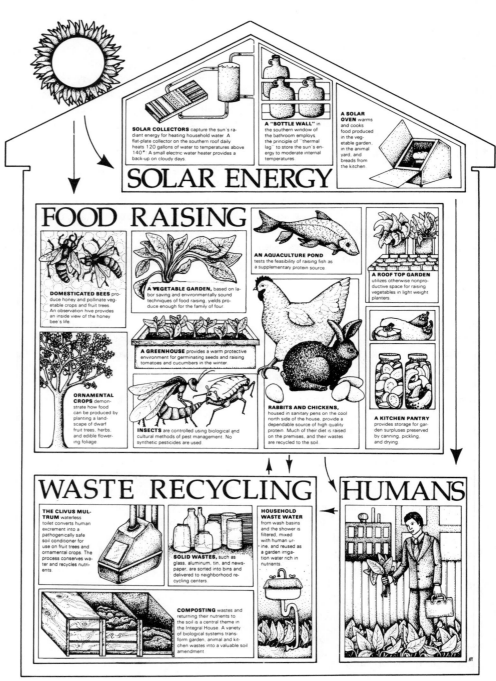

Figure 2
Habitat & life support system of an integral urban house

An old, condemned house was bought in a mixed, commercial-residential area of Berkeley not far from the bayside freeway. Since the plan was to create an experimental setting, open to the public for casual visits as well as workshops and classes, a house with larger than usual backyard was chosen, to accomodate groups of people (Figure 3). The interior of the house was also planned with reception and seminar rooms, offices and large workshops in mind. It was not a typical family dwelling in those respects, but nevertheless served the goal of exploring self-reliance in an urban setting.

Efforts were made to harvest solar income directly (Figures 4 and 5). A solar hot water and space heating system and a greenhouse were eventually installed (Figure 6). Supplementary heat is available through wood-burning and electric facilities, but is rarely required because of the mild climate and the great lengths undertaken to insulate the house and provide the windows with protective shutters. Biogas or methane production was judged to be best undertaken at the block or small neighborhood level, so was not included. A savonius windmill is used to harvest solar energy indirectly and aerate a pond in which a variety of aquatic food studies have been undertaken (Figure 7).

The food production systems were designed to attempt to get the most food out of small spaces with the least amount of effort and attention from the house inhabitants, and with as few imports from outside the house as possible. Experiments along these lines are still being undertaken at the house by a small group of dedicated staff.

A key process was turning organic kitchen wastes and garden debris into a compost that could return nutrients to the garden. Using this compost as a thick mulch also reduced both watering needs and weeding chores.

Similar food-growing techniques, designed to accomodate busy working urban people, were adopted from the authors' studies and experiences, more completely described elsewhere (Figure 8).[3] Greywater, waste water from sinks and showers, is also returned to the garden. This was a great boon during two consecutive drought years, and thousands of people came from

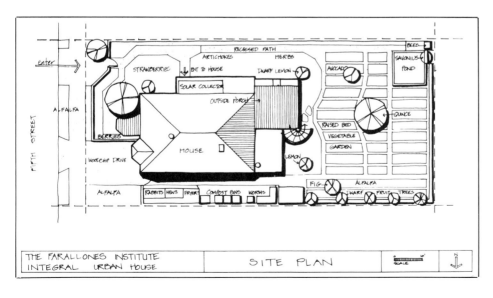

Figure 3
The integral urban house, site plan

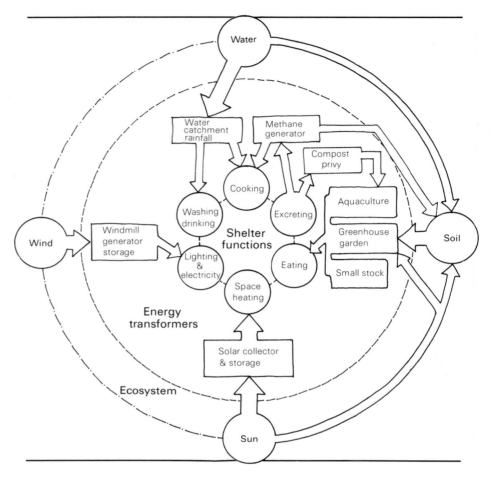

throughout the Western drought area to see this simple and inexpensive solution to urban water problems.

Human manure is collected in a Clivus Multrum composting toilet and the final compost applied to the few ornamentals in the landscaping. Urine is used regularly in the garden to recapture the nitrogen, with the yearly addition of some lime to flush away the accumulating sodium (See Table 3).

The north side of the house, too shady for raising vegetables, shelters small animal systems—primarily egg and meat chickens, and rabbits for meat and fur (Figure 9). Alfalfa is grown as a "lawn" to feed the rabbits, flies are trapped to feed the chickens, bees are raised above the fish pond so that the dead bees can provide protein to the fish.

These and other systems in the house are described by the authors and other Farallones Institute members in a book published by Sierra Club Books.[4]

The authors ceased to have daily contact with Farallones Institute in the fall of 1977 and have continued to experiment with food and waste management systems under the auspices of their own Center, a division of the John Muir Institute. Our major focus has been developing alternatives to pesticides, including biological control

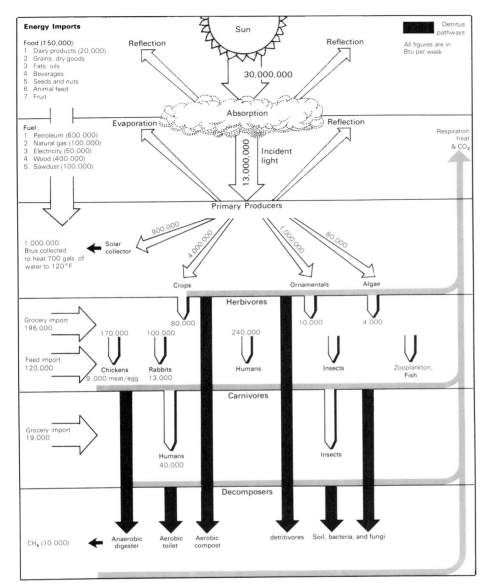

Figure 5
Energy flow at the integral house— biophysical

of insects. But we are interested still in evaluating components of and the concept of an integral house.

3. *What Did We Learn?:* The major questions asked of Integral Urban House designers and residents are : Are you self-sufficient? How much food can be produced in how little space? The questioners are often looking for "gee whiz" type facts that make good copy but ultimately have little real util-ity. This is because they cannot be ap-plied to other circumstances and tend to stand abstractly independent of the important variables that characterize the individual circumstances within which they might be applied.

No effort was ever made to be food self-sufficient. (The raising of grains or dairy products was never contem-plated, for example.) The goal was to reduce negative impact on the planet

Figure 6
View of greenhouse and side yard (which is used to grow herbs, artichokes and lemons).

while developing some level of family and individual self-reliance in relation to basic life support. Has the goal been reached? Unquestionably, but so has it been in every instance where people insulate their houses, install solar hot water heaters, keep a compost pile going and raise some tomatoes, lettuce, and zucchini instead of buying them at the store. How much food can be raised? This is a function of many variables at least as important as how much space is available and exposed to the sun, and the climate. Variables include the level of interest or motivation on the part of the food raisers; the information they have about basic soil-plant relationships, as well as time-saving methods of raising food, and environmentally sound pest management; the strength, resources, and opportunity they have or can find to construct the initial systems.

So, what did we learn? We learned from the tens of thousands of people from across the United States and every continent who have visited and corresponded with the House, that there is a hunger in urban people to see demonstrations of small-scale systems

that work and to learn the technology for duplicating them. We have also confirmed our belief that traditional agricultural technologies cannot be imported wholesale into cities to satisfy urban needs. Modified and new systems are required that can flourish under urban constraints of space, time, light, building codes, proximity of neighbors and lead fallout from gasoline, among other constraints. We saw that the rehabilitation and redesign of older urban dwellings to take advantage of solar income not only provides a measure of self-reliance to its residents, but starts them thinking and then working toward the next level: integral urban blocks and neighborhoods. The latter must include community-shared spaces for food raising and recycling as they do places to park cars and for children to play.

A rooftop experiment

During 1975, while we were developing the Ecology and Natural Systems Program for Antioch College / West, we started a small rooftop food production system on the warehouse where the college was then located (Mission St. near 7th in downtown San Francisco). This is an area of busy streets and narrow alleys edged with small manufacturing enterprises and shops below, slum dwellings above, interspersed with large warehouses. Some of the latter have been converted to office buildings. Many of these warehouses have flat roofs, structurally strong because of early building standards that required their support of huge water cisterns as a hedge against another catastrophe such as the great San Francisco earthquake and fire in 1906.

A step out onto the roof showed other roofs in all directions, each receiving abundant solar input. It was easy to visualize a greening of the inner city above the noise of traffic, air pollu-

Figure 7
A Savonius windmill aerates a pond used for aquaculture. Bees are raised above the fish pond so that dead bees can provide protein for the fish.

Figure 8
Organic kitchen wastes and garden debris are turned into compost and used for intensive food cultivation. Shown here are rooftop planter boxes and a solar food drier.

Table 3
Nitrogen Manu-
facture in Urine,
by Homo sapiens
Average daily output
of urine: Volume:
1.75–2.875 pints
(0.8–1.3 liters): ★
Dry weight: 0.09–
0.13 lb. (40–59
grams); (Dry weight
calculated from 96%
moisture.)

Chemical composition of urine from a 180-lb. man, producing 1500 cc urine:

Salts	Dry Weight	Percent Nitrogen	Amount of Nitrogen (produced/liter urine)
Urea	30.0 grams	46.7	14.0
Sodium chloride	15.0	—	—
Potassium	3.3	—	—
Phosphoric acid	2.5	—	—
Sulfuric acid	2.5	—	—
Creatinine	1.0	37.0	0.37
Ammonia	0.7	78.0	0.58
Uric acid	0.7	33.3	0.23
Hippuric acid	0.7	7.8	0.05
Magnesium	0.6	—	—
Calcium	0.3	—	—
Others	2.8	—	—
	60.1 gm.		15.2 gm./day; 12 lb./yr.

Adapted from A. J. Carlson and V. Johnson, *The Machinery of the Body* (Chicago: University of Chicago Press, 1941) and from H. Gotaas, *Composting,* World Health Organization Monograph no. 31, 1956.

Note: Urea is the main source of nitrogen in urine.
   One quart = 0.947 liter or about 95% of 1 liter.
   To add 50 lb. N per acre, use one quart urine per 27 sq. ft. (3 ft. × 9 ft. of land) once a month. If possible, dilute urine five times with water and use a sprinkling can. Since urine is high in sodium, add 1 lb. gypsum or dolomite lime per 100 sq. ft. once a year to help remove the sodium from the clay in the soil.
   Conversion factors for above calculations:
   1 pint = 0.47 liters
   1 acre = 4.356 × 10⁴ ft.²
   1 lb. = 453.6 gm.

tion, and hazards of vandalism. The goal was to develop the project from the waste resources of the immediate community, so all involved spent a great deal of initial time checking out what resources were available.

First we located a source of nitrogen and other plant nutrients. These we would obtain from the food wastes of a number of nearby restaurants. The finely ground residues from juicing machines were particularly welcome since they were likely to decompose very quickly (due to the large surface area provided by the small size particles). Carbon was secured in the form of sawdust from a cabinet shop in the alley behind the warehouse. The two waste products together, organic garbage and sawdust, with the addition of liquid in the form of urine and water, were all we needed to make a good quality compost to use as a light, balanced growing medium.

Figure 9
The shady north side of the house is used for raising chickens for eggs and meat and rabbits for meat and fur pelts. Instead of a suburban lawn, alfalfa is grown to feed the rabbits. Fly traps are used to provide supplemental feed for the chickens.

The next step was to protect the roof, a tar coating topped with gravel, from foot traffic. We used old pallets, discarded in great numbers in the industrial areas of large cities, as decking material. Upon this deck we built our compost bins (about a cubic yard each, with fly-tight sides and weatherproofed lids). With our first compost started (normally taking three weeks for completion), we turned our attention to building deep planter boxes, a henhouse with enclosed yard, and rabbit hutches. Indoors, in a sunny window, we germinated seeds. Protected from the weather and insects they grew quickly. Some were ready to set into the planter boxes by the time the first compost was ready to receive them. We soon were producing lettuce, broccoli, and other vegetables, and obtaining eggs from the chickens.

By constructing deep planter boxes, we kept the soil level eight or more inches below the top. This provided a windbreak for the seedlings and a sup-

port for the old windows which we scavenged to use as temporary cold frames. We had to import a large percentage of the animal feed, but the manure provided an important addition to the compost. High on the roof both vegetables and animals were protected from vandalism.

Had the project continued we would have focused on locating waste food products that could have been used to supplement a greater part of the diet for both chickens and rabbits. We would have trapped flies, produced abundantly in the back alleys, to use as supplementary chicken feed (after solar cooking in a jar placed in the sun) along with waste grain products. Waste greens from the supermarket are a good addition to the alfalfa pellets for the rabbits. All of these systems we had experimented with elsewhere. The task remaining was incorporating them into the rooftop project.

When we shifted our classes from San Francisco to the East Bay we were no longer able to supervise the project and it ended less than a year after it started. Although short-lived, this experiment lasted long enough to prove to us that viable food production systems could be designed for the flat roofs of the inner city utilizing waste products from surrounding areas.

What's next?

It is possible that the human species will destroy itself through either the cataclysm of nuclear war or other disasters, or through the more subtle influence of nuclear wastes. If human civilization continues without bringing upon itself such an end, then a number of potential development scenarios are possible. If one assumes that the number of people producing food in backyard and community gardens will continue to grow, then what could be some of the next set of developments?

Food surpluses from these gardens will start to find their way to local markets. Food trading will be accelerated. New markets and marketing systems will evolve. Small support businesses will develop to install, help install, and maintain these gardens. Small scale seed, nursery, and germ plasm centers will develop and multiply.

Similar developments could occur for the built environment: design, installation and maintenance reconstruction businesses would continue to spring up to install other solar systems such as hot water, space heating, weatherizing, cooling, refrigeration, cooking, and solar forges and furnaces for small scale, but high-quality, industrial applications.

As these concurrent developments in food and structure begin to mature and as the economic system readjusts to fossil fuel reductions, synergism between the two areas will become possible. Extraction of raw materials from major organic sources will occur, as can be observed today with the recycling of waste materials. Relatively small-scale developments will continue to spring up. The raw materials for more industrial processes will be produced from and with solar sources. The future will bring high-quality processing to larger numbers of craftspeople operating out of their homes, garages, basements, and leased buildings. Solar stills will produce alcohol as a fuel or fuel ingredient and other solar extraction processes will provide such raw materials for local use. Where it is ecologically easier to produce herbs, citrus, mushrooms, cotton, potatoes, silk, or oils there it will flourish. As a result the current industrial urban monoculture will be superceded by a bioregionalism that will diversify and invigorate our culture. Electronic communications may reduce overall movement of people and goods, saving resources, and helping to foster this bioregionalism. All these developments will become possible and real when we put our minds and hands to work to create these changes. The most serious limiting factor we see now to such a vision is the lack of awareness that such a future is desirable or achievable. Personal action, commitment to learn new skills, and communication about these explorations are ways our individual futures will be created.

References

1. Bruce Anderson and Michael Riordan, *The Solar Home Book,* (Harrisville, N.H.: Brick House Publishing Co./Cheshire Books, 1976).

2. United States Department of Agriculture, *Potential Cropland Study,* Soil Conservation Service, Statistical Bulletin no. 578, (1977).

3. Helga Olkowski and William Olkowski, *The City People's Book of Raising Food,* (Emmaus, Pa.: Rodale Press, 1975).

4. Helga Olkowski, William Olkowski, and T. Javits, *The Integral Urban House,* (San Francisco: Sierra Club Books, 1979).

12 | The Cheyenne Community Solar Greenhouse

Gary M. Garber

ON *SUN DAY,* May 3, 1978 as America was officially beginning the "solar age," President Carter was standing in the rain at the Solar Energy Research Institute (SERI) in Golden, Colorado examining an array of sophisticated solar devices that had been hastily set up for his benefit. While the rain that day may have dampened his spirits regarding solar energy (he later slashed his solar budget), people less than a hundred miles to the north were celebrating the beginning of a genuine commitment toward energy independence.

The sun broke through the clouds over Cheyenne, Wyoming just long enough for dedication ceremonies at the nation's largest community solar greenhouse. Cheyenne received 17 inches of snow that afternoon, but while the sun was shining hundreds of people visited the 5,000-square-foot prototype solar greenhouse and harvested bushels of vegetables that had been growing since January. It was not only amazing that these crops were being reaped a full month before the start of the growing season but that they also were grown in a greenhouse heated entirely by the sun (Figure 1)!

Design and planning

The Cheyenne Community Solar Greenhouse was built by Community Action of Laramie County (CALC) after a successful greenhouse project, involving 15 low-income youths, brought the group national acclaim in 1976. The young people, all in the program as an alternative to jail, built three 16-by-20-foot solar greenhouses on vacant lots in Cheyenne. These structures worked so well they are still being used to provide food for a group home of 35 handicapped people. That fall the teenagers made a presentation on these greenhouses to the National Energy Policy Advisory Board for Community Services Administrations and laid the groundwork for similar projects all over the country. That same year Cornell University completed a $35,000 study confirming what was already known in Cheyenne—solar greenhouses work!

While work was proceeding on the three prototype greenhouses, a grant proposal to the Community Services Administration's Food and Nutrition Program was being prepared by CALC. With the success and excite-

Figure 1
*The Cheyenne Com-
munity Solar Green-
house survives the cold
Wyoming winters (one,
the coldest on record)
while continually pro-
ducing food for the city's
poor. The 156-ft.-long
structure was built in
three sections to create
three growing environ-
ments.*

(Photo by Gary Garber)

ment generated by work in progress, CALC anticipated success in the new project even before this proposal was completed. The idea was simple—to develop a commercial scale solar greenhouse to be operated by low-income elderly volunteers that would provide a continual source of low cost food for the city's poor. In addition to this large commercial structure the proposal included plans for the con-struction of attached solar greenhouses on three homes owned by elderly citi-zens. Not only would these residential greenhouses provide food, but they would also supply a significant fraction of winter space heating needs of the homes involved.

The basic concept of the large com-munity greenhouse was to involve vol-unteers from Cheyenne in all phases of the program from planning and design to construction and operation. In De-cember 1976 a grant for $42,700 was received and CALC immediately began to organize an intensive one-week workshop to develop program goals and objectives and implementa-tion strategies.

The workshop group included about thirty people, including high school students, as well as unemployed, re-tired, and professional people. This self-selected group of community vol-unteers responded to a local media campaign. Had more (or fewer) people responded, CALC was prepared to in-volve them. It is interesting to note that the workshop stimulated the high school student participants to return to their school to present a program on energy and renewable energy technol-ogy issues. As part of this program these students prepared small-scale demonstration devices (e.g., a solar food drier, a flat-plate hot water collec-tor, and a working model of a movable insulation system for solar green-houses). This spin-off not only helped the students to learn more deeply about appropriate technology but also had the effect of broadening local aware-ness of the community greenhouse project and the potential of solar en-ergy in Cheyenne.

To reduce the workshop group to a more workable size, participants were divided into three groups: (1) Design and Construction, (2) Greenhouse Op-erations and, (3) Project Management.

While it was not planned by the workshop organizers, there was a natural tendency for participants to divide themselves up according to interest and expertise. The result was a high level of enthusiasm and competence in each group.

The goals of the Design and Construction group were to: (1) design the greenhouse and back-up heating system, (2) locate potential sites, (3) identify and conform to local codes and ordinances and, (4) estimate materials costs and locate possible donors of materials. The initial design idea was to build a 50-by-100-foot structure, but after attempting to solve some engineering and economic problems the group decided to actually build the greenhouse in three sections. This approach not only allowed for construction to proceed in three phases (to compensate for the anticipated lack of money down the road), but provided for three complete growing climates. It also solved potential fire code problems by creating three separate control zones for fire safety—an important issue in a large public facility such as this. By the end of the week this group had completed its design in the form of a scale model. Even though it was a crude effort, this presentation technique served to generate enthusiasm for the work ahead as well as communicating design ideas in a form understandable by all workshop participants and the local officials who attended the summary session on this last day of the workshop.

The Methane Digester group, a subgroup of Design and Construction, worked to develop a back-up heating system. Based on information supplied by one consultant group, it was initially estimated that a 3,000-gallon digester system would be able to supply all back-up heating needs with an input

supply of waste organic matter from the greenhouse and a daily truckload of manure from local ranches. While the hardware for such a system was eventually built and installed in the greenhouse, it was later determined, based on the analysis of a second consultant, that the initial estimates were greatly overstated. It has now been concluded that, while the concept of a methane digester as a heating system for greenhouses is still valid, the scale of the system is crucial to the success of the idea. In this case, especially with the need to import more manure than originally expected from distant sites, the system would not have been able to supply even a fraction of the supplemental space heating needs at a cost that would be affordable. As an alternative, homemade oil-barrel stoves were eventually built by a local high school welding class to provide back-up heat for people (the environment for plants is adequate without a back-up). However, since the building is so airtight for control of infiltration heat loss, the woodstoves tend to smoke and, consequently, have only been used on two occasions in two years. As a result, the facility is now, in effect, 100 percent heated by the sun. (See later section on Thermal Performance, this paper.)

The Greenhouse Operations group was responsible for determining local marketing demand in order to decide what produce should be grown, and, consequently, what design conditions would have to be maintained in the greenhouse environment. The market survey was carried out by soliciting information on produce sales from local food stores. From this, the ten most popular food crops were identified. They included lettuce, tomatoes, green peppers, and onions. It is interesting that these are also among the easiest crops to grow in solar greenhouses. A separate survey determined what items people would buy more of if they were more readily available, were of higher quality, and / or were less expensive. A combined list of types of produce from both surveys was analyzed to estimate greenhouse productivity potential and the cash value of each crop per unit area of greenhouse space. While all of this research was necessarily "quick and dirty" due to the time and expertise limits of the workshop format, it did establish the fact that the produce that could be grown in a solar greenhouse would indeed be a welcome addition to local diets.

To further explore the economic value of such a project, the Greenhouse Operations group made contacts with potential consumers of excess produce, including local restaurants, retail outlets, and special food programs such as "meals on wheels" and Goodwill Industries. The potential of direct sales through a farmer's market was also investigated. The result of these studies was to firmly establish, in the minds of the workshop participants, the viability of the project.

In addition to these questions, the Greenhouse Operations group made a list of issues that required more detailed study. These ranged from the question of how many barrels of water would be needed for thermal mass in order to regulate diurnal temperature swings to determining the size and layout of growing beds. These issues were decided as the project proceeded toward implementation.

Finally, the Project Management group was charged with the task of overall planning and coordination of the project. This group developed a step-by-step procedure and time-line for completing the project. Within this framework, the group looked at everything from the issue of how to acquire land to the question of what licenses and permits would be needed. They attempted to define responsibilities of project participants and outlined lines of authority and responsibility. The Project Management team also assumed responsibility for mapping out a public relations program aimed at maximizing community understanding and involvement in the implementation of the project.

The final day of the workshop was spent briefing local and state officials on the project. This was the beginning of a working relationship with key agencies whose cooperation would be necessary for the duration of the program. Community interest was maintained by constant news releases and radio and TV talk show appearances which began during the workshop and have continued throughout the project, from construction to its present operation.

The workshop was an enormous success. Not only was a design concept developed but an implementation plan was set in motion and the entire Cheyenne community had been made aware of the project and how they could help to complete it. However, this was just the beginning and many problems, anticipated as well as unanticipated, would have to be overcome before the idea was to become a reality.

Site selection and construction

Since the workshop had taken place in December, project implementation had to wait for spring and good weather. That left time for a search for a suitable site, a task which proved quite frustrating. Miles of red tape stood in the way of acquiring any government land and negotiations with various city and county officials proved fruitless. Just as it was beginning to look hopeless, a family that had heard of the project and its troubles in finding land, offered two acres just outside the city limits on a long-term renewable lease basis completely free of charge. While the greenhouse planners had hoped to locate an in-town site, this location has since proved to have many advantages, not least of which is greater flexibility due to the less rigid county codes and regulations.

Shortly after this, land was made available and the construction process began. The surveying was done by a retired highway engineer, who had participated in the workshop. By the middle of May 1977 the staff of one of the consultant groups had converted all the workshop sketches and ideas into architectural drawings, and actual construction, under the supervision of two paid carpenters, was started. The labor force, like the design workshop, was composed of high school students, retired people and weekend volunteers. Construction funding for wages and materials came from the Community Services Administration grant of $42,700.

The plan to build the greenhouse a section at a time proved to be a wise decision—the project ran short on money twice. On one occasion, the Laramie County Commissioners allocated $2,000 to keep the work going while Community Action staff worked on additional funding through CSA's Community Food and Nutrition Program. Another $13,000 then was secured to complete the construction. Community Action's Weatherization Program Policy Advisory Committee allocated $6,000 to build the methane digester. Thus, final construction financing came to a total of $63,700 or $12.74 per square foot for the 5,000-square-foot greenhouse. This included plumbing (including a $5,000 well,

bathrooms, and a septic tank and branching field system), and electrical work as well as construction of the building shell itself (Figure 2). (Financing for raised beds was provided by later supplemental grants).

The project was made possible, to a large extent, by the ready availability of skilled volunteers. Electrical work, for example, was supervised by an electrician layed off from his regular job by a leg injury. The plumbing was supervised by 57-year-old Molly Rivera. Her mentally retarded son also helped. All plumbing, including a gray water recovery system, was in place by mid-summer. Molly's dedication to the project won her Cheyenne's Volunteer of the Year Award presented annually by the Mayor.

The foundation, requiring 120 yards of concrete, was insulated all along the outside with discarded polyurethane and then back-filled to create an earth berm to retain heat within the greenhouse. The building was then caulked and weatherstripped to stop possible infiltration. Inner surfaces were painted white to reflect incoming light throughout the greenhouse. The complete south side of the building was double glazed with corrugated "Filon" on the outside and Monsanto '602' on the inside (Table 1). Volunteers, working with 45 squares of multicolored shingles and six cases of beer worked out a unique patchwork design that makes the greenhouse very easy to locate.

In December 1977, as Wyoming's winter began closing in, a second workshop, this time focussing almost entirely on construction, was conducted. More than two hundred 55-gallon oil drums were painted black, filled with water and placed inside the greenhouse to capture the sun's heat during the day and re-radiate it back

Figure 2
Roofing the Cheyenne Community Solar Greenhouse took 4,300 sq. ft. of donated and discarded shingles and plenty of beer. The roof later received hail damage and even though CALC could then afford to buy roofing in one color, they chose to duplicate the original patchwork design.

Glazing:	4,100 sq. ft. at 45° angle: Filon panels for exterior; Monsanto '602' for interior
Foundation:	120 cu. yd. concrete with 2-in. polyurethane insulation on exterior
Insulation:	Rock wool and cellulose; 8 in. in walls, 10 in. in north roof. (These materials settled after the first year and we had to fill up the gap. We recommend fiberglass if affordable.)
Wall Construction:	2 by 8s, 4 ft. on centers for both roof and walls

Table 1
Summary of construction materials

into the greenhouse at night and on cold, cloudy days. A local high school welding class completed the two wood-burning stoves from oil barrels to serve as a back-up heating system.

While finish details were being completed during the day, workshop organizers from CALC held several evening presentations on the greenhouse aimed at locating volunteers interested in using the greenhouse to grow food crops for the winter. In spite of blizzard conditions during these presentations, approximately twenty-five construction volunteers and a small number of older citizens expressed a willingness to believe that a structure entirely heated by the sun could actually create conditions suitable for plant growth during Cheyenne's long, cold and windy winters.

Greenhouse Operation

By January 1978 the greenhouse was substantially completed and crops were being planted in the center section of the structure by a handful of former construction volunteers supervised by horticulturalist Shane Smith. By March, when the first crops in the center section were being harvested, the west section was planted and bedding plants and food crops were ready in May. Following the May harvest, the first summer season was started in both the center and west sections with a large planting of tomatoes and other warm weather crops. In addition to greenhouse space, an area 150-by-50-feet to the south of the structure was made available in 10-by-20-foot plots as community garden space. Many greenhouse participants as well as other

area residents took advantage of that opportunity for growing more food.

Fall crops in the center and west sections were planted in September and October 1978, and in early 1979 the east section was completed and planted commercially to raise and sell bedding and ornamental plants, and organic gardening supplies (Figure 3). Initial materials cost for this enterprise, which is coordinated by greenhouse horticulturalist Shane Smith, was $500, and in the first year returned over $3,000. (Second-year sales are expected to be even greater). This income is helping to make the greenhouse financially self-sufficient, providing salaries for the horticulturalist and a greenhouse manager. Other staff positions are provided by Green Thumb and the Comprehensive Employment and Training Act (CETA) programs. Income also must support all materials and supplies. At present the greenhouse is owned and operated by CALC and is governed by a broad-based community board with strong representation by low-income and elderly citizens.

Through local television talk shows, radio programs, and newspaper coverage the success of the food production effort became known to larger numbers of area residents. As a result, the number of people desiring to work in the greenhouse increased dramatically to its present level of approximately 80 gardeners. Instead of allocating private plots, as in many community gardens, all plantings are selected, based on criteria of maximum yield potential, by greenhouse staff and work roles are scheduled to insure healthy plant growth throughout the structure. In effect, the crops are communally maintained. Participants are assigned specific tasks such as watering, pollinating, or transplanting, according to a daily and weekly schedule. Since harvesting is done on a continual basis, individuals simply take what they need. In some cases, people who may work at the greenhouse three or four days a week for several hours a day may choose to take little or nothing while an individual with less time to spend but more need might take whatever is ready to pick. So far, after two complete winter and summer seasons, there have been no problems with this system of distribution. It seems that people get to know each other through working side-by-side in the structure and develop strong bonds of mutual understanding and respect. This has been one of the least anticipated and most heartening aspects of the project.

Participants range in age from ten to ninety-two years and include a large percentage of retired citizens as well as handicapped persons from Goodwill Industries. Many young people also "work-off" jail sentences and fines by working in the greenhouse. At present, on any given day, a visit to the greenhouse is likely to reveal a broad cross-section of the Cheyenne community working on their food crops and sitting in lawn chairs visiting with their neighbors (Figures 4, 5, and 6).

Figure 4
Cukes or cows, this cowboy knows about both. Montan enjoys a "roll-yer-own" outside the greenhouse as he displays a day's cucumber harvest.

Figure 5
Two greenhouse workers, Howard Morrison and Ben Sanchey, take a breather from pollinating tomatoes.

Figure 6a & b
Young or old, there is
always plenty of work
(and food) for
everyone.

Typically, elderly participants arrange for their own transportation once or twice a week or get rides from project staff. Arrangements for more regular public transportation would greatly increase demand for garden space and open up the facility to the community's least mobile population.

Thermal performance

Due to the fact that the methane gas back-up heating system has never operated and the woodstoves have been turned on only twice, the greenhouse has operated for two full years heated entirely by the sun. The lowest inside air temperature recorded during that time was 32°F in January 1979, a record cold month. Outdoor air temperatures remained well below zero for nearly two weeks (Table 1). While there was an unusually high percentage of clear sky radiation that year, Cheyenne's typically strong winds provided an additional heating load.

The most serious thermal problem to date has been overheating in the summer months (Table 2). While typical outdoor temperatures range from a high around 80 to 85°F to a low of 50 to 55°F, greenhouse temperatures have remained in the 80 to 105°F range. Not only are these temperatures too high for the many elderly growers but the productivity of many plants is sharply reduced, and many beneficial insects are unable to survive. As a result of upsetting the bilogical control balance in this way, produce output was reduced by an estimated one third during the first summer season.

To remedy this situation, large power vents have been installed. These design changes have made it possible to maintain a more stable and acceptable temperature regime throughout the overheated season (Table 3).

Greenhouse performance*

Based on nearly two full years of crop production it is becoming increasingly clear that traditional outdoor gardening methods just don't apply in a solar greenhouse. The most obvious environmental difference in the solar

* Shane Smith is the author of the sections on greenhouse performance and food production.

Date	Outside Temperature (°F)		Center Greenhouse Section Temperature (°F)	
	High	Low	High	Low
1	4	−18	84	33
2	14	−24	60	32
3	10	−10	48	34
4	24	4	60	34
5	26	4	48	33
6	10	−3	80	33
8	18	−2	82	34
9	20	5	90	42
10	22	7	74	40
11	30	0	76	40
12	34	4	68	45
15	43	4	81	33
16	26	−4	88	46
17	38	16	76	46
18	40	16	80	50
19	40	20	56	44
21	41	20	60	36
24	14	6	79	40
25	39	14	92	46
29	22	−10	86	40
30	12	−6	54	36
31	13	−10	84	36

Table 2
Thermal Performance During January 1979 (a record cold month)

Note: Even though water freezes at 32°F, most plants grown in the Cheyenne Greenhouse during the winter are cool-season crops and can withstand temperatures as low as 28°F. No plants died due to low temperatures. Soil temperature never dropped below 45°F during the month.

greenhouse is the widely fluctuating temperature. Extreme highs and lows can cause lower total crop yields. Warm-season crops (those grown for their mature fruits, such as tomato, eggplant, and melon) prefer temperatures between 55 and 85°F. Fruit set, usually, will not happen when temperatures are out of this optimal range for extended periods. Cool-season crops (such as cabbage, lettuce, and broccoli, grown for their vegetative parts) prefer temperatures between 45 and 75°F. Growth and quality are greatly diminished when the cool-season crops experience temperatures beyond this range. Incidence of disease, insect problems, and deformed growth also occur beyond optimal temperature regimes.

Light is another important environmental difference in solar greenhouses. Insufficient light levels result in slower growth, lower yields, elongated stems, and sparse foliage. Since the Cheyenne facility is enclosed and insulated on the north wall and roof, and on the east and west walls, the light is reduced

Table 3
Thermal Performance During August 1978 (with inadequate ventilation)

Date	Outside Temperature (°F)		Center Greenhouse Section Temperature (°F)	
	High	Low	High	Low
1	78	52	95	64
2	82	61	94	64
3	75	47	83	60
9	63	47	71	58
11	90	45	98	60
12	85	54	98	64
14	93	51	105	66
15	77	46	85	56
16	75	42	93	60
17	83	50	94	64
18	84	48	90	60
21	86	37	100	55
22	86	58	92	68
23	83	53	88	66
24	89	52	100	66
25	90	55	100	67
28	90	48	98	63
29	74	50	94	64
30	75	43	88	60
31	77	48	89	63

even further during the short days of winter.

By practicing proper scheduling and crop placement, however, the problems associated with light and temperature have largely been overcome. For Cheyenne, it has been found that there are two growing seasons: winter (September 15 through April 13) and summer (March 15 through October 15). (These seasons are specific to the latitude, altitude, and climate of Cheyenne and may vary in different climates and for different building designs.) While the best yields in the winter are achieved with cool-season crops (and in the summer with warm-season crops), it is possible to reverse schedules if special varieties of "cold hardy"

and "heat tolerant" crops are grown. However, this does result in lower quality and yield.

In addition to paying close attention to season-specific planting schedules, the potential problems of disease spread and pest control must be dealt with in special ways in a solar greenhouse. Since chemical pesticides can be dangerous to human operators, they should be avoided wherever possible. This is especially important when using biological pest control since the chemicals will destroy beneficial insects more easily than they will kill pests. Biological pest control is important, especially in community greenhouses, because: (1) chemical spraying will delay harvesting for many days

Date	Outside Temperature (°F)		Center Greenhouse Section Temperature (°F)	
	High	Low	High	Low
5	86	32	92	52
8	88	4	76	56
12	88	47	94	52
13	90	50	92	63
14	90	51	97	64
15	89	53	90	64
18	77	42	84	52
19	84	44	87	54
20	85	48	92	57
21	86	48	94	59
22	89	53	94	64
25	87	53	93	63
26	87	51	91	63
27	89	53	96	60
28	87	52	92	64
29	88	52	91	62

Table 4
Thermal Performance During June 1979 (with new fans and extra door)

while waiting for the residue to disappear; (2) the greenhouse must be evacuated while spraying; (3) pests readily develop resistance to synthetic chemicals.

At the Cheyenne greenhouse the food-producing sections (center and west) are managed exclusively with biological pest controls. (In the commercial east section, where bedding plants, flowers, and house plants are grown, botanical pesticides are used to ensure that products can compete with other totally bug-free commercial greenhouses). The best way to deal with pest problems is to prevent them by maintaining healthy plant growth. To accomplish this, a variety of strategies are employed, including: (1) companion planting to confuse the pests and diseases and to provide overall plant health through mutually beneficial plant associations; (2) planting a large variety of species of plants and types of the same plant to maintain genetic diversity; (3) encouraging a rich and diverse microbial soil community with the frequent addition of compost; (4) using plant varieties that are specially bred for resistance to greenhouse pest problems (e.g., certain varieties of many vegetables that are resistant to specific diseases); (5) maintaining adequate ventilation (during winter months, air is circulated inside the greenhouse with a small fan for 20 minutes a day); (6) treating insect infestations as they occur and, if necessary, removing diseased plants. Perhaps the most important preventive maintenance is in the area of greenhouse sanitation such as removing and composting dead leaves or decaying matter, keeping floors free of trash and plant parts, and thoroughly washing all plant containers before reusing.

When pests do become a problem there are a number of biological pest controls that have been found to be effective at the Cheyenne greenhouse. For example, there is a small parasitic wasp known as *Encarsia* that is most effective in controlling whitefly population, a typical greenhouse pest. Since these wasps are very expensive to purchase initially and the species purchased through the mail cannot reproduce in the fluctuating solar greenhouse environment, the greenhouse staff has developed a special "solar high-bred" by crossing a California variety that thrives at a constant 70°F with a high altitude type that can withstand the fluctuating temperatures. This new variety is thriving in the Cheyenne greenhouse.

To control aphids, another recurring problem in greenhouses, a variety of beneficial insects has been used. These include ladybugs, green lacewings, spiders, and syrphid flies.

This combination of techniques for creating and maintaining a healthy and diverse garden ecosystem in the greenhouse has kept disease and pest problems within easily manageable bounds for the entire operating history of the Cheyenne greenhouse. The greenhouse research program continues to monitor the effectiveness of these and other approaches to organic solar greenhouse gardening without chemical pesticides.

Food production

Solar greenhouses are of no value unless they can produce adequate amounts of year-round fresh food for the people involved as well as passive space heating. The food grown in a solar greenhouse should be high-value crops such as lettuce, tomatoes, and cucumbers rather than low-value crops such as potatoes and dried grains. This is based on cost per pound. Year round production can vary greatly from season to season with the temperature, light, maturity of the crop being grown, and the scheduling involved.

It is also hard to place an average production figure in pounds as it's hard for a pound figure on yields to give an accurate view of value produced. For example, one 10-by-10-foot bed can produce 3 bushels of tomatoes weighing in at 160 pounds. The same 10-by-10-foot bed can produce 3 bushels of green peppers which would weigh only 50 pounds. The total nutrition of the tomato and the pepper is similar so the pound yield figure doesn't really help. This is similar with many crops. Conversely the same 10-by-10-foot bed could be set up to produce edible single-celled food products using types of algae based on NASA space colonization ideas. Thinking in these terms, that same bed could produce 800 pounds of food.

Food production can also be variable as to the type of horticulture used. A chemical intensive (pesticides, growth regulators, hydroponics) growing system will produce more food per square foot but the many questions relative to world ecology and human health may make this option questionable.

The yields can still be quite substantial in a solar greenhouse that utilizes "organic" techniques and maintains active biological balances. This is the option we have taken for our food production here in Cheyenne. It is hard to present an average on food production in Cheyenne in just two years of operation. Harvest yields have been continually on the upswing as the horticulture for the solar greenhouse is being worked out. (See Table 5.) Yield projections based on our type of crops and planting schedule would be approximately 100-pounds per 1,500-square-feet greenhouse section per month in the winter months and 250 pounds of produce per section (1,500 square feet) per month during summer months.

Conclusion

The Community Solar Greenhouse means much to the people of Cheyenne. It is an alternative energy park where people can learn not only how to save energy, but how to create it. It is a center where senior citizens can find meaningful work, and where young people can gain work experience and interact with older people. The greenhouse not only provides fresh food for Cheyenne's poor people, it is an information center and botanical garden where children can gain insight into their daily food.

A visitor at the greenhouse may be greeted by a retired school teacher, a little girl, or a weather-beaten old cowboy. Any of them will gladly conduct a tour and explain how everything works. A visitor will see a cross-section of the community—young and old, rich and poor—working side by side. Some are there to socialize, some to learn, while others need the food.

Eighty-year-old Sarah Tulchinsky works at the greenhouse twice a week and is "the healthiest woman you can find." She summarized her feelings about the greenhouse as follows: "They always give me different work—I've learned so many wonderful things—there's something for everybody. The other day a group of little kids came in with their mothers. It was so nice to see them all working side by side. Out here everybody is happy, it is a different world—our government has done such a wonderful thing for our country."

Cheyenne Goodwill Director, Chester Johnson, who believes the sun can work miracles, placed one 56-year old

Table 5
Food Production in Cheyenne Community Solar Greenhouse*

Summer

Early July 1979, one week using two thirds of greenhouse area

Cucumber	49 ½ lb.
Squash	24 ½ lb.
Tomato	6 lb.
Bean	7 lb.
Onion	1 lb.
Spinach	10 lb.
Fresh herbs	3 lb.
	101 lb.

Winter

February 1979, one week using two thirds of greenhouse area

Greens	49 lb.
Cabbage	2 ½ lb.
Peas	4 lb.
Broccoli	2 lb.
Fresh herbs	2 lb.
Carrots	4 lb.
Radish	3 lb.
Cauliflower	2 lb.
Kohlrabi	4 lb.
Tomato	⅛ lb.
Turnip	2 lb.
	74 ⅝ lb.

* Gross area, 3,350 sq. ft.; net, 3,000 sq. ft.

mentally and physically handicapped "untrainable" client at the greenhouse as a last resort in March 1979. He describes what happened, "We couldn't find any work that he was suited for until we took him to the greenhouse. He loved it. If his progress continues at this rate I know we can place him in a job at a commercial greenhouse by next year. I've never seen anything like it—it is a miracle."

One volunteer and his 83-year-old mother constructed an Indian style adobe oven next to the greenhouse to bake bread and rolls for monthly solar dinners where people gather to share the fruits of their labor. Many city and county officials have gone away with more than some new recipes for beet jelly or cabbage rolls. They leave with the knowledge that solar energy is here now and that communities can solve their own problems using available resources.

Dennis Holloway, an architect in Colorado (see Chapter 14), sees the Cheyenne Solar Greenhouse as "a prototype of the future." He said that the appeal solar greenhouses are having with low-income groups will expand to the middle class in the near future.

CALC hopes to expand the concept of decentralized food production even further. An adobe walk-in food drier, a solar heated rabbit hutch, and a beekeeping operation will be phased in by the summer of 1980. The group also hopes to cut its $10 to $15 montly electricity consumption by harnessing the ever-present Wyoming wind.

They have also produced a slide show highlighting the project and conduct periodic greenhouse food production seminars. A food production manual that covers all aspects of growing food in a solar greenhouse is also available.*

Hopefully, in the near future people won't have to visit Cheyenne to experience a community-run solar greenhouse. Maybe a visit to the closest senior center, school, or park will do.

* For a food production manual, contact the CALC Public Relations Department at 1603 Central, #400, Cheyenne, Wyoming 82001 (price available on request).

13 | The Davis Experience*
Marshall Hunt and David Bainbridge

WHILE THE ROLES of states and the federal government are fiercely debated, the role of local government in solar energy commercialization has been largely ignored. Davis, a university town of 35,000 near Sacramento, California, is a case study of what local government officials and the citizens who elect them can do. In October 1975, Davis adopted the nation's first comprehensive energy-conserving building code designed to meet the needs of the local microclimate. This was a landmark event in a process that is still going on. It was accompanied by the adoption of solar-use planning policies by the city's staff and citizen commissions.

Work on the code began in the spring of 1972, when a newly elected city council, committed to controlled growth and environmental quality, commissioned a study of energy-saving ways and means as part of an overall rewriting of the city's General Plan. The council's action was prompted by a report on energy consumption from a

* Reprinted with permission from *Solar Age,* Church Hill, Harrisville, N.H. 03450, May 1978

citizen advisory group, finding that Davis residents used a third more electricity per capita than the U.S. average. It appeared that the poor adaptation of Davis houses and apartments to the relatively mild local climate accounted for much of the surprisingly high use. In an attempt to correct this situation the city hired a research team including Jon Hammond (designer and solar expert) Marshall Hunt (microclimatologist and solar expert), Richard Cramer (architect), and Loren Neubauer (engineer and natural heating and cooling expert), to design a building code that would reduce energy use. The project was supported by the city, the University of California, and the CASE Institute. Two years later the work was further supported by a HUD innovative project grant. By that time the research team had evolved into Living Systems, a solar design, research, and consulting firm.

At that time there was no energy code for any type of structure in Davis. The team quickly reached the conclusion that the new code should complement the existing building code, and that the study should also result in a set of planning guidelines and criteria. The development of such a code seemed at first a straightforward problem of identifying appropriate physical design strategies for the local climate. However, interaction with local building designers and homeowners soon made it clear that cultural factors were equally important in promoting energy-efficient housing. Education, therefore, was the first task. Few people, including architects, knew how to design such housing, or how to operate existing houses efficiently, how to choose well-designed housing, or how to improve thermal performance.

Neubauer and Cramer provided a body of knowledge about design with climate, based on their cumulative twenty-five years of research. A comprehensive set of techniques for calculating heating and cooling needs (based on ASHRAE practices)—technically useful to the research team of engineers and designers—were simplified for more general use by developers and builders. The problem of convincing people that the calculations and research data meant they could be comfortable without large furnaces and air conditioners remained. The team therefore decided to emphasize analysis of existing buildings in Davis to dem-

onstrate how *real* buildings worked, and how important orientation and architectural design features are. Their report, *A Strategy for Energy Conservation,* was submitted in 1974.

The Davis energy-use study

Davis is located in California's great Central Valley, in a climate characterized as temperate Mediterranean. Winters are cool (2,819 heating Degree Days), with temperatures averaging around 45°F and seldom colder than 25°F, and with 55 percent of possible sunshine (Figure 1). The average rainfall, 16 inches per year, falls almost entirely during the winter. Summers are warm, with daily maximums around 95°F (1,063 cooling Degree Days). Temperatures over 105°F are not uncommon during hot spells. Fortunately, the sun's energy and the area's geography combine to generate sea breezes through the Carquinez Straits that make natural cooling relatively easy. These reach Davis, typically, in the late afternoon or early evening, cooling the area to an average summer nighttime low of 53°F. With such natural diurnal cooling it was absurd for

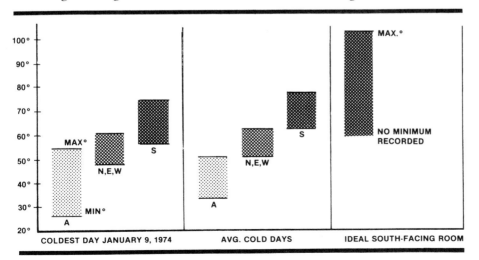

Figure 1
Winter temperature ranges on sunny days. Stonegate and Cranbrook apartments.
A: Outside air temperature; N, E, W: North, East & West-facing apt.'s inside temp; S: South-facing apt's inside temp.

Davis residents to be paying as much as $200 for summer air conditioning. The elimination of central air conditioning in new construction saves enough initially to pay for passive solar systems.

Natural cooling is particularly important in Davis because the demand for residential air conditioning occurs during one of California's peak electrical demand periods. Reduction of this demand could reduce the need for additional expensive generating capacity.

In measuring performance, apartments proved to be particularly useful in that some complexes had identical units directly facing each of the four compass directions, so that orientation, window size and location, and roof overhang could easily be compared to interior temperature, energy use, and level of comfort. During July and August of 1973 the team monitored temperatures in unoccupied units of three two-story complexes, all built according to conventional standards, all insulated to existing FHA standards of R-7 in walls, R-11 in ceilings. At 99°F outside, those apartments facing east and west on the top floors were 24° hotter than units faced north-south on the ground floor.

Pacific Gas and Electric Company supplied data on energy use in twenty-seven occupied apartments in a three-story part of one complex. Subtracting average winter month's electric use from average summer month's use to separate energy used by the air conditioner from normal electric use, the top floor apartments under inadequately designed roofs consumed twice as much energy as second-floor units and nearly three times as much as bottom-floor units. Units on the upper east side were worst because excessive heat gain through the roof was supplemented by early morning direct heat gain through the large east-facing windows, demon-strating the vital importance of window orientation. Experiments showed that interior drapes on east- and west-facing windows only reduced the temperature 1° to 5°F. Exterior shading devices proved the only effective protective measure.

A series of good sea-breeze-cooled nights during the test period, when windows in monitored units were opened at dusk and closed early in the morning, showed temperatures substantially lower in these units than in other, unvented apartments—but there was no reduction of daytime maximum temperatures because of a lack of thermal mass in the structures. This led to provisions for thermal mass in the building code and in the passive solar houses designed by the team as examples.

During the winter of 1973–1974, research showed that south-facing apartments with good solar exposure were significantly warmer. On several occasions temperatures in the 80s were registered on sunny winter days—for several days 24°F above ambient, and 17°F above temperatures in north, east, or west facing units. The apartments had solar glazing equal to only 10 percent of their floor area, and no thermal mass, but comparisons of natural gas used for space heating in occupied apartments confirmed the value of direct solar heat provided by south-facing windows. Units facing south used as much as 30 percent less gas than other apartments.

Gas-use and electricity-use data were obtained from a sample of typical houses to evaluate the difference between detached houses and apartments. They showed that the average Davis apartment uses 25 percent less electricity and 39 percent less gas per square foot than the average Davis detached house. Common walls and reduced outside surface area account for the apartments' superior performance. Energy use in various neighborhoods was also compared. The oldest part of Davis had the lowest electricity use but a surprisingly high gas use per square foot—explained when we remember that older houses are usually shaded by mature trees so that they need little air conditioning, but they often have poor insulation and leaky windows, and therefore tend to use more gas for winter heating.

Conclusions

The study of Davis buildings made certain conclusions inescapable.

- The basic frame construction methods commonly used in Davis could produce buildings that would perform reasonably well in the Davis climate.

- Simple principles of climatic design were consistently ignored by the local building industry.

- Existing city policy and citizen review processes were inadequate, and in some instances resulted in reduced energy efficiency.

- High levels of energy efficiency would be achieved only if building code changes required future buildings to adapt design to climate.

- Neighborhood planning policies also would need revision to facilitate certain aspects of proposed code requirements.

The team decided that the new code, to be workable, would have to be based on performance requirements, not inflexible standards. It would have to be easily understood, and would need to avoid rasing construction costs significantly. Compliance that used standard building technology and prac-

tice would have to be possible. And the code must help to save significant amounts of energy and consequently money.

To allow maximum design flexibility the code provided two alternatives. Path I is prescriptive, providing a set of rules with possible tradeoffs. Path II sets a minimum performance standard. It describes a calculation technique and specifies a design day for determining the compliance of buildings that do not conform to Path I, with certain requirements for heat loss or heat gain per day per square foot of floor area. For example, a 2,000-square-foot house could not exceed a heat loss of 192 Btus per square foot per day on the winter design day, or 95 Btus heat gain on the summer design day (infiltration was not included in these figures).

Path II allows almost complete design flexibility, to encourage innovative solutions in adapting buildings to the local climate. Path I allows compliance without the need for detailed calculations. As the research group expected, almost all buildings have used Path I. Some of its more important provisions are:

- Wood frame walls must use R–11 insulation; roofs must use R–19 (this is the state requirement). Some exceptions are made for houses with brick or concrete walls, if the decreased insulation is outside the mass.

- All glazing is regulated as a percentage of floor area. "Unearned" glazing is set at 12.5 percent of the area in single-pane glass. More area can be "earned" by using double-pane glass or by using south-facing windows backed by thermal mass. All but a small percentage of these windows must be shaded in summer.

- Good natural or artificial cross-ventilation must be provided.

- Light colors must be used on roofs to reflect summer heat, unless 30 percent thicker insulation is used.

Local builders helped to estimate the economic impact of these requirements. The analysis showed that slight increases ($0 to $200) in design costs, insulation, and shading devices for a typical 1,500-square-foot house would save more than $5 per month in utility costs—and with projected energy cost increases of 10 percent a year these savings will also increase considerably.

To show how far the proposed standards were from what could be done by more refined solar buildings, Jon Hammond and Marshall Hunt spent several weeks in the spring of 1974 with Steve Baer and Zomeworks, learning what would later become known as passive solar energy solutions to designing with climate, and experimenting with and designing low-cost solar buildings. New approaches to both building codes and solar design were intertwined in the Davis study, and although the building code has received more attention, it cannot stand alone.

City planning for solar use

It does little good to design the perfect solar house or system for a subdivision where design and zoning regulations allow the sun to be blocked in the winter, or the breeze to be hampered while excess solar heat is stored in wide and unshaded streets in the summer. Therefore, a set of planning policies were developed to complement the building code. Planning affects the environmental quality of the community, noise levels, transportation patterns, air pollution levels, the conversion of prime agricultural or other valuable land to urban use, and the consumption of energy in all levels of society. The energy conservation and solar use planning package developed for the city of Davis included these major policies:

Lot orientation

Simply by facing houses toward the south, we can assure better thermal performance, summer and winter. In Davis, this change was accomplished at little or no increase in development cost. In areas with more complex terrain, solar exposure must still determine, or at least influence, land-use decisions (Figure 2).

Setback flexibility and minimum lot size

Neighborhood planning policies that encourage large lots promote sprawl and increase the area covered with pavement—thereby increasing summer heat problems. Sprawled development increases travel time, distance, and energy use. Setback flexibility allows orientation of houses for natural heating and cooling and for solar domestic water heating. Houses could be set on the extreme edges of lots for proper orientation by removing standard restrictions through the use of Planned Unit Development zoning or other innovative concepts (Figure 3).

Fences

In most areas existing controls are excessive and may allow shading of the south wall with extreme setback requirements. This is a particularly controversial issue in Davis—in *all* of California—where the mild climate, high cost of land, and lifestyle make opaque 6-foot fences a standard feature in subdivisions. But as lot size drops below 6,000 square feet fencing makes little sense—particularly when it adversely affects use of the sun and the climate for natural space conditioning. As a result of our work, setbacks and height controls were made more flexible (Figure 4).

Solar rights

If there is no system to assure long-term shade-free solar access, it is of little use to orient buildings toward the sun. Large investments are involved; therefore a guarantee of solar rights is necessary in new residential developments. Colorado, Oregon, and New Mexico have already adopted such laws, and they have been introduced in the U.S. Congress and in California. We suggested that developers be required to provide easements guaranteeing solar access. It was a controversial issue and has not been adopted. A solar rights bill affecting vegetation alone (the most critical issue) has been introduced in the California legislature (Figure 5).

Street widths

The city heat-island effect is well documented and predictable. It is caused primarily by substitution of dark, hard, non-evaporating surfaces for vegetation. Research in nearby Sacramento had demonstrated that at the extreme this can cause a rise of 10°F on hot summer days. Any built environment will necessarily have non-evaporating surfaces, but the use of landscaping and planting to minimize the impact is essential. The design of streets is particularly important. Narrow streets save valuable land and can be shaded more easily. They are more comfortable and safer for bicyclists, pedestrians, and motorists because they reduce the thermal heat load on people

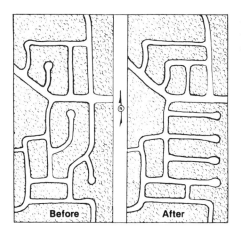

Figure 2
Subdivision was re-oriented for solar access.

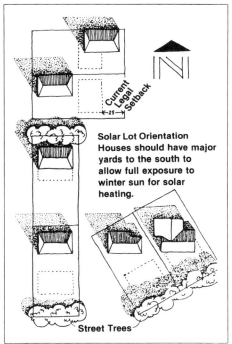

Solar Lot Orientation Houses should have major yards to the south to allow full exposure to winter sun for solar heating.

Figure 3
Standard restrictions often dictate house placement. Flexibility is more functional.

using the streets, as well as traffic speeds. The use of parking bays rather than on-street parking can promote shading both over the bays and over the narrower streets. We developed a set of resolutions and ordinances that will facilitate use of pedestrian and bicycle systems as a means of moving people around the city. Most of these have now been adopted.

Figure 4
Regulations on fencing for privacy must consider sun.

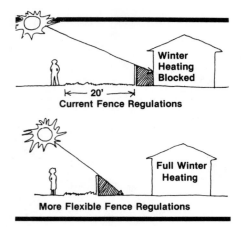

Winter Heating Blocked

← 20' →
Current Fence Regulations

Full Winter Heating

More Flexible Fence Regulations

Figure 5
Sun rights are three dimensional—a state ordinance guaranteeing solar access is pending in California.

climatic and financial benefits must be accompanied by appropriate landscaping. Large deciduous trees like oaks, hackberries, sycamores, and ashes provide cooling shade, evapotranspiration, and a quiet beauty that gives older Valley towns much of their character and livability. These shed their leaves in winter to allow the warm sun in. Shading and landscaping may often be the determining factors in individual decisions to walk or bicycle instead of riding in an airconditioned car. Glaring unshaded asphalt creates desert micro-

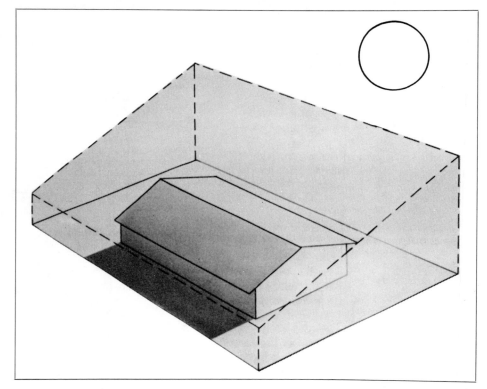

Landscaping

The environmental quality and beauty of a community is largely a function of its architecture, its street layout and grid system, its parks, and its landscaping. The last three elements are all within municipal control and operation. Narrower streets for micro-

climates in the summer. We developed several resolutions, code amendments, and ordinances to encourage the shading of streets and parking areas that have been adopted.

The city should also encourage the widest possible use of home gardens to realize energy savings in the food sector. For each calorie of food produced

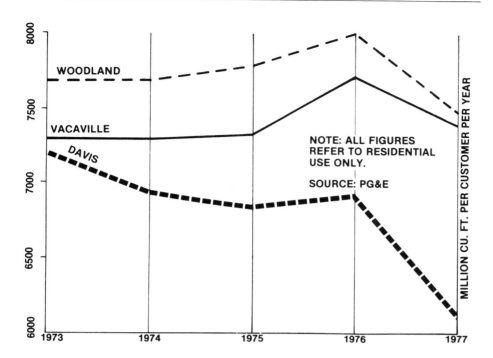

Figure 6
Kwh per customer per year.

WOODLAND

VACAVILLE

DAVIS

NOTE: ALL FIGURES
REFER TO RESIDENTIAL
USE ONLY.

SOURCE: PG&E

MILLION CU. FT. PER CUSTOMER PER YEAR

by agriculture ten calories are expended. A home gardener can do much better.

Village Homes

At approximately the same time the city council embarked on the energy conservation studies, a local builder/developer was proposing a 70-acre subdivision that raised many of the same issues in a site-specific manner. The solutions proposed by Mike Corbett for Village Homes included many innovative features like solar heating, natural cooling, and continued use of the prime agricultural land on which Davis is located.

It is important that the role of this private enterprise in the Davis experience be understood. Just as the solar housing research gave builders an idea of how little the proposed code asked for, so Corbett's subdivision became a real demonstration of the principles of wise land use the research team proposed. Though there was little coordination between the two groups, primarily because both were too busy doing their own work to coordinate strategies, this demonstrates the level of understanding and innovation that now exists in Davis.

The overall density of the Village Homes master plan is the same as that in a standard subdivision, but the organization of the land creates major common areas that are controlled by the Village homeowners association. The subdivision will not be completely built until 1982, and will doubtlessly evolve as the democratic will of residents is expressed, but it is already an interesting and pleasant place to live.

The impact of code and planning policies

The new code has now been in effect for more than two years. The majority of builders who opposed it initially have been convinced that it works and

Figure 7
Natural gas use.

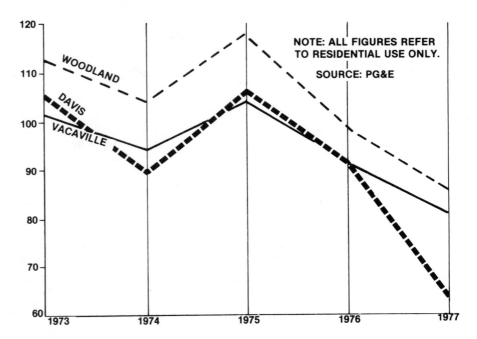

NOTE: ALL FIGURES REFER TO RESIDENTIAL USE ONLY.

SOURCE: PG&E

are now strong supporters. The City Building Inspection Department has done a very good job of implementing it, with the help of Living Systems and support from HUD. Almost 1,000 single-family houses and more than 600 apartment units have been built under the code, at a construction value of about $40 million.

The planning policies have been in effect for more than a year, and were more commonly accepted from the very beginning because in many cases they reduced development costs. More than 90 percent of new lots are oriented for solar use. Local streets have been reduced from more than 40 feet wide to a mere 26 feet. And many other ideas and suggestions have been incor-

porated in the development review process.

The energy savings have been even better than expected (Figures 6 and 7). Code and related education measures have caused a dramatic change in the trend in energy use in Davis. Energy use has been significantly reduced and a viable solar industry has been established in the area. Most important, however, is the fact that the people of Davis have broken the myth that the energy problem is far beyond our control and can be handled only by far-away men of great power and expertise. While no one thing will save the world, there are those activities that make real contributions toward, at least, giving it a chance.

14 | The Appropriate Technology Vision and the Future of Our Communities

Dennis R. Holloway

I BELIEVE our existing communities will undergo tremendous physical and social changes in the next decades as a consequence of the inevitable shift away from waning fossil fuels and dangerous nuclear energy. The oil embargo of 1973 prompted all of us to look more closely at the relationship between the conditions of our existence and world fossil fuel supplies. We began to ask questions about the amount of energy we consume and the technology with which we consume it. And there was the dawning question about the real limitations of fossil fuels —the "energy of freedom"—and the foundation of our affluent "modern" suburban lifestyles.

These questions became the basis for a new and increasingly vocal movement peopled primarily by a younger, environmentally conscious generation that sought answers in the alternative, renewable, cost-effective, and ecologically sound energy sources of sun, wind, and bio-fuels. The list of the movement's gurus is long, but it includes de Tocqueville, Thoreau, Gandhi, Mumford, and Schumacher— all men who had, in their own times,

understood the human propensity towards technological addictions, and who sought the right connections between self, society, and environment. The Appropriate Technology movement, as it is sometimes called, is developing an optimistic vision of the future of civilization that is in stark contrast with the visions conjured by the Three Mile Island disaster and Garrett Hardin's "tragedy of the commons." In this paper, I present the work of my university students who have attempted since 1973 to define and express this Appropriate Technology vision.

When the "lights went out" in 1973, I was teaching at the School of Architecture and Landscape Architecture of the University of Minnesota. Since 30 percent of the U.S. energy budget is consumed by the built environment, it seemed natural to ask my students if there were new techniques for designing tea kettles, buildings, and even whole communities which would conserve fossil fuels while making major use of renewable energy sources such as solar, wind, and bio-fuels.

To my surprise, the students were

Figure 1
Ouroboros/South: Plan view of experimental structure built by University of Minnesota students in Rosemount, Minnesota.
(By Dennis Holloway)

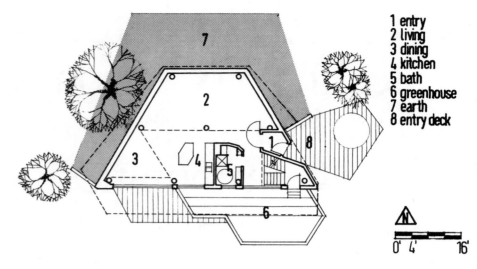

1 entry
2 living
3 dining
4 kitchen
5 bath
6 greenhouse
7 earth
8 entry deck

0' 4'   16'

"turned on" by these assignments. It was for all of us, undergraduate students and teacher, an exciting opportunity to work on a new frontier of design with radical departures from the energy-affluence paradigm of the *modern movement* in architecture. It was also a liberation to reflect on the best technologies from the past, which the modern movement had heretofore ignored. Some of these older, saner technologies gave us new insights into energy conservation possibilities for the future. We rediscovered that history is not only for historians.

The first project, Ouroboros / South, a solar heated, wind-powered house, begun in 1973, was designed and constructed by interdisciplinary teams of architecture, landscape architecture, mechanical engineering and electrical engineering students. Named after the mythical serpent that survives by consuming itself, a metaphor for the ecological movement, Ouroboros was designed as a new rural structure intended to test various residential energy conservation and solar technologies (Figures 1, 2, and 3). The trapezoidal plan of this house optimizes the area of the south-facing, flat plate solar col-

lector, and a sod covering on the north roof keeps the house cool in summer and warm in winter. The large overhanging solar collectors, developed by mechanical engineering student John Ilse, shade the vertical south facing windows during the summer. Other energy and resource conserving features of the house include a waterless composting toilet, a passive solar greenhouse, and, in the future, an aerogenerator for lighting and cooking.

In addition to learning a great deal about the functioning of these building systems we discovered that it is possible for the necessary funds and materials for such a large-scale educational experiment to be found in the local community. By taking this approach to the implementation of this project, we not only eliminated the time-consuming process of government grant writing, but we actively involved the local community in the process of design and construction and gave them a real stake in the outcome.

The success of Ouroboros / South, our first project, paved the way for a second project, Ouroboros / East. Realizing that energy- and resource-conserving new housing construction can

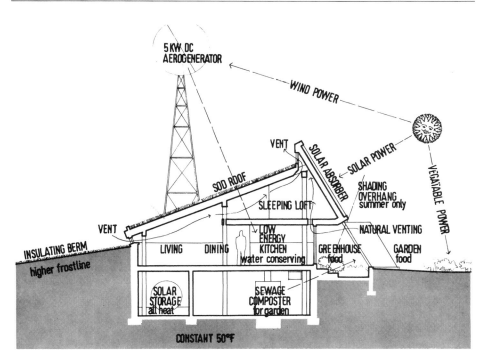

Figure 2
*Ouroboros/South:
Section view showing
various residential
energy conservation and
solar technologies
being tested.*
(By Dennis Holloway)

only make a small contribution to the total energy use of existing communities, we decided to "retrofit" an existing St. Paul house (ca. 1910) with similar energy-conserving solar and recycling technologies (Figure 4). This project was the first solar-retrofitted house in the upper midwest. Like Ouroboros / South, it utilizes a flat plate solar hot water collector system, a passive solar greenhouse, a *Clivus Multrum* composting toilet and a variety of insulation and window retrofitting techniques. Designed as a neighborhood center for demonstration and education, the house includes a community tool shop in the basement, classroom space and a resource library on the first floor and staff living space on the upper two floors. An outdoor courtyard space in the front of the house (for meetings and demonstrations) and an urban food garden in the back complete the educational facilities (Fig. 5).

This project required many public community meetings to convince the

Figure 3
*Ouroboros/South:
Large overhanging flat
plate solar water
collectors cast shadows
on south windows
during summer.*
(Photo by Dennis
Holloway)

Figure 4

*Ouroboros/East:
Located in St. Paul,
this was the first solar
retrofitted house in
the upper midwest.*
(By Dan Feidt)

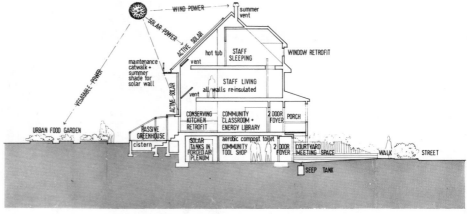

Figure 5

*Ouroboros/East: A
section view showing
various energy con-
servation and solar
technologies being tested
and demonstrated.*
(By Dennis Holloway)

local neighborhood of the soundness of the experiments. People who came to these meetings wanted to know if solar space and water heating was practical in an older house. Would there be too much reflection from the solar collector glazing and odor problems with the composting waterless toilet? In answering these questions, we began to understand the importance of involving the community with full-scale actual energy education projects. And we began to understand that projects like Ouroboros could be the key to organizing and restructuring neighborhoods towards greater self-reliance.

In the third project, begun in 1975, we extrapolated the findings of the Ouroboros projects and proposed the energy conservation retrofitting of an entire city, Winona, Minnesota. This approach to conservation and alternative energy sources by an entire community is the work that I will concentrate on in the latter part of this paper. The Winona project shows how people's individual actions to retrofit dwellings and neighborhoods are steps toward the rebuilding of our towns into ecological, energy-conserving, self-managing cooperative communities.

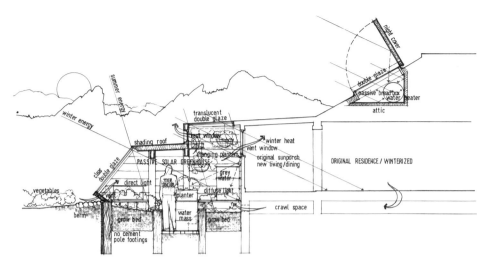

Figure 6
House of Essentials (HOE): Located in Boulder, Colorado, this house has been retrofitted with low-cost, passive solar technologies.
(By Dennis Holloway)

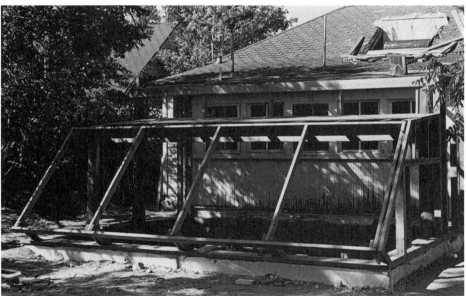

Figure 7
House of Essentials (HOE): Passive solar greenhouse and hot water heater shown during construction.
(By Dennis Holloway)

The findings from these Minnesota projects are now being economically refined and extended at the College of Environmental Design, University of Colorado, in a project called the House of Essentials (HOE) (Figures 6 and 7). My students are constructing low-cost, passive solar greenhouse additions, solar water heaters that cost less initially than natural gas water heaters, gray water recycling systems, and a new passive Trombe wall solar house constructed with beetle-kill pine beams and rammed earth bricks that cost three cents each. This latest cost-effective, labor-intensive work by my students has convinced me that the vision of an energy-conserving community, described in the following case studies of Winona, Minnesota and the Montclair Community in Denver, Colorado, is realizable very quickly—perhaps in a decade.

Neighborhood and community case studies

Winona: Toward an energy-conserving community*

INTRODUCTION   In 1975, I instructed the students of my Energy Design Studio at the University of Minnesota to carry out a nine-month feasibility study for making a typical Minnesota city energy- and food-self-sufficient by the year 2000. This project does not presume to be a blueprint. Rather, it is a glimpse of possibilities. Put simply, it says that if we, as individuals, begin by altering our own lifestyles, local habitats, and neighborhoods with muscle supplied by ourselves and those around us and technology supplied by the new renewable energy systems, the affluent western nations will be able to cut energy consumption drastically, thereby alleviating the inhuman conditions of the Third World and insuring the well-being of future generations.

The City of Winona was chosen because:

(1) Its size, age, and economic activity make it typical of many upper-Midwest river towns;

(2) With a population of 27,000, it is manageable in terms of energy conservation;

(3) It has a state university and two private colleges;

(4) It is a center for the surrounding agricultural communities of southern Minnesota;

(5) It is not suffering from an out-migration, due to the fact that young people remain or return;

* The author thanks Huldah Curl, Editor, Continuing Education in the Arts, University of Minnesota, for her editorial assistance in the original publication "Winona: Towards an Energy Conserving Community" University of Minnesota (1975).

(6) Its weather (from -30°F in winter to 95°F in summer) is sufficiently challenging to make it a good test case.

The Studio made a thorough and careful on-site study of Winona in preparation for this project. Consideration was given to the effect of rising energy costs on systems of transportation, food production, shelter, and communications and the consequent effects on people and their neighborhoods. Discussions were held with the Winona Planning Commission and Winona Chamber of Commerce, and the public was invited to several open meetings.

The machinery and technology advocated throughout this project are not new or revolutionary. Windmills, dotted throughout rural America until the Rural Electrification Adminstration changed the country in the 1930s and 1940s, were invented in principle in 7th Century Persia. The direct ancestor of today's solar collectors was built in 18th Century Holland. Methane gas, direct from the sewers, was once used to light the streets of London. In-filling between buildings is simply reviving the idea of the row house. The A. B. Clivus Company has been making composting toilets for Sweden for more than 15 years.

What *is* new and unique in this project is the application of energy-conserving technology as a retrofitted infrastructure for a *total existing community* as a possible direction for the city with its evolving physical, social, and economic needs in an age of dwindling traditional energy sources.

Not all proposed energy-conserving methods are fully tested, and improvements in these technologies are constantly being made. Moreover, developments are taking place at such speed that there can be gaps in communication while new techniques are being investigated. This project is therefore aimed at stimulating thinking and planning at all levels of the community. It emphasizes what individuals and neighborhoods can do by themselves without fighting city hall or big government; it shows possible ways an entire community can change creatively; and it demonstrates that a better quality of life is possible with less energy consumption.

GOALS AND STRATEGIES   The Winona project shows that, in the process of achieving the goal of community energy conservation and localized energy and food production, a number of other goals may also be achieved:

- *Social goals* — To create a more cooperative community, in which "neighbor" means "helpmate," and to enrich the world experience for special populations (e.g., children, housepersons, handicapped and elderly);

- *Economic goals* — To encourage local production and distribution of goods and services; and to maximize worker control over decision-making about production, distribution, working conditions, and so on;

- *Architectural goals* — To maintain a sense of history by building preservation and neighborhood character preservation, and to diversify environmental experience by mixing land uses;

- *Ecological goals* — To maximize recycling of waste, water, and materials, and to develop a sense of common ethics toward the future environment of the planet.

NEIGHBORHOODS   While there is a wide range of proposals for various parts of Winona, the general strategy for change involves a gradual and continuous series of locally initiated changes analogous to successive biological evolution, moving from energy and resource systems based entirely on use of fossil fuels to systems and practices based upon the use of income-energy sources — the sun, wind, and biofuels.

Since the home and the neighborhood are the environmental units most responsive to the initiatives of individuals, families, and small neighborhood groups, it seems natural that any strategy for change at the community level would begin with change in the neighborhoods. The neighborhood proposals, like the suggestions for other parts of the city, are based on a three-part structure of changes:

Phase I: Energy conservation within the existing physical environment;

Phase II: Replacement of existing fossil fuel systems with renewable-source energy systems;

Phase III: Development of a more diverse cooperative community.

Over a period of twenty-five years, student Rolf Stoylen argues, a typical Winona neighborhood could quietly evolve into a renewable energy-based cooperative community. He envisions the use of shelter belts along existing streets, urban orchards, hedges for birds and small animals, and beehives (Figure 8). The former service station shown in the lower right section of Figure 8 has, in this proposal, been converted into a live-in car pool repair shop, and garages have been converted into passively solar heated cooperative shops and barns for small animals (Figure 9).

Other ideas include the joining together of two existing small houses to

Figure 8
*A typical Winona
neighborhood moves
toward energy self-
reliance.*
(By Rolf Stoylen)

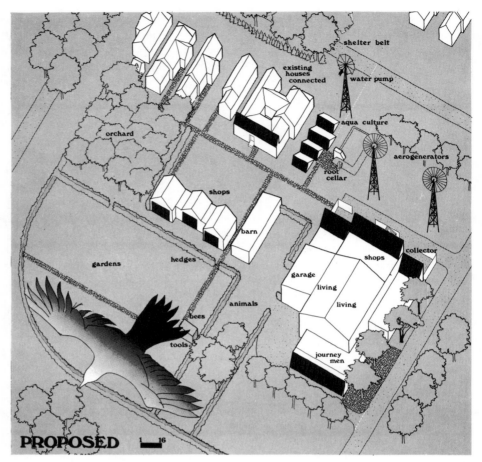

create a solar-heated residence for an extended family group (Figure 10). Adjacent to this structure, a greenhouse equipped with fish culture tanks and a root cellar, have been constructed over the foundations of houses which have been demolished for economic reasons (Figure 10).

While utilizing similar ideas, other students developed a variety of different ideas for transforming other neighborhoods. For example, Greg Oltvedt proposes the retrofitting of existing streets, (unnecessary in a town largely without automobiles), as pedestrian bicycle parkways (Figure 11). This scheme utilizes brick paving, trees, benches, gardens, children's playgrounds at intersections, and water-

connecting elements supplied by the Mississippi River.

Phase III of Gary Nyberg's neighborhood proposal shows the center of city blocks being utilized as garden and aqua-culture coops (Figure 12). New institutional buildings for the community (e.g., the Living-Working Center) and new shops serve the daily needs of the basically pedestrian world of the neighborhood. Notice also that this proposal revives the old electric trolley system by uncovering the existing tracks. In this neighborhood scenario, a local Catholic church and a group of locally-based architect-builders join to become the moving forces behind the restructuring of the neighborhood.

NEIGHBORHOOD MARKETS The various neighborhood proposals for an energy self-reliant Winona are tied together by the creation of a city-wide food cooperative with neighborhood markets. This concept is based on the recognition of the fact that, in the United States, we put five times as much energy into food production as we get back out of the food produced. Energy used in current U.S. food production is as follows: 33 percent for food processing, 30 percent in the home, 18 percent for actual growing (including energy costs of fertilizer, pesticides, and fuel for farm machinery), 16 percent in trade (staff, advertising, and packaging), and 3 percent on transportation. This can be cut at all five levels by a Winona Food Cooperative with seven branch markets. The branches can be strategically located throughout the city so that daily walks to the markets would be possible for everyone (Figure 13).

At the small scale of the neighborhood market, much of the processing, chemical preserving, and refrigeration of food can be done away with. When

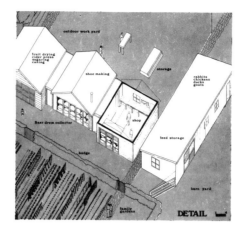

Figure 9
A detailed view of garages converted into passively heated cooperative workshops and small animal barns.
(By Rolf Stoylen)

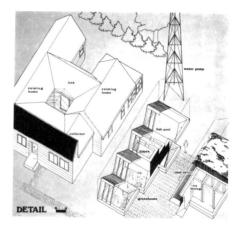

Figure 10
An example of how two small homes could be joined to create a solar-heated residence for an extended family group.
(By Rolf Stoylen)

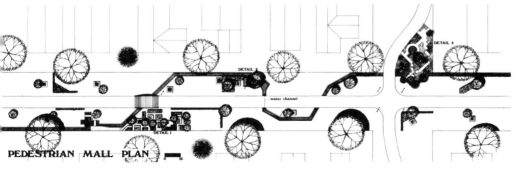

PEDESTRIAN MALL PLAN

Figure 11
A proposal to create pedestrian/bicycle parkways, complete with an artificial water channel, in place of existing neighborhood streets.
(By Greg Oltvedt)

produce is bought and sold pretty much on a daily basis, the ice house, the smoke house and the root cellar are reasonable substitutes. Naturally dried foods can replace mechanically dehydrated ones. Quick-process foods should be eliminated entirely: they not only cost more and use more energy but provide less nutrition than unprocessed food. A canning plant, powered with wind and solar energy, can stock the markets in the wintertime.

At the household level, people should be encouraged to eat less meat and more vegetables. Livestock (depending on the kind) use eight to

Figure 12
In this scheme the centers of existing residential city blocks are utilized as garden and aquaculture coops.
(By Gary Nyberg)

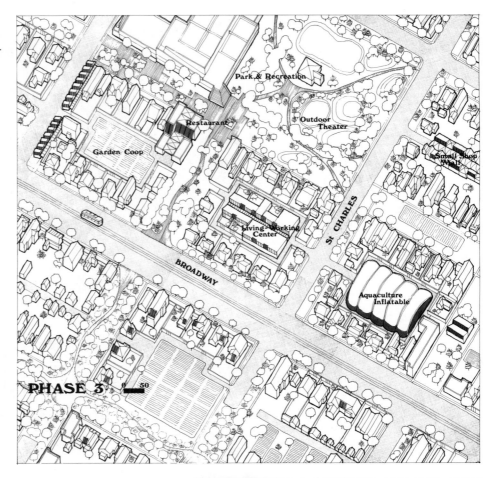

Figure 13
Plan view of city-wide food cooperative and neighborhood markets.
(By Doug Derr, Dwight Doberstein, and Rick Rampe)

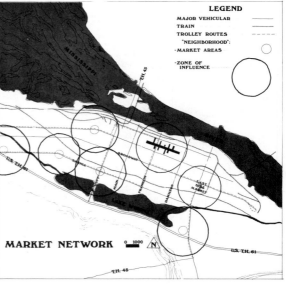

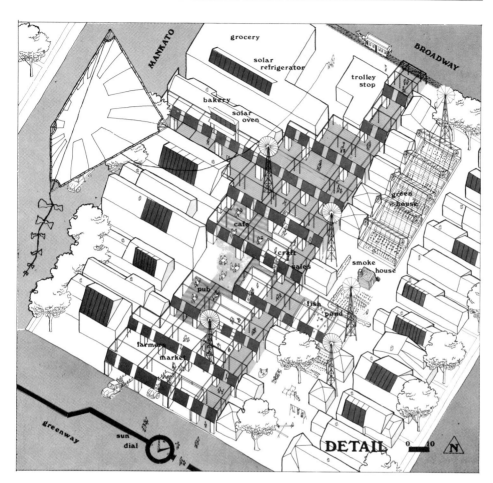

Figure 14
Detailed view of a typical neighborhood market.
(By Doug Derr, Dwight Doberstein, and Rick Rampe)

twenty times the amount of energy needed for vegetable growing. Vegetables need less cooking than meat, and many need no cooking at all. Household refrigerators can be smaller when they are replenished by daily trips to the market. Home canning can replace the freezer.

As one of the biggest local buyers of farm produce, the cooperative can use its influence on farming methods. It can support labor-intensive as opposed to energy-intensive agriculture. In collaboration with the Agricultural Experiment Station, and the proposed School of Environmental and Energy Technology at Winona State, it can explore more natural ways of pest con-

trol, (bugs that eat other bugs, plants that repel bugs). It can influence local growers toward more vegetable production and less emphasis on livestock.

One of the main purposes of the cooperative is to get food from farmers to people with as little salesmanship and as few middlemen as possible. Since it will be owned by its own customers, the cooperative will not need advertising campaigns, coupon promotions, and grand openings with arc lights. Its customers won't need to pressure-sell their own food to themselves. The staff can be a combination of employees and volunteers.

Transportation costs will automatically be cut since the cooperative will

Figure 15

A view of the main receiving and distribution center for the Winona Food Cooperative.

(By Doug Derr, Dwight Doberstein, and Rick Rampe)

ISOMETRIC

Figure 16

Phase I of the conversion of a central city neighborhood into a revitalized shopping district, complete with a local neighborhood market.

(By Bruce Johnson)

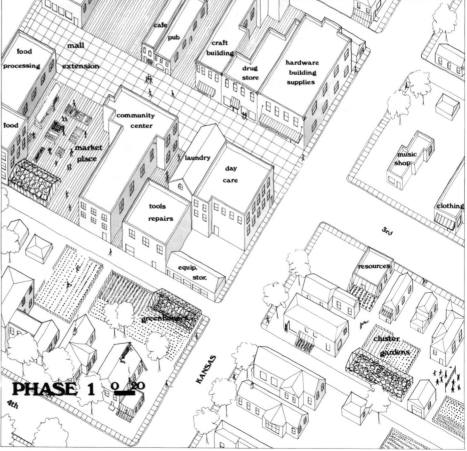

PHASE 1   0   20

rely mainly on local farmers. Most of the shipping can be done by railroad or barge. Produce will be redistributed from the main receiving center to the neighborhood branches, since it takes less energy to ship commodities to people than to transport people to commodities.

The network of markets would teach good nutrition and set up occasional demonstrations and exhibitions as well as sell food. It would sell starter plants and advise people on their backyard gardens. It would be a natural vehicle for passing on improved organic farming methods to area farmers.

The main receiving and distribution center in Winona could be set up in the Peerless Building on 2nd Street between Walnut and Market (Figure 15). The Peerless Building is directly on the railroad and near the existing barge terminal. It is also close to the Bay State Milling bins and the Northrop King Building. Offices to run the entire operation could be set up in the latter.

This proposal for a food cooperative and neighborhood markets by Doug Derr, Dwight Doberstein, and Rick Rampe is similar to the ideas developed by Bruce Johnson, who examined the possibilities of creating an interface between a central city neighborhood and a revitalized central shopping district (Figure 16). Once again, the local production and distribution of food is seen as the key to remapping the existing neighborhood.

The valuable urban space now taken up by streets and parking would be made available for gardens, bikeways, and walkways. The scale of the neighborhood makes walking a perfectly reasonable way of getting about. The introduction of food processing plants, as well as gardens, would reduce transportation, storage, and packaging and allow the daily harvesting and sale of fresh vegetables during the growing season. In-filling between houses would reduce heat loss during winter. Solar collectors and wind generators could be built which would serve the entire neighborhood and reduce the demand on the city power system.

The shopping district on 3rd Street is already a neighborhood focal point. A translucent, removable tensile membrane of treated canvas, which provides for ventilation and drainage, will be suspended above the street (Figure 17). It would not only offer shelter against the sun, rain, and snow but also maintain a winter street temperature of between 45° and 50°F. Businesses could use the sidewalks year-round for displays, and sidewalk cafes could remain open during most of the winter. The membrane street-covering is not expensive and could be used in similar Winona neighborhoods. It would pay for itself in savings in heating and cooling alone in short order—quite aside from making an atmosphere which would attract people (and customers).

THE CENTRAL BUSINESS DISTRICT
Downtown Winona, like that of many other small towns, is rapidly losing its effectiveness as a center for commerce. Rather than succumbing to the pressures of new suburban shopping malls, which would only increase community energy consumption and further erode the vitality of the downtown area, students Kevin McDonald and Bill Rust have proposed a three-stage process of revitalization for the central business district (Figures 18 and 19).

The first step would be to get people back into the area. Toward this end, an energy efficient public transportation system is suggested. In addition, a new downtown stop on the Amtrak line would make it easier for people from the suburbs and outlying hamlets to

Figure 17
A detailed view of Proposal Phase III, showing the solar retrofitting of existing buildings, the conversion of secondary streets to urban gardens, and the creation of a tensile membrane street covering over the existing shopping street.
(By Bruce Johnson)

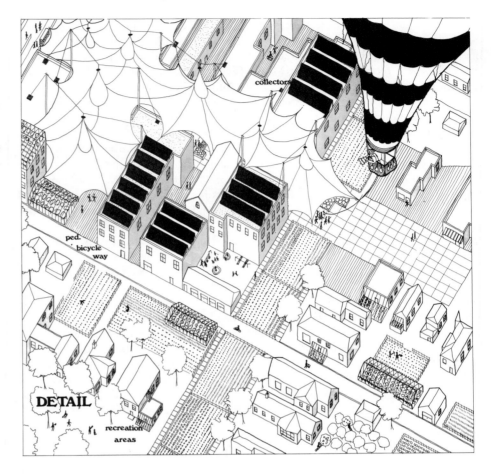

get to the area conveniently, and with much less energy consumption and pollution than the present system of automobile transportation.

The next phase would involve efforts aimed at increasing residential density in and near the downtown area. Not only would this new pattern of population distribution create more demand for retail outlets and related services, but the entire project would increase the city tax base, making future city improvements possible. By adding apartments to buildings such as the architecturally significant Latsch Building and the largely vacant two- and three-story buildings surrounding the square in front of it, while keeping stores and businesses on street level, it would be possible to increase both residential and retail occupancy. Renovation could include heavy insulation, solar collectors and even rooftop gardens and greenhouses.

The third step is to make the entire area more attractive and exciting. This could be accomplished by converting the square in front of the Latsch Building into a sunken pedestrian plaza, bordered by shops and professional offices and fronting on an open, covered arcade which would be enclosed during the winter (Figure 19). Other changes would include the restoration of the waterfront, an important part of Winona's heritage. The land behind the

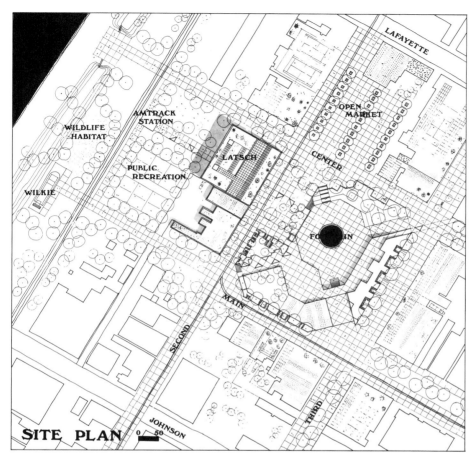

Figure 18
Plan view of a proposal for a revitalized central business district.
(By Kevin McDonald and Bill Rust)

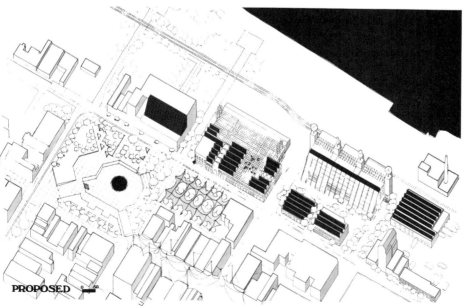

Figure 19
Detailed view of revitalized, pedestrian-oriented central business district.
(By Kevin McDonald and Bill Rust)

Figure 20
Diagram of a proposed
new food and waste
complex: a miniature
spaceship earth.
(By Drew Erickson and
Scott Williams)

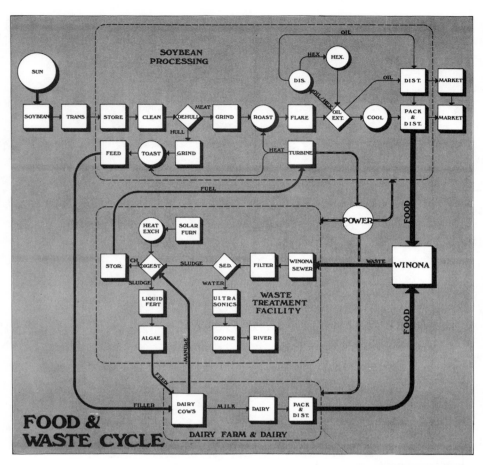

Figure 21
Site plan of
proposed food and
waste complex.
(By Drew Erickson
and Scott Williams)

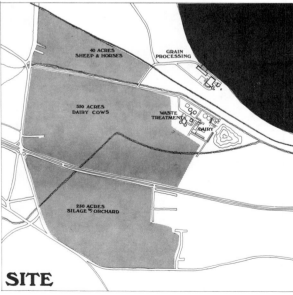

Latsch Building could become a public park with direct access to the river along Center Street: the dike would remain intact except for a section on Center Street which could be opened at low water through the use of gates. The Levee Park, on the flood plain beyond the dike, could become a wildlife sanctuary.

These changes, along with the creation of the neighborhood food cooperative network, not only would conserve energy and create new local business opportunities; they would improve the quality of life for the entire community.

Food and Waste Complex, A Miniature Spaceship Earth The Food and Waste Complex Plan by Drew Erikson and Scott Williams illustrates how a variety of systems and functions, usually separated in time and space, can be integrated to produce a synergy which makes good business and ecological sense.

The diagram of the system, in Figure 20, shows how a community-owned waste-treatment facility, dairy farm

and dairy, soybean processing facility and co-op markets could be integrated for optimum energy savings. This complex could be built on a 600-acre site along the river which includes the city sewage plant (Figure 21). The area is already zoned for commerical use and has existing roads and railroads. The complex would include a soybean processing plant, a dairy, a livestock and dairy farm, an ultrasonic water purifier and a new anaerobic digester to replace the current aerobic system. Construction, beginning with the ultrasonic water purifier as a first step towards reducing river pollution, would be phased over a five-year period. Construction would also include wind pumps and generators, algae ponds and drying beds, water storage, and barge docks.

With the conversion of the sewage plant to an anerobic digester, methane gas could be produced from both city sewage and livestock manure. The gas would power a turbine generator supplying power for the digester itself, for the dairy, and for about three-quarters of the processes at the soybean plant

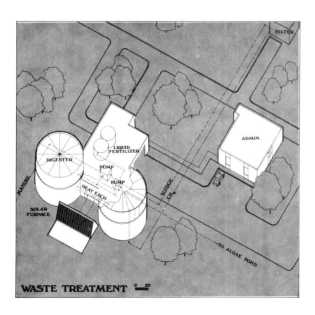

Figure 22
Waste treatment plant converted to an anerobic digestor to produce methane gas from city sewage and livestock manure.
(By Drew Erickson and Scott Williams)

Figure 23
The soybean plant
would process beans
grown along the river
into food products for
human consumption as
well as food supple-
ments for the cattle and
livestock farm and
dairy.
(By Drew Erickson and
Scott Williams)

SOYBEAN PROCESSING

(Figure 22). The turbine would also produce excess heat which could be used to dry and roast soybeans. Gas production would be speeded up by a solar furnace and heat exchanger. Sludge from the digester would be pumped for fertilizer to algae ponds, a source of high-protein cattle food.

Waste water from the digester, most of which would inevitably end up in the Mississippi, could be purified in tanks using ultrasonic waves and ozone (which breaks up into oxygen in water and leaves no pollution). The ultrasonic process eliminates both the need for energy-consuming filter beds and the need for chlorine, which is not only expensive, but dangerous to produce,

transport and store. Some of the purified water could be used for livestock, pumped through a carp pond and stored in reservoirs suspended in the windpump towers.

The soybean plant (Figure 23) could process 75 tons of beans, produce 54 tons of meal, 15 tons of oil and 6 tons of hulls each day. The meal could be further processed in the city into flour, meat extenders, and lecithin. The oil could be used for cooking, margarine, and paint. The hulls, ground and mixed with algae and waste fruit and vegetables, could be used as livestock feed. Beans for the plant could be grown on 26,000 acres along the river (about one-fifth of the total agricultural acreage of Winona County) and shipped by low-energy barge transportation. One benefit of soybeans as a crop is their capacity to fix nitrogen in the soil, permitting crop rotation.

The cattle and livestock farm and the dairy (Figures 24 and 25) would be located on the same grounds to minimize transportation and milk spoilage; both would be close to the new sewage digester for easy transportation of manure. Three double-six milking parlors in herringbone formation would handle the entire herd in two hours. Milk storage, lockers, and wash-up areas would be next to the milking parlors. Deep-well pumps, powered by wind, would provide cooling water for the milking parlors and the milk house. This pure water would also be used for washing and sterilization. The dairy would supply 1,000 gallons of milk a day, about 70 percent of what the city needs. The remaining 30 percent would come from privately owned cattle in the city and immediate area. Cows, sheep, and horses would be housed and yarded on the dike of the existing sewage plant. Calves, yearlings, dry cows, bulls and feed lots would be located on the pasture lands to the south. For insulation, the farm buildings would have thatched roofs, such as are used throughout Scandinavia today.

A two-story cow barn would house 300 cows in milk on the upper story, while 60 calves, 60 yearlings, and 120 dry cows would be housed on the lower floor. Twenty bulls would be housed separately in pens connected with enclosed exercise yards. A stable would provide housing for 20 horses. A loose shed, divided into four pens, would house 80 sheep with a woolhouse, and shearing and dipping areas nearby; lambs would live in a separate pen.

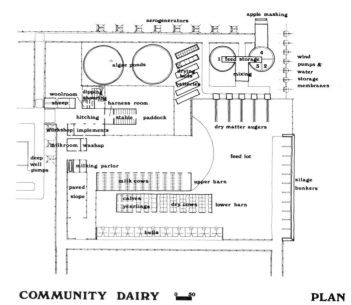

COMMUNITY DAIRY   **PLAN**

Figure 24   *Plan view of dairy, to be located adjacent to the soybean plant and the municipal methane gas plant to minimize transport of feed and manure.*

(By Drew Erickson and Scott Williams)

COMMUNITY DAIRY

PERSPECTIVE

Figure 25   *Aerial view drawing of community dairy.*

(By Drew Erickson and Scott Williams)

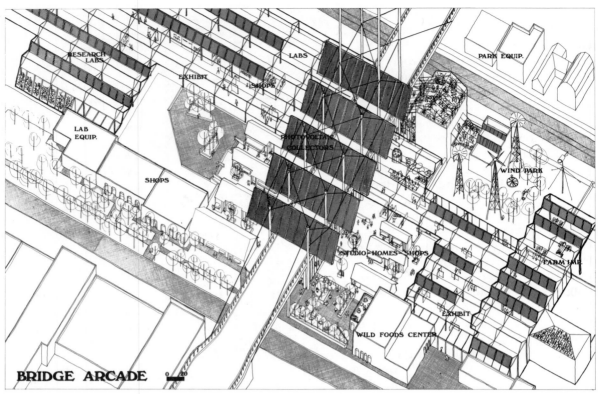

BRIDGE ARCADE 0 20

Figure 26
Riverfront Research and Exposition Center, a new gateway to Winona.
(By Mike Lopac and Dan Moldenhaver)

Some of the abandoned facilities from the old sewage plant could be put to new uses. The two 135-foot diameter filter beds would make ideal ponds for growing algae on digested sludge from the new anaerobic digester. The algae would be coagulated and harvested by autoflocculation, a process which can be done chemically (with lye) or, as proposed here, by keeping the sludge at 95°F using the heat exchanger at the digester and the sun's heat during the day. The coagulated algae would be pumped by wind pumps to glass-covered beds for drying. Two tanks remaining from the old sewage plant would be used to mix and store dry food (soybean hulls, dried algae, and dried waste fruit and vegetables) to be auger-fed to the livestock at the feed lot.

This proposed complex would be publicly owned and, by introducing new industry, would provide needed jobs. It is a concrete example of how energy-conserving planning can interlock a variety of systems so that they approach self-sufficiency.

NEW INSTITUTIONS   One of the implications of a reduction in energy and resource consumption on a community scale is that no part of the town can be underutilized. The entire range of environmental, aesthetic, and social experience, now available in a single day by automobile over a 100-to-200-mile radius, will have to be incorporated within geographical limits established by the new, dominant modes of transportation—walking, bicycling, urban electric cars, and energy-efficient public transportation. The mini-world of the small town and neighborhood will have to become more intensely inhabited and used by a broader cross-section of the local population.

Toward this end, students developed a series of ideas for how a city, no longer dominated by the automobile and subjected to the impoverishment created in local communities by transcontinental and global transportation patterns, could become a richer, more satisfying place to live. While these proposals are specific to the town of Winona, every community in this country has similar problems and opportunities.

Riverfront research and exposition center

Most communities have a largely abandoned series of residual open spaces near rivers or railroad tracks which could be put to good use. This proposal (Figure 26) by Mike Lopac and Dan Moldenhauer includes a large photovoltaic array which acts as a new gateway to Winona and a new research and exposition center to serve the technological development needs of the entire city.

Riverboat community on Latsch Island

Latsch Island, located in the Mississippi across from the central business district, contains a park, a beach, and a municipal harbor. There are permanent residents on the island, some of whom live year-round in houseboats in a back inlet. They have a very special lifestyle with a unique relationship to the river, which supplies them with carp, driftwood for fuel, and a cheap, non-polluting means of transportation by rowboat. The temporary residents, who come from Winona and nearby communities, use their houseboats as a poor man's yacht or vacation home on the river. In spite of their slightly raff-

ish reputation, the permanent and temporary residents combine to form a low-energy community which would be strengthened by any scheme aimed at promoting energy self-reliance for Winona.

In the proposal by Timothy Sullivan and Franz Hall (Figure 27), the houseboats could be oriented towards the south in winter, with larger windows in the bows and increased insulation in the sterns; in the summer they could reverse their direction. In the winter, they could huddle together to reduce heat loss and in the summer they could anchor further apart to increase natural ventilation. Small service centers as shown in Figure 27 for ten to fifteen houseboats could be built to provide waste recycling and methane gas production, water storage, power from wind generators, and workshops for small-boat repair and storage.

In addition to making these changes, which would enhance the ecological ef-

Figure 27
New solar heated service centers, along with slightly redesigned houseboats, improve the energy efficiency and quality of life of the existing houseboat community on Latsch Island.
(By Franz Hall and Tim Sullivan)

Figure 28
Site plan of an existing
abandoned monastery
converted to a vocational
rehabilitation center.
(By Paul Snyder)

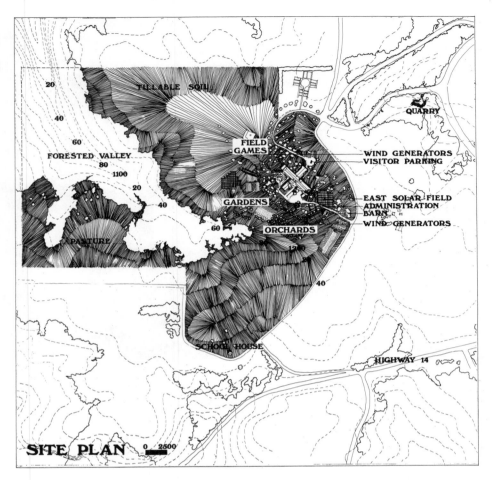

ficiency of the existing community of houseboat "squatters," the students proposed the construction of a new solar-heated public community center on the island, with a cafe, shops, and recreation facilities to serve not only Winona but the entire river traffic in the area. This kind of community-center pattern at each city along the river could revitalize the productive value and health of the entire "river community."

Vocational rehabilitation center

Nearly every community has an abandoned building worth saving. A proposal by Paul Snyder envisions a socially-innovative, adaptive reuse of one such building in Winona, an abandoned Catholic monastery built on a high hill overlooking the city (Figures 28 and 29). By converting this unused resource into a center for vocational rehabilitation, the important point is made that a shift towards energy self-reliance is not just a technological proposition but is primarily a restructuring of social relationships and can mean an improvement in the quality of life for all the citizens of a community.

The cruciform monastery (Figure 30) would be a live-in center for elderly and handicapped people with a volunteer staff from the community-at-large. The center would be a small

EXTERIOR

Labels within image: 3rd LEVEL DECK, ENCLOSED RAMP, WALKWAY GALLERY, COMMUNITY FORUM, WIND PUMP, RESIDENT ENTRIES, HOBBY GREENHOUSE, 3rd LEVEL, 2nd LEVEL DECK, GARAGE, FIRE RAMP, PARKING, SERVICE YARD, LOADING

Figure 29
Detailed view of the proposed vocational rehabilitation center.
(By Paul Snyder)

community, supported by the surrounding monastery agricultural lands and by the larger community of Winona.

Winona State University: Catalyst for change

Student Timothy Whitten addresses the general issue of how existing institutions, especially educational institutions, could be refocused toward an emphasis on public service and lifestyle and lifeway experimentation in his plan. The campus, (see Figure 30), becomes a model for solar retrofitting, and the curriculum shifts towards the organizational skills and new technolo-

gies necessary for a swift social transition into the renewable energy age.

Winona in retrospect

When the students completed the Winona Study, the project was exhibited as a traveling show in Winona and other nearby southeastern Minnesota communities. Because this area is agriculturally and economically stable, younger people, after formal education or other world travels, have tended to return to their hometowns. Consequently, Winona has a dynamic, relatively well-educated young population which sees its hometown within a wider context. And for this group of future community leaders, the Winona Study provided a tangible, comprehensive vision of a possible future worth working for. The dialogue that developed between students and this younger population was the most exciting aspect of the whole project. The study, however, did not address the greater question of how these citizens can move the city into the directions we proposed, which we later realized was the question uppermost in people's minds. We learned that changes in a community's environmental systems, however interesting or exciting, must stem from carefully coordinated social changes that involve individual and neighborhood organizational inputs

from the beginning of the study.

The Winona Study was exhibited at the United Nations Habitat Conference in Vancouver, British Columbia in 1976. More than 100,000 people saw the show. We were deeply moved by the positive response from the international audience, who had similar ideas but had never thought to ask what a community retrofitted with renewable energy systems might really be like.

From our experience with the exhibits at these local and international forums, I am convinced that further academic, service-learning in the community-scale energy context is (especially for design schools) extremely relevant now and in the foreseeable fu-

Figure 30

A proposal to transform the campus of Winona State University into a center for solar retrofitting and experimentation with new energy-conserving lifestyles.

(By Timothy Whitten)

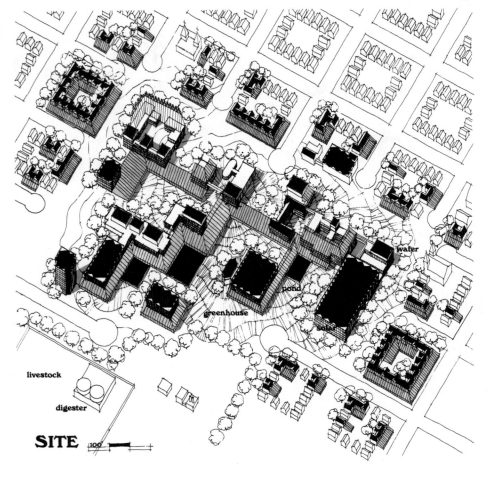

livestock

digester

SITE 100

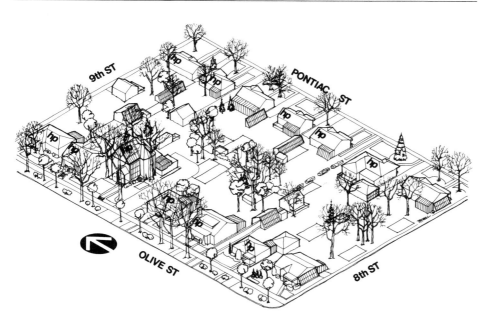

Figure 31
*A view of a proposed
retrofitting of a typical
city block of the
Montclair neighborhood
in Denver, Colorado.*
(By Joe Troxell)

ture. The next step is to begin the task of understanding the dynamics of local community politics, power, and self-motivation, and to begin the complex educational process of withdrawing from energy-intensive technology and applying energy-conserving technologies that are realizable through cooperative actions between the individual and the local neighborhood.

Montclair Community, Denver, Colorado

My students at the College of Environmental Design at Colorado University in Boulder and I are developing a planning strategy for energy retrofitting of the middle-income neighborhood of Montclair in Denver. We were invited to undertake this project by the Montclair Community Association, which is involved in a study of its future energy needs (the Future Power Project).

Besides developing the first comprehensive survey of existing socio-economic conditions and solar applicable residential conditions, the Montclair study proposes specific changes that are possible on each block (Figure 31). Implementation of passive solar greenhouses and cold frames, vegetable gardens, orchard-lined streets, water-conserving landscaping, solar wall and solar collector retrofits, and heat pumps are among the proposals.

Because the students are working more closely with the neighborhood residents, this plan is more specific and realistic than the Winona Study. It is our hope that the gap between the vision of possibilities and their realization will be narrowed as a result of this close working relationship between the student architects and the community residents.

Conclusion

Based on these projects to date I am more convinced than ever that the University is still (despite what some of us thought in the 1960s) the most viable institution in which to develop and organize new forces for social and technological change. Some of the reasons are:

- Availability of experimental public lands;

- Proximity of interdisciplinary students and faculty;
- "Service-learning" and "learning-through-application" are now widely accepted pedagogic methods;
- Possible large numbers of students can provide the necessary momentum to on-going applications research projects of relatively large-scale and comprehensive scope;
- "Failure," a necessary precondition of genuine creative processes, is still a valid expression of learning in the university.

* * *

Thus far, I have shown how a number of classroom questions led to some startling proposals for community transition in the near future. But this work is merely touching the "surface" of the future. More important questions about the changing energy picture continue to loom, and these questions must also be asked by the young generation:

- What strategies exist for altering community consumption patterns?
- How must our community values change during the transition from a wasteful to a frugal society?
- How can neighborhood government be organized from the grassroots?
- How can community formation occur in our mobile society?
- Can communities organize and implement self-help labor pools?
- Can we increase aspiration and satisfaction while consuming less?

The last question is most intriguing for our American culture, unaccustomed to limited resources.

In Japan, there is a traditional way of sitting during conversation. Japanese houses once were without central heating; the primary source of heat was a small charcoal brazier in the center of the room. There were cushions for sitting in the Zen manner on each side of the brazier so that two people could sit facing each other as they talked. A quilt placed over the brazier also covered the hands and folded legs of the two friends. With hands and legs warmed by the charcoal fire and backs warmed by heavy robes, only the faces were exposed to the cold air. Two warm bodies and two cold faces conversing about some aspect of the human condition. This is the literal expression of Taoism of the East—an experience of beauty founded upon contrast, in this case the contrast between hot and cold.

Examples of aesthetics founded upon contrast are also profuse in our own Western literature. Herman Melville in *Moby Dick* tells how wonderful it is to be in a nice warm bed with one foot extended into the cold air. How uninteresting our modern, uniformly heated environments seem in comparison to these two examples. Can we be satisfied while consuming less?

We must not forget that we are living in our childrens' house. Everything that we do in our lifetime is going to affect the next generation more drastically than all previous generations. I believe we have already affected future generations in a dangerous way by allowing technology to control our world unchecked. We must feel and accept the tremendous responsibility to alter the "hard" course we have taken so that our children have a chance to live on a healthy planet.

Let us begin.

Biotechnology
and Regional
Integration

IF, AS HAS BEEN SUGGESTED, the end of the fossil-fuel-based age of industrialism implies the need to redistribute population and restructure human habitat through a process of rural development and urban decentralization, then it is also clear that action toward these ends must occur within some larger, more comprehensive framework. Completely *ad hoc* and piecemeal change will not produce the kind of balanced and healthy cultural form that is the final aim of a resettled America. There must be a shared vision of possibilities and an appropriately scaled administrative and planning unit that will ensure that short-term change and local action will not undermine long-term viability and broader collective purpose.

At a minimum, any future society must be biologically adaptive, that is, it must be able to be sustained indefinitely without disrupting the ecosystems upon which it depends for survival. This suggests that the search for an appropriate organizing framework for the creation of a new society should begin with the commonly experienced fact that the earth is not a single, homogeneous biological unit, but is, rather, a complex web of highly differentiated yet interacting assemblages of life forms and processes. These separate but interdependent systems have been referred to as biogeographic provinces, or more generally as bioregions.[1]

Through a combination of geologic structure, topography, soil type, vegetation, animal life, and climate, each bioregion achieves its own unique identity. The systemic whole that is thereby created exists in a state of dynamic equilibrium. Any change in a part requires some change in the whole. Through this quality of internal coherence the bioregion sets natural limits on human intervention. To be adaptive, human culture must first recognize and then attempt to enhance the innate character and potential of these biogeographic areas. Thus, the bioregion can be viewed as a fundamental biological and social unit and the foundation for planning in the postindustrial age.

However, while each bioregion can be differentiated from every other, it is important to recognize that, unlike the surveyor's lines on a map, there are no clear boundaries between them. As one region shades into another, there tend to be intermediate zones that share the characteristics of two or even more adjacent systems. The bioregion, then, like any other idea, is as much a category of thought as it is a reality of nature. So, while the bioregion should be considered as a basic "fact" of nature, it must also be recognized that any such "fact" is also a reflection of human perceptions, goals, and purposes.

Rather than eliminating the variety and diversity among naturally occurring bioregions, human culture tends to intensify their differences. This is even true in those cases where modern industrial economies have reduced entire regions to monocultural production units for world markets. While most of Kansas may be devoted solely to the production of wheat, the fact that it is wheat and not corn is directly related to the limits on action set by the ecology of the Great Plains Region. While any sane society would reject the idea and practice of a regional monoculture, any alternative that is based on polycultural farming and the promotion of intraregional stability through diversity would still be limited by the problems and potentials given by the bioregion.

In addition to its selective influence upon occupation and economy, the bioregion provides the common context for everyday life. People living within a given bioregion breathe the same air, drink the same water, see the same landscape, and experience the same pattern of weather. Historically, these commonalities, which are rooted in the biology, geology, and climate of the area, have tended to unify the inhabitants and to differentiate them from the members of other regions.[2]

Regional planning, then, takes as its starting point the unique mix of resources and the common background provided by the region. Its aim is to reshape the given state of nature into a humanized landscape that more completely fits the physiological, aesthetic, emotional, social, and economic needs of the human inhabitants of a given area. However, within such a humanly managed bioregion there must be room for both the wild and the tame, nature in its primordial state as well as its humanized form. The overall goal, as Rene Dubos has defined it, is to create a new symbiosis between nature and culture:

> Symbiotic relationships mean creative partnerships. The earth is to be seen neither as an ecosystem to be preserved unchanged nor as a quarry to be exploited for selfish and short-range economic reasons, but as a garden to be cultivated for the development of its own potentialities of the human adventure. The goal of this relationship is not the maintenance of the status quo, but the emergence of new phenomena and new values. Millennia of experience show that by entering into a symbiotic relationship with nature, humankind can invent and generate futures not predictable from the deterministic order of things, and thus can engage in a continuous process of creation.[3]

While a society that takes the bioregion as a fundamental unit for planning and administration would tend to aim toward a higher degree of economic self-reliance than the overspecialized monocultures of today's industrial economies, that does not imply that it is either necessary or desirable to seek complete regional self-sufficiency. Rather, it suggests that the social, political, economic and biological health of a region depends upon the development of all its potentials in a way that ensures its long-term viability. Only if basic human needs are met in such a way within the region is it possible for interregional relations to be characterized by the free and open exchange of ideas and goods. A region that survives only by importing cultural values and basic goods and supplies from distant centers exists solely at the pleasure of locally unaccountable decision-makers. Such unhealthy dependencies, which now characterize relations within as well as among modern national economies, not only tend to erode the local support capacities of the earth, but they also tend to create the kinds of dependency-based psychological and social conflicts that lead to individual neurosis and blind social revolt. Economic regionalism attempts to provide a solid foundation for the nurturance of personal and cultural independence as well as the development and spread of truly productive, universalizing trends among regions and peoples.

Regional planning, because of its concern for the development of the latent human and biological potential of larger-scale areas, is uniquely suited to the task of redistributing population so that human demands are matched to the long-term carrying capacity of the earth. While metropolitan planning and rural new town planning is necessary to coordinate the growth and development of smaller scale concentrations of population, regional planning attempts to integrate such centers of population into the larger landscape upon which they depend for survival. This is a theme that was eloquently formulated more than fifty years ago by the Regional Planning Association of America, (RPAA). Unfortunately, the prescient insights of this small and loosely associated group of biologists, architects, planners, and cultural historians were not grasped or implemented by the nation at large. However, the new relevance of the ideas of this group to the enormous future task of resettling America can be seen in the following definition of regional planning by historian and RPAA member Lewis Mumford:

> Regional planning asks not how wide an area can be brought under the aegis of the metropolis, but how the population and civic facilities can be distributed so as to promote and stimulate a vivid, creative life throughout a whole region —a region being any geographic area that possesses a certain unity of climate, soil, vegetation, industry and culture. The regionalist attempts to plan such an area so that all its sites and resources, from forest to city, from highland to water level, may be soundly developed, and so that population will be distributed so as to utilize, rather than nullify or destroy, its natural advantages. It sees people, industry and the land as a single unit. Instead of trying, by one desper-

ate dodge or another, to make life a little more tolerable in the congested centers, it attempts to determine what sort of equipment will be needed in the new centers. It does not aim at urbanizing automatically the whole available countryside; it aims equally at ruralizing the stony wastes of our cities.[4]

Regional planning, as conceived by Mumford and others in the RPAA, is viewed as a process that would integrate the analytical rigor of the sciences with the collective will as expressed through a fully participatory democratic process. The role of the sciences primarily is to discover and describe the rough outline and innate potentials of the bioregion. But, even this task is seen by Mumford as an instrument of community education and a means of creating and sustaining a shared sense of local and regional identity. The regional survey, which would include an analysis of soil, climate, geology, biology, industry, agriculture, and the history and present pattern of human settlement and local culture, is seen as the foundation for the education and socialization of the young. It would break down the present segregation of the young from the practical affairs of public life and provide a means of making science relevant to the task of creating life and values. The region as a whole, with its plant and animal life, its people, its landforms and waterways, in short, its total life, is the context within which all the inhabitants of a region, from childhood on, would be able to integrate abstract and specialized bodies of theory and knowledge with the concrete and particular experiences of everyday life.

> When the landscape as a whole comes to mean to the community and the individual citizen what the single garden does to the individual lover of flowers, the regional survey will not merely be a mode of assimilating scientific knowledge: it will be a dynamic preparation for further activity. . . . Once this more realistic type of education becomes universal, instead of being pieced into the more conventional system, we will create a whole generation that will look upon every aspect of the region, the community, and their personal lives as subject to the same processes: exploration, scientific observation, imaginative reconstruction, and finally, transformation by art, by technical improvement and by personal discipline.[5]

Clearly, any conception of regional planning that does not, as a basic premise, include the idea of community education and full community participation in all phases of planning, from the survey of potentials to their realization in physical, social, and political form, would simply be an expansion of the technocratic regime of experts. However, the kind of regional planning envisioned by Mumford would not only provide a scientifically and politically sound foundation for collective action, but it would also provide a sense of personal and regional identity that would transcend narrow and arbitrary political units such as the state or nation-state. By nurturing the differentiating forces of local identity, the possibility of building a world order based on the universalizing forces of a common humanity would be greatly enhanced. Thus, regionalism at its best is an historically new expression of the movement toward world community rather than a regression to old forms of village and small town parochialism or the violent assertions of complete autonomy claimed by the large-scale, centralized nation-state.

The bioregion, then, is an imaginatively constructed collective work of art. But the creation of any work of art requires, in addition to an understanding of the medium of expression, full access to the materials to be shaped into new form. A painter without knowledge of the principles of color, lacking skill in the use of the brush, and only intermittently able to gain access to canvas would be a poor bet to produce a great painting.

The same is true in the case of regional planning. In addition to a scientifically informed and participatory planning process, it is necessary to have a legally and appropriately constituted administrative unit for implementing the common will. To accomplish this, there needs to be some form of land ownership that guarantees individual security as well as the common good. The current system of private land ownership, which is based on the assumption that land is a commodity that can be divided up, sold and used as the owner (corporate or individual) sees fit, regardless of effects on the community at large, must be replaced. The idea of regional planning almost requires a new system of land tenure based on the community ownership of land, with individual and group use rights guaranteed, within limits established by the regional community.[6] At a minimum, these limits would be aimed at meeting basic human needs while protecting the integrity and long-term health of the regional and local ecology.

We have already seen, in the case of rural new town development, that community land trusts and regional land "banks" are essential to the success of that form of rural development.[7] Not only would the community ownership of land protect the leaseholders from the loss of access to their land during hard times, but it would ensure that any increases in land values created as a result of social arrangements would accrue to the community that created them rather than to profiteering private landowners. Also, since regional communities are more stable and longer-lived than individuals or corporations, they would be willing and able to make improvements to the land and to regulate its use in such a way that the needs of present and future generations would be adequately provided for. If land was held in common it might be possible, for example, to prevent the short-sighted mining of ground water by competitive private landholders trying to survive in a market economy. The long-term needs of the whole might be judged as more important than the short-term gain of the part.

In any case, the common ownership of land would make it possible to make informed and rational decisions about resource development and population distribution that are all but impossible to make at present. But such changes in land ownership, like regional planning itself, are not ends in themselves. The common ownership of land "is merely a means toward creating a system of dressing and keeping the land as it must be dressed and kept for an advanced civilization."[8] And while it might be possible to maintain the current system of private ownership of land along with a broad program of public education and regulation aimed at ensuring the common good, such a hybrid approach would likely be cumbersome to administer, burdensome to the private owners, and ultimately less effective than the community trusteeship of resources that are inherently limited and vital to the health and survival of everyone.

Since the common ownership of land would, if carefully worked out through a system of leasehold possession, guarantee individual use rights and security of tenure as well as protecting collective interests and shared values, the public control of land for the benefit of the region as a whole may well be an idea whose time has come. While it may seem politically impractical, if not impossible, at present, the notion is likely to become more attractive as energy and resource scarcities and escalating costs begin to force us to make a major commitment to population redistribution and careful resource management toward the creation of more regionally self-reliant economies based on the efficient use of income energy sources and the wise recycling of capital as well as nutrient and mineral resources.

Peter van Dresser, along with Lewis Mumford and other members of the RPAA, has been proposing the idea of regional planning based on the principle of creative stewardship of the land for more than forty years. His "Goals for Regional Development," the first paper in this section, is excerpted from his excellent study, *A Landscape for Humans.*[9] While van Dresser's book outlines how the innate cultural and ecological potentials of the northern New Mexico Uplands region would be identified and developed, the paper included in this book speaks to the general goals of regional planning. As van Dresser points out, the linked phenomena of "urban hypertrophy" and "rural and provincial disintegration" have accompanied the spread of industrialism throughout the world, leading to the destruction of regional ecologies and the creation of widespread poverty and despair in the ghettoes of megalopolis as well as the wasteland of the abandoned countryside. Rather than trying to regulate and police the worst depredations of this imperial order of industrialism, van Dresser suggests that a radically new approach, based on the development of all the potentials of a region, will be required to remedy the situation. His proposed goals, which include population redistribution toward greater local and regional self-reliance in basic necessities as well as the development of information- and skill-intensive production technologies based on income energy sources, provide a comprehensive platform for meaningful change. Anything less will simply be more of the same, and, as the current, and possibly terminal, crisis of urban-industrial civilization demonstrates, more of the same will simply not work.

Given the difficulties of overcoming the inherent inertia and resistance to change in our overdeveloped regions, van Dresser suggests that "a social evolution of this general type can best occur in the 'under-developed' and provincial areas of the nation, where cities and towns are still of manageable size, populations are still low, and land and biotic resources are still relatively accessible and uncompromised."[10] Rather than trying to introduce such radically new patterns of development where the knot of industrialism is thickest, van Dresser believes that we should begin at the source of raw materials supply rather than the "mouth" toward which all resources flow. Change should begin with the simple and move toward the complex.

In a remarkable essay, "The New Exploration: Charting the Industrial Wilderness," published in 1925, Benton MacKaye made essentially the same argument.[11] Viewing the history of "industrial empire" as the progressive transformation of a natural wilderness into an urban one, he described the physiology of industrialism as analogous to the watershed of a river system. To illustrate how his program for recharting the urban wilderness could begin, he took as a case study a small crestline valley in the Berkshire–Green Mountain Range located partly in Berkshire County, Massachusetts and partly in the state of Vermont. He analyzed the history of this exemplary "sphere of origin" and showed how a settled life could be created around the development of the region's natural resources of timber and water power.

Perhaps it is merely coincidence, but it is interesting to note that two projects described in this section, which illustrate substantive strides now being made toward the realization of van Dresser's goals for regional development, are taking place in approximately this same area of Massachusetts and Vermont.

The first case study, described by David Pomerantz, is a grass-roots attempt by citizens in Franklin County, Massachusetts to map out a "soft energy path" for the year 2000. Since energy is the lifeblood of human society, the Franklin County study is focussed on the issue of how to sustain valued human activities from the renewable energy sources of sun, wind, flowing water, and green plants and the wise use of small amounts of fossil fuels. In the belief that our energy problems are indicators of larger problems caused and perpetuated by large-scale, centralized, and unresponsive systems, Pomerantz suggests that the issue of energy planning is a political problem to be resolved by the community of those affected, rather than merely a technical problem to be solved by engineers. In his words, it is "a social question with technical parameters."

Besides demonstrating that it would be technically feasible as well as economically, politically, and morally desirable for Franklin County to make a transition to a renewable energy base, the Franklin County energy project is pioneering an implementation strategy that is based on community control rather than corporate and government management. The work that is described illustrates the belief, that in this sunset phase of the fossil fuel age, energy planning is the integrating thread of the growing movement toward decentralization and the restoration of democratic values and processes to our political economy. It clarifies the idea that the realization of an ecologically sound meta-industrial society is simultaneously our best hope for the fulfillment of our most cherished ideals and values.

For any policy of regional development to succeed, it is also necessary to link food supply with food demand in a way that minimizes unproductive transportation costs associated with the current system of agribusiness. Resolving this logistical problem, along with the problem of energy supply from local, renewable sources, is the key to any rational policy of population redistribution. Toward this end, George Burrill and Jim Nolfi describe their landmark studies of food self-reliance for Vermont. While they clearly recognize that bioregions, which would be the basis for planning such food systems, do not necessarily follow existing and somewhat arbitrary political boundaries, they have chosen to test and develop their methodology for planning within the reality of existing political decision-making units.

Utilizing readily understandable computer-modeling techniques, Burrill and Nolfi have mapped a variety of diets, from existing ones to purely vegetarian, against the physical production potential of the state's existing farmland. They reached the conclusion that all the food needs of Vermont could be supplied by production within the state with surplus for sale outside the state while affording an equal or better economic situation for the state's farmers. The Burrill and Nolfi study thus shows that the present energy intensive and land exploitive system of agriculture is a creation of political and economic forces which have favored corporate farming for national markets. Once that is recognized, and once the hidden human, ecological and energy costs of current practices become more evident, the vision of possibilities contained in this paper should provide a solid foundation for change toward a richer, more varied and sustainable system of regional food production.

The issue of the sustainability of regional agriculture is taken up in detail by Earle Barnhart and Wes Jackson in the final two papers in this section. From an analysis of the inherent flaws in the existing system, which range from the erosion and salinization of topsoil, and the depletion of ground water to the pollution of ground and surface water supplies and the wholesale destruction of delicate ecological processes, Barnhart develops a proposal for an agriculture that is modeled on the principles and functioning of naturally occurring ecosystems. Describing the pioneering experiments of the New Alchemy Institute, of which he is a member, Barnhart describes in some detail the kinds of biotechnologies that would allow both high and sustainable yields from agricultural landscapes designed and managed for permanence rather than short-term profit. Through the creation of an integrated human ecology of information and skill-intensive horticulture, aquaculture and agricultural forestry, combined with the de-

Figure 1
At the New Alchemy
Institute, *experiments
in biotechnology pro-
vide new agricultural
forms for the landscape
of Cape Cod.*

velopment of bioshelters and solar villages, it is shown that it is within our power to create a culture and agriculture that restores rather than destroys the earth. As Barnhart observes, such a human ecology would give visible expression to the ancient but all-too-often forgotten wisdom of all the world's great spiritual and religious traditions. Although the reason for creating such a culture might be, at root, ethical and moral, the results would inevitably prove to be practical as well as economical.

Like the New Alchemy Institute, The Land Institute, which is located in Salina, Kansas, is dedicated to a search for alternatives in agriculture, energy, shelter, and waste management as well as to an exploration of the alternative world view necessary for the imagination and creation of a radically new culture. In addition to projects involving the design and application of renewable-energy-based technologies aimed at "regional semi-self sufficiency" (e.g. wind electric and water pumping systems, solar collectors and wood stoves for space heating, adobe and rammed earth blocks for building construction, and organic methods of food production), The Land Institute is also an alternative school which attracts students from many disciplines and all regions of the country. By equally dividing the day between "hand" and "head" work, students attempt to develop a holistic world view capable of expression in everyday life.

While New Alchemy and The Land share many values and are working on the development of many similar technologies and ideas, the work of each group grows out of the unique character of the bioregion in which it is rooted. Located in coastal New England, New Alchemy has focussed on the development of integrated systems of food production such as tree cropping, aquaculture, and intensive organic horticulture. Based, as it is, in the grain belt of the vast and open Great Plains region, the concern of The Land Institute has turned quite naturally to the search for a new form of seed-producing agriculture that does not produce dust bowls as its necessary side-effect.

Figure 2
*Raising a windmill
at the Land Institute
in early spring.*

Figure 3
*Class on wind
generators, the Land
Institute.*

This point is crucial. Unless the search for an alternative agriculture addresses the question of how to produce, on a sustained yield basis, the grains which have always been and are likely to continue to be the staples of the diets of "civilized" peoples, the split between nature and culture which was inaugurated by the agricultural revolution ten thousand years ago will remain unhealed. While new techniques of ecologically-derived food production, e.g. aquaculture, tree culture, and organic horticulture can provide an important supplement (especially protein) to a cereal-based diet, it is clear that they are not the answer to the present or long-term food needs of the majority of the world's people.

The central fact about the present system of industrialized agribusiness is that it is not sustainable. In addition to its addiction to rapidly depleting fossil-fuel intensive pesticides and fertilizers, modern agriculture is eroding topsoil in many areas of the country at a rate which far exceeds replacement. As Wes Jackson, the co-founder of The Land Institute and author of the last paper in this section, points out, 84 percent of U.S. farms are losing more than 5 tons of soil per acre per year, with an average loss of 15 to 16 tons per acre per year. For U.S. crop production to be sustained, soil loss will have to be reduced by one-half or more. Moreover, the rate of soil loss seems to be relatively unaffected by the use of conventional Soil Conservation Service practices. Even if energy and resource shortages force the abandonment of the most destructive practices of today's agriculture before it is possible to totally strip away our rich dowry of topsoil (we have already lost one-third of the topsoil we found when this country was settled), the long sad history of soil erosion, ground water depletion and desertification which has accompanied the decline of almost every civilization before the industrial age suggests that we are yet to invent a social form other than hunting and gathering which is compatible with the needs of the earth. In short, the crisis of modern agriculture is merely the latest chapter in the historical failure of all forms of agriculture to prove sustainable.

According to Wes Jackson, the anti-ecological nature of all agricultural systems to date can be traced to the fact that they have all been based on the monoculture of annuals, which necessarily involves the creation of inherently immature, fragile, simple, and unstable ecosystems which deplete rather than build topsoil. Rather than proposing the usual piecemeal remedies, such as crop rotation, increased labor intensity and the use of organic fertilizers, Jackson asks what nature will require of us if we are to create a high-yielding and permanent agriculture. Like the New Alchemists, who have asked the same basic question and have begun to forge an ecologically-derived approach to the design of integrated agricultural landscapes, Jackson and his students and colleagues at The Land Institute have assumed that the careful examination of nature's strategy for permanence as revealed in naturally occurring climax ecosystems will provide the clues necessary to reconfigure the present food system into an historically unique and sustainable human ecology. By thoroughly understanding how the native prairie accumulates rather than erodes biological capital while furthering the aims of life, Jackson feels that it should be possible to create a domesticated analogue of these natural systems which can be continuously harvested (with agricultural machinery yet to be invented) within the limits of sustainability. Paradoxically, then, Jackson proposes that because of the development of machine harvest and modern science it is now possible for us to think seriously of polyculture harvest in a return to a pattern of life more like the hunting and gathering one within which we evolved as a species. We can escape the ecological destructiveness of historical forms of agriculture because we now have the knowledge and technology as well as the pressing need to do so.

Since the polyculture of perennials is dominant in nature's strategy for survival, and since the cultivation of grains has always been basic to agricultural society, Jackson suggests that the search for a sustainable and desirable agriculture, especially in the "grain belt," would lead to an agriculture dominated by the polyculture of herbaceous perennials for seed/fruit production, an approach which is nearly the opposite of the present monocultural cultivation of high yielding annual cereals and legumes.

Since Jackson is, in effect, calling for the invention of an agriculture never before seen in human history, it might be worthwhile to summarize what could be gained should we succeed in what is sure to be a momentous undertaking. An agriculture dominated by the production of herbaceous perennial seed-producers in polyculture would: (1) virtually eliminate soil erosion (by keeping the soil covered year round); (2) reduce energy consumption for seed bed preparation and cultivation (which would now be done by the system itself); (3) reduce energy use in the preparation of fertilizers and pesticides (which would be almost completely unnecessary due to the broad genetic base and natural disease resistance of such an agriculture); (4) reverse the decline of our domestic genetic reservoir; (5) provide new germplasm for breeding more disease-resistant, high-yielding annuals; (6) increase the crumb structure of the soil, leading to increased resistance to fluctuations in rainfall and other climatic variables; and (7) reduce the time spent in many tasks of mechanical power weeding (only harvesting, occasional fertilizing, pest control, replanting, genetic selection, and management would remain).

Clearly, such an agriculture, which would virtually eliminate the most destructive practices and outcomes which have plagued human civilization since the invention of agriculture, can be seen as a desirable and, perhaps, a necessary goal. But is it feasible? Jackson does not underestimate the enormous obstacles, e.g., the dilemma of combining high-yield and perennialism, the problem of inventing new harvesting machinery, etc. However, as the preliminary results of research undertaken at The Land indicate, there is good cause to believe that it is possible to solve these problems over the next fifty years through a coordinated program of research and development.

What has been lacking so far is the holistic vision which links unacceptable levels of soil loss with the monoculture of annuals, a blind spot in our collective vision which Dr. Jackson has successfully removed in this article. Rather than using our vast educational and research establishment to invent high-yield crops which are designed for harvest by huge soil compacting machines and which depend for their survival on the continuous injection of rapidly depleting and costly fertilizers and pesticides, it would seem that the goal described by Jackson would be a far more valuable focus for our future efforts. Rather than continuing to promote a "Green Revolution" whose time has passed, it should be clear that the development of a permanent agriculture based on the cultivation of herbaceous perennial seed-producers is a task whose time has come. We can no longer afford to forsake the "wisdom of nature" for the "cleverness of humans." If, as Jackson argues, we use "wilderness as the standard against which we judge our agricultural and cultural practices," we may yet create a civilization worthy of our human potential.

All the papers in this section make it clear that we do not lack the knowledge of how to "live lightly on the earth." We lack only the wisdom necessary to see the need for change and the courage to begin. Unfortunately, should we fail to act soon, we shall also lack the time necessary to succeed.

As Peter van Dresser has said,

The rethinking and restructuring of our purposes, our institutions, and our private and public policies needed to effect such changes in the direction of our social and economic evolution on the scale that will be necessary is a colossal, dismaying, and fascinating task. As the final and most difficult phase of the ecologic transformation towards which all people are groping, its long-term consequences must, if we succeed, dwarf even those of the industrial revolution in permanence and ultimate meaning. May our vision sustain us over the difficult coming century.[12]

References

1. Raymond Dasmann, *Environmental Conservation,* (New York: John Wiley & Sons, 1959). While the idea of bioregions has been used for nearly a half century in relation to plant and animal communities it was first used in relation to human ecology by Raymond Dasmann in the 1950s. Also see Dasmann, "Biogeographical Provinces," in *Co-Evolution Quarterly,* no. 11 (Fall 1976): 32–37.

2. Lewis Mumford, "Regional Planning," in Carl Sussman (ed.), *Planning the Fourth Migration: The Neglected Vision of The Regional Planning Association of America,* (Cambridge: MIT Press, 1976) p. 201.

3. Rene Dubos, "Symbiosis Between the Earth and Humankind," *Science,* 193: 462.

4. Lewis Mumford, "Regions—To Live In," in Sussman, ed., *Neglected Vision,* p. 90.

5. Lewis Mumford, *The Culture of Cities,* (New York: Harcourt Brace Jovanovich 1938) pp. 385–386. Mumford provides a thorough and comprehensive summary of his thoughts on regionalism as the basis for a new social order. The thoughts on regional planning and regional identity presented in this introduction largely follow those of Mumford in this fine book. For other examples of approaches to learning that would facilitate the creation of a metaindustrial society based on respect for bioregional ecologies, see Gary Coates, ed., *Alternative Learning Environments* (Stroudsburg, Pa.: Dowden, Hutchinson Ross, 1974).

6. See Mumford, *The Culture of Cities,* pp. 327–331 for a discussion of the idea of common ownership of land.

7. See Shimon Gottschalk, "Rural New Towns for America," in this volume.

8. Mumford, *The Culture of Cities,* p. 329.

9. Peter van Dresser, *A Landscape for Humans: A Case Study of the Potentials for Ecologically Guided Development in an Uplands Region,* (Albuquerque: The Biotechnic Press, 1972).

10. Ibid., p. xix.

11. In Sussman, ed., *Neglected Vision,* pp. 94–110.

12. Peter van Dresser, "Goals for Regional Development," in this volume.

15 | Goals for Regional Development

Peter van Dresser

Metropolitanization — A dominant process

THE OVERWHELMING FACT we must recognize is that the basic dynamic of our industrial civilization, since early in the 19th Century, has been in the direction of population concentration and "metropolitanization," at the cost of rural communities and provincial towns, cities, and regions, no matter where they are located nor what their cultural derivation.

In the U.S.A., this dynamic has accelerated the decay, or worked against the economic maturation, of major provinces of the nation as diverse as old New England industrial and farming regions, the entire eastern Appalachian backbone, huge sections of the West, Middle West, and South, and countless lesser "pockets of poverty" scattered throughout the land. People of Anglo-Saxon, Scotch-Irish, Scandinavian, African, Middle-European, or Spanish extraction have been equally affected by this process. Most of the current furor about the "plight of our cities" is caused on the one hand by the inability of the few metropolitan sectors, where opportunity is supposedly concentrated, to absorb the overwhelming influx of displaced persons from de-

pressed rural or provincial areas and, on the other hand, by the inability of the stranded towns and cities in those same depressed areas to maintain themselves as going communities.

This phenomenon is, of course, not limited to the United States and is even further advanced in numerous foreign countries. "The Highlands of Scotland," writes a contributor in 1944 to the *Journal of the London School of Economics,* "is a derelict area where geological denudation finds a parallel in the disappearance of population . . . The younger members of the population are tending to disappear as they reach the last years of school age, and the rising standard of living accelerates the movement . . . The process of economic, sociological, and cultural deterioration can be found in almost every corner of Scotland . . . "[1]

A 1961 report by an international committee of European agricultural experts and economists comments, "After the second world war, the mountain regions of Austria, Germany, Italy, and Yugoslavia were recognized as priority targets for emergency aid . . . The tendency of the

Alpine population to age because of the exodus of the young to cities and industrial centers is a special and particularly aggravated form of the exodus from the countryside . . . Mountain regions are depressed areas from the economic standpoint . . . "[2]

The French historian Aries wrote a generation ago, "A whole section of the population of the Savoy Alps used to live in the forest, but in the second half of the 19th Century, the forest was closed off . . . the population was deprived not only of work, but of a reason for existing . . . the inhabitants left . . . "[3]

Examples of this universal process of rural and provincial disintegration, paired with a corresponding urban hypertrophy, can be drawn from every corner of the world. It affects lands as diverse as England, India, Thailand, Peru, Brazil, or Haiti. In some of these lands, it approaches the dimensions of a national calamity. The process works impartially in Mao's China, in Soviet Russia, in monarchist Ethiopia, in parliamentarian Canada.

The trend is so powerful and universal that generations of people of almost all ideological persuasions have come to regard it as virtually synonymous with progress. Economic theory has rationalized it in terms of the flow of capital into areas of maximum productivity, with a resulting most effective utilization of scientific technology. Industrial and managerial practice has facilitated it, and a great deal of scientific research has been directed to meeting its demands. Public policy has expedited it. Banking and financial tactics support it. Education has dedicated itself almost exclusively to preparing and training the oncoming generation for its requirements. Highway systems are being continually designed, redesigned, built, and rebuilt to meet the ever-increasing traffic loads it generates. Enormous sums are expended and serious environmental risks are accepted to open up new sources of energy to meet its fantastically increasing power demands. The entire fabric of social organization, values, and motivations has adapted to the conditions of life this hyper-urbanizing trend imposes.

The long confrontation

The impact of this trend on non- or proto-industrial folk or agrarian societies throughout the world is well documented over the nearly 200 years since the commercial and industrial revolution began to spread out from the coreland of northwestern Europe in the latter 18th century. A characteristic sequence of effects has repetitiously accompanied this impact, as follows:

1. The disruption of localized, relatively self-sufficient economies, with their supporting technologies and logistic arrangements.

2. Expropriation of land and other natural resources from tribal, peasant, yeoman, or local aristocratic ownership, and their concentration in larger units for machine-intensive management capable of maximizing export surpluses and yield on investment.

3. Monetization of local exchange to replace distribution of goods at least partially through barter or through customary arrangements sanctioned by family, tribe, or religion.

4. Dislodgement of dispersed agricultural or pastoral populations, with a resulting influx to the cities, a rapid increase in the urban proletariat, and an accelerating rate of urbanization.

5. A resulting disintegration of communities, folkways, skills, and life

styles which crystallized around, supported, and embellished the traditional modes of livelihood. This process inevitably involved the disruption of deepseated patterns of work, sacrament, and attachment to homeland, and has been responsible for much of the disorientation, apathy, or anger which marks the psychology of what we currently speak of as "disadvantaged minorities." (That this sort of collective trauma is essentially due to derangement of customary patterns of livelihood and life style, rather than to clashes of purely linguistic or ethnic dichotomies, is well evidenced by its repeated historical occurrence *within* nations of relatively homogenous culture and language. England, in the days of the early textile mill boom and the Luddite uprisings, is an example.)

We may note, in passing, that almost from its beginnings in Europe, these effects of industrialism on traditional societies were trenchantly criticized in humanitarian terms by individuals such as Dickens, Ruskin, and Zola. They were also resisted physically by generally ineffective peasant, clan, or petty-national protests and Jacqueries everywhere. Much of the history of the 19th Century is, in fact, the chronicle of how these resistances were overcome through a combination of financial and commercial leverage, entrepreneurial energy, military might, missionary zeal, and the sheer impressiveness of scientific technology in action. The resultant of this combination of factors was that, over the past two centuries, countless minor folk and agrarian societies in virtually all corners of the globe were obliterated, and countless millions of rural and provincial dwellers abandoned their farms, villages, towns, and minor cities to migrate (all too often) to the slums of the nearest metropolis or industrial center.

The problems of metropolitanization

The very universality of this trend tempts us to accept it as inevitable. There is indeed a rationalization of long-standing respectability ready at hand to justify this conclusion. The socioeconomic deterioration of "bypassed" backward societies and communities, according to this rationalization, is a transitional effect—the sad but necessary price of progress towards scientific civilization. When the transition is completed, when the necessary regrouping into the new era urban-industrial complexes is achieved and the essential re-education and re-training of the people perfected, the full benefits of industrially generated affluence will begin to flow, and mankind will reach a new plateau of wellbeing and material abundance. In the meantime, the disruption and demoralization of old and sentimentally valued ways of life is to be regretted. Such painful experiences should be tempered as much as possible by enlightened eleemosynary and public policies, but the all-important process of assimilation and acculturation is the only final answer and should be expedited in every possible way.

During the earlier formative stages of this process, this formulation of the ethics and praxis of industrialization (for which term "colonization" might, of course, be substituted in very many cases) could remain plausible, if only on the basis of benefits to be realized in the not-too-distant future. Humanitarian objections could be set aside as the well-intentioned but impractical gestures of romantics not in touch with the stern but just operations of the economic world.

In recent decades, however, and especially in the period since the close of World War II, the entire rationalization is on the verge of breakdown. The slow historical "drift to the cities" has accelerated into a dismaying proliferation, worldwide in extent, of urban slums, ghettos, *barriadas, favelas,* and the like, mostly populated by the residues of demolished rural and provincial communities and societies. This proliferation has vividly demonstrated the widespread inability of contemporary industrial economies to integrate uprooted masses into their systems in any useful, humane, or ecologically sound way. The arsenal of technological wizardries at the command of these economies has spectacularly failed to alleviate the results of this trend.

The drain on natural resources— fossil fuels, soils, forests, ores, waters, now even the atmosphere itself—imposed by the gigantic logistic mechanisms necessary to maintain these nonproductive but cancerously growing agglomerations of humanity even at the bare subsistence level, threatens to overwhelm our hopes for mankind's future. The psychic strain engendered by the overcrowding, deprivation, and frustration of the new superghettos has already generated massive civil disturbances and promises greater ones to come. At the same time, the bypassed and semi-abandoned rural and provincial regions from which the new urban masses come, continue to decay, deteriorate, and spread.

Urban-industrial civilization in crisis

It seems a tragic circumstance that most of our accumulated "conventional wisdom," as it bears on eco-

nomic progress and technological development, leads only to intensification of trends that contain the seeds of self-destruction. The classic formulas calling for mass production and mass merchandising, for capital-intensive mechanization and automation, for massive public investment in "social infrastructure," and for massive corporate investment in machinery and plant are, after all, operative only where they can recreate or intensify the megalopolitan environment, with all its entrainment of increasingly unmanageable problems.

The fact seems to be that urban-industrial civilization itself—under whatever political ideology it operates —is entering a transitional, if not a crisis, phase. The computer-borne projections of the economists, demographers, and planners of all nations, with their foreshadowings of unprecedented population congestion, natural-resources depletion, mass famines, land-water-and-air pollution, and the like, are deeply disquieting indications of uncertainties ahead. . . .

Characteristics of a new pattern of development

Popular reaction against the disturbing uncertainties of this looming future (which, in fact, began as long ago as the late 18th Century) is expressing itself currently at high intensity in a literature of protest under the general banner of "ecology." Manifesto after manifesto has appeared denouncing the pollution-generating operations of the great metallurgical, chemical, automotive, agribusiness, and power corporations; control legislation has been debated in most state capitals and in Washington, and some of it has even been adopted; conservation candidates and parties have appeared; pickets and boycotts have been mounted; lists of austerities to be practiced by conscientious citizens have been drawn up and circulated.

Much of this agitation implies no basic questioning of the underlying premises of industrial society. Accepting as irrevocable the present trends in population growth and concentration, it takes for granted that the needs of the swarming generations to come must be met through a ceaseless refinement of the machine systems on which we have become dependent, and of the complex mass habitats in which we must dwell.

It assumes that the general apparatus of production and distribution will continue to function at even higher levels of output, efficiency, and complexity in the future, but that its harmful side effects will be eliminated by increasingly sophisticated technical and legal controls. Accordingly, this wing of the ecologic front calls for such ends as "action now" against belching smokestacks and spewing outfalls; for campaigns against waste and littering; for a halt to excessive scarifications and mutilations of the earth. It proposes, in short, to police the emerging landscape of megalopolis through intelligent planning, enlightened engineering, and responsible administration.

Such goals, commendable though they are, and realistic though they seem in the light of current conventional wisdom, are probably inadequate to the depth of the long-term ecologic crisis ahead. There are strongly argued opinions expressed in many quarters that even with the best of policing and decontamination measures, the web of life on earth can survive for no more than a few decades the continued expansion of our vast apparatus for planetary exploitation. A true reading of the ecologic "handwriting on the wall" confronting us, it is argued, unequivo-

cally signals that our civilization must make a more profound adjustment to the vital processes of the biosphere than merely recycling our wastes, precipitating our effluents, banning persistent pesticides, and landscaping our freeways and borrow-pits.

It is very possible, despite such ameliorative efforts, that the sheer deadweight of urban aggregations, the insatiable materials-processing, transport and energy requirements built into our present pattern of economic organization will continue to intrude so insistently, so massively, and at so many points into the tissue of our living environment, that the damage may soon exceed the natural world's self-healing capability.

An obvious adjustment to this likelihood could be a slowdown in human multiplication, a stabilization of population, hopefully even an eventual reduction in absolute numbers in many parts of the world. This is a highly visible and widely discussed issue which could be described as the second major campaign front of the drive for ecologic reform. Although, as yet, distressingly little effect is visible in the growth-habits of most nations, an increasing number of organizations and public agencies are concerned with it, and much scientific research is devoted to the very difficult social, political, religious, and medical problems it poses.

A third and probably the least understood and explored aspect of the ecologic challenge is the strategy of adaptation through modifying our industrial system so as to drastically reduce both our per capita and total appetite for energy and for extracted, processed, fabricated, and transported things, while at the same time continuing to improve our level of civilization in terms of the more genuine material needs and cultural amenities.

The general outlines of this strategy have been sketched in by various explorers in such fields as urban, cultural, and political evolution, town and regional planning, human geography, speculative economics, and the like. The restructuring of our socioeconomic organization which could lead towards such results runs somewhat as follows:

1. There should occur a redistribution and regrouping of population, of means of production, and of patterns of trade in such a manner as facilitates greater local and regional self-sufficiency in the production of goods, services, and amenities.

2. As part of this regrouping, the smaller range of "urban places" (villages, towns, provincial cities) must undergo a renaissance as vital functional elements in the economic and cultural order, and this should be accompanied by corresponding diminishment in the relative importance of major cities and metropolitan conglomerations.

3. An increasing proportion of our over-all social effort should be diverted away from ubiquitous mechanized commutation and massive mechanized transport and distribution, and towards the enrichment and diversification of localized production within efficient smaller communities, as the enlightened solution of the "logistic" problem.

4. A type of production technology should be encouraged which is adapted to the utilization of renewable "flow resources" (vegetative growth, climatic cycles and energies, etc.) on a small-scale, intensive, science-, skill-, and manpower-basis, rather than on a large-scale, extensive machine- and mechanical-energy-basis.

5. There should be a corresponding development of an ecologically grounded science of community design, adequate to guide the recolonization of vast semi-abandoned and under-used provinces of the nation on a sustained-yield, symbiotic basis with the soil, climatic, and biotic regimens of such regions.

6. Communication and education techniques should be developed such as will allow this organic type of population dispersion, renucleation, and regionalization to occur, while maintaining a high level of social and ecological awareness, and a degree of scientific and intellectual competence which will effectively counteract the dangers of parochialism and insularity.

The rethinking and restructuring of our purposes, our institutions, and our private and public policies needed to effect such changes in the direction of our social and economic evolution on the scale that will be necessary is a colossal, dismaying, and fascinating task. As the final and most difficult phase of the ecologic transformation toward which all people are groping, its long-term consequences must, if we succeed, dwarf even those of the industrial revolution in permanence and ultimate meaning. May our vision sustain us over the difficult coming century.

References

1. Hugh Quigley, "The Highlands of Scotland: Proposals for Development," Agenda of the London School of Economics and Political Science, 3 (1944).

2. Food and Agricultural Organization of the United Nations, "Rural Problems in the Alpine Region" (1961).

3. Philippe Aries, "Histore des Populations Francaises" (1948).

16 | A Renewable Energy Future for Franklin County, Massachusetts[*]

David Pomerantz

An energy overview

WITH A WORSENING energy situation people are becoming more confused and angry over what the problems are, who is to blame and what possible solutions exist. Whether one thinks the oil and utility companies are at fault, that government is incapable of handling the problems or that international economic and political happenings are the cause, the energy problem hits home directly when waiting in line for gasoline or wondering if there will be enough home heating oil for the winter. What many people have yet to realize is that energy is the lifeblood of society, and to paraphrase a current television commercial, "Without energy, life itself would be impossible."

In only several years, this country has experienced major changes in how it deals with energy. Before the oil embargo of 1973–1974, few people paid any attention to energy. It was always assumed that energy would be available in plentiful amounts and at cheap prices. People simply drove their cars

into the gas station for fuel, called the oil company for home delivery or flipped on a light switch. Now, with prices soaring and supplies diminishing, people are more conscious of energy and how they relate to it. As people change vacation plans, refigure household budgets and fret about the next energy price increase they are asking, "What happened?"

What did happen? In a nutshell, government, in a general sense, and the energy companies never took the time or cared to examine the implications of using finite, expendable resources known as fossil fuels (oil, natural gas, and coal) and other finite energy sources such as uranium. Everyone always thought that tomorrow would take care of itself and that answers to problems would be found. Profits became more important than planning, jobs, the environment and democratic principles.

Historically, energy use has been based on always increasing energy supplies to meet projected demands. No attention was paid to how that energy would be used (in what form for what purpose). Until several years ago, energy demand was based solely on extending the past into the future, thus resulting in exponential energy growth. Such forecasts were done on a macro-level and never considered conservation, efficiency, or price. Utilities worked on annual energy consumption increases of 7 percent and only after 1973 did they begin to realize that demand was affected by price. Since 1973, utility demand forecasts have continued to drop, and in certain areas of the country, growth forecasts now stand at 2 percent per year. Unfortunately, even these projections do not include potential savings that can accrue to both utilities and consumers from conservation. It is now widely acknowledged that it makes more economic sense for a utility to invest in conservation then to develop new energy generating capacity. Due to decreasing energy demands, many utilities are finding themselves with half-completed, multi-billion dollar power-generating facilities. With investors shying away from utilities, ratepayers are being forced to supply capital for unnecessary utility ventures. This situation is already forcing people to pay higher and higher rates, a situation which can lead to severe economic problems.

Forecasts based solely on extrapolation now appear to be technically and economically unworkable. The skills, industrial capacity and managerial ability to maintain rapid expansion of energy technologies may not exist. Also, it is increasingly clear that the capital needed to develop and fuel capital-intensive, high-risk energy technologies will not be available.[1] With decreasing supplies of nonrenewable energy resources, it will become more costly and pose greater risks to find additional amounts of fuel to convert into premium forms of energy such as electricity.

Consequences and options

While the amount of oil imported by this country is sizable, (nationwide imports stand at 55 percent), New England finds itself in a more precarious situation. Recent studies indicate that 80 percent of New England's energy comes from oil, all of which is imported from other states (21 percent) or from abroad (79 percent). New England is tightly bound to overseas oil-producing countries and to events within their borders. Some energy analysts predict that there are about 10 to 15 years supply of oil within the continental United States. At the end of that time, New England will stop sending energy dollars to Texas or Alaska, and send them entirely overseas.

Whether energy is imported from Texas, Venezuela, Alaska or the Middle East, dollars are leaving the New England region, creating a regional balance-of-payments deficit. Recent calculations indicate that about $15 million a day leaves New England for imported energy. Each week, a typical family of four in New England sends $22 abroad to purchase energy.

As oil supplies diminish and prices increase, supply interruptions will begin to occur. While new supplies may be waiting to be discovered, the point will be reached where it is simply too expensive to get energy out of the ground. Increasing energy prices will begin to consume an ever larger amount of a family's income, and other basic needs will go unmet. There are signs already of this trend, and when energy becomes too expensive to afford, social distress will occur. This will happen not because there is no energy, but because people cannot afford to buy it.

The recently enacted National Energy Act prescribes various remedies for the country's energy woes. To a large degree, the Energy Act is merely a continuation of the past, business as usual as its called, where many large-scale, centralized coal and nuclear-generating stations will be developed to help curtail the country's dependence on imported oil. While the Energy Act contains provisions for implementing conservation measures and various solar technologies, the overall projected energy future of the country is based largely on macro-solutions where decisions about how to deal with energy problems are left up to government officials and large corporations. Energy planning will still focus on increasing supplies to meet hoped-for demands and will ignore energy efficiency (matching supply to demand), conservation, health, water, land use and air pollution questions, financial impacts, regional problems and potentials. Most importantly, it will continue to exclude people from the energy decision-making process.

The National Energy Act focusses on the supply side of the energy question and projects major changes in energy supplies over the next 25 years. But satisfaction of energy needs is not solely a technical issue to be solved by engineers. How this society will meet its energy needs is basically a social issue involving a host of value-laden decisions. Surrounding the social questions are technical parameters and boundaries.

Who picks the solutions

A key bias of all current energy planning is that it is being done for people by the government and energy companies, not by the people for themselves. It is assumed by both the planners and the planned-for that the solution will come from national experts trying to fulfill national needs. Business, however, was not always done this way. In the late 1800s, if one wished to build a factory, one started with the assumption that the source of energy needed to be created. Now, when one founds a new factory, one assumes that plugging into an existing energy course will occur. This leads to users not taking responsibility for supply and leads to numerous problems such as wasteful plant designs, processes and products, since the difficulty in securing energy is hidden from view. There is also a surrender of power to the energy suppliers in doing business this way. The local community which hosts the new manufacturing facility does not see the full impacts of the plant since the energy supplying equipment may be placed many miles away.

Are there any options?

When energy problems are presented in terms of corporate utilities, national politics and international economics, the sense of helplessness that people have is understandable since a homeowner or businessowner is placed in the position of trying to figure out what "I" can do. This aspect of helplessness is intensified since the public perceives government as being unwilling or unable to grasp and handle energy problems. There is no real long-term energy planning going on in this country today. As with so many other issues, action is only taken when situations reach crisis proportions and then the response is too little, too late.

Energy problems are indicative of greater maladies caused by large, centralized, unresponsive systems. Individual and local needs are ignored and people at the local level have no power and control over what happens to them. In an attempt to rectify those problems people are actively examining new ways of doing things. They are trying to bring about social changes which can be grouped under the heading of decentralization. Under decentralization, technology is environmentally safe, responsive to citizen control, possibly developed locally, and is of a scale that is accessible and understandable to individuals. With decentralization there is local ownership, democratic decision making is followed, and individuals have more control and responsibility over their lives. Right now, energy is in the forefront of the decentralization movement.

Within the energy movement, a growing amount of studies, literature, and thinking describes a system of energy built around environmentally benign, renewable energy sources. Systems which utilize natural, non-polluting sources of energy production include: wind generators; facilities to convert municipal waste, sewage and wood residues into methane gas and transportation fuels; active and passive solar systems for heating and cooling; solar photovoltaics for the generation of electricity; hydroelectric facilities; and, wood for heating and the generation of electricity.

Such energy systems are decentralized in nature since they are spread out over the landscape, either serving communities or individual buildings; some of them are intermittent, working only when the wind blows or the sun shines; they are flexible and understandable technologies; and, they are matched in scale and geographic distribution to the needs they will meet. The characteristics of renewable energy resources dictate that people get involved in deciding what energy systems will be developed, where and how. By developing renewable energy resources, opportunities and processes are presented

for people to participate in making important decisions concerning other issues as well.

The decentralized renewable energy movement covers a broad spectrum of people and programs. For example, individual homeowners, citizen groups, local officials, state legislatures and private businesses are engaged in numerous activities including public education programs, research and feasibility studies, hydroelectric and solar demonstration projects, building greenhouses, and passing legislation offering tax credits for conservation activities and solar hot water systems. The *Franklin County Energy Study* and Energy Project is one such local energy program.

Franklin County: Local energy planning

Under a grant from the Department of Energy, the Future Studies Program at the University of Massachusetts at Amherst developed a decentralized solar energy use scenario (solar is used to describe all forms of renewable energy) for Franklin County, Massachusetts for the year 2000. The technical positions of Amory Lovins, that societies could utilize innovative methods to solve their impending energy problems, were applied to Franklin County, a small, rural area located in northwestern Massachusetts (Figure 1). The *Franklin County Energy Study* was an eight-month project completed in the spring of 1979 and was one of three studies done for the Department of Energy under the solar technology assessment program.

To examine a solar energy future for Franklin County, two separate scenarios were developed: one for life as it is likely to be if traditional fuels and energy production systems are used; and,

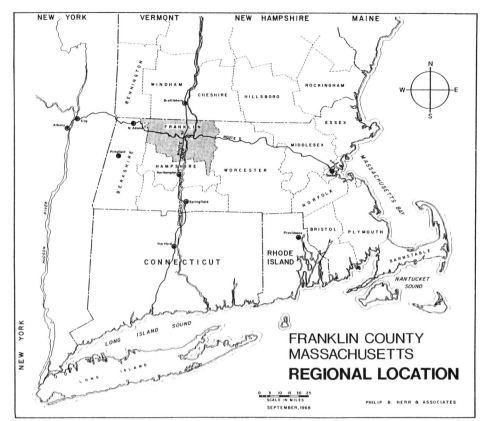

Figure 1

FRANKLIN COUNTY
MASSACHUSETTS
REGIONAL LOCATION

0 5 10 15 20 25
SCALE IN MILES
SEPTEMBER, 1968   PHILIP B. HERR & ASSOCIATES

one describing life as it could be if renewable energy sources were used. Social, environmental, and economic implications of both scenarios were assessed in order to show that renewable energy resources and conservation are viable options for the county to meet future energy needs.

Through the use of scenarios, which differ from the traditional energy planners' mode of operation of numbers extrapolation, the *Franklin County Energy Study* attempted to present the effects of various energy options. It allowed for the involvement of the general public and the institutions servicing the county in examining and developing those possible energy futures.

While the main goal of the study was to construct a solar energy scenario for Franklin County, a second goal was to educate the public and local decision makers about a malleable energy future and allow them to chart their own futures, something traditional energy planning has totally ignored by choice.

A citizen involvement component was woven into the study format because an energy transition to renewable energy resources must involve the people who will use that energy in the future if the transition is to be successful. If people are to play a role in determining the energy future, complex and technical energy information must be presented in an understandable form. Then, various energy proposals can be evaluated by the public. The *Franklin County Energy Study* followed a course which made information available to the public which they could then act upon.

The *Franklin County Energy Study* led to the development of a new program aimed at implementing the proposals generated in the study. The Franklin County Energy Project is working with county and town officials, groups and citizens to coordinate energy efforts and supply technical assistance. Concurrent research, demonstration and education projects are planned and will be discussed further on in this chapter.

To set the stage for the *Franklin County Energy Study,* the following statements served as guidelines for research:

1. In the year 2000, Franklin County can obtain significant amounts of its required energy by utilizing renewable energy resources located in the county.

2. Money paid by county residents for energy obtained from renewable energy systems would result in a higher standard of living for the county as measured by: employment statistics, pollution indices and other environmental factors and the shape of the county economy resulting from local purchases.

3. The presence of an alternative energy vision for the county would result in significantly greater awareness of the problems facing the county.

4. Increased comprehension of warnings about energy issues would result in increased political action in the county to support energy conservation and the development of new technologies.

The following methodology was used to develop the solar scenario:

1. Reviewed literature on New England's energy history and projected future.

2. Reviewed literature on renewable energy technologies and sources.

3. Compiled historic energy use and cost data for the county for the period 1950–1975 and assessed the impacts of energy on the county for that period.

4. Compiled an inventory of available renewable energy resources within the county.

5. Applied accepted techniques for energy forecasting to historic data to develop an energy future which uses traditional fuels and energy production systems.

6. Estimated the economic, social, and environmental ramifications of following the traditional energy future.

7. Calculated future energy demands for the county for various sectors of the economy based on the implementation of stringent conservation programs.

8. Developed an energy supply mix utilizing renewable resources which would meet conservation-oriented demands. The year 2000 supply mix is based on various constraints (physical availability of resource, citizen attitudes and acceptability and economics).

9. Estimated the economic, social, environmental, and political implications of implementing the renewable energy scenario.

10. Compared and contrasted the two scenarios in a form readily understandable by the general public.

11. Met with citizens and officials in the county throughout the study.

What is Franklin County

In order to understand the relationship of energy to Franklin County, the first step in the study involved developing a perspective on the county by examining it in terms of land use, population, housing, and economics.

Franklin County is predominantly rural, with over 75 percent of the land area forested. Only one of the county's 26 towns has a population greater than 10,000, and the 1975 population of 63,000 made Franklin County one of the least densely populated counties in the state.

Situated in the Connecticut River Valley, the county has some of the choicest agricultural land in the Northeast. Five watersheds cover the county, including the Quabbin Reservoir, whose 25,000 acres provide drinking water for the metropolitan Boston area.

About 36 percent of the households in the county are classified as low-income, and the 1975 median family income of around $9,000 was lower than the state median. The county's industrial base is comprised of firms producing fabricated metal products, non-electric machinery, paper products and food. Manufacturing and agricultural activities have declined since 1950 and have been replaced with service-oriented activities including retail trade, finance, insurance and real estate. Forest products, tourism and recreation also support the county economy.

An energy history

To comprehend and use the solar scenario, the year 2000 energy look had to be placed in context. To do this, energy use and cost patterns were examined from 1950 to 1979. A combination of federal, regional, and local data were used to examine the industrial, residential, commercial and transportation sectors.

Only energy purchased by the end-user was considered, versus that consumed by the producer, since it presented trends more clearly to those policy makers who would be reading the study. Local data is the most valuable and precise and was used whenever it could be found. During some of the years included in the historical review study, little attention was paid to energy. Therefore, some data was simply nonexistent. In such cases, various assumptions had to be applied.

Figures 2 through 7 show 1978 energy use for the county (by end use and by sector) and gross energy consumption trends between 1950 and 1978. (End use refers to energy consumption categories within sectors. For the residential sector this would include space heating, lighting and appliances. For the inductrial sector, lighting, hot water and direct process heating are considered end uses.) Franklin County experienced continuous increases in energy consumption through 1972, the year before the first oil embargo hit. Consumption dropped drastically for the next several years, but 1978 figures showed that electric consumption was again increasing.

An interesting point concerning consumption is that energy levels were the same for the two years 1965 and 1976 even though population and housing increased during that period and the economic base was larger in 1976 than in 1965. This situation clearly dispelled the myth that continuous increases in energy consumption are necessary in order for economic growth and an increased standard of living.

Collecting energy consumption data for a local area and on a frequent basis can provide a very accurate picture of changes in total energy use and energy use by sector. While overall consumption in Franklin County has either lev-

Figure 2

1978 Energy use by sector

Note: Sector and end use breakdowns for Figures 3–5 barely changed between 1975 and 1978.

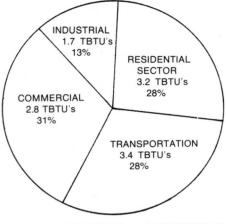

Figure 3

Residential sector 1978 end use breakdown of energy

Source: Stephen Dole, *Energy Use and Conservation in the Residential Sector: A Regional Analysis,* The Rand Corporation, Santa Monica, CA, June 1975, p. 66, (R-1641-NSF)

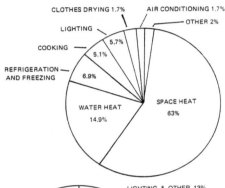

Figure 4

Commercial sector 1978 end use breakdown of energy

Source: J. Brainard, et al., *Perspectives on the Energy Future of the Northeast United States,* Brookhaven National Laboratory, Upton, New York, June 1976, p. 4.

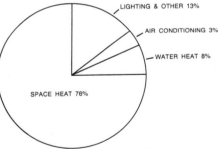

eled off or risen at about 1 percent annually for the past several years, energy mixes by sector have undergone substantial changes. Both the residential and industrial sectors use less oil than in 1975. The industrial sector has shown an increase in the use of electricity which may be indicative of a growing trend toward electrification. This could be occuring in an attempt to guarantee a steady energy source for the future. Wood is clearly displacing oil in the residential sector. While oil consumption decreased about 10 percent between 1975 and 1978, the use of wood jumped by almost 50 percent. That information was obtained through a countywide telephone survey.

While energy consumption started dropping in 1973, costs have risen at accelerating rates, with skyrocketing price increases between 1978 and 1979 (Figure 8). Between 1950 and 1970 the county's energy bill increased by $20 million, and by that same amount between 1970 and 1975. The total energy tab rose by another $10 million between 1975 and 1978, and then jumped by $27 million between 1978 and 1979. Of the $84 million paid by the county for energy in 1979, about $71 million left the county, never to return. In New England it is a standard rule that 85 percent of every dollar spent on energy leaves the local area. Only 15 percent of every dollar spent on energy is recycled back through the local economy.

The main intent of a local energy study is to present information in clear and concise terms, and in a manner that people can relate to. Along with examining the total county energy bill, that portion of all energy costs borne by households was calculated. According to Figure 9 this amount equaled $43 million, and represented just under half the total 1979 county energy bill. That

$43 million was paid by some 23,000 households whose median disposable income (money remaining after taxes) hovered around $8,500. Energy costs per household in 1979 were estimated to be between $1,800 and $1,900, and may be increasing as much as $200 per year. It is clear that incomes are not keeping pace with escalating energy costs and the average Franklin County resident now may be putting over 20 percent of his disposable income toward energy. For many, choices have to be made between necessities and luxuries. For others, the situation is such that a decision has to be made about what necessity to spend on.

Again, to bring complex energy data down to a human level, the total household energy bill for 1975 was compared to the payrolls of major employers in the county. (Updated data for certain employers was not available.) As can be seen from the following graph, in 1975 the top ten employers, in terms of number of employees, paid their workers only slightly more than the total for household energy costs. One way of looking at this is to say that the employers existed solely to help county residents meet the costs of their energy needs (Figure 10).

Hard numbers and human attitudes

Any local renewable energy planning work must involve an assessment of peoples' attitudes, feelings, preferences and fears concerning various issues from economic growth to political processes. Such an examination must be correlated with hard numbers and projections for population, housing and economic changes. In Franklin County, population and housing projections were used when calculating new energy demands and in assessing

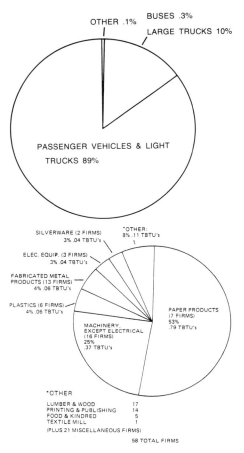

Figure 5

Transporation sector 1978 end use breakdown of energy

Source: Franklin County Energy Conservation Task Force, *Franklin County Energy Profile, 1975–1978*, p. 5.

Figure 6

Industrial sector 1975 breakdown

Sources: U.S. Dept. of Commerce, *Census of Manufacturing*, U.S. Bureau of Census, Washington, D.C., 1976 Franklin County Chamber of Commerce, *Franklin County Economic Profile and Statistical Abstract*, Greenfield, MA., 1974. Franklin County Energy Conservation Task Force, *Franklin County Energy Profile, 1975–1978*, p. 5. Department of Energy, *Federal Energy Data Series, 1960–1975*, Table V-Industrial

the contribution of renewable energy resources.

Local areas frequently lack economic growth forecasts and, for numerous reasons, state or federal forecasts are inapplicable to specific geographic areas. Such was the case with Franklin County, although county economic development officials are now formulating economic projections for the area.

The *Franklin County Energy Study* utilized several general growth policy documents to determine what might happen to the local economy over the next decade. The policy papers expressed residents' attitudes toward issues such as agriculture, industrial development, the county's rural character, a proposed nuclear power plant,

Figure 7
Energy use history
Franklin County,
Massachusetts
1950–1978

Energy-use data for 1976–
1977 became available
from the Department of
Energy after the historical
review had been com-
pleted. Information for
these two years was added
to the overview. Data for
1978 was obtained from an
updated version of the
Franklin County Energy Pro-
file, compiled by the
County Energy Conserva-
tion Task Force.

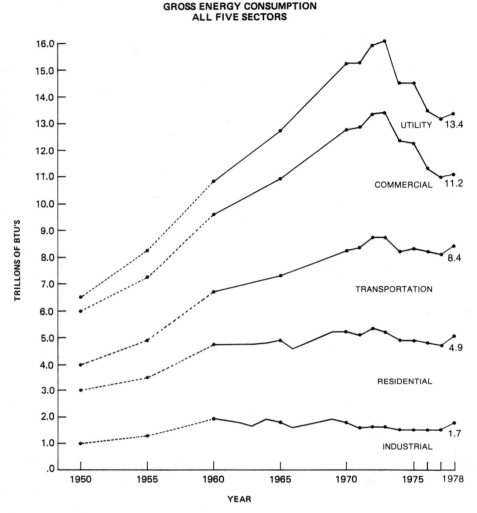

**GROSS ENERGY CONSUMPTION
ALL FIVE SECTORS**

and zoning. The development of renewable energy resources would pose a
host of additional questions to be addressed along with the above issues.
What people must realize is that energy
is tightly bound to all those issues and
the county's ultimate survival.[2]

One group the study worked closely
with was the Franklin County Energy
Conservation Task Force. This unique
citizen-based, county-supported organization and its member town energy
conservation committees are working
to expose energy problems, conserve
energy, and develop a sound energy future for the county. During its three-
year existence, the task force has
published two energy profiles of the
county, compiled an inventory of hydroelectric sites, conducted an energy
conservation survey and developed an
energy policy document. The conservation survey details residents' attitudes toward energy conservation, the
potentials for alternate energy sources,
public transportation, and recycling.
Some of the key responses to the conservation survey, which was conducted
in 1977, are presented on page 434 and
clearly show that energy is a major

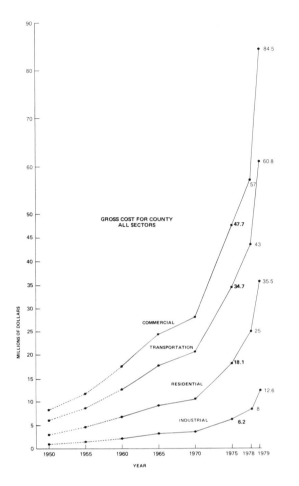

Figure 8

*Economics of energy
history, Franklin
County, Massachusetts
1950–1979*

Sources: U.S. De-
partment of Energy,
*Federal Energy Data
Series, Massachusetts,* 1977,
Tables I, II, III, IV
New England Federal Re-
gional Council, *New En-
gland Energy Situation and
Alternatives for 1985*
Franklin County Energy
Conservation Task Force,
*Franklin County Energy Pro-
file, 1975–1978*

concern of county residents. Such a survey or similar studies are beneficial since they allow people to get involved and present their views on critical issues and can serve as tools for education and future planning efforts.

Business as usual

For comparison, Franklin County's past and present energy make-up was extended out to the year 2000. Various federal and regionally-tuned, energy-growth forecasts were applied to Franklin County in a manner which took present energy-use patterns and said what they will be in 2000. The models chosen all depict annual increases in energy consumption, al-

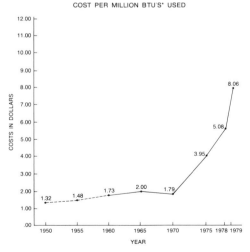

* 1 BTU = THE AMOUNT OF HEAT REQUIRED
TO RAISE THE TEMPERATURE OF 1 LB. OF
WATER 1°F.

Figure 8-A

*Economics of energy
history, Franklin
County, Massachusetts
1950–1979*

Sources: U.S. De-
partment of Energy,
*Federal Energy Data
Series, Massachusetts,* 1977,
Tables I, II, III, IV
New England Federal Re-
gional Council, *New En-
gland Energy Situation and
Alternatives for 1985*
Franklin County Energy
Conservation Task Force,
*Franklin County Energy Pro-
file, 1975–1978*

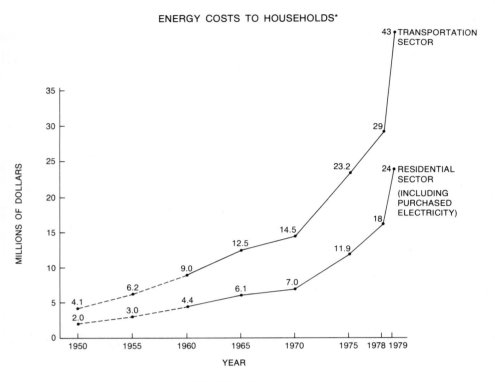

Figure 9

Economics of energy history, Franklin County, Massachusetts 1950–1979

Sources: U.S. Department of Energy, *Federal Energy Data Series, Massachusetts,* 1977, Tables I, II, III, IV New England Federal Regional Council, *New England Energy Situation and Alternatives for 1985* Franklin County Energy Conservation Task Force, *Franklin County Energy Profile, 1975–1978*

ENERGY COSTS TO HOUSEHOLDS*

* COSTS INCLUDE PURCHASED ELECTRICITY
PLUS 75% TRANSPORTATION COSTS
PLUS RESIDENTIAL SECTOR

though factors such as conservation and supply were taken into account. The "business as usual" approaches all bespeak of energy supplied by traditional technologies and fuels, but do not consider economic, environmental, and quality-of-life constraints.

A conservative annual energy price increase of 3 percent was added to the four models which were then applied to Franklin County. The 3 percent price increase was extremely conservative considering that energy prices increased by 55 percent between June 1978 and June 1979. The most important understanding to come from this exercise was that, while it may be possible to supply various amounts of energy to the county in 2000, the county will not be able to afford the bills for the energy. At some point in the near

future, the county may go bankrupt in its attempts to pay for energy (Figures 11 and 12).

Under the traditional approach, sizable economic infusions will be required to maintain the present flow of money and level of goods and services over the next decades. These infusions will need to offset the burden of rising energy costs. Since the county has virtually no indigenous resources capable of driving hard-energy technologies, the ability to recycle funds within the county is minimal. Money will not merely change hands faster as energy costs increase, but in addition, money will be flushed out of the county in ever greater amounts, never to return.

To drive home the point about the economic ramifications of a *business as usual* approach to energy, a comparison

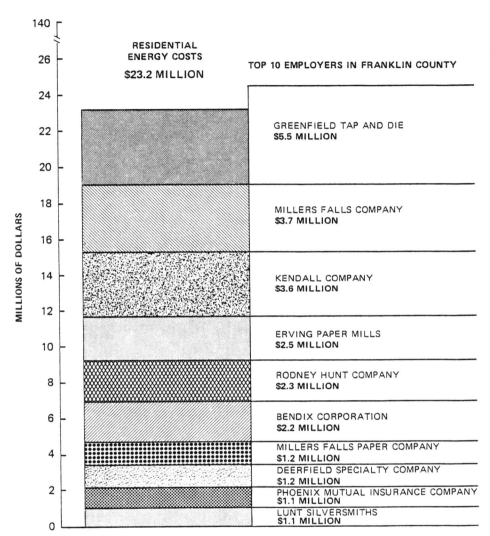

1975 RESIDENTIAL HOUSEHOLD COSTS COMPARED TO INDUSTRY PAYROLL

RESIDENTIAL
ENERGY COSTS

$23.2 MILLION

TOP 10 EMPLOYERS IN FRANKLIN COUNTY

MILLIONS OF DOLLARS

GREENFIELD TAP AND DIE
$5.5 MILLION

MILLERS FALLS COMPANY
$3.7 MILLION

KENDALL COMPANY
$3.6 MILLION

ERVING PAPER MILLS
$2.5 MILLION

RODNEY HUNT COMPANY
$2.3 MILLION

BENDIX CORPORATION
$2.2 MILLION

MILLERS FALLS PAPER COMPANY
$1.2 MILLION

DEERFIELD SPECIALTY COMPANY
$1.2 MILLION

PHOENIX MUTUAL INSURANCE COMPANY
$1.1 MILLION

LUNT SILVERSMITHS
$1.1 MILLION

Figure 10

Economics of energy history, Franklin County, Massachusetts 1950–1975 some useful comparisons

Source: Massachusetts Department of Labor and Industry, Division of Statistics

was made between annual increases in the county's energy bill and new industrial development. This analysis was similar to the one made for the relationship between household energy costs and manufacturing payrolls. County energy costs can be said to be the equivalent of various county employers payrolls. Similarly, it can be argued that an industry with a payroll equal to the increase in energy costs per year would have to be developed in the county each year in order for the county to keep pace with rising energy costs.

Based on various yearly increases for the low- and high-end, *business as usual* models, industries of a certain size would need to be constructed every one or two years (Figure 13).

Energy Conservation

a. Almost 80 percent felt that home heating and gasoline consumption are the two areas where conservation can do the most.

b. 93 percent said they had reduced energy consumption since the 1973 oil embargo (52 percent reduced consumption by 10–25 percent; 25 percent reduced consumption by 25–49 percent; 8 percent reduced consumption by more than 50 percent).

c. 55 percent believed that energy conservation does not mean a reduction in lifestyles.

d. 76 percent believed there is a serious energy problem and 86 percent had "pro" attitudes toward energy conservation.

e. 68 percent would be willing to pay 10–15 percent more initially for energy savings appliances if it meant lower costs later on.

f. 82 percent supported energy efficiency labeling on major appliances.

Households

a. 40 percent used a secondary heating system and of that amount 65 percent used wood.

b. 14 percent used wood as a primary heating source.

c. 42 percent of those using wood as a primary heating source intended to install another heating system and 64 percent of those said it would be wood.

d. Homeowners, as compared with renters, are more likely to take energy saving measures.

e. Renters, as opposed to homeowners, are more likely to keep their thermostats at a lower setting during the daytime, but not lower it during the evening.

f. 57 percent felt their homes were adequately insulated.

Alternate Energy Sources

a. 59 percent believed that hydroelectric power could contribute a lot to meeting local energy needs.

b. 55 percent believed that wood could contribute a lot to meeting local energy needs.

c. 39 percent felt that solar could contribute a lot to meeting local energy needs.

d. 31 percent felt that waste recycling could contribute a lot to meeting local energy needs.

e. 21 percent felt that wind could contribute a lot to meeting local energy needs.

f. Concerning the factors that would encourage one to install an alternate energy system in their home: 35 percent wanted figures on projected energy savings, 27 percent wanted financial assistance, 22 percent wanted proof that the system would work in this area.

g. Concerning the factors which would discourage one from installing an alternate energy system in their home: 59 percent said it would be the cost of changing or adding another system, 27 percent felt it was the uncertainty of possible savings.

Transportation

a. 48 percent are willing to carpool.

b. 86 percent were in favor of continuing public mass transit and 62 percent were in favor of expanding public mass transit.

c. About 50 percent said they drove up to 100 miles per week.

d. 35 percent felt that gas-guzzling cars should be penalized via taxes.

Recycling

a. 65 percent currently recycle various materials.

b. 70 percent said they would recycle more if there were convenient collection points.

Citizen participation

The most important aspect of local energy planning is that citizens play a key role in creating a renewable energy future. In Franklin County, the following groups participated in the research process by providing information and attending meetings: the county commissioners, the county energy planner, the county energy conservation task force, economic development officials, representatives from the local community action agency and the county extension service.

A countywide public meeting was held partway through the research effort to present findings to the county. At a meeting attended by officials, citizens, utility representatives, the media and various groups and organizations, the validity of presenting energy information in comprehensible terms was revealed. Changes in energy consumption were understandable when explained in terms of population and housing growth, economic development and rising energy prices. Likewise, the cost of energy for the county and households was made clear when expressed in terms of manufacturing payrolls and median disposable income. Finally, the impact of continuing along the traditional energy path was brought home when explained in relation to necessary new jobs needed on an annual basis if the county is to stay even with skyrocketing energy costs. Depicting the county as a bucket with an enlarging hole in the bottom is a graphic way to explain the ever-larger amounts of money which must be dumped into the top.

The impact of the meeting was borne out by comments expressed afterward and on evaluation sheets passed out to the audience. "Now that you've scared the hell out of us, what can we do," was indicative of the audiences' response to the presentation. Even a former president of the county Chamber of Commerce, who is also a district manager for one of the two electric utilities servicing Franklin County admitted that he had never really thought of energy the way it was presented at the meeting.

A solar scenario

The renewable energy scenario developed for Franklin County, entitled a

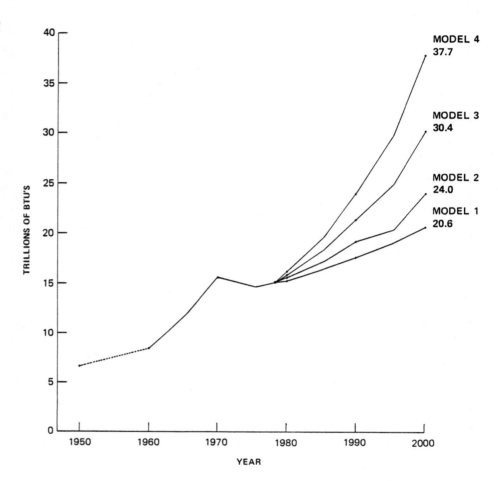

Figure 11
*Energy use forecast
Franklin County,
Massachusetts 1950–
2000 business as usual*

COMPOSITE – ALL FOUR MODELS

MODEL 4
37.7

MODEL 3
30.4

MODEL 2
24.0

MODEL 1
20.6

TRILLIONS OF BTU'S

YEAR

Technical Fix-Solar Scenario, posits fundamental shifts in traditional consumption patterns. While advocating changes in habits, no projections were made of any major changes in the quality of individual lifestyles, since that is an extremely difficult point to define and qualify.

At first, the intention was to develop renewable energy models similar to those used in the non-renewable energy section of the study. Since none existed, attention was turned to Sweden, which is pioneering a stringent conservation-transition energy sce-

nario. Too many fundamental differences existed between Sweden and Franklin County to use it for comparison with the county. What evolved was a locally tailored plan, based on integrating the county's natural resources with its human potential.

Conservation is the cornerstone of the solar scenario. In two years, the CETA funded-Cooperative Extension Service administered Energy Conservation Analysis Project (ECAP) has conducted more than 1,000 home energy audits throughout the county. They discovered that if homeowners

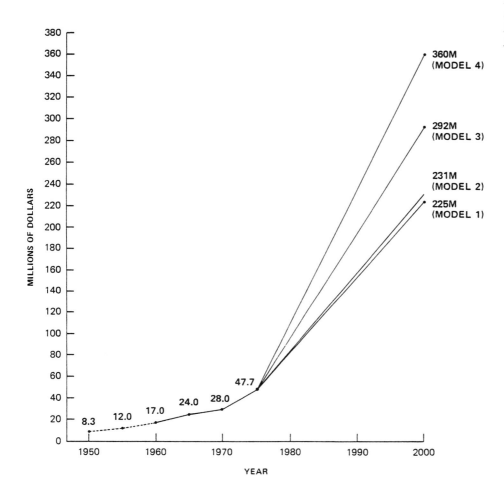

GROSS COST FOR COUNTY ALL SECTORS

360M
(MODEL 4)

292M
(MODEL 3)

231M
(MODEL 2)

225M
(MODEL 1)

47.7

28.0

24.0

17.0

12.0

8.3

MILLIONS OF DOLLARS

YEAR

Figure 12
Energy economics fore-cast, Franklin County, Massachusetts 1950–2000 business as usual

followed prescribed procedures for in-sulating and weatherizing their homes, there could be average reductions in space-heating demands of at least 40 percent. Before ending last fall, ECAP had begun audits of municipal build-ings in Franklin County.

Recommendations such as ECAP, and others derived from exhaustive lit-erature searches and reviews of other studies, began to coalesce into a model called the Technical Fix-Solar Scenario. Technical fixes cover actions that will reduce energy consumption and in-clude insulating homes, driving more

fuel-efficient cars and using more effi-cient appliances. Incorporated into these fixes are social acts such as car-pooling, lowering thermostats, and turning off unnecessary lights. Explicit in the Technical Fix-Solar Scenario is the notion that intensive energy conser-vation programs must be put into prac-tice first before renewable energy sys-tems are developed. It does not make any sense to put a solar collector on the roof of your house if the building lacks insulation, and storm doors, and windows.

Each end-use by sector was exam-

Figure 13
Energy Economics Forecast, Franklin County, Massachusetts 1975–1980. Some Useful Comparisons

Increased residential energy costs translated into new economic demand

Year	Cost Increase (Millions of Dollars)	
1975–1976	Model 1	$1.0
	Model 4	$1.6
1976–1977	Model 1	$1.1
	Model 4	$1.7
1977–1978	Model 1	$1.1
	Model 4	$1.9
1978–1979	Model 1	$1.2
	Model 4	$2.0
1979–1980	Model 1	$1.2
	Model 4	$2.1

Growth Needed Every Year

Under Model 1
- A new Millers Falls Paper Company (175 employees)
- or Deerfield Specialty Company (170 employees)

Under Model 4
- A new Rodney Hunt Company (355 employees)
- or two Lunt Silversmiths (150 employees)

Growth Needed Every Two Years

Under Model 1
- A new Bendix Corporation (320 employees)
- or Rodney Hunt Company (355 employees)

Under Model 4
- A new Millers Falls Company (600 employees)
- or a new Erving Paper Mills (390 employees) plus a Millers Falls Paper Company (175 employees)
- A new CETA program about the same size as current (500 employees)

ined to determine the theoretical energy reductions possible via conservation. The application of conservative figures revealed that countywide net energy savings in 2000 could reach 50 percent. This takes into account increases in population and housing stock and, on a more general basis, economic and industrial growth.

Beyond the savings that could be realized from the implementation of ECAP's insulation and weatherization recommendations, passive solar-designed new single and multi-family dwellings could reduce energy consumption by another 20 percent. Additional savings could be realized from retrofitting schools, warehouses, offices and businesses with passive solar systems and by having industry practice cogeneration. (Cogeneration refers to the use of the same fuel to produce power and useful heat. Utility plants and industry are prime candidates for cogeneration since the production of electricity and manufacturing processes both produce usable "waste" heat.) In addition, building low-cost solar greenhouses onto existing homes would result in more space-heating savings, not to mention creating a new household food-growing option.

To develop the solar scenario, an in-depth inventory was conducted of renewable energy resources located in the county. A wide array of data and information were used to ascertain how much wind, solar, hydroelectric,

Example of the graphic illustrations developed by the Franklin County Energy Study to show citizens what their communities might look like if the solar scenario were implemented.

wood, and biomass resources there are. (Biomass refers to organic matter that can be converted into energy and includes municipal sewage and solid waste, agricultural residues and manure, wood residues and specifically grown agricultural crops such as sugar beets and potatoes.) As with the conservation-oriented future energy demand projections that were developed, resource availability figures must be refined by conducting in-depth field analyses. For example, over 100 sites were identified for possible wind generators. A field program using anemometers must be conducted to determine the actual wind potential at each of the sites.

Figure 14
*Residential sector—
soft path, 2000*

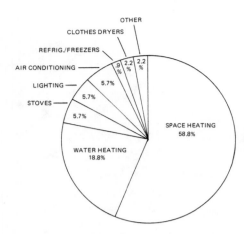

CATEGORY	DEMAND	% REDUCTION FROM 1975
SPACE HEATING	1.34 TBTU's	37
WATER HEATING	.43	16
AIR CONDITIONING	.02	0
STOVES	.13	24
CLOTHES DRYERS	.05	17
REFRIG./FREEZERS	.13	43
LIGHTING	.13	32
OTHER	.05	37
TOTAL	2.27	44

Figure 15
*Commercial sector—
soft path, 2000*

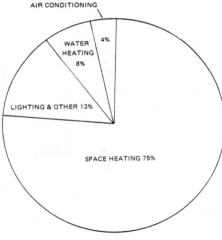

CATEGORY	DEMAND	% REDUCTION FROM 1975
SPACE HEATING	1.80	36
WATER HEATING	.20	35
AIR CONDITIONING	.07	30
LIGHTING & OTHER	.31	39
TOTAL	2.40	35

Assuming the existing housing stock is completely weatherized, it would be possible to provide about 57 percent of the annual heating requirements for such homes by installing 20-by-40-foot solar panels on half the homes in the county. For new, passive designed homes, the solar systems could achieve the same results but would only need to be two-thirds the size of the systems installed on existing homes.

An important element of the solar scenario is using wood to make up heating deficits in December, January, and February, the months when solar energy potential is at its lowest. Right now, nearly half the homes in the county use wood either as a primary or secondary heat source. In addition, the solar scenario describes placing 10-by-10-foot solar photovoltaic panels on half the county's homes to transfer the sun's light into electricity.

A half-dozen hydroelectric facilities in the county are now owned and operated by various utility companies. The study calculated that the county currently produces more electricity than it consumes, and that electricity is used to support peak demands within the New England grid. Using a hydro-electric site inventory prepared by the Energy Conservation Task Force, 137 existing, former, and never-developed hydroelectric sites were identified for further examination. While numerous hydroelectric sites could be developed to provide power for the county and to sell to outside areas, the major issue is not so much one of supply, but one of ownership and distribution.

With the development of renewable energy resources, the questions of control and distribution are as important as supply. Counties and towns have certain options open to them as far as setting up their own power companies, but the use of renewable energy resources on a decentralized basis will require regulatory and policy changes at higher levels. The study recommended that the county take over the existing hydroelectric facilities, although it would be extremely difficult to do at this time due to various Massachusetts laws.

The *Franklin County Energy Study* envisions a coordinated approach to using the county's ample forest resources. At this time, approximately 70,000 cords of wood are harvested annually for fuelwood and sawlogs. The study proposes a wood-fired power plant to help meet electric demands, with such a plant consuming 50,000 cords of wood per year. A lack of sound forest management practices in New England has resulted in poorly growing forests and yields could be doubled if the forests were cleaned up.

Finally, biomass materials were examined in terms of providing a substitute for natural gas and as a fuel for transportation. Sludge from paper mills could be used for ethanol production, and may be an option for the county to pursue. Another possibility is producing ethanol from crops such as sugar beets. Under this caveat, a large portion of agricultural land in the county would have to be given up to meet liquid fuel demands, and this would decrease the amount of land available for food production. Such trade-off questions exist with each renewable resource and must be decided by all the citizens of the county.

Implementation

The *Franklin County Energy Study* represents a first-level examination of a potential new energy future for a specific geographic area. The intent is to take the study from the theoretical to the realistic via implementation and

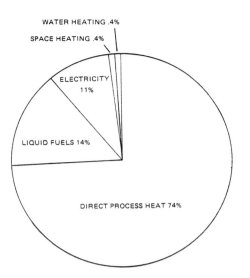

Figure 16
*Industrial sector—
soft path, 2000*

WATER HEATING .4%
SPACE HEATING .4%
ELECTRICITY 11%
LIQUID FUELS 14%
DIRECT PROCESS HEAT 74%

CATEGORY	DEMAND	% REDUCTION FROM 1975
SPACE HEATING	.004 TBTU's	97
WATER HEATING	.004	97
ELECTRICITY*	.11	39
DIRECT PROCESS HEAT	.73	11
LIQUID FUELS**	.14	33
TOTAL	.99	55

* ELECTRICITY IS FOR LIGHTING & OTHER
** LIQUID FUELS FOR INDUSTRIAL VEHICLES

using local energy planning. That work is now beginning in the form of the Franklin County Energy Project, an advocacy program developed as a result of the study.

In moving from here to there, (and no specific time frame is presented since the entire implementation process surely will be one of trial and error), there are several key areas of work that local energy planning must take into consideration. Those issues to be addressed under implementation would include:

1. Public education.

2. Further research concerning the development of renewable energy systems and an assessment of their social, economic, and environmental impacts.

3. The development of various dem-

Figure 17
Franklin county fuel requirements (millions of gallons)

Year	76	80	85	90	95	2000	
Need for Scenario A: fleet avg. 27.5 mpg @ 2000 A.D.	23.9	20.2	16	16.3	16.5	16.7	(gasoline)
			24.2	24.7	25	25.3	(ethanol)
			32	32.6	33	33.4	(methanol)
Need for Scenario B: fleet avg. 37 mpg @ 2000 A.D.	23.9	20.2	16	14.6	13.5	12.4	(gasoline)
			24.2	22.1	20.4	18.8	(ethanol)
			32	29.2	27	24.8	(methanol)
Need for Scenario C: mass transit fleet/mercedes diesel	—	—	—	1.7	3.0	4.2	(gasoline)
				2.5	4.5	6.7	(ethanol)
				3.41	6.0	8.4	(methanol)

onstration projects on various scales to test a certain technology, program or concept and determine its feasibility.

4. A determination of financing mechanisms available for education and demonstration programs and for the development of renewable energy systems.

5. Development of specific programs and priorities to address the pressing needs of low-income citizens.

6. An investigation concerning municipalization of energy facilities and the development of public energy companies to manufacture energy systems and produce power.

7. An investigation of numerous utility-related issues including: selling and buying power; who owns certain equipment; the quality of power fed to utilities; rates; load management; storage; control; and local distribution capacity.

8. The development and implementation of strong conservation programs to cover all sectors and areas of energy use.

9. The investigation and redesign of land use policies to incorporate energy conservation concepts and the development of decentralized en-

ergy systems. This can include building codes, zoning ordinances, subdivision regulations and land-use plans.

10. An examination and revitalization of local political processes to ensure that citizen involvement in democratic energy decision-making can occur.

In working on energy issues it quickly becomes apparent that many other subjects come into play which require consideration: jobs and economic growth, citizen involvement and control, community stability, land use, and public-private decision making. Initiating local energy planning can reverse a trend which has continued for some time now—the loss of control at individual and community levels.

In Franklin County such losses and their resultant impacts are readily apparent: the county once consumed locally produced energy, but the area is now part of a multi-state electric grid system run by a conglomerate of utilities. These groups are far removed from the county and have no specific interest in the well-being of the area; the loss of prime agricultural land and small farms; the loss of downtown businesses to malls run by corporations located away from the local scene; and, the increase in the number of political

Resource	Annual Available MW[a]	Annual Available MK Whrs.[b]	Monthly Available (AV.)MKWhrs.	Uses
Wind	Scenario I[c]·225	727	6–13	Electricity
	Scenario II[d]·75	245	12–31	
	Scenario III[e]·30	103	34–94	
Hydro.	Existing	443.3	12–62	Electricity
	Potential	489.6[f]	12–87	
Solar	7.22 Quads[g]		(Jan) 420BTU's/ft² (July) 1900BTU's/ft²	Process heat, Space heating, Water heating, Electricity

Biomass	Municipal Solid Waste			
	400 million cubic feet synthetic gas **or** 40,000 tons organic residue		Constant throughout the year	Process heat, Space heating, Water heating, Electricity, Natural gas substitute, Fuel oil uses, Transport, Fuels
	Sewage			
	310 million cubic feet synthetic gas **or** 1 million gallons methanol		Constant throughout the year	Natural gas substitute, Transport, Fuels
	Agricultural dairy, Feedlot and Field Wastes			
	92.4 million cubic feet synthetic gas		Seasonal	Transport, Fuels, Natural gas substitute
	Timber Harvesting and Lumbermill Residues			
	4–10 million gallons ethanol fuel **or** 745 million cubic feet synthetic gas **or** 74,585 tons		Relatively constant throughout the year	Process heat, Space heating, Water heating, Transport, Fuels
	Specially Grown Crops			
	25–33 million gallons ethanol fuel		Seasonal but supply is constant	Transport, Fuels
	Wood			
	7.7 trillion BTU's[h]		Relatively constant	Electricity, Firewood, Lumber, Wood products, Process heat, Gas production, Transport, Fuels
	9–13 trillion BTU's[i]			
	8–12 trillion BTU's[j]			

Figure 18
Energy resource summary

a. Megawatts
b. Millions kilowatt hours
c. 150 1.5 MW wind machines
d. 150 500 KW wind machines
e. 300 100 KW wind machines
f. Includes sites larger than 5 MW, existing unused sites and older, once used or small, never developed sites
g. County wide total
h. Yearly 1978–2000
i. By year 2000
j. Per year after 2000

Sector	1975				2000			
	Electric	Non-electric <350°F	>350°F	Liquid Fuels	Electric	Non-electric <350°F	>350°F	Liquid Fuels
Residential	.86	2.54	—	—	.50	1.77	—	—
Commercial	1.00	2.80	—	—	.40	1.99	—	—
Industrial	.18	.54	.57	.21	.11	.36	.38	.14
Transportation				3.4[a]			(.725)[h]	(4.1)[b]
								(3.1)[c]
								(1.0)[d]
								(3.2)[e]
								(2.3)[f]
								(0.8)[g]
Total	2.04[i]	5.88	.57	3.61	1.01 (1.795)	4.12	.38	(4.24) (3.24) (1.14) (3.34) (2.44) (0.94)

a. Equivalent of 27 million gallons of gasoline
b. Methanol demand for passenger fleet at 27.5 mpg (33.4 millions gallons)
c. Methanol demand for passenger fleet at 37 mpg (24.8 million gallons)
d. Methanol demand for mass transit (8.4 million gallons); difference between two fuel efficiencies for passenger fleet
e. Ethanol demand for passenger fleet at 27.5 mpg (25.3 million gallons)
f. Ethanol demand for passenger fleet at 37 mpg (18.8 million gallons)
g. Ethanol demand for mass transit (6.7 million gallons); difference between two fuel efficiencies for passenger fleet
h. Electric demand for passenger fleet
i. Does not include utility percentage of electric consumption

decisions made at the federal and state levels which are imposed on local areas.

As was pointed out earlier, energy planning is now being carried out by non-elected civil servants and energy companies, not the optimal situation for the evolution of social policies affecting energy use. Along with developing renewable energy sources, local involvement can lead to citizens assuming much of the decision-making work now out of their hands. Satisfying energy needs is not a technical issue, but is a social issue with technical boundaries.

The next steps

While the original work plan for the *Franklin County Energy Study* included provisions for interaction with citizens and institutional groups in the county, it became clear that a more substantive relationship with the county would be beneficial to the goals of the study and the people of the county. The study had to be moved from its university setting into the county, and a presence had to be established which would allow for the project's involvement in local energy work.

	Process Heat	Space Heat & Hot Water	Cool-ing	Elec-tricity	Fuels
Solar					
ON–SITE PASSIVE SOLAR		X	X		
ON–SITE ACTIVE SOLAR		X			
DISTRIBUTED SOLAR HEATING		X			
SOLAR PROCESS HEAT	X				
SOLAR COGENERATION	X	X		X	
Hydroelectric					
ON–SITE HYDROELECTRIC				X	
DISTRIBUTED HYDROELECTRIC				X	
Wind					
ON–SITE WIND				X	
DISTRIBUTED WIND				X	
Biomass					
MUNICIPAL SOLID WASTE (STEAM)	X	X			
MUNICIPAL SOLID WASTE (ELEC)				X	Natural gas substitute
MUNICIPAL SOLID WASTE (METHANE)					
MUNICIPAL SOLID WASTE (PYROLITIC OIL)					Fuel oil uses
MUNICIPAL SOLID WASTE (METHANOL)					Transport. fuel
SEWAGE (METHANE)					Natural gas substitute
AGRICULTURAL, DAIRY, FIELD AND FEEDLOT WASTE (METHANE)					Natural gas substitute
TIMBER HARVESTING RESIDUES (STEAM)	X	X			
LUMBERMILL RESIDUES (STEAM)	X	X			
AGRICULTURAL INDUSTRY WASTE (STEAM)	X		X		
WOOD (STEAM)	X	X			
WOOD (AIR)	X	X			
WOOD (ELEC)				X	

Figure 20
Energy supply options to meet energy demands

The first step in making the transition was a presentation of the solar scenario before the Energy Conservation Task Force. The group voted to establish a liaison committee to assist the study in becoming the Franklin County Energy Project. The liaison committee and study staff met several times to outline steps for introducing the study and relocation plans to key decision makers and interested parties.

What followed were separate briefings for the County Commissioners, the Greenfield Town Energy Conservation Committee, the Franklin Community Action Corporation, the Franklin County Cooperative Extension Service, the Greenfield Town Selectmen and a

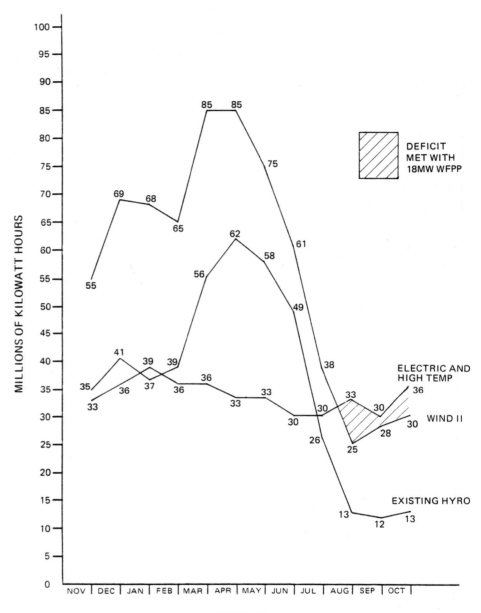

Figure 21
*Electric and Industrial
High Temperature De-
mands Met with Exist-
ing Hydroelectric,
Wind, and Wood*

special presentation before the county's economic development officials and the Rural Development Corporation. What emerged from those meetings was a clearer understanding of the various roles groups could play in renewable energy planning and some of the issues to be addressed:

1. Education activities would further highlight energy issues for local elected officials.

2. Support was given for the creation of an energy resource center and a broad-based education effort.

3. A special training program con-

cerning energy options and economic development was requested by the economic development specialists.

4. The Franklin County Energy Project would initially assume responsibility for working with the Task Force and Town Energy Conservation Committees to strengthen their capabilities for doing renewable energy and conservation work.

5. The Project could work closely with the county's energy planner in developing a county energy conservation plan.

6. The Project could act as an informal clearinghouse for various groups or individuals seeking funding or technical assistance for projects.

7. The Project would assume an informal, but recognized, role to perform an oversight-coordination function for energy planning work in the county.

During 1979–1980 the Energy Project divided its time between education, outreach, and research activities. Some of that work was done outside Franklin County since the staff were frequently asked to lecture and consult on local energy planning to private and public groups. The Energy Project has concentrated on working with individual towns across the county and coordinating the efforts of various energy actors around the county. As part of its education and planning work, the Energy Project recently completed a countywide Technology Assessment Program (TAP).

Based on the solar scenario or blueprint for a renewable energy future contained in the *Franklin County Energy Study*, the TAP project involved the dissemination of the energy study findings to the citizens of Franklin County and the solicitation of information from those residents concerning their attitudes, desires and goals about the future of Franklin County as it relates to energy and specifically about the solar scenario.

On the surface, the TAP project would appear to be the logical mechanism to use to initiate local energy work and to get citizens to take a more active role in energy decision-making and planning. This was only partially the case in Franklin County since energy concerns have been a high priority for officials and citizens since 1977 when a county energy conservation task force and town energy conservation committees were formed. Since that time, a variety of research, education and conservation programs, and, lately, renewable-energy development projects have been undertaken as the county continues to practice what it preaches: that energy issues are matters of survival and that many energy concerns are local in scope and can best be addressed through locally generated solutions. Therefore, in Franklin County, the TAP program's main accomplishments were to solidify and expand upon the already sturdy and active official–citizen energy planning apparatus.

The TAP program was organized to accomplish the following:

• To help Franklin County to use energy more efficiently (by disseminating pertinent information) and to continue developing a renewable energy base;

• To strengthen town energy conservation committees as an established foundation and network for local energy planning and activities;

• To identify further work areas for the Energy Project, which already has a positive working relationship with county and local government throughout the county, but due to its being a non-profit advocacy group can initiate projects that cover a variety of topics and have definite political overtones.

Finally, the TAP program was structured to include a wide variety of activities and to facilitate a high degree of citizen participation. This path was pursued since it best fit in with ongoing county energy activities and encompassed many of the recommendations contained in the *Franklin County Energy Study*.

The Energy Project, with co-sponsorship by various town energy conservation committees, held six regional meetings around the county. The format of each meeting was structured in the following manner:

• A brief overview of energy activities in Franklin County since 1977 and an assessment of the impact of national energy policy and international happenings on the county;

• A presentation of the Franklin County Energy Study and solar scenario (this involved a slide show of the numbers, shots of various operating renewable energy projects and graphics which portrayed what the solar transition might look like);

• A broad-ranging discussion with the audience about what their towns have done or could do and obstacles to be overcome.

Each meeting was attended by town energy conservation committee members, interested citizens and usually a local and/or appointed offical so that the discussions addressed a wide array of topics and concerns. As a result of the meetings several towns formed energy conservation committees and some dormant committees have been reactivated. The Energy Project was able to identify issue areas to concen-

trate on, which was a difficult task since so many groups and agencies in the county are now carving up the energy pie. Table 1 shows where the Energy Project will be placing its efforts in the months to come. Overall, the TAP program was seen as a catalyst, something that served a variety of purposes but could be said to have moved the county one step closer toward a full and comprehensive movement to address its energy problems and potentials.

Options for Franklin County

Along with tapping into the state and federal network to take advantage of energy-related programs and money, the county can immediately commence work on building a new energy future. Numerous local projects can be undertaken without waiting for state or federal action:

1. Place restrictions on new subdivisions and moratoriums on new shopping centers until appropriate land-use policies are adopted.

2. Develop and implement an energy efficient building code similar to the ones in use in Aspen, Colorado and Davis, California.

3. Work toward the assurance of sun-rights for property owners.

4. Establish a county resource team to monitor energy problems, to further study county energy resources, to investigate funding sources for proposed projects and to pass along information to individuals and organizations. Identified money could be used for construction, renovations, improvements, new businesses and education. Sources of money include tax revenues, municipal bonds, private investments, and state and federal money.

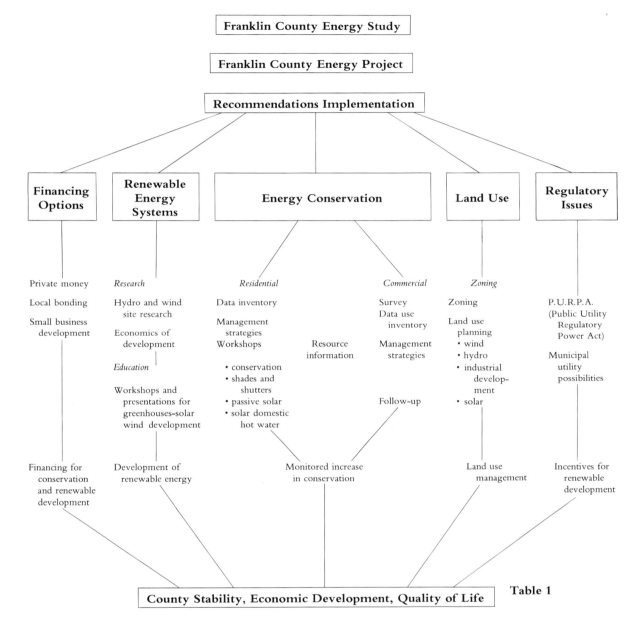

Table 1

5. Get merchants to stock energy efficient appliances with information on life-cycle costing.

6. Reduce lighting levels where appropriate.

7. Conduct energy courses at schools, community colleges, technical schools, and extension services.

8. Examine the potential for industrial cogeneration.

9. Examine ways to curtail water use and waste since this cuts down on energy consumption and costs. Reductions in pumping and treatment also cuts down on maintenance requirements and extends the life of systems.

10. Examine ways of dealing with waste disposal and landfill problems by expanding recycling programs.

11. Under transportation, investigate car pooling opportunities and van pooling, the development of a regional transportation authority and the enlargement of the current mass transportation system. Examine having gasoline stations offer engine inspection and maintenance programs which can cut down on fuel consumption, and developing bikeways, pedestrian malls, and walkways.

12. Conduct door-to-door surveys of household energy use, lifestyle preferences and attitudes, transportation needs, commuting patterns, and income levels. Assess capital resource requirements for renovations on a sector by sector basis, identify amounts and types of energy waste, and conduct building stock and land surveys to locate salvageable and vacant structures. Also, examine land for agriculture, recreation, and energy production uses.

13. Formulate, adopt and publicize a resolution stating that the county will work toward energy conservation and efficiency and the development of renewable energy resources. Get as many private and public groups, organizations, and agencies as possible in the county to endorse the resolution.

14. Explore the opportunities for using local materials and labor for energy conservation and renewable energy systems projects.

15. Maintain complete monthly records for energy consumption by fuel type and amount for various activities in all sectors.

16. Continue recycling work in the county through education, the reuse and recycling of materials, and the development of town recycling stations.

17. Encourage the recently created Community Development Corporation to support energy-related projects and examine county-wide economic implications of conservation and renewable energy resource programs.

18. Enforce the life-cycle costing law for all new buildings.

19. Develop programs such as fuel banking, bulk fuel purchasing and cooperatively organized wood fuel, weatherization, and solar technology activities.

The development of community-scale energy systems must occur in the most coordinated and public way possible. It will be vital that all citizens be informed and be able to fully participate in any decision making process. A three-to-five year time frame is envisioned for developing concurrent research, education, planning, and demonstration progams. Since the nature of participatory local energy planning is not now well understood, flexibility will be the key to any successful long-term effort. It must be clearly recognized that community energy planning is a new experience for citizens and communities. Certain ground rules for success will only become evident after various programs have been tried. In Franklin County, as in other places where energy work is going on, the key to increased activity often has been through the interests and visions of particular groups or individuals in the community. Federal and state programs for those efforts will have to respond to diverse activities.

Final responsibility and accountability for community-scale energy systems resides within those frameworks which a particular community chooses for itself. Whether it is a neighborhood, town or county, the community is in the best position to evaluate the strengths and weaknesses of its energy activities. This viewpoint requires, however, shared authority and a measure of trust in creating an effective partnership between community, state, and federal renewable energy efforts.

Within the realities of the work currently being done by the Franklin County Energy Conservation Task Force, the Town Energy Conservation Committees, the Franklin County Community Action Corporation, the County Planning Department, and increased utility and industrial involvement and individual efforts, the Franklin County Energy Project will take its place. The combined efforts of all these groups will make a clear statement that effective renewable energy activity can and will be carried out at the local level.

References

1. Amory Lovins, *Soft Energy Paths: Toward a Durable Peace,* (New York: Harper & Row, 1979).

2. Several public planning agencies have begun to include energy when developing their master plans. For example, see: St. Lawrence County Comprehensive Land Use Plan, St. Lawrence County Planning Board, Potsdam, N.Y. (June 1978); *Citizen Based Energy Technology Assessment Program,* Southern Tier Central Regional Planning and Development Board, Corning, N.Y. (December 1978).

17 | Strategies for Bioregional Food Systems

George Burrill and James Nolfi

BY TRADITIONAL STANDARDS the United States is one of the most agriculturally productive countries in the world. However, this statement obscures important questions concerning the price that has been paid to construct our present system, as well as the desirability and feasibility of maintaining it into the long-term future. There already exist serious problems which may not allow the structure of the present agricultural system, and its practices, to continue.

The purpose of this paper is, within an ecological perspective, to: (1) provide an overview of major reasons why the present system of production and consumption is inadequate; (2) propose the consideration of a bioregional systems approach;[1] and, (3) outline initial work that the authors have done toward developing a sustainable bioregional agricultural production and consumption system.

The present U.S. system of agriculture

Since World War II, agriculture in the U.S. has become highly mecha-nized, energy-intensive, and increasingly organized into monocultural operations. Higher and higher levels of capitalization and increasing farm size are required to compete within the market system. Over this same period of time we have seen population increases in the United States and abroad resulting in increased demand for food. We have also seen increased urbanization and loss of farmland and farms.[2] In the United States increased demand for food has been met by increased productivity per acre and per farmer, despite the loss of actual farmland and farms. However, this trend of improved productivity is now reaching biological limits.[3] Plant geneticists seem to agree that plant breeding for increased photosynthetic efficiency has been pushed about as far as it can go, and quantitative feed-conversion efficiency in animals seems near its limit as well. For these and other reasons, given the present system and its paradigms, agricultural productivity in the United States seems at a plateau.

Overall demand levels for food are not likely to diminish, nor is the pressure to take farmland out of production. Pressure to export food to aid our balance of payments and to feed an increasingly hungry world, particularly when diplomatically expedient, will be with us for some time to come. Despite the opinion of USDA officials that increased export of United States' food will not affect consumer prices, it is difficult to see how domestic price increases can be avoided. Furthermore, from a humanistic standpoint, it doesn't seem justified to take an isolationist stance. The United States must make food available to all the world. What needs to be considered is the way that this is done. We cannot consider the world our garden place, dictating by economic and military hegemony what is to be planted and harvested. Rising consciousness of nationalism and anti-imperialism in former colonial regions means that people will not long continue to produce foods for export on all available land, and starve in the process.[4] National concern over the disappearance of agricultural land is also evidence of a pressure that is not going to change. Topsoil is being lost at a very significant rate through wind and water erosion; salinization of soils in areas with high levels of irrigation has caused significant losses in productivity. Formerly rich, productive soils have become sterile support media, requiring greater and greater inputs of inorganic nutrients, and at least in some regions, productive agricultural land is being irreversibly blanketed with asphalt, concrete, or development tracts.[5]

In short, productivity has leveled and pressures for food will be maintained or increased, with surpluses being a short-term aspect of the normal food and agricultural cycle. All of this means increased food costs. Americans will have to pay a greater portion of their disposable income for food. In ef-

fect, we are going to become more like the rest of the world. If present trends toward larger farms and more corporate farming continue, increasing amounts of food production will be linked to return on investment comparable to other investment alternatives, and this will increase costs to the consumer.[6] (The calculations and need for cash return are very different with family farm ownership structures.[7])

However, these factors are merely symptoms of more basic problems. These problems are rooted in societal values, and in the ways society has interacted with the environment. We have exploited the environment to achieve our present "standard of living," but in the process we have developed social institutions, structures, and values that put us in the Alice-in-Wonderland situation where it takes all the running we can do to stay in the same place. The voting public doesn't want to consider a change in the present standard of living or lifestyle, and so doesn't face the problems. Therefore, the political leadership certainly won't face them. Business leadership has no incentive to face them when profit is the motive and is calculated on a 5- to 20-year basis. The result is a social situation wherein natural resources are depleted at accelerating rates with more and more people demanding increased material wealth, based on a belief in the necessity of increasing GNP and an ever-expanding or growth-oriented economy.[8]

To not question the values that support our present economic concept of growth, and the institutions and structures that operationalize and perpetuate it, will only serve to increase and complicate the difficulty of changing the paradigm upon which we act and build our society. Employing a paradigm that has been exploitive rather than symbiotic and sustainable means that as time passes we may become increasingly vulnerable to having our production systems disrupted. Resource shortages and degradation of our life support system are the two areas in which society has begun to be aware of the need for change. Later, we shall discuss both of these issues in relation to U.S. agriculture, but first let us look at the major resource problem today—the energy issue—within the context of our present discussion.

The United States agricultural system has become an energy sink. An energy sink is a system that has the capacity to "absorb" large energy inputs without these inputs being reflected in greater energy-containing outputs. For example, increasing fossil fuel inputs in corn production are necessary to maintain a constant output in corn yield. For example, it takes more energy to get the same (or proportionately less) energy out.[9] The whole food production and distribution system uses an average of 18 percent of our national energy consumption. To provide one kcal of food energy to the table (this includes packaging and transportation) the system uses 16 to 20 kcals, with only about 4 to 5 kcals of this going for on-farm production uses. Clearly massive amounts of energy are used to transport items from other climates (Mexico and Central America), across the U.S. continent, and in packaging and preparing modern convenience items. Disturbingly, the trends in energy consumption, and the trends in production and marketing, are all moving towards more energy use and more specialization despite the obvious energy problem. From a long-term view it matters little whether fossil fuel energy shortages come in the 1980s or the 2020s. The important matter is that shortages will come and that any changes we introduce that improve our energy efficiency will be helpful in altering the energy sink picture.

It is not a simple matter to change present food system energy use patterns. For example, in on-farm energy use, given the energy-intensive methods and types of production systems we now have, farms producing the same product are not equally energy efficient. Variation occurs because of different management strategies, size of operation, geographic location of the farm, and choice of available technology, to identify only some of the major reasons.

Moreover, it is rarely possible to make general statements about energy efficiency across presently practiced production systems or products. For example, one cannot say categorically that large farms are more energy efficient than small farms (or even the reverse). Some research results show that large egg farms are generally more energy efficient than small ones, but that large dairy farms are generally less energy efficient than small ones.[10] Economy of size in energy utilization must be examined on a product by product basis and specific production strategies must also be taken into account. However, at a certain point, with most present practices and systems, there is an energy plateau—getting larger does not mean greater energy efficiency. Most of modern agriculture has reached this plateau.

Farmers producing agricultural products by specific methods and systems that require a proportionally greater amount of energy for each additional unit of production will find that substantial increases in energy costs limit the possibility of increasing net profit by increasing the size of operation. Those attempting to "stay ahead" by adopting energy intensive strategies and increasing size will find themselves caught in a financial squeeze with rising energy prices and inflation. Increased production will afford little relief in maintaining real net profits, due in part to multiplier effects of direct and indirect energy costs. On the other hand, staying the same size will allow an increase of the present economic pressures which are already placing a severe strain on farmers.

Therefore, the problem is that in order to get off the treadmill, in order to change production techniques, the farmer must take steps that run counter to the present major practices of U.S. agriculture. The farmer must question all energy-intensive strategies, even though the technical support people and social / economic structures tell him to become more energy intensive. In fact, the marketing structure of food is such that the large chains only want to buy in large volume from big suppliers, which builds in more impetus to get bigger, become more capital and energy intensive, and more specialized. This situation exemplifies the value-based conflict which is heightened by an ill-founded ecological paradigm.

A situation has been created in which economic and social structures may soon be unable to function as we would like, due to reliance on patterns of energy use which cannot continue given finite resources. Paradoxically, however, our economic and social structures demand a continuation of present energy use patterns. We have this "Catch-22" situation because the energy crisis is a symptom of the larger problem of our relationship to the natural environment. Until we face the deep-set nature of this problem we will not be able to really improve or correct our present energy-use patterns. Therefore, in solving issues of energy use in agriculture, we must look care-

fully at energy flows and the natural cycles within our life support systems. Because of the energy crisis and the resulting need to partially re-design and re-tool, we have a unique opportunity to depart from increasing dependence on linear systems of food production to more cyclical systems in balance with the natural environmental system. In economic terms, linear systems emphasize "throughput" rather than attempting, as cyclical systems do, to attain production while "recycling" and emphasizing maintenance of "capital stock."

Linear systems, such as a large beef lot, function within a short-term economic view rather than a long-term, sustained-yield ecological view. Our present energy problems merely point directly to the fallacious position of using linear systems as anything more than what they are—short-term solutions for the goal of increased production in single production units. But we should hardly be surprised. *Our food-production systems have become production oriented factories because of the economic values and perspective which drive them. We should merely recognize that our external structures always reflect our internal concepts of life, values, and all our dominant paradigms.*

In order for the farmer to break his energy "habit" he must break with present practices, and this means operating under a different value structure. As with the present situation, this different value structure can also be described or exemplified in agricultural practices and in the concomitant surrounding economic and social structure.

Energy is only one of the resource-related problems that agriculture is faced with. Serious consideration must be given to other problems that may cause increased prices, less availability of food and potentially severe break-downs in our present production system. Included in these are loss of soil fertility due to erosion, salt accumulation and excessive use of chemical fertilizer, herbicides, and heavy equipment use.[11] Increasing pesticide use means increasing costs, and more important, that insects seem to be winning the battle by developing resistance faster than man can develop new pesticides.[12] Human health issues are also raised by our present use of pesticides and chemical food additives. Also, water availability is a serious problem for agriculture. Water in the Western United States is coming under more competing use pressure each year, and mining of water with center pivot systems of irrigation cannot continue for very long. In many locations water tables are dropping and the recharge rate is far below what is being taken out for irrigation. In sum, large monoculture systems do not seem to have long-term ecological stability, even with constant human attention. We may not be able to stay ahead of the present and future problems we are creating. It is our belief that in 10 to 20 years significant decreases in production, with relative increases in food prices for the consumer, could occur. Moreover, there is the real concern for nutritional quality of the food that is produced through this system.[13] That is, loss of nutritional value due to farm practices, transportation, processing, and storage may not be always necessary. There are other ways to design the food system so that it would yield high-nutrition foods.

We cannot develop a healthy and sustainable human ecology without developing a different paradigm and a different system for food production, distribution, and consumption. We believe that the bioregional approach is a major element in this paradigm. This means developing sustainable practices (those that can be carried on for centuries without major ecological damage) of agricultural production that are based in the biological realities of the region. Such production would bring our food system more into line with long-term environmental and resource concerns. It also means bringing production into line with consumption, and bringing perceived needs into line with long-term production resource potential. Implied is the collective determination of "needs" and of allocation of natural and human resources in the production process. Also implied is the necessity for major changes in control of land, production, resource allocation, and therein the relationship of human society to the rest of the natural world. We feel that relative self-sufficiency is the only kind which can be realized in any conceivable future with a culture remotely resembling the one in which we live. Thus, a "movement-in-the-direction-toward" process, or transitional forms is an important aspect. We need not wring our hands because of our dependency; it is much more useful to begin the process of addressing our problems.

To achieve immediate collective action by society on a generally perceived problem too often requires labeling the situation a "crisis." The "crisis" in this sense is not yet upon us, and is in all probability some time away (barring unforeseen climatic disaster or war). In the U.S. and world-wide, all we have seen so far have been slight dislocations. The task of creating a long-term ecologically sound production/consumption system is made more difficult because it requires farsightedness, both on a local level and in our large government bodies. If this vision is lacking, and if history has anything to teach, we will in time be confronted with "crises" that will not go away in the spring.

Given the present technology, what changes in agricultural production and marketing are desirable and possible? What are reasonable expectations for technological change? What are the constraints and supports in the marketplace? How would any or all of the above changes affect the quality of life and of food?

The next section of this paper discusses our attempts to address these questions and issues.

The biological approach: An initial analysis of the food system

The Center for Studies in Food-Sufficiency was established in 1974 to investigate the relationships between energy, food, humans, and the environment. A major issue that was confronted from the outset was the potential to make Vermont self-sufficient in food; that is, to produce locally to meet the consumption needs of the population. While there were numerous opinions to the contrary, little actual data was available. *Land, Bread, and History* was published in 1976 and summarizes the results of our interdisciplinary study. The history of agricultural production in Vermont was carefully studied, a variety of estimates of food consumption by commodities were made, and a computer-mapping technique was developed to examine the physical food-production potential in Vermont.

A basic fallacy that needs to be addressed at the outset is the concept that "things have always been as they are, things will continue to be as they are." From an historical perspective, most of the world, most of the time that

humans have existed as a species, was sustained by food produced or obtained locally. Only in the center of a few great empires in the past, since World War II in the United States and in most of the highly industrialized world, has food production become so aregional and aseasonal. The astounding tales of Roman emperors who had exotic foods brought to them at incredible expense to suit their momentary whim is uncomfortably close to our present food system if all costs (energetic, environmental, social) are included.

What is essential to the development of models for future food systems is the development of a new paradigm. Kuhn, in *The Structure of Scientific Revolutions,* has indicated the necessity and power of shifts in the conceptual framework through which perceptions of the world are organized. The present agricultural system has been evaluated primarily in terms of production (yield) per acre, or production per hour of labor. Also, a very limited and short-term economic analysis has been utilized. It does not adequately incorporate protection of the environment, resources, and future generations. New criteria, analysis, and mechanisms for their operationalization need to be developed. Biodynamic Agriculture, as articulated by Rudolf Steiner in 1924 calls for the simultaneous consideration of three factors: (1) yield of production, (2) inputs to production system, (3) maintenance or enhancement of soil fertility. To this scheme, a fourth element should be added: (4) social impact of the farming system; that is, impact on the farmers themselves and on the social infrastructure of the rural communities of which they are a part. Although the original research was done some time ago, Goldsmith's study of two California towns is the most significant demonstration of the impact of consolidation and agri-business on rural life that has been made to date.[14] In that study, the town with numerous small family farms had a much richer, more diverse, and more stable social infrastructure than the town with large corporate farms. Rural towns may not have changed their population numbers in the last 100 years, but with residents commuting 25 to 150 miles each way to work, and the loss of active farms, and other sources of employment, has come a loss of theatrical societies, church socials, fraternal organizations, and diverse local commerce. Perhaps this graphically illustrates Fukuoka's statement that "the purpose of agriculture is not simply the production of food, but the cultivation and perfection of human beings."

The historical development of U.S. and Vermont agriculture

The food system of the past was different in quality and in organization from the present system. Today's food system, with little local production of food to meet local needs, highly centralized marketing and distribution components with a few large operators didn't just happen. It, like the planning of planned obsolescence, was a logical development of national trends toward increasing centralization in capital, production, and government.[15] Recent USDA figures indicate that 4 percent of farms in the United States with gross annual income of $100,000 or more, produce more than 50 percent of the food and fiber for the nation. While a portion of these are "family farms" and another group are production components of vertically integrated food industries, many are purely investment holdings of banks, insurance companies, and conglomerates. Perpetuation of production of the latter type of holding is strictly related to tax structure and return on investment capital, not a commitment to agriculture as a way of life or a family tradition.

To be sure, from the point at which people began to live in cities (probably directly as a result of the development of agriculture) the city market has determined what crops a farmer could profitably produce. Once agriculture moves from subsistence to market orientation, the countryside is "an economic dependency of the metropolis." As Schlebecker states, ". . . the concentric zones of specialization from the city outward would read: (1) truck gardens, (2) milk and poultry, (3) corn-hogs and cattle feeding, (4) wheat and small grains, (5) grazing, and (6) furs, spices and gold. The several zones would change as transportation improvements were introduced or consumer preference changed." Thus, agricultural history can be seen as more closely correlated with industrialization, urbanization, and change in transportation technology than with limitations of climate, soil, or the regional identity of its population. Certainly, the case has been well made for Vermont. The historical record from diaries and records of 19th century farmers, and from the Census of Agriculture (1840 to present) documents this very clearly.

By way of review, the colonial expansion into Vermont brought clearing and cultivation, first of hill land, followed by cultivation of the river and lake valleys. Subsistent, individually self-sufficient farmsteads initially produced very little surplus for off-farm sale or barter. As urban markets opened up, and transportation methods became available, a shift from self-sufficient farms, to commercial market-oriented production developed. Europe, Boston, and New York served as major markets for Vermont products. Vermont farmers struggled to make choices of commercially viable products in light of general economic trends and competition with Western goods, simultaneously reducing local production of diverse products for local on-farm and regional needs, and imported staple products of feed and food from other agricultural regions. With the closing of the frontier, Vermont's proximity to urban markets in the Northeast gave a comparative advantage for certain Vermont products such as dairy, particularly fluid milk. The production of dairy products was tied directly to fuel, feed, seed, machinery, and other items produced out-of-state, and brought into the state, making Vermont farmers increasingly dependent, not only for markets, but also for the material means of production necessary to continue agricultural productivity.

In general, the statistics follow the information presented in the preceding narrative: general decline in production of meat livestock after 1840–1850; decline in production of grains from 1840–1850, with recovery or, in some cases, peaks during the 1870–1880 period; shift to dairying and rise in hay production following the rise in number of dairy cows; increased silage with shift in dairy feeding practices; shift from maple sugar to maple syrup; decline of sheep numbers and wool production; food production peaks in periods from 1900 to 1920 and in 1940 with declines following; general patterns of decline in agricultural production, consolidation into larger production units, and retreat to the "better" farm land.

History seems to tell us that the reasons for past changes that have the most relevance for us today are eco-nomic rather than physical production limitations of soil and climate. Society, therefore, presumably has control over potential food self-sufficiency even if physical factors mitigate against it.

The Vermont food self-reliance study

We knew that the physical and biological potential to produce a good diet was present in Vermont, but we needed to find out two important additional sets of data. First, what were Vermonters eating. Second, what foods could be grown, where in the state, and in what amounts. Only then would it be possible to find out the upper potential for a more self-sufficient food system while using the general agricultural practices now employed. A change in practices: more solar greenhouses, greenhouses on homes, people growing more of their own food on small plots, and recycling biomass for fuel and animal food, could make self-sufficiency an even greater possibility. However, in this initial analysis we wanted to stay quite close to existing production practices and dietary patterns.

In order to develop plans for production to meet local consumption needs, it is necessary to determine those consumption needs in amounts of each commodity consumed per person per year. We attempted to determine food consumption patterns for the population of Vermont based on an approximation of diet and buying habits. (If people change diets, for example, eat lower on the food chain, this naturally will change the food production needs.) We used data from USDA and directly from the food-marketing sector based on records kept by cooperating housewives (*Food Consumption of Households in the Northeast, Seasons and*

Figure 1
*Addison County Crop
Potential Map*

Corn for Grain

There are a total of 1,458
cells (4,000 × 4,000) in the
county. On 229 of these
cells, corn can be grown.
There are 497,689 acres in
the county. Corn can be
grown on 81,301 of them.

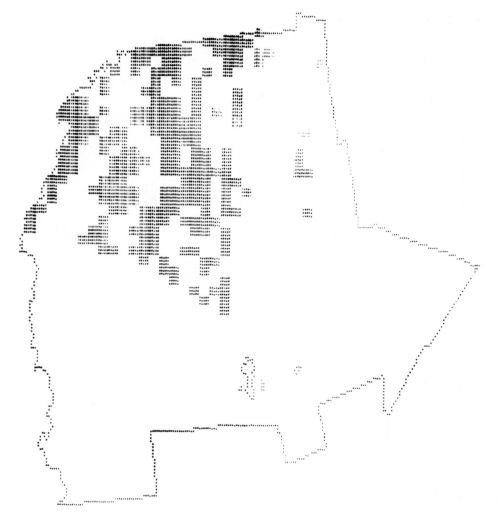

Year 1965–66) and projections based on survey data collected by the Center from supermarket chains and independent grocers in Vermont (1974).

In order to determine estimates on food production we developed a computer-mapping system that generated physical production potential maps for a variety of crops.

A grid system was laid over the area to be studied, and all data related to plant growth and cultivation available for the region was determined for each "cell" in the grid system. This data when fed into the computer gives a base from which determinations of the total area and distribution of areas suitable for cultivation of a given crop can be calculated. Results are obtained by arriving at the *design parameters* for the crop in question (that is the limiting factors for successful cultivation at least at the level of physical possibility for cultivation in terms of appropriate soil types, land use, and climatic variables for the crop) and matching them against the computerized data base. Examples of major design parameters are: type of present land use, slope, shallowness of soil, elevation, annual

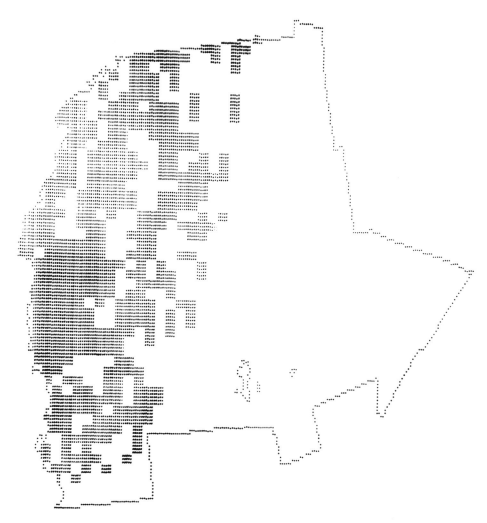

Figure 2
*Addison County Crop
Potential Map*

**Wetland rice with
irrigation**

There are a total of 1,458
cells (4,000 × 4,000) in the
county. On 427 of these
cells, wetland rice can
be grown. There are 497,689
acres in the county.
Wetland rice can be
grown on 151,574 of these
acres.

precipitation, frost-free period, quarterly annual mean temperatures, growing degree day requirements, soil types, growing season rainfall limitations, and drought limitations.

The mapping project was initially envisioned as being concerned with crop production potential for the whole state of Vermont. However, limitations of time and money demanded that a single county be picked for a pilot study to develop the method more precisely. Addison County was chosen because it is currently, and has been since 1840, one of the most agri-

culturally productive counties in the state. Typical maps are shown in Figures 1, 2, and 3.

The Center used the output of crop potential maps as input for a new data base consisting of the summation of crop potential for each cell. Knowing the population of the county, and assuming a particular diet for generating estimates of per capita food consumption patterns by commodity, the annual food requirements for the population can be determined. Total amounts required for staple crops such as corn, wheat, and potatoes can be deter-

Figure 3
Addison County Crop Potential Map

Soybeans

There are a total of 1,458 cells (4,000 × 4,000) in the county. On 80 of these cells, soybeans can be grown. There are 497,689 acres in the county. Soybeans can be grown on 28,613 of these acres.

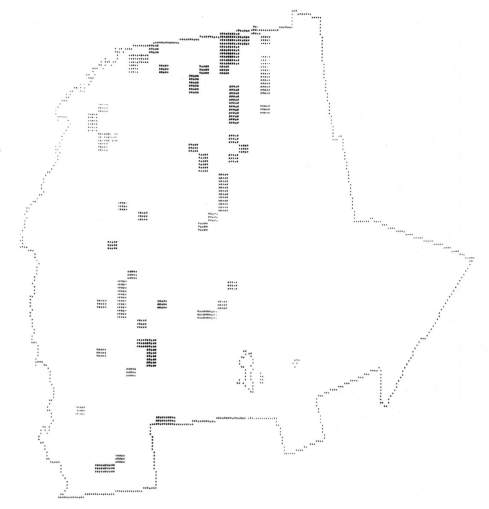

mined, and using estimated productivity per acre, total acreage needed for each crop can be determined. Requisite amounts of meats and dairy products can be expressed in terms of acreage of pasture, feed and forage necessary to produce a pound of finished beef, an egg, or a quart of milk. Table 1 shows a series of equations used by the Center in applying the above method to Addison County.

The diet used was taken from preference and consumption levels for 1974. The diet is essentially the one now eaten by Vermonters. Production figures for each crop were based on average figures taken from USDA and Census data on Addison County. These figures are listed in Table 2. Output relating the diet to land needs with a population of 25,000 is presented in Table 3.

Based on the above diet (vegetables are not included but will be explained later in this paper) and production, the total amount of Class I land needed to support the present population of Addison County is 26,665 acres. The county has approximately 158,213 acres of Class I land.[16] If all available

1 lb.	Beef	= .0013 pasture + .0012 hay + .0002 corn
1 lb.	Veal	= .0010 pasture + .0003 hay + .0015 corn
1 lb.	Lamb	= .0088 grassland
1 lb.	Pork	= .0014 corn
1 lb.	Chicken	= .0012 corn + .0016 soybeans
1 lb.	Turkey	= .0018 corn + .0033 soybeans
1 doz.	Eggs	= .00156 corn + .00216 soybeans
1 lb.	Milk	= .00024 corn + .00049 hay + .00016 pasture
1 lb.	Cheese	= .003 corn + .0006 hay + .002 pasture
1 lb.	Butter	= .0053 corn + .0011 hay + .0036 pasture
1 lb.	Bakery products	= .00078 spring wheat

Table 1
Equations relating food products to crop acreage (all figures in acres)

Hay/acre	4,000 lb.
Corn Silage/acre	27,260 lb.
Corn Grain/acre (with cob)	4,368 lb.
Soybean/acre	696 lb.
Flour/acre (wheat)	1,806 lb.
Potatoes/acre	15,000 lb.

Table 2
Addison county production figures

Class I and Class II land were effectively utilized there would be approximately 18 to 20 percent less land in the county for dairy farming than at present. Nevertheless, taking conservative agricultural production figures, and present market prices for agricultural products, it is highly unlikely that total cash receipts to farmers would decrease under this totally self-sufficient scenario.

Although we did not have a data base of each county on which we could apply the mapping program, in order to arrive at some understanding of the available land in terms of production potential, we calculated the above-mentioned diet for each county with the appropriate 1974 population level and adjusted production levels peculiar to each county. The total amounts of Class I and Class II land needed are listed below in Table 4. Given the present population and present diet, 21.5 percent of Class I and II land is needed to meet the food consumption needs.

It is clear that such a change in production patterns would have an immense impact on the Vermont dairy industry. It would not, however, mean Vermont could no longer export large amounts of milk if that was deemed desirable. Figure 4 shows the acreage that could be utilized in Addison County for fluid milk production. A conservative estimate of the amount of milk that could be produced for export would be 178-million pounds with all the feed for its production produced within the county. This is 65 percent of the approximately 275 million pounds produced in the county in 1974, utilizing large amounts of grain concentrates produced outside of the state. We have just completed a careful analysis of the potential for a "Vermont Home-Grown Vegetarian Diet" which is now in press. This work indicates that perhaps the *best* diet is one which combines grains and vegetables with small amounts of meat or fish. This becomes

Table 3
Land area needed for present diet, population of 25,000

Food	Quantity	Hay	Pasture	Corn	Soy	Other
			Acres Needed of			
Beef	85.23 lb.	2556.90	2683.56	375.19		
Veal	0.99 lb.	7.76	25.20	18.28		
Lamb	5.06 lb.		1084.29			
Pork	19.45 lb.			667.93		
Milk	566.00 lb.	693.35	2251.03	1632.69		
Eggs	33.82 lb.			422.81	1217.89	
Chicken	35.30 lb.			474.22	1144.68	
Turkey	28.04 lb.			609.84	1913.65	
Cheddar	16.13 lb.	164.66	534.59	387.59		
Hard Cheese	16.13 lb.	246.99	801.88	581.61		
Butter	13.47 lb.	366.68	1190.48	863.86		
Bread	135.03 lb.					1252.35
Margarine	14.40 lb.			2113.99		
Potatoes	228.95 lb.					381.58
Totals		4036.30	8571.00	8147.7	4276.20	1633.93

Total acres needed = 26,665.25   Present Class I land = 158,213

a diet in which meat is a condiment, as in oriental diets. Rather than austerity, we can envision a kind of dietary elegant-frugality. The total acreage needed in the state for a pure vegetarian or a lacto-ovo diet is in Table 5 and 6.

Dairy and poultry farming would still provide some meat for consumption. Because the vast majority of the population on the lacto-ovo diet would not eat meat, the amount of land required would be lessened by 44,757 acres (or 9 percent of the land required for the present diet) while in a totally vegetarian diet, the amount of land needed is lessened by 194,940 acres (or 40 percent of the land required for the present diet). It is possible to change types of vegetables or grains in these diets to fit personal preference. How-

ever, the general land area needed would remain about the same.

However, there would be obstacles in attempting to utilize Vermont's land in this manner. What are the costs of putting into good improved condition Class I and II lands, recently fallen into disuse or poor management? What ownership or environmental constraints render some of this land (and in what amounts) unavailable for use? Such optimization of land use would require greatly increased land-use planning at both state and local levels. But, the land resources do exist. Allowing present trends to continue will increase poor land management and will contribute to potentially decreased production totals. What becomes clear is that the root of the question lies not

County	Population	Acres Needed	Class I Land		Class I + Class II Land	
			Acres	% Needed	Acres	% Needed
Addison	25,000	26,665	158,213	16.8%	247,469	10.7%
Bennington	30,000	30,651	32,241	95.0%	69,778	43.9%
Caledonia	23,000	25,890	71,092	36.4%	175,698	14.7%
Chittenden	102,000	99,142	79,737	124.0%	190,278	52.1%
Essex	6,000	6,877	9,280	74.1%	33,532	20.5%
Franklin	32,000	34,931	116,934	29.8%	221,407	15.7%
Grand Isle	4,000	4,203	24,438	17.2%	41,762	10.0%
Lamoille	14,000	16,077	38,166	42.1%	102,846	15.6%
Orange	18,000	19,808	52,041	38.0%	216,675	9.1%
Orleans	21,000	24,052	94,908	25.3%	242,015	9.9%
Rutland	54,000	54,729	54,355	100.6%	183,438	29.8%
Washington	48,000	50,600	78,863	64.2%	158,552	31.9%
Windham	34,000	36,821	25,057	146.9%	135,673	27.1%
Windsor	45,000	48,260	53,033	90.9%	206,400	23.4%
State Totals	456,000	478,706	888,358	53.9%	2,225,523	21.5%

Table 4
Land area needed for present diet

This does not include acres for vegetable production.

Consumption/Person			Acres Needed
Eggs	68.25	lb./yr.	44,866
Milk	748	lb./yr.	110,308
Cheese	108	lb./yr.	132,748
Soy	156	lb./yr.	102,201
Barley	20	lb./yr.	12,701
Oats	20	lb./yr.	7,164
Rye	20	lb./yr.	2,619
Wheat	60	lb./yr.	21,342
Vegetables	190	lb./yr.	11,809
Total			445,758

Table 5
Lacto-ovo diet

only in wise land management but also in recognizing and dealing with its economic and political nature. For example, in an attempt to address economic and political issues, we modified the computer-mapping technique to utilize a cell size of one hectare (2.5 acres). The technique was then used to test a hypothesis concerning conversion of agricultural land. Nationally, it has

Figure 4
Use of Agricultural
Land for County's
Food Needs and for
Milk Export

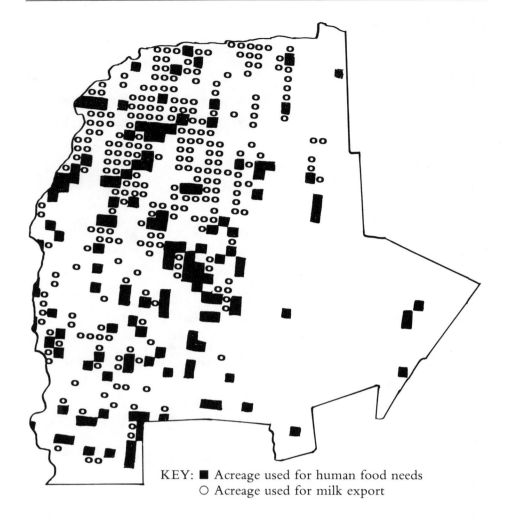

KEY: ■ Acreage used for human food needs
○ Acreage used for milk export

been argued that the land going out of production has been the least productive agricultural land.[17] We examined the town of Middlebury for the period from 1942 to 1974 and tested the hypothesis that a greater proportion of less-productive agricultural land than of prime agricultural land has gone out of production during a given time period.[18] We were unable to demonstrate any significant difference in the percentage of land of any agricultural quality going out of production during the period 1942 to 1974. What we did find, however, was that the land of highest quality was lost to develop-

ment at about twice the rate of lower-quality land. This technique graphically illustrated the economic and political struggle in the town of Middlebury between development interests and agriculture.

Perhaps significantly, after the publication of this study, the first development in the state was denied a land-use permit because it was utilizing high-quality agricultural land. The newly appointed Commissioner of Agriculture for the State of Vermont, William Darrow, has noted that the "selling of Vermont" runs counter to the interests of Vermont farmers.

Consumption/Person			Acres Needed
Soy	156	lb./yr.	102,202
Barley	58.5	lb./yr.	37,151
Oats	58.5	lb./yr.	20,954
Rye	58.5	lb./yr.	10,585
Wheat	58.5	lb./yr.	20,808
Apples	208	lb./yr.	5,511
Strawberry	208	lb./yr.	7,901
Broccoli	65	lb./yr.	5,880
Cauliflower	65	lb./yr.	1,906
Spinach	65	lb./yr.	47,424
Lettuce	65	lb./yr.	23,505
Carrots	65	lb./yr.	1,096
Potatoes	65	lb./yr.	1,956
Squash	65	lb./yr.	1,644
Tomatoes	65	lb./yr.	3,526
Total			295,575

Table 6
Vegetarian diet

Appropriate technology and regional food self-reliance

We at the Center see one primary task at present: to continue to be involved with research on aspects of appropriate technology related to regional self-sufficiency. This work is particularly critical when it has the potential to impact on the viability of transitional options. More precisely, we need to assist local farmers / producers, and local consumers to be able to negotiate a relationship which allows both to exist in a competitive short-term economic marketplace that supports both, and in a better way than the present system. An appropriate technology is one that is locally appropriate; that is, it is suited to the solution of a locally-perceived problem. Appropriate technology emphasizes: (1) Labor intensiveness, where possible, over capital and machinery; (2) Comparatively light capital costs; (3) Technologies that can be understood, used, and maintained locally; (4) Technologies compatible with local social conditions; (5) Optimum use of locally-available and renewable resources.

Daniel Bell puts forth a categorization of technology that is helpful in clarifying any approach to technology.[19] This categorization also provides a means of organizing information about how comprehensively technology affects our lives. Bell identifies machine technologies, intellectual technologies, and social technologies. Machine technologies are the physical tools and hardware, big and small, simple and complex, that we create. Intellectual technologies are those theories, models, and techniques by which we analyze and give meaning to complex phenomena of the world around us.

	Machine Technologies **A**	Intellectual Technologies **B**	Social Technologies **C**
Fertilizer 1	1. A methane system for dairy farms with a liquid-pipeline handling of manure. 2. Nitrogen-fixing crops. 3. Improved composting machines	The paradigm from Bio-Dynamic agriculture contained in the concept of balance between yield, nutrient inputs, and maintenance or enhancement of soil fertility.	Development of institutional arrangements and reward system to make possible separation of municipal household wastes, composting, and then returning it to the land.
Feed 2	Development of local and appropriate farm machinery for more economical and energy-efficient production of local feeds.	Development of a use theory of value for feeding systems.	The use of educational programs and advertising to make people aware of the nutritional value and energy savings of range-fed animals.
Tillage 3	1. Inter-cropping 2. Minimum tillage 3. More energy-efficient machinery design	Practices generated by the ecosystem concept of agriculture.	An energy-credit cooperative organized for methanol production
Transportation 4	Use of solar greenhouses to extend the local growing season and reduce regionally imported food.	Development of an economic paradigm which favors local production to meet local needs.	1. (Public Policy) Changes in transport regulations. 2. (Business) Changes in marketing patterns of chain-food stores. 3. Organization of community-storage facilities

Table 7

Examples of appropriate technologies in agriculture which could positively impact on energy use

Social technologies are organizations, institutions, and other formalized decision-making entities that allow us to manipulate and improve our social and economic life. Agricultural technologies (those that can be used to improve agriculture) are to be found in each of these categories. As a design- and problem-solving perspective, as well as specific hardware, appropriate technology cuts across all of these categories.

Table 7 shows appropriate technology solutions to energy-use issues and problems in agriculture.[20] This matrix provides a conceptual tool for organizing typical appropriate technology approaches and for indicating how the appropriate technology perspective can be used in all major areas of agricultural energy usage. Examples of appropriate technologies that have existed for some time could be placed in each box of the matrix to give an indication of present possibilities. Or, some of the most promising future technologies could be used to show the research and demonstration direction that the appropriate technology perspective can provide.

Most technologies affect energy use in several boxes in the matrix, that is, solar greenhouses affect tillage and fertilizer energy-use practices as well as exemplifying a strategy by which it would be possible to increase local production and thereby reduce transportation of food produced far away from the point of consumption. A technology may produce energy savings (or increases) in areas other than in the place categorized. However, the overall effect and goal should always be one of reduced non-renewable energy use and net energy-gain.

The matrix indicates that the appropriate technology perspective offers a holistic and comprehensive problem-solving and design approach to agricultural technology in its broadest sense.

Fertilizer, feed, tillage, and transportation are the four major energy-use areas in agricultural systems. Any technological approach that is to have a major impact on energy problems must be capable of providing economically, socially, and environmentally acceptable solutions in these major areas. In fact, for most types of animal production in the Northeast, such as dairy or poultry, feed and fertilizer represent the vast majority of energy input. For farms raising food crops, fertilizer and field operations represent the majority of energy input.

While these energy technologies may affect net income of farmers to some extent, their primary function is to help small local producers reduce dependency on fossil fuels and petrochemicals, which may undergo acute shortages in the near future.

Appropriate technology solutions for other aspects of the local production to meet local needs issues are presently being sought by researchers at the Center. One recent study by the Center examines farmers' markets in Vermont and their capacity to provide a decent return to producers, and at the same time, provide quality products at an affordable price.[20] Another study, the previously mentioned *Vermont Vegetarian Diet,* focusses on the proposition that it is possible to produce a healthy vegetarian diet in Vermont. This work, utilizing sound dietary standards, computer techniques, and good sense, builds necessary production around a complete and healthy vegetarian diet.

In the short five years of the Center's existence, it has been possible to begin to show that needed research on relevant agricultural issues can be done by a group with little funding support, and no elaborate research establishment. There was a time a century or more ago when the most sophisticated agricultural research was done, not in the University by scholars, but on the farm, by the farmers, with the results of experiments communicated through the journals of agricultural societies. Appropriate research may come out of the educational institutional research establishment, but we believe that much needed work in this decade, and in the next, will come from the efforts of other non-traditional groups such as ours.

Summary

It is hard to evaluate the impact of our work, separable from the milieu in which it has arisen. However, there has been a growing interest in Vermont and the Northeast on questions of food production and the future of agriculture. Politicians and the public media have begun to use our materials. We are contributing to a growing consciousness of our dependence on out-of-region sources of food, and that physical potential is less important in determining what is produced agriculturally than the larger (national / international) economic arena. We have helped similar research centers, and have supplied specific data to individuals, groups, and agencies, which heretofore had not been assembled. Perhaps, more significantly, we have, with several other groups in the region, made it demonstrably clear that the schools of agriculture, and extension services, no longer have a monopoly on valid agricultural research. We have helped to raise questions about why these institutions supported by state and national tax revenue do not work in a more effective manner toward meeting peoples' needs.

Clearly, there are contradictions in our work. The community with which we work most directly is not "the people" themselves, but elected and appointed officials, state and town planners, agricultural-extension agents, soil conservationists, college professors, and some farmers. Also, dealing with perceived needs as direction for future changes and developments is somewhat short-sighted, so we must simultaneously work on both short-term problems as well as longer-range alternative solutions. For example, on a global level, population pressures and need for foreign exchange by third-world nations prevent many areas from immediately developing strongly regionalized food systems. Only a look at the long-term spectrum and resolution of the concomitant social issues of population control will allow for desirable solutions.

Certain social and economic limits influence which solutions can be implemented in the context of contemporary America. For example, the strongly held social values discussed early in this paper, along with the strong momentum of our economic institutions and their reliance on the market-price mechanism to make our decisions for us, are all very large barriers to developing more regional systems. Also, countering big-business power, handling coordination of national social programs, and national defense, are all some of the main forces that support maintenance of a strong federal gov-

ernment. However, the previously mentioned pressures will probably cause contemporary America to change as rapidly in the future as it has in the past. Hopefully, interplay of these limits and pressures will create a new set of system dynamics that will allow for implementation of solutions, now almost impossible. Such new dynamics could allow for increased local diversity and potentially a more healthy situation economically, culturally, and ecologically. Food is obviously a key ingredient for human existence. Any decentralist vision is incomplete without considering food production / consumption within its perspective.

In order for such changes to occur, people will have to perceive the pressures as indicating that major structural adaptions must be made. Values and thereby economic and political institutions will have to change, along with the necessary legislation, public policy, and social adaptation. However, strong political pressure and public consciousness-raising will be needed to bring about the necessary system changes. This is not a chicken-and-egg situation —people will have to take the personal responsibility to change themselves (perhaps under extreme duress) by changing their values and actions.

Diversity need not be entropic. Decentralization in the latter 20th century could place the ideals of Jeffersonian Democracy in a modern workable context. Local political and social activity can be as important as national activity, and may in reality be more effective. As De Tocqueville noted, local government has been the school of democracy. There is nothing in the American tradition or our basic concepts of democracy that prevents a movement towards decentralizing some major aspects of our political / economic system.

In fact, to the contrary; we need only redefine efficiency. Perhaps, with new ecological awareness, we will come to develop ways to calculate efficiency beyond a monetary basis, by taking into account long-term resource availability and use patterns, social costs, and the relative value of a product or service to society. This awareness will also aid us to understand what cannot be centralized without creating disequilibrium and systems unresponsive (or, responding inappropriately) to environmental information in its broadest context. This would be a major change from what has happened previously in the course of human history.

It is difficult to imagine how a highly centralized, conglomerate agriculture could co-exist with highly decentralized, libertarian, political-process or social-institutional structures. This does not mean that at the federal level there might not be very centralized functions, but that these functions (powers) would make sense within the new ecological-value paradigm and concomitant social/economic values.

Therefore, if we desire a self-determining, participatory culture, then we must create participatory processes in not only the political arena, but also in our economic and social life as well. Production and consumption of material items will have to be based on long-term ecological constructs and reflect to some extent these participatory and libertarian values. Otherwise, we will perpetuate negative-conflict situations (as opposed to dialectics which result in positive development) with the environment and between people. Therefore, bioregional strategies must avoid (and should not be seen as) parochialism. The purpose of decentralist and bioregional strategies should be to create more symbiotic situations and less isolationist conflict-producing situations and structures. Diversity does not have to mean parochialism. In fact, we believe the present system has more potential for regional isolationism and a me-first mentality than an ecologically value-based bioregional system would possess.

How can a state or region develop an economic base not totally dependent on the national, and international market economies? Can the concept of "real income," that is, the ability to have an adequate amount of decent food, heat, housing, clothing, health care, meaningful work, and time for recreative play, be incorporated into economic development of a state or region? Can a research facility which is to meet the needs of people in a community be supported by subscription or a tax from the community it serves? Can such community-based research be locally appropriate—bioregional—and still be transferable to similarly scaled decentralized units in other geographical areas?

These are all questions which we feel compelled to address. To us at this point, as when the Center was founded, these questions form a background against which specific research takes place. Without an awareness of context, and sense of community, our work would be much less meaningful.

References

1. Natural biotic regions exist due to the complex interaction of topography, climate, soils, and other factors. Because of the varying physical characteristics of these bioregions, distinct plant and animal associations have evolved. These differences mean that both the bioregion's carrying capacity for hu-

mans and the ecologically sound ways in which humans can interact or use the bioregion's resources vary greatly. Bioregions transcend state and national political boundaries, and traditionally have had profound effects on human culture, trade, and source of livelihood. While the notion has been used in relation to plant and animal associations for nearly half a century, the concept was first used in relation to human populations by Raymond Dasmann in the 1950s. See Raymond Dasmann, *Environmental Conservation*, (New York: John Wiley & Sons, 1959).

2. Lester R. Brown, *The Worldwide Loss of Cropland*, Worldwatch Paper 24, (Washington, D.C.: Worldwatch Institute, October 1978).

3. See David Pimental, E. Hurd, A. C. Bellotti, M. J. Forster, I. N. Oka, O. D. Sholes, R. J. Whitman, "Food Production and the Energy Crises," *Science*, 182, 1973, pp. 443–449. See also David Pimental, et al., "Energy and Land Constraints in Food Protein Production": *Science*, 21 November 1975, pp. 754–761.

4. For an excellent in-depth examination of the international ramifications of U.S. food policy, see Frances Moore Lappe and Joseph Collins, *Food First: Beyond the Myth of Scarcity*, (Boston: Houghton Mifflin Co., 1977). See also, Keith Griffin, *The Political Economy of Agrarian Change* (Cambridge: Harvard Univ. Press, 1974).

5. See, for example, Deborah Barlow, George Burrill, and James Nolfi, *A Research Report on Developing a Community Level Natural Resource Inventory System*, (Burlington, Vt.: Center for Studies in Food Self-Sufficiency, 1976).

6. See Robert W. Kastenmeier of Wisconsin in the House of Representatives, January 18, 1977, and the Report by the U.S. General Accounting Office, *Changing Character and Structure of American Agriculture: An Overview*, (Washington, D.C.: Government Accounting Office, 1979).

7. Phillip M. Raup, "Some Questions of Value and Scale in American Agriculture": *American Journal of Agricultural Economics*, May 1978, pp. 303–308.

8. See Herman Daly, ed., *Toward a Steady-State Economy*, (San Francisco: W. H. Freeman & Co., 1973). See also Hazel Henderson, *Creating Alternative Futures: The End of Economics*, (New York: Berkley Publishing Corp., 1978).

9. Pimental, et al., "Food Production and the Energy Crisis."

10. George Burrill and James Nolfi, et al., Energy Utilization in Vermont Agriculture, Parts I and II, (Washington, D.C.: National Technical Information Service, U.S. Department of Commerce, 1976). See also, George Burrill and James Nolfi, *Land, Bread, and History: A Research Report on the Potential for Food Self-Sufficiency in Vermont*, (Burlington, Vt.: Center for Studies in Food Self-Sufficiency, 1976).

11. Vernon Carter and Tom Dale, *Topsoil and Civilization* (Norman, Okla.: Univ. of Oklahoma Press, 1974). See also Eric Eckholm, *Losing Ground: Environmental Stress and World Food Production*, (New York: W. W. Norton & Co., 1976).

12. Robert Van den Bosch, "The Pesticide Problem," *Environment*, 21, no. 4 (May 1979).

13. R. H. Hall, *Food for Naught: The Decline in Nutrition*, (New York: Random House, 1974).

14. W. Goldsmith, *As You Sow*, (Montclair, N.J.: Allanheld, Osmun & Co., 1978).

15. Harvey Salgo, "The Obsolescence of Growth: Capitalism and the Environmental Crisis," *Review of Radical Political Economics*, Fall, 1973.

16. For a description of land classes, see James G. Sykes, *Vermont Land Classes,* (Burlington, Vt.: Univ. of Vermont, 1964).

17. See O. Krause and D. Hair, "Trends in Land Use and Competition to Produce Food and Fiber" in *Perspectives on Prime Land, Background Papers for Seminar on the Retention of Prime Lands,* USDA, Washington, D.C., 1975. See also, M. L. Cotner, *Land Use Policy in Agriculture: A National Perspective,* USDA, Washington, D.C., 1977.

18. Barlow, Burrill, and Nolfi, *Developing a Community Level Natural Resource Inventory System.*

19. Daniel Bell, *The Coming of the Post-Industrial Society,* (New York: Basic Books, 1976).

20. George Burrill, "An Appropriate Technology Approach to Energy Use in Agriculture," paper presented at Northeast Agricultural Leadership Assembly, March 20–22, 1979, (Washington, D.C.: National Science Foundation, 1979).

Selected Bibliography

BARKLEY, PAUL W., "Some Nonfarm Effects of Changes in Agricultural Technology," *American Journal of Agricultural Economics,* May 1978, pp. 309–315.

BARNES, PETER, *The People's Land* (Emmaus, Pa.: Rodale Press, 1975).

BELDEN, JOE and GREGG FORTE, *Toward a National Food Policy* (Washington, D.C.: Exploratory Project for Economic Alternatives, 1976).

BERRY, WENDELL, *The Unsettling of America: Culture & Agriculture* (San Francisco: Sierra Club Books, 1977).

BRAITERMAN, MARTA, JULIUS GY, FABOS, and JOHN H. FOSTER, "Energy Saving Landscapes," *Environment,* July/August 1978, pp. 30–41.

BROWN, LESTER R., *By Bread Alone* (New York: Praeger, 1974).

BROWN, LESTER R., *The Global Economic Prospect: New Sources of Economic Stress,* Worldwatch Paper 20 (Washington, D.C.: Worldwide Institute, May 1978).

BURRILL, GEORGE, *An Evaluation of the Aquaculture Extension Project at Goddard College* (Burlington, Vt.: Center for Studies in Food Self-Sufficiency, 1978).

COMMONER, BARRY, *The Closing Circle: Nature, Man, and Technology* (New York: Alfred A. Knopf, 1971).

EPSTEIN, S. S. and R. D. GRUNDY, "Consumer Health and Product Hazards of Cosmetics and Drug, Pesticides, Food Additives," *The Legislation of Product Safety* 2 (Cambridge: M.I.T., 1974).

FLINT, MARY LOUISE and ROBERT VAN DEN BOSCH, *A Source Book on Integrated Pest Management* (Washington, D.C.: Office of Environmental Education, Department of Health, Education, and Welfare, May 1977).

FRITSCH, A. J., L. W. DUFACK, and D. A. JIMERSON, "Energy and Food: Energy Used in Production, Processing, Delivery and Marketing of Selected Food Items," *C.S.P.I. Energy Series VI* (Washington, D.C.: Center for Science in the Public Interest, 1975).

FUKUOKA, M., *The One-Straw Revolution* (Emmaus, Pa.: Rodale Press, 1978).

GARDNER, B. DELWORTH and RULON D. POPE, "How is Scale and Structure Determined in Agriculture?" *American Journal of Agricultural Economics* (May 1978) pp. 295–302.

HIGHTOWER, JIM, *Eat Your Heart Out:*

How Food Profiteers Victimize the Consumer (New York: Crown, 1975).

HIRST, E., *Energy for Food: From Farm to Home* Trans. A.S.A.E. 17, no. 2 (1974).

JACOBSON, M. and C. LERZA, *Food for People Not for Profit* (Washington, D.C.: Center for Science in the Public Interest, 1975).

KUHN, THOMAS, *The Structure of Scientific Revolutions* (Chicago: Univ. of Chicago Press, 1972).

LAPPE, FRANCES MOORE, *Diet for a Small Planet* (New York: Ballantine Books 1971).

MAHR, RUTH M., *Appropriate Technology in Agriculture in the Northeast: The Impact on Labor* (Ithaca, N.Y.: Cornell Univ., Program on Regional and City Planning, 1979).

MERRILL, RICHARD, *Radical Agriculture* (New York: Harper & Row, 1976).

MOLES, JERRY A., "Discussion," *American Journal of Agricultural Economics* May 1978, pp. 316–321.

PIMENTAL, DAVID, DONALD NAFUS, WALTER VERGARA, DAN PAPAJ, LINDA JACONETTA et al., "Biological Solar Energy Conversion and U.S. Energy Policy," *Bioscience* 28, no. 6, (June 1978): 376–381.

SCHLEBECKER, J. T., *The Use of the Land,* (Lawrence, Kan.: Coronado Press, 1973).

SMITH, ELIZABETH B., "A Guide to Good Eating the Vegetarian Way," *Journal of Nutrition Education,* July/September 1975.

STEINER, RUDOLF, *Agriculture* (London: Biodynamic Agriculture Association, 1974).

STEINHART, J. S. and C. E. STEINHART, "Energy in the U.S. Food System," *Science* 184, (1974): 307–316.

STOKES, BRUCE, *Local Responses to Global Problems: A Key to Meeting Basic Human Needs,* Worldwatch Paper 17 (Washington, D.C.: Worldwide Institute, February, 1978).

USDA, *Monoculture in Agriculture: Extent, Causes, and Problems,* Report of the Task Force on Spatial Homogeneity in Agricultural Landscapes and Enterprises (October 1973).

WELLFORD, HARRISON, *Sowing the Wind* (New York: Grossman, 1972).

18 | Agricultural Landscapes: *Strategies Toward Permanence**

Earle A. Barnhart

The nature of the problem

IT IS BECOMING CLEAR that America's agricultural production cannot be sustained at present rates of erosion and under gradually increasing energy costs. Studies by the General Accounting Office, state agricultural colleges and private resource analysts indicate that modern farming practices result in erosion rates higher than at any time in our history.[1,2] Approximately one third of the topsoil originally present on our land has already been lost. It is estimated that topsoil losses and salt build-up on irrigated land are beginning to reduce the capacity of the soil to produce food, even assuming conventional levels of fertilizers and equipment. Soil degradation of that degree should be reason for alarm. In the long history of human societies which exploited their original land resources to build their civilizations, most of them ultimately suffered severe environmental degradation from deforestation, erosion, over-grazing

and faulty irrigation practices.[3] Eric Eckholm in *Losing Ground* chronicles the population declines and agricultural difficulties in some of those depleted regions today. Many have suffered partial desertification, irreversible salting of the soil, loss of soil and plant cover from hillsides, and recurring cycles of floods and droughts.

It is somewhat surprising that we humans would consistently exploit new territories to the point of ruin, but it is even more surprising that we can disturb them to the degree we do. While most populations of plants and animals necessarily use the food and space around them to grow and reproduce, they are gradually restricted from exponential increase by various disease, behavior, and competition constraints. Humans are uniquely successful in bypassing most of these constraints. One important reason is our extreme maleability to diverse habitats and food sources. Another is our capacity to manipulate energy. By using only a small amount of physical strength we can skillfully direct other energy in the environment to benefit us. Tools, to be sure, are an aid to accuracy and finesse, but the advantage that typifies human

Our losses from a technology never lie on the same dimension as our gains. We see the gains because they're new, but they blind us to the slipping away of other things that may be of greater importance yet which never get measured in the balance.

Tom Bender
Rain *May 1977*

475

dominion derives from manipulating energies other than our own. Fire, draft animals, water power, wind, fuels or nuclear heat are all directed by us to alter our ecosystems.

Humans lived as hunter-gatherers for millions of years using only hand tools, producing only minor eddies in the flows of the biosphere and leaving few traces. But when fire was put to chasing game and clearing fields, oxen used to carry and plow, and water or wind turned to grinding and pounding, then agriculture as we think of it became a major force on the face of the earth. Manipulating available energy to derive resources from an ecosystem is not inherently bad, but doing so without regard to some fundamental dynamics of how ecosystems work leads to disaster. Unfortunately much agriculture has been based on short-term planning and a narrow linear conception of our role in nature. The price has often been gradual land degradation that limits future generations and gradual migration to other regions. In far fewer societies have people understood living ecosystems well enough to adopt agricultural techniques which are permanently sustainable.

Living systems, whether plants, animals or ecosystems, have slowly evolved ways to sustain themselves by intercepting, storing, and degrading energy. The energy is used to grow and maintain structure and to develop protection from extremes of weather and climate. In an ecosystem, each year's solar energy is absorbed by the plant community and secondarily maintains the animal food chains which live from the plants. In the annual growth and reproduction of the system, materials such as minerals and water are conserved and recycled within the community. Some living communities such as forest, meadow,

or pond have developed over centuries, accumulating a rich storehouse of organized nutrients and building a strong resilience against forces of wind and rain. Eugene Odum in *Fundamentals of Ecology* believes that to be successfully self-protecting, a terrestrial community needs to invest about half its annual growth in processes of protective structure and nutrient cycling.[4] This means that branches, roots, and fallen leaves are important structurally to protect the soil against wind and water. Organic detritus and humus below ground physically absorb and hold water, decomposing slowly to recycle minerals and energy to soil microorganisms and plant roots.

The accumulated fertility and structural diversity of an undisturbed ecosystem is somewhat analogous to capital investment—the land needs its capital to effectively intercept as much solar energy as possible and use it for basic maintenance and some annual growth. An exploitive harvest such as clear-cutting, over-grazing, or total-crop removal takes away more than the land's annual growth and in fact reduces the communities' capacity to intercept energy and hold nutrients for the future. Symptoms of exploitation include erosion of surface soil, leaching of minerals into the water table, rapid disappearance of soil organic matter and a reduction of animal diversity.

Hunters and gatherers harvest by periodically collecting useful food and materials which have accumulated in the ecosystem over time, and then move away while the system recovers by rebuilding its supplies. The yields at harvest can be large but not detrimental if the total growth / harvest cycle is long. Some harvest cycles by herdsmen in Africa or by swiddening cultures in the tropical forests are measured in years. More common is annual harvest by hunting and seasonal grazing. By moving through a landscape and skimming off stored food, the energy efficiency, that is, the amount of energy expended in the collected food compared to the energy expended in work is often very high for hunter-gatherers. Consequently the fraction of their time spent on food production is small.

Agriculturalists, rather than collecting what food occurs naturally, instead try to annually transform some of the nutrients of an ecosystem into domestic plants or animals of their choice. Farmers typically must first disrupt the existing plant / micro-organism associations of the soil by cultivation or burning to release minerals for their crops. Ranchers protect domestic grazers from predation and competition while allowing them to eat local plants into useful meat. Farming and ranching both replace some of the original biota with fewer domestic species and unintentionally lose many of the recycling and self-regulating functions needed by the land. Sustained agricultural yield is then only possible if the displaced self-regulating functions are successfully performed by the farmer, either manually or with help from machines and outside energy. Energy invested wisely in the affairs of the ecosystem is repaid with food and in sustainability of yield.

A far-sighted farmer (or society) should spend time and effort on both production activities that linearly transform nutrients into food and on protection activities that maintain a high reservoir of nutrients cycling in the system. Production activities include the work of releasing nutrients from the soil community (cultivation, burning, mowing); performing the reproductive activities of the food plant (seed collection/storage/planting, plant breeding); and eliminating competition

(herbicides, weeding, pest control). Protection activities include work of holding the topsoil in place (terracing, cover cropping, mulching, windbreaks) and accumulation or recycling of nutrients and energy (fertilization from other ecosystems, crop rotation, irrigation, and growing of nitrogen-fixing plants). Typically, farmers spend more effort on activities leading to direct and rapid yield than on soil maintenance, and often agriculture is defined to consist of the production practices alone. In the short term, "mining the soil" by investing only in production and ignoring conservation is highly profitable. But in the long run the land's capacity to produce is gradually diminished and more and more energy must be invested to get the same yield. Odum speculates that as industrial agriculture tries to get greater and greater yields from land the energy required to do so seems to increase exponentially. In straining for maximum yield the modern farmer tries to stabilize more and more of nature's variables and also to compensate for past soil deterioration and lost nutrients.

Human labor or fossil fuel energy can be applied to agriculture with either finesse or recklessness; the amount of work expended to get food in return is less with increased skill of application. Some of the most energy-efficient farmers in the world are Asian peasant farmers who use no fossil fuel at all and get very high yields per acre.[5] Their success is due to manually tending crops with an awareness of micro-climate and soil and tailoring each task to subtleties of season, weather, and ecological side effects. Energy-intensive industrial farmers attempt to get the same yields by performing the same tasks, but use "clumsy inventions," machines which roll over large areas with mindless ignorance of subtle variation. Machine work and chemical control normally lack the versatility to respond to micro-climates and often accidentally create undesired effects as well as desired ones. The principle is analogous to Amory Lovins' phrase "using a chainsaw to cut butter"; in addition to the cut butter one also gets exhaust fumes, piercing noise, vibration, and butter on the walls. Similar side effects of industrial agricultural machinery and chemicals are: (1) large machines physically compact the soil, reducing water absorption and destroying soil habitats; (2) bare plowed soil exposes the soil to rains, summer drying and oxidation; (3) biocides are mobile in the biosphere and cause damage at other times and other places than where intended; (4) soluble fertilizers are usually applied annually in quantities larger than the crop can completely absorb, resulting in runoff of soluble nutrients which concentrate in the ground water table or in streams and rivers; (5) almost all plant and animal habitats in the vicinity of the crop are disrupted, including beneficial species such as earthworms, predatory and parasitic insects, and beneficial birds.

Another energy perspective is that a barrel of oil has in it the equivalent of about 1,000 days of human manual labor. So when a USA corn farmer uses five barrels of oil per hectare in his production activities, the overall process has some of the entropic qualities of 30 people tramping, digging, eradicating plants and animals, and single-mindedly tending the corn on that hectare every day for the entire season. Small wonder the corn grows well and the soil looks abused.

The working hypothesis which can be drawn from interactions of ecosystems, energy, and agriculture is that while an undisturbed ecosystem tends to accumulate, conserve, and protect its resources, we as humans can harvest from it only to its recuperative limits without degrading its productivity. By investing energy in ways that reinforce its own maintenance processes we can remove a larger harvest. Furthermore, the agricultural return on investment of work depends upon the skill and knowledge with which it is applied; some ecological functions are more amenable to fossil fuel subsidy than others and ecological wisdom and insight will reduce the energy needed to obtain a given yield.

The nature of the solution

As we and the biosphere begin to pay for some of humanity's past gains, a slow awareness is developing that everything is connected and that the trend toward absolute human dominion must be tempered with humility for the unexpected complexity of nature. Some of the biosphere's larger interconnections only begin to appear "in the long run," such as slow but constant soil erosion or effects of carcinogens in our food chains. The changes may be subtle over the lifetime of any individual, but the cumulative effects eventually are undeniable as well as irreversible. Long-term effects of nuclear technology and abuse of toxic wastes will similarly be subtle but cumulative and will be bourne most directly by people who follow us: our children, our grandchildren and all future generations.

Humanity is at a unique point in history, having at its disposal the greatest amount of historical and scientific information ever before available. In that body of information are clear examples of historical mistakes that should not be repeated. Today satellites can chart on-going examples of atmospheric pollution, river contamination, erosion, silting, flooding, and regional vegetation damage inflicted by one community upon another from a distance. In light of such obvious time-delayed and remote damages resulting from conventional agriculture and industrial activities we are compelled to look for alternative patterns of living which minimize costs imposed upon others, for these effects will ultimately be returned to us. Development of life-support strategies which are sustainable and environmentally benign is the only way of reducing the probability of future famine, disease and war. The most pertinent design criteria for the task are those by which organisms and ecosystems live and successfully maintain themselves and their environment. Some of nature's fundamental adaptive principles of design include: (1) the capacity to absorb and use pulses of energy; (2) accumulation, conservation, and recycling of materials; (3) multiple functions performed by each component; (4) development of storage mechanisms as a source of resilience to seasonal and annual weather and energy pulses; (5) bioregional differences in structure and function to match the variation of latitude, altitude, and climate.

Many of society's activities are obviously antithetical to the way living systems operate. Voluntary restraint in deference to future needs has never been an important part of the American land ethic. Early American settlement always assumed further room for expansion or migration if production levels dropped. More recently, modern agribusiness has defined agricultural success as maximum profit per acre based on annual planning in which the major controlling factors are external costs and prices. The economic context of farming includes financed debt for land and equipment and a government which is pursuing deficit spending.

Within such an infrastructure, conservation efforts by a farmer result in bankruptcy rather than security. High profits and yields are a hollow achievement if the land is destroyed in the process.

Raymond Dasmann has suggested that the Earth's remaining fossil fuel be committed to facilitate a transition to a sustainable society. The fossil fuel would be consciously invested in the development of renewable sources of energy and recycling processes for materials. Applied ecology in this case is identical with good long-term economics. Preserving the fertility of land and maintaining its capacity to produce is a kind of cultural insurance. A distinction must be made between a commitment to invest energy in strategies of permanence and a commitment to obtain more energy. Energy of any form can as easily subsidize exploitation as preservation. For example, conventional agribusiness uses unprecedented amounts of energy yet produces unprecedented amounts of erosion. Studies of agricultural land use show that high production and good stewardship depends largely on ecological skill rather than on great energy subsidy. Transition to a post-petroleum society requires intensive education and local planning in addition to the development of structures and hardware. Our representatives in Congress, who are theoretically responsible to oversee the nation's resources and promote the general welfare, have shown little foresight in land-use planning since the Dustbowl crisis many decades ago. Even now, balance-of-trade programs highlight food exports which actively degrade our soil at record rates. The challenge at hand requires concerted action at all levels of society if the transition is to be successfully made.

Ecologically-derived agriculture implies a new synthesis of technology and biology which carefully considers the qualities and advantages of each. Technological hardware is seductive in its property of simplifying or speeding up one particular process while carrying hidden social costs in its manufacture, use, maintenance, and disposal. In many cases biological processes can perform similar services (albeit sometimes more slowly) but with more favorable overall side effects. For instance, prior to pesticides farmers were often aware that populations of certain birds were beneficial around orchards and would contribute to insect pest control. Accordingly they would maintain nesting trees and other necessary habitat in the landscape to nurture them. The costs included the space committed to the nesting trees and a willingness to accept less than absolute control over insects, but the benefits included freedom from toxic chemicals, no spraying schedule or machinery costs, and selective destruction of only certain insects. The aesthetic value of watching the birds and the trees is a matter of personal taste. Similarly around many European gardens were planted herb plots and various hedge plants which provided protective habitat for parasitic and predatory insects, beneficial birds, and resident toads.

Crop rotation is a biological substitute for the manufacture and distribution of nitrogen fertilizer. It also reduces the power requirements for cultivating soils which have little organic matter and poor structure.

Single-product farms of today, which separate grain crops and hayfields from the livestock that consume them, require transportation technology and energy subsidy to move both feed and livestock wastes. When the livestock and crops are grown far from consumers, more transportation is needed to get the food to its place of consumption. Before abundant fossil fuels, farms of mixed crops and animals were managed as an integral unit. Livestock were moved through pasture and fields, creating very short food and waste loops and minimizing transport of materials.

Once during a discussion of these ideas a Vermont farmer noted, "You know, people are biological solutions, too." We humans have a unique capacity to carry out a wide range of ecological functions which in nature are usually divided among specialized organisms. The most remarkable example is peasant farmers in heavily populated parts of Southeast Asia who manually do all the maintenance work of the ecosystem with the help of draft animals and moving water. With these few energy inputs, they recycle wastes, control rain water for irrigation and regulate populations of crops, animals, and pests. Each task is carefully planned to conserve soil and nutrients. These farmers use virtually no fossil fuels but obtain up to 40 units of energy for each unit of work energy invested. Their success is due in part to the highly-organized association of domestic plants and animals used, each species being a multi-function multiuse element. Terrestrial and aquatic systems are carefully combined to cycle nutrients rapidly, turning waste products into food products. Ecologically, the situation is unusual in that the entire landscape is domesticated: each of the many plant and animal niches is intentionally filled with a chosen useful organism. Also a very large fraction of the landscape's productivity is channeled into human food for the people who maintain it. The result is a symbiosis between the humans and the landscape, each totally dependent upon the other.

Subsistence agriculture should not be equated with low yields or with drudgery. The effort required to provide a family's basic food needs depends greatly on population density and available energy. A low population density allows a large area to be harvested for each person at a lower intensity of effort; typically, pre-industrial agriculturalists work only 15 to 25 percent of their work day on food-related tasks. As increasing amounts of human and animal work are put into the process, yields per acre rise linearly. When energy of fossil fuels is added, yields per acre continue to rise but begin to show diminishing returns. The ideal situation is one in which the concentrated energy of fossil fuels is made to perform the most time-consuming tasks. Fossil fuels, wind, and water power, which are not extracted from the immediate living community, are particularly valuable since they are an addition to the total biological energy flow of the ecosystem and can be used for management without suppressing the food potential.

To create new agricultures, we need to first strive for the biological sophistication of the Chinese peasant farmer, drawing upon the wide range of useful food organisms used in different bioregions and recombining them into integrated polycultures. We need to identify those ecological processes that are most amenable to energy subsidy or machine work and that reduce labor time without inflicting environmental damage. Finally, we must create landscapes that fulfill social and spiritual needs as well as physical needs. Individual well-being as a species may just require some physical labor outdoors, some immediate and obvious personal reward for work, fresh food and air,

and the pleasures of children learning from parents how the seasons unfold and how we each are connected to the earth. As a species, our mutual well-being requires some serious changes, soon.

Merging the practical, the scientific and the sacred: The work of the New Alchemy Institute

A friend who studies the phenomenon on warnings and social crises finds that most people will agree with the warnings but they will not change their habits unless presented with a ready alternative. The work of the New Alchemy Institute is an exploration of alternative ways of living. The main task is design and testing of human support systems that are environmentally sound and economically efficient. Our intention is to create biotechnologies which anticipate the decline of fossil fuels and use instead the renewable energy of the sun and wind. By merging modern scientific tools and information with traditional knowledge, we want to create more benign methods of providing food, shelter, and energy. We are evolving a theory of design that turns to nature for models of sustainable communities and translates them into design principles for meeting basic human needs.

An implicit belief is that we are part of the larger tapestry of the biosphere and our well-being depends upon an understanding of ecological limits. Fundamental design criteria are:

1. *The biosphere's needs are as important as our own.* This concept has perhaps the most far-reaching implications for human culture, as it calls to question our freedom as a species to proliferate without regulation or self-imposed limits. With adequate

"Would you tell me, please, which way I ought to go from here?" asked Alice.

"That depends a good deal on where you want to get to," said the cat.
Lewis Carroll
Alice in Wonderland

energy supplies *Homo Sapiens* is exceedingly clever at by-passing normal population constraints such as food shortages, disease, climatic stress and intraspecies predation. Consequently we are literally overrunning the earth, able to occupy almost any habitat and eliminate any competition. But this phenomenal growth and expansion is only transitory, if, in the process, we totally consume the limited fossil fuels or the biological capital of the biosphere. On our present course, limits will soon be reached as cumulative toxic wastes and soil erosion peak during the same period fossil fuels run out. The larger biosphere provides the gases we breathe, the soil for our food, and purification of our wastes. Only by sustaining the life around us can we hope to sustain ourselves.

2. *Food, energy, and shelter techniques for different regions should be as variable as the biology in the different regions.* People in each biogeographical region should look for the "comparative advantages" of that region when choosing food plants, energy sources, and architectural forms. A demand for conditions radically different from local conditions (such as exotic foods, foods out of season, or populations above the food production capacity of the land) usually creates higher energy costs.

3. *A majority of people should participate in the processes that supply them with food, energy, and shelter.* Tending of a landscape for food is a physical commitment to place and to the future, bringing to the human experience a heightened awareness of the close link between our bodies and the biosphere. To watch a landscape change through the seasons is a profound lesson in the larger ebbs and flows of energy on the planet and in the ways other living things live on the earth.

4. *Variable but dependable energy sources —the sun, wind, flowing water and biofuels—should be the primary inputs to the sustenance of the living community.* The welfare of a biotic community depends upon its resilience to variations in weather and energy supplies. Typical responses to seasonal pulses are: migration during scarcity or extreme weather; storage of products from rich periods for use in times of shortage; protective structure, or architecture, that protects from climatic extremes. Most human communities can exist in their present form only because of cheap energy for transportation of food and materials from other places. The most useful strategies for permanent communities without energy subsidy are local storage and protective architecture. Transparent materials provide the entirely new option of growing food crops in transparent shelters for winter food production.

5. *Information can replace hardware.* Knowledge of ecological dynamics can result in more efficient use of tools and machinery.

Biotechnologies

Drawing upon such diverse fields of knowledge as agriculture, ecology, architecture, electronics, engineering, materials science and systems dynamics, the New Alchemy Institute has begun to develop biotechnologies on a small scale which fuse biology and technology to form the physical basis of regional self-reliance. The first task has been to explore the nature and limits of ecological agriculture, that is, food production techniques which acknowledge and anticipate the long-term health and environmental implications of the agricultural process. Intensive gardening, aquaculture, solar greenhouses for fresh winter food and agricultural forestry are major areas of research. Each food system is created as an agricultural analog of a terrestrial or aquatic community.

INTENSIVE GARDENING Until very recently family-scale vegetable gardening was a fundamental part of life in most human cultures, traditionally supplying foods locally in neighborhoods. In this century fossil fuel gradually displaced labor, and people began to rely on larger mechanized producers to supply their daily needs. The resulting gains in convenience and extra leisure were exchanged for losses of freshness, control of purity from biocides, and responsibility for soil conservation. Since the introduction and widespread use of pesticides over the past three or four decades, many people are no longer aware that food can be grown without them. Our purpose is to demonstrate that intensive vegetable production using biological pest control can be highly productive and energy efficient while maintaining the fertility of the soil. Our gardening strategy incorporates beneficial insects and birds as pest control, waste organic materials as fertilizers and a high diversity of food plants in polyculture. Experimentation is directed to discover the minimum land, labor and fossil fuels needed to supply a person's food. The average production thus far indicates that a skilled gardener can produce an annual supply of vegetables for 13 adults from 1/10 acre of Cape Cod soil, using no machines, no biocides and indirectly only small amounts of fossil fuel to transport materials. Current research is underway to incorpo-

rate grains and poultry into the production cycle and to compare the production and efficiency of perennial crops with annual crops. Intensive vegetable production of this type compares favorably with the yields and energy efficiency of conventional agriculture, with the added advantage that the fertility of the soil is gradually improving each year.

AQUACULTURE Aquaculture is the process of managing aquatic organisms, usually fish and shellfish, to produce food. On a family scale it is a substitute for traditional livestock, utilizing a small area to provide high-quality protein. The simplest form of fish culture takes place in small ponds or submerged cages in lakes: small fish are grown to larger edible size by supplemental feeding. More intensive production is possible using water circulation, aeration, increased sunlight or polyculture to increase yields. The model for polyculture comes from Asia where mixtures of herbivorous and omnivorous species are cultured in ponds with aquatic plants. The ponds usually receive animal wastes as feed. The resulting aquatic ecosystem develops internal food chains and efficiently converts sunlight and organic wastes into fish and other foods.

These various aquaculture systems demonstrate the general rule that auxiliary energy used wisely to manipulate the system can greatly increase yields. For instance, additional sunlight reflected into a pond increases algae growth and water temperature, both of which normally result in faster fish growth. Wind energy, if used to circulate, stir or aerate water in the pond, will increase the nutrient turnover rate and make more nutrients available to the organisms for faster growth. Energy of feed added to the pond (grain,

Figure 1
Research into intensive gardening is an on-going part of New Alchemy's work.

Figure 2
Compost: recycling of nutrients is essential for sustained productivity.
(Photo by Hilde Maingay)

worms, insects) raises the yield over that produced by photosynthesis alone. Finally, if fossil fuel or machinery is used to provide heat, light, or water movement within the pond, the yields can also be greatly increased.

SOLAR PONDS   Solar ponds are an intriguing example of the synergistic benefits made possible by combining biological and structural elements in new ways. A solar pond is a translucent fiberglass aquaculture pond which is above ground and receives sunlight through its sides and top. The additional sunlight striking the water column from the sides increases the population of algae which can grow there and secondarily warms the water with much of the absorbed sunlight. The increased algae produce more oxygen during the day, take up more fish waste nutrients, and provide more food to filter-feeding herbivores. In effect, the solar pond is a novel biological membrane that is permeable to light but not to water. Functionally it enables sunlight and algae to do the work that normally is performed by machinery in conventional intensive fish-production systems.

BIOSHELTERS   Bioshelters are energy-conserving, solar-heated struc-

tures that protect vegetable gardens, aquaculture ponds, and a living area for the people who tend them. They are a unique melding of biology and technology into an entity with biological qualities somewhere between an organism and an ecosystem. Within the climate-buffering architectural membrane are nurtured productive agricultural and aquacultural ecosystems. The architectural structure employs modern techniques of glazing, insulation, and thermal mass to absorb and smooth daily pulses of solar energy to

3   4

Figure 3
*Intensive aquaculture
in floating cages ef-
fectively utilizes
natural pond and lake
resources.*
(Photo by Hilde Maingay)

Figure 4
*Fish harvest from
floating-cage aquacul-
ture in a natural lake*
(Photo by Hilde Maingay)

Figure 5
*Solar aquaculture
ponds within the Cape
Cod Ark are essential
heat storage elements as
well as food production
systems.*
(Photo by Hilde Maingay)

protect the contained community. The semi-closed ecosystem within includes food plants, aquaculture ponds, interacting populations of pests and beneficial insects, and a living area for those who tend and benefit from the production.

Within the bioshelter, sunlight is directed to perform multiple functions as it is captured, stored, and slowly degraded. Some of the sunlight grows vegetables and algae. A larger part of the light is captured as heat by warming the soil, stone terrace walls, solar ponds and concrete foundation walls. Additional heat is captured and stored as hot air and water vapor from plant respiration and evaporation. At midday in winter, heat in the air is actively stored in a rock storage chamber for later release at the coldest time of the night. Heat stored each day is thus released slowly, keeping fish ponds, plants and air warm through the night, eliminating the need for heating with fuel.

Within the agricultural zones some space is committed to "ecological is-

Figure 6
Cape Cod Ark with
solar courtyards.
(Photo by Hilde Maingay)

lands," areas of plants and soil which create permanent habitat for beneficial pest-controlling insects and other desirable organisms. Food crops in nearby areas are periodically harvested and replanted, but the ecological islands remain undisturbed and provide cover for the parasitic or predatory insects which live there and make forays into the crops to feast on aphids, whiteflies, and other greenhouse pests. Other special micro-climates have been designed into the structure: areas on raised terraces where the temperatures are always a little warmer; areas in partial shade for propagation of tree cuttings, and; full sunlight areas for vegetable seedlings and breeding populations of warm-water fish for later distribution to outdoor areas in the summer.

Multiple-function (structure as simultaneous thermal storage) is an important design principle, as is the use of by-products of one process as input to another. Heat lost from the solar ponds warms the agricultural areas; rainwater from the roof is stored for use in fish ponds; nutrient-laden fish pond water is used as fertile irrigation water for the gardens, and; some garden weeds and vegetable wastes are fed to the fish. As our gardening cycles gradually become linked to aquaculture ponds, as solar and wind energy are used to enhance biological processes in solar ponds and greenhouses, and as agricultural forms begin to combine diverse plants and animals which assist each other, we begin to glimpse the structural and functional symbiosis characteristic of biological systems and begin to approach the design integrity of nature.

AGRICULTURAL FORESTRY The natural biotic tendency of New England is a mixed deciduous forest, a polyculture of perennial plants and associated animals. Forests can thrive permanently on sloping land where conventional row crop agriculture causes constant erosion; they are also highly efficient at capturing gases, water and nutrients, and holding them within their community. As with agricultural and aquacultural ecosystems we are studying natu-

Figure 7
Plan and cross sections of the Cape Cod Ark.

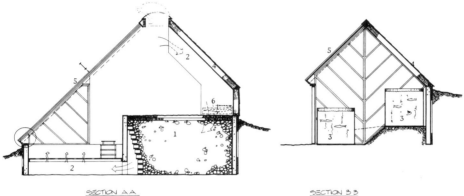

1 - **Courtyards (Not Shown) Housing 33 Solar-Algae Ponds Connected to Interior Aquaculture Facility**

2 - **Solar Pond Aquaculture Elements — Warm Water Heat Storage**

3 - **Demonstration Pool**

4 - **Rock Hot Air Heat Storage**

5 - **Experimental Economic Plant Culture Zone**

6 - **Production Zone**

7 - **Food Crop**

8 - **Insulated North Reflective Interior Surface**

9 - **Research Laboratory Pedestal**

10 - **Fan for Removing Hot Air to Rock Storage**

SECTION AA   SECTION BB

1 - **Rock Storage**

2 - **Air Flow**

3 - **Translucent Solar-Algae Pond for Intensive Fish Culture**

4 - **Insulated North Wall**

5 - **Fiberglass (Double Layer) Southern Exposure**

6 - **Fan**

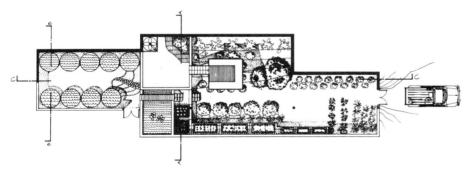

ral forest structure and function as models for the design of agricultural forests. These would be humanly-designed polycultures of useful trees and shrubs, producing fruit, nuts, forage, timber and other useful materials. Useful food trees from other regions of the earth with similar climates would be integrated with native species and nitrogen-fixing trees and shrubs would be interspersed through the forest. "Ecological islands" would be established as habitat for beneficial birds and other biological pest-control organisms.

By utilizing steep, rocky, wet or

Figure 8

Biological pest control within greenhouses: This lizard resides in an "ecological island" of bamboo between forays into food crops to eat pests.

(Photo by Earle Barnhart)

other marginal soils for culture of tree crops, food can be produced on what is now considered non-agricultural or useless land. On sloping land, agricultural forests would take the form of a park-like orchard of tree crops with pasture and livestock beneath. Soil erosion on such slopes will be minimized with resulting benefits to springs and streams of the watershed. Rather than the periodic flooding and silting which occurs below a cultivated hillside, the watershed will experience a cleaner, steadier flow.

Figure 9

Prince Edward Island Ark, a bioshelter which includes living space for a family as well as a commercial greenhouse for vegetable production, tree seedling production, and aquaculture. With its experimental hydraulic wind electrical system (the Hydro wind), this structure operates entirely on solar energy (solar and wood heating).

VILLAGE DESIGN   Most of the modern buildings, towns and cities we live in are dependent upon cheap energy for their operation and viability. These existing structures are relatively difficult to alter into energy-conserving shelters. The large amount of new rural ·and suburban housing being built could however make immediate use of solar architecture and food production processes in anticipation of future conditions and needs. The village is the functional level of society which is probably most suited to incorporating locally cohesive food, energy and recycling processes into its initial design. New Alchemy is beginning to explore village-scale design, linking together the biotechnic sub-elements into larger wholes.

Few examples yet exist of new communities intentionally designed to use solar, wind, and biofuels for energy sources and which choose to incorporate food and waste-cycling processes into the very structure of the village. Early designs of solar villages are necessarily incomplete as further techniques of integration are discovered and incorporated. Major design studies need to be carried out on the concept of large climatic envelopes, membranes that create bioshelters over acres of land. If new villages can be developed with economic advantages due to self-reliance in the areas of food and heat, an option of a new social unit and new form of security emerges: locally produced and controlled basic human needs.

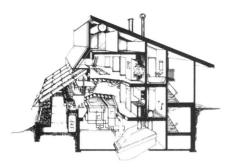

Section through Residential Greenhouse,
Hot Water Heat Storage, Composting Toilet and Living Areas.

Ark Section through Barn, Rock Storage and
Greenhouse Areas. Solar-Algae Aquaculture Ponds
are in Two Rows Down the Middle.

Figure 10
Prince Edward Island
Ark.

Figure 11
The PEI Bioshelter,
combining agriculture
and human habitation
in a northern climate.
View of residential
section looking east.
(Photo by Hilde Maingay)

Figure 12
North side of PEI Ark
showing residence on
right, research office
and barn in middle,
and commercial green-
house on left.

Figure 13
Agriculture and aqua-
culture within the
Prince Edward Island
Bioshelter

Integrated landscapes and future technology choices

Trend is not destiny.
René Dubos

Many cherished beliefs about modern industrial society have been shattered by recent social and environmental disruptions. With sudden realization, we discover that economic growth is very dependent upon fossil fuels, that many industrial technologies produce side effects which pose serious threats to human health, that conventional agriculture is not sustainable in its present form, and that large quantities of goods and services do not necessarily result in social security, well-being, or contentment. With these facts in mind we should seriously begin to use our dwindling-oil days to redesign our habits and our landscapes. A transition strategy must be developed for sustaining human societies with less energy and with a reasonable chance of long-term security.

The transition strategy used by nature is mutation and selection. Many different alternatives need to be developed in the hope that the best ideas will spread. Biological agriculture and aquaculture, solar- and wind-assisted bioshelters, and agricultural forests are options that can co-exist within the present culture and can ultimately be linked together into restorative landscapes if widely adopted. Land-use planning would be a necessary step in the careful integration of sustainable agricultures and renewable energy sources, and "agricultural zoning" based on watershed topography would be the first step. These zones would be developed to conserve soil and water within watersheds, absorbing rainfall, and gradually releasing it into ponds, lakes, streams, and rivers below. Steep hillsides must either be forested or terraced to prevent severe and irreparable erosion. Forested mountain slopes tra-

ditionally produce timber and wild game, harvested periodically. Terraces on steep slopes are used when population density requires intensive gardening and a high harvest per acre. Though terracing seems an enormous labor investment, it is instructive that many mountain peoples have found the effort worthwhile and probably essential to long-term productivity.

Gently sloping land should be grown to pasture or orchards of perennial crops. Polyculture of tree crops together with grazing livestock can produce sustainable yield of food and materials on slopes which, if plowed, would cause eventual soil and water damage to the watershed.

Natural level lands or artificial land behind terraces can be intensively cultivated with vegetables, grains, and other row crops. It is important to remember that a small area intensively managed can produce the same yields per acre as a larger one with less intensive management.

As rainfall is absorbed on the land and slowly released downstream, the natural water course can be modified for purposes of aquaculture and water power. On a water course, a series of ponds, lakes, and streams can productively recover dissolved nutrients and silt and act as supplies for water mills and turbines producing mechanical power. Chinese aquaculture is the best example of sophisticated multiple-use of water: as it flows downstream it passes successively through fields for irrigation, ponds for aquaculture, watermills for power and even in the lower levels of rivers and estuaries flows through suspended fish cages and shellfish rafts where the last nutrients are extracted that would otherwise be lost to the sea.

In Chinese aquaculture many organic wastes are transformed into food

CATEGORY	ARK	ORTHODOX HOUSING
UTILIZES THE SUN	Source of Heating, Climate, Purification, Food Production and Much Interior Light.	Some Interior Light – Often Negative Role Necessitating Air Conditioning
UTILIZES THE WIND	A Source of Electrical Energy from Windmill Wind-Driven Circulation through Composting Toilet.	Only Negatively, Increasing Fuel Demands through Infiltration.
STORES ENERGY	YES – in Three Systems and Growing Areas.	NO.
MICRO-CLIMATOLOGICAL SITING	Integral to Design.	Rare.
WASTE PURIFICATION	YES – Except for Grey Water which is Piped into Leaching Bed.	Wastes Untreated and Discharged to Pollute.
WASTE UTILIZATION	Purified Wastes are Nutrient Sources in Interior Biological Cycles.	NO.
FUEL USE	Wood, a Renewable Source, as Supplemental Heat.	Heavy Use of Gas, Oil or Inefficient Electricity.
ENERGY CONSERVING	YES – Also Uses Energy to Serve Simultaneous Functions.	NO, or Rarely.
ELECTRICITY CONSUMPTION	About same as Orthodox House but Electricity Used for Many Productive and Economic Functions.	Fairly Heavy Consumer.
FOODS	Diverse Foods Cultured Year-Round	Not Within – Often Summer Gardens.
AGRICULTURAL CROPS	Vegetables, Flowers and Young Trees	NO.
AQUACULTURAL PRODUCE	Fish for Market.	NO.
ECONOMIC UNIT	YES – Viability to be Determined.	NO – Financial Burden.
OPERATIONAL COST	LOW – Ultimately Exporter or Power.	HIGH – Particularly in Fuels and Electricity.
INITIAL COST	HIGH – Due to Energy and Biological Components – Uses Larger Amounts of Quality Materials.	Moderate.
VULNERABILITY TO INFLATION AND SHORTAGES	SLIGHT.	SEVERE.
IMPROVES CLIMATE AND LOCAL ENVIRONMENT	YES – Locally by Windbreak and More Broadly through Reforestation.	RARELY – Most Intensify Weather.
TEACHES ABOUT THE LARGER WORKINGS OF NATURE	YES.	NO.
INCREASES SELF-SUFFICIENCY	YES.	Rarely.
STIMULATES LOCAL AND REGIONAL SOLUTIONS	Possible.	Unlikely.

Figure 14
A comparison of the Ark with orthodox housing.

in the aquaculture systems, including animal wastes, food processing wastes and human wastes. Conversion to food is generally faster through an aquatic system than through the slower cycle of composting, spreading the compost,

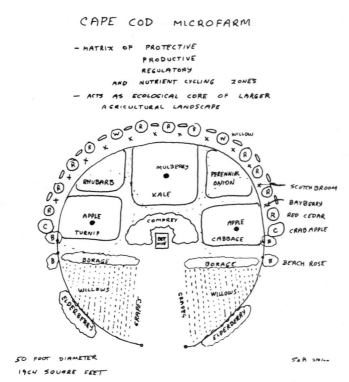

CAPE COD MICROFARM

- MATRIX OF PROTECTIVE
  PRODUCTIVE
  REGULATORY
  AND NUTRIENT CYCLING ZONES
- ACTS AS ECOLOGICAL CORE OF LARGER
  AGRICULTURAL LANDSCAPE

50 FOOT DIAMETER
1964 SQUARE FEET

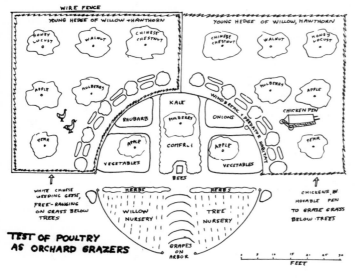

TEST OF POULTRY
AS ORCHARD GRAZERS

Figures 15 and 16
*Agricultural forests, polycultures of perennial plants and associated
animals, are being investigated as a means of eliminating soil loss
while meeting human food needs from marginal land.*

and eventually eating the crop a year or more later. Human wastes are organic materials which must cycle back into an ecosystem and be reused to avoid toxic accumulations and ground water contamination. Planning for reuse of human wastes rather than disposal into the subsoil or into external water bodies is an essential step in a sustainable society. On a local level several options exist for productive utilization. Aquaculturalists in California have developed a municipal-scale version of Chinese waste conversion in which a series of connected ponds treat sewage with special combinations of aquatic plants, fish, shrimp, and other organisms.[6] As the wastes slowly flow through the ponds they are broken down and transformed into plant biomass and edible fish or shrimp. The water finally emerges pure enough for reuse.

On a home scale, standard septic systems can be redesigned to supply subsurface irritation to food trees and shrubs, instead of the standard leach field that drains to the water table out of reach of the plant roots. Household greywater has successfully been used in a greenhouse version of subsurface irrigation. Water from baths and washing is filtered through deep vegetable beds which remove particles and nutrients and produce clean water for other irrigation or aquaculture processes. With such a water reuse system, solid wastes are completely separate from the grey water, usually entering a composting toilet for slow decompositon and ultimate use as fertilizer, or in periodically shifting shallow outhouses beneath trees.

Bioshelters in future landscapes will be the center of many of the food and waste-cycling processes already described. More than just a house, they will function simultaneously as human habitation, food production and waste-treatment facilities for the inhabitants, and as focal points for agricultural expansion in the wider community. As energy-conserving shelters they provide an environment of sunlight and gardens through the often bleak cold months of winter. As nurseries they act as epicenters for the landscape around them, producing vegetable seedlings, tree seedlings, and young fish in hatcheries. Used for storage of summer foods grown outdoors, such as edible-size fish held in ponds for winter eating and frozen foods, they replace the storage functions of barns in previous rural communities. The production of fresh winter vegetables supplies vitamin-rich foods now transported in winter from California or Mexico. Wind energy (and water power, where available) is envisioned as providing mechanical power for the air and water-pumping work and for mechanical operation of freezers and refrigerators for food storage. Both pumping and freezing are mechanical tasks which can absorb intermittent pulses of energy and which store their product for periods of lull. Pumped water and air are stored physically in containers until time of use, and a refrigeration compressor produces storable "cold" in well-insulated, walk-in freezers: the waste heat of compression is used for domestic water preheating or warming of greenhouses or fishponds.

In our society there are high energy costs due to separation in space and time of agriculture, living and eating, and waste disposal and treatment. Often the fertilizers supplying farms are imported from other continents, food is removed from the farm, and the food wastes and human wastes are eventually deposited in still another place instead of being returned to the farm. As these now separate activities become more closely linked into localized wholes, they mutually reinforce one another and transportation costs are gradually reduced. Transport becomes more important for moving people to meet other people, and for moving tools and information from one area to another. Available fossil fuels, rather than being burned, have their greatest value in the manufacture of durable materials and structures that contribute longer-term benefits. If living systems in nature can be said to have a general goal, it is to invest in mechanisms leading to long-range survival. Fossil fuels, as an unearned legacy from the past, should be likewise invested to strengthen the chances of well-being for our own and future generations.

Conclusion

Quite obviously the analysis and ideas proposed here about the future assume a perception of nature and our proper role in it which is not widely held. For instance, it seems radical to propose that our society, which has access to most of the accumulated knowledge of history, should avoid repetition of obvious agricultural blunders of the past. It seems utopian to propose that remaining fossil fuels be used consciously to create sustainability for the present human population. And, tragically, it seems reactionary to reject nuclear technologies which are biologically lethal to ourselves, our children and all future generations.

It may be that we as an animal species cannot escape our biological destiny of population boom and bust brought about by exploitive agriculture and fossil fuels. On the other hand, as intelligent beings we have finally developed the cybernetic capacity to perceive the global implications of some

We will not cease from exploration, and the end of all our exploring will be to arrive where we started, and know the place for the first time.

T. S. Eliot

Figures 17 and 18
The principles of agri-cultural forestry and biological climate con-trol can also be applied to urban areas, re-ducing energy costs (up to 30 percent from the use of windbreaks) and increasing local food supply (which also reduces energy use).

NORMAL CITY STREET

TRANSITION STAGE

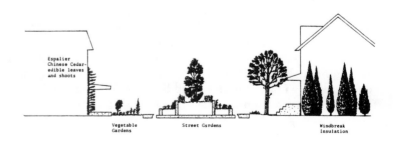

Espalier
Chinese Cedar-
edible leaves
and shoots

Vegetable
Gardens

Street Gardens

Windbreak
Insulation

MATURE URBAN AGRICULTURE

of our actions. If Gaia (the ancient Greek name for the earth) has indeed slowly evolved a protective atmospheric body on the planet, we may well be part of a lately evolved but powerful central nervous system in the biosphere. So far, our culture is ignoring its global memory of the past and has, in effect, relinquished its control over its future destiny.

In a world where more money is invested in military technology than in energy, health, food production, and environmental protection combined, one concludes that modern intellectual and political paradigms are failing to create a path to future peace and well-being. Gregory Bateson once alluded to the idea that many ancient philosophical and religious truths, perceived in moments of enlightenment by prophets and mystics, are, in essence, the deep internalization of a fundamental natural law or pattern of natural history. And, in fact, traditional wisdom passed down from widely different cultures has taken a conceptual form similar to the notion of Karma:

"Do unto others as you would have done to you."
"The sins of the father are visited upon the following generations."
"Give prayers of forgiveness and thanks before killing game."
"Spirits inhabit all things and thus all things are to be respected."
"The Earth is Mother and Sacred."

In our time these concepts have been subsumed under the joint notions that "Everything's connected" and "There is no such thing as a Free Lunch."

Beneath all the rhetoric, the intellectualization, and the scientific abstraction favoring right livelihood, it will probably be such simple, virtually religious perceptions that will eventually turn the tide toward striving to enhance rather than diminish life on the planet. The information, materials, and energy needed to live lightly are available to all at a modest cost, and the wisdom of how best to use them can be obtained with a little digging. The will to try is all that is missing, and, fortunately for us, that is free.

References

1. David Pimental et al., "Land Degradation: Effects on Food and Energy Resources," *Science* 194 (1976): 149–155.

2. Eric P. Eckholm, *Losing Ground,* (New York: W. W. Norton & Co., 1976).

3. Vernon G. Carter and Tom Dale, *Topsoil and Civilization,* (Norman, Okla.: Univ. of Oklahoma Press, 1974).

4. Eugene P. Odum, *Fundamentals of Ecology,* (Philadelphia, Penn.: W. B. Saunders Co., 1971).

5. Gerald Leach, *Energy and Food Production,* (Washington, D.C.: Institute for Environment and Development, 1975).

6. For information on community-scale wastewater reclamation by controlled environment, ecological processes contact Solar Aqua Farms, Inc., P. O. Box 88, Encinitas, CA 92024. See also the following works by The New Alchemy Institute: *The Book of the New Alchemists,* (New York: E. P. Dutton, 1977); *Journal of the New Alchemists* 4 (1977): *Journal of the New Alchemists* 5 (1979). For information about membership and subscription to the *Journal* of the *New Alchemists,* contact: The New Alchemy Institute, P. O. Box 47, Woods Hole, MA 02543.

Selected Bibliography

ANDERSON, EDGAR. 1952. *Plants, Man and Life*. Berkeley, Cal.: Univ. of California Press. A description of human dependence on and domestication of plants.

BERRY, WENDELL. 1977. *The Unsettling of America: Culture and Agriculture*. San Francisco: Sierra Club Books. Berry shows that agricultural practices in America have gradually been turned away from cultural common sense under the pressure of the exploitive strategies of agribusiness.

CARTER, VERNON G. and TOM DALE. 1974. *Topsoil and Civilization*. (Norman, Okla.: Univ. of Oklahoma Press. A review of the rise and fall of past civilizations as a function of their care of the soil.

DUBOS, RENE. 1976. "Symbiosis Between the Earth and Mankind." *Science* 6, (August 1976): 459–462. Meditations on the fact that humans and their local ecosystems coevolve, even now.

DUCKHAM, A. N., J. G. W. JONES and ROBERTS. 1976. *Food Production and Consumption: The Efficiency of Human Food Chains and Nutrient Cycles*. New York: North Holland Publishing Co. A technical treatment of energy conversion as it passes through various crops, livestock, and food products.

ECKHOLM, ERIC P. 1976. *Losing Ground*. New York: W. W. Norton & Co.

ECKHOLM, ERIC and LESTER R. BROWN. *Spreading Deserts — The Hand of Man*. Worldwatch Institute Paper No. 13. Worldwatch Institute, Washington, D.C. Tragic erosion on a planetary scale is occurring and is a one-way street of declining food productivity.

FORBUSH, EDWARD HOWE. 1905. "Useful Birds and Their Protection." Massachusetts State Board of Agriculture. Many birds eat pests and those birds can be cultured with very little effort. An underexplored biological pest control process.

HUFFAKER, C. B. and P. S. MESSENGER. *Theory and Practice of Biological Control*. New York: Academic Press. A long look at the current knowledge of biological pest control, including many classical cases of fruit tree pests.

HYAMS, EDWARD. 1952. *Soil and Civilization*. New York: Harper / Colophon Edition. Similar to *Topsoil and Civilization* but more descriptive of the agricultural crops, methods and land ownership patterns in each civilization.

JACKSON, WES. 1978. "Soil Loss and the Search for a Permanent Agriculture," *The Land Report,* Salina, Kans. (February 1978): 10–16.

KERN, KEN. 1975. *The Owner-Built Homestead*. Oakhurst, Cal.: Owner-Builder Publishing Co. Kern suggests a polyculture orchard with built-in succession.

KING, F. H. 1911. *Farmers of Forty Centuries*. Emmaus, Pa.: Rodale Press. Parts of Southeast Asia have been farmed continuously while other cultures have eroded away. King shows some of the strategies involved.

LAPPÉ, FRANCIS MOORE *and* JOSEPH COLLINS. 1977. *Food First: Beyond The Myth of Scarcity*. Boston: Houghton Mifflin Co. Lappé states that most regions can produce adequate food if given a favorable matrix of land ownership, education, and free market. Malnutrition is a socio-political malfunction.

LARSON, DON. 1976. "Nitrogen-Fixing Shrubs." *The Futurist,* (April 1976):

74–77. Let shrubs make your nitrogen fertilizer, then use shrub prunings.

Lerza, Catherine. "U.S. Soil: The Dustbowl Syndrome." *The Elements,* (July 1977).

Merrill, Richard, ed. 1976. *Radical Agriculture.* New York: Harper Colophon Edition. Where to from here? *Radical Agriculture* proposes that there is an "Economics of Permanence" which demands a revamping of U.S. agricultural policy along different paths of research, land use and food production.

Mollison, Bill and David Holgren. 1978. *Permaculture One: A Perennial Agricultural System for Human Settlements.* Australia: Corgi Books, Hedges and Bell. See also, Mollison, Bill. 1979. *Permaculture Two: Permanent Design for Town and Country in Permanent Agriculture.* Tasmania, Australia: A Tagari Community Book. Available from International Tree Crops Institute, Box 1272, Winter, CA. 95694. Far and away the most comprehensive vision of how one might create new agriculture ecosystems using patterns from nature. Books to be adapted to every bioregion.

Odum, Eugene P. 1971. *Fundamentals of Ecology.* New York: W. B. Saunders Co. A requirement for ecosystem designers. Particularly pertinent are the sections on domestication and energy subsidy in agriculture.

Robinette, Gary O. 1972. "Plants, People and Environmental Quality." U.S. Government Printing Office, no. 024–005 00479-3, catalog no. 129.2: p. 69. A clear handbook on how to place trees in the human landscape for greatest practical and aesthetic effect. Probably the one book to buy in this section if you want to explore the possibilities of using plants.

Robinson, Gordon. 1976. "Forestry As If Trees Mattered: A Bold Stand." *Not Man Apart,* (August 1976) pp. 1–4. The United States is not exempt from poor management of soil and forest. These articles describe the rapid decline of farm soil productivity and the short-term exploitive practices of Federal forest management.

Smith, J. Russell. 1950. *Tree Crops: A Permanent Agriculture.* New York: Devin-Adair Co. From the most energetic proponent of tree crops, a compelling argument that tree crops should be the backbone of agricultures meant to last.

Udvardy, Miklos D. F. 1975. "A Classification of the Biographical Provinces of the World." *I. U. C. N. Occasional Paper No. 18.* International Union for Conservation of Nature and Natural Resources, Morges, Switzerland.

Map of World Biogeographical Provinces. The CoEvolution Quarterly, P. O. Box 428, Sausalito, CA 94964. Udvardy's paper and map by *The CoEvolution Quarterly* reminds us of what would be growing on Earth if we weren't controlling things. An important perspective is that it takes energy to resist these tendencies of nature and more energy to patch things up afterward.

Wilson, Helen Van Pelt. 1978. "Plantings for a Bird Watcher's Landscape." *Horticulture,* 56, no. 1 (January 1978): 68–74. A short list of the best bird-forage plants and the birds which eat them.

19 | New Roots for Agriculture*

Wes Jackson

The Grass Is Rich and Matted, you cannot see the soil. It holds the rain and the mist, and they seep into the ground, feeding the streams. . . . It is well-tended, and not too many cattle feed upon it; not too many fires burn it, laying bare the soil. Stand unshod upon it, for the ground is holy, being as it came from the Creator. Keep it, guard it, care for it, for it keeps men, guards men, cares for men. Destroy it and man is destroyed. . . .

Alan Paton
Cry, The Beloved
Country

NOWHERE IS the human–nature split more dramatic than in the manner in which land is covered by vegetation. To maintain the "ever-normal" granary, the agricultural human's pull historically has been toward the monoculture of annuals. Nature's pull is toward a polyculture of perennials. This is not to say that we humans exclude perennials from our agricultural endeavors, just as nature does not exclude the annual plant as part of her strategy to keep vegetation on the ground. Certainly the numerous nut and citrus trees, grapes and berries (be they blue, black, rasp or straw), along with other perennial plants, are important to our species. As for nature, no naturalist need remind us that her annuals are widely dispersed in natural ecosystems.

The main purpose of this paper is to consider the implications of these opposite tendencies, with an eye to the serious work involved in healing the split. Nature is at once uncompromising and forgiving, but we do not precisely know the degree of her compromise nor the extent of her forgiveness. I frankly doubt that we ever will. But we can say with a rather high degree of certainty that if we are to heal the split, it is the human agricultural system which must grow more toward the ways of nature rather than the other way around.

Nature rewards enterprise on a limited scale. A weedy annual is enterprising. Not only will it cover bare ground quickly, but it will yield an excess of potential energy besides. This is probably the reason our most important crops, such as corn and wheat, arose as weedy annuals. A small amount of annual vegetative biomass promotes the production and survival of a rather large number of seeds during a growing season. This is usually assured by one of three things or even a combination of all three: (1) the storage of plenty of food in the seed, (2) the set on of many seeds and (3) the ability to colonize a disturbed area. Many perennials may have these three characteristics, but it is less critical for them to come through in a particular season, for there is always another year. For that matter, there is always another year for many

---

* Reprinted by permission from Wes Jackson, *New Roots for Agriculture,* (San Francisco: Friends of the Earth, 1980).

annuals too, as their seed will remain viable for more than one year. But overall the colonizing annual has had to rely on enterprise. The ancestors of our current crops may well have been camp followers, colonizers of the disturbed ground around the campsite. They were obvious candidates for selection by humans because of their availability and their inherent ability to produce an excess of potential energy. They are the enterprisers of the higher plants.

We don't know whether the early agriculturists were faced with famine or not. But when they began to plant annuals in fields, they were beginning to reward this enterprise. The monoculture of annuals, the enslavement of enterprising species, was a big new thing in the history of the earth. The face of the earth was changed.

By and large, the patient earth has rewarded patient ecosystems, but it would seem that enterprise has always been rewarded too, though on a very limited scale. It would seem to be a good strategy for an ecosystem to have such species present, for these quick colonizers could rapidly cover the ground made naked by a migrating buffalo which had wallowed and dusted himself, or by an excessive flood or an insistent wind. The ecologi-

(Photo by Terry Evans)

Not content with the authority of either former or present day husbandmen, we must hand down our own experiences and set ourselves to experiments as yet untried.

Columella,
1st century A.D.

cal capital which had been sucked from parent rock material or stolen from the air could be retained to promote more life for future generations of all species in the system.

The selection of enterprising plant species has rewarded all humans bent on enterprise in food production.

But there is the second consideration, the likelihood that we have a psyche predisposed to take from the environment with little thought for the future, especially when the connection between the product and the source is separated by numerous links. It is the combination of these two psychological characteristics, enterprise and taking with little thought for the future, which has resulted in a rub yet to be reckoned with in the four hundred generations since humanity started keeping track of seed time and harvest. The problem is this: to maintain any system, agricultural or natural, bills must be paid eventually. In nature's prairie, the bills are paid automatically and with amazing regularity. The wild forms have evolved methods for dispersing seed, recycling minerals, building soil, maintaining chemical diversity, promoting new varieties and even controlling weeds, e.g. through shading. The prairie has been successful because close attention has been paid to seeing that these jobs get done. Most biologists believe that natural selection alone was up to these tasks, and that purpose was not necessary.

This "no-free-lunch law" applies just as much to human agriculture as it does to the biotic cultures of nature. For when agricultural humans substitute their annual monoculture on this land, be it corn, wheat, milo sorghum, rye, oats or barley, the same bills have to be paid or failure is inevitable. Mechanical and commerical preparation of the seed and planting, the application of fertilizer, chemical and power weeding, mechanical soil preparation, pesticides and fungicides and plant breeding are all clumsy inventions we have devised for paying the same bills nature pays.

In contrast to the system of nature, which relies solely on the daily allocation of solar energy, in the industrialized world our inventions for the successful monoculture of the annuals require the stored light of the geologic past. Efficiency in energy use is the way of nature, not of industrialized people.

I mentioned at the beginning that the human-nature split was at its most dramatic in the manner in which land is covered with vegetation. Soil loss certainly ranks alongside our other major problems in importance. As a resource, soil is every bit as depletable as petroleum and the consequences of depletion are worse for more of earth's people. An over-populated planet can fare better without fossil energy than it can without soils to grow food. If soil loss were not such a reality, it would be much more difficult to argue that the way of nature is inherently better than the way of the agriculturists in the developed world. Energy use is not the major consideration.

The monoculture of annuals leads to soil erosion. The methods almost inherent in the monoculture of annuals require that ground be devoid of vegetation for too long a time, often during critical periods of the year. The forces of wind and rain can now rapidly move soil seaward. Even during the growing season, especially for the row crops, the loss is substantial. Crops such as corn, cotton and soybeans have much of their holding power destroyed between the rows as the farmer loosens the earth to cultivate. For this reason, J. Russell Smith called corn, "the killer

Figure 2
Wes Jackson, Phil Hayes, and Jim Peterson examine the spatial relationships among a species in a native prairie (the Fent Prairie) which has never experienced forced grazing. This research, which will provide baseline data for an understanding of the strategy nature uses in maintaining soil and creating abundant plant growth, will help the Land Institute to develop ways to create a high-yielding, sustainable agriculture (Photo by Terry Evans)

of continents . . . and one of the worst enemies of the human future."[1]

The polyculture of perennials is another matter, however. The more elaborate root system is an excellent soil binder. It has been estimated that before Europeans came, fires were sufficiently common and any given area became burned at least once in a decade.[2] Though the top organic matter may have been absent for brief periods, the roots at least were alive and binding the soil.

What will nature require of us?

It seems doubtful that nature will uncompromisingly insist that the polyculture of perennials is the only way humans can peacefully co-exist with her. As I mentioned earlier, she employs some annuals in her own strategy. One might begin a limited systematic inquiry into the nature of a high-yielding sustainable agriculture by asking whether it is the annual versus perennial condition of the plant or monoculture versus polyculture we need to investigate first.

In a more thorough-going systematic study, we may have to contrast, not just annual versus perennial, or monoculture versus polyculture, but the woody versus the herbaceous condition and whether the human interest is in the fruit / seed product or the vegetative part of the plant. When we consider these four contrasting considerations, in all possible combinations, we have sixteen categories for assessment.

We can eliminate four of these sixteen categories listed in Table 1 for they involve woody annuals, an unknown phenomenon in nature. This leaves us with twelve categories for consideration. Eleven of these remaining combinations are currently employed in the human enterprise. But category five, which involves the polyculture of the herbaceous perennials for seed / fruit production, is almost the opposite of our current high-yielding monoculture of annual cereals and legumes.

Fruit / seed material is the most important plant food humans ingest. This is so because of the readily storable, easily handled, highly nutritious nature of the seeds we call grains. Unfortunately, none of our important grains are perennial, or when they are, as with sorghum, basically a tropical plant, they are not treated as such. If a few of them had been, we might not have so thoroughly plowed from the edge of the eastern deciduous forest to the Rockies. Where we did not plow or where we did plant back nature's herbaceous perennials in polyculture, our livestock have become fat on the leaf and seed products. Throughout this entire expanse, the mixed herbaceous perennials have not been cultured for the purpose of harvesting the seed except for the occasional times when collections were made to plant more mixed pasture.

In the eastern tall grass region, the white settler substituted the domestic tall grass, corn. In the middle or mixed grass region, he substituted a domestic middle-sized grass, wheat. Part of the problem of the Dust Bowl is that we tried to substitute the middle-sized grass in what was short grass prairie.

The Dust Bowl followed the great plowing of the teens and twenties. When the dry winds blew in the thirties, the bad reputation for the region became firmly implanted on the American mind. We have had other severe droughts in the area since, and the wind has blown just as strong. All the work done by the Soil Conservation Service and others to prevent other dust bowl conditions should be ap-

Poly vs. Monoculture	Woody vs. Herbaceous	Annual vs. Perennial	Fruit/Seed vs. Vegetative	Current Status
1. Polyculture	Woody	Perennial	Fruit/Seed	Mixed Orchard (both nut & fleshy fruits)
2. Polyculture	Woody	Perennial	Vegetative	Mixed Wood Lot
3. Polyculture	Herbaceous	Annual	Fruit/Seed	
4. Polyculture	Herbaceous	Annual	Vegetative	Dump Heap Garden,* Companion Planting
5. Polyculture	Herbaceous	Perennial	Fruit/Seed	
6. Polyculture	Herbaceous	Perennial	Vegetative	Pasture & Hay (Native or Domestic)
7. Monoculture	Woody	Perennial	Fruit/Seed	Orchard (both nut & fleshy fruits)
8. Monoculture	Woody	Perennial	Vegetative	Managed Forest or Wood Lot
9. Monoculture	Herbaceous	Annual	Fruit/Seed	High-Producing Agriculture (wheat, corn, rice)
10. Monoculture	Herbaceous	Annual	Vegetative	Ensilage for Livestock
11. Monoculture	Herbaceous	Perennial	Fruit/Seed	Seed Crops for Category 12
12. Monoculture	Herbaceous	Perennial	Vegetative	Hay Crops (Legumes & Grasses) & grazing

* See *Plants, Man & Life* by Edgar Anderson for the splendid chapter on Dump Heap Agriculture   ***Table 1***

plauded. It is truly the work of thousands of diligent and dedicated people who have spent most of their productive lives thinking and working on the problem, but still the most sobering fact cannot be ignored. The soil is going fast. On some flat land there may be very little loss, but on rolling land the loss can be as high as sixty tons per acre per year. According to the General Accounting Office, the average yearly loss is 15–16 tons per acre. Based on a random sample, eighty-four percent of the farms are losing more than five tons of soil per acre each year.[3] Furthermore, there is little difference between farms participating in USDA programs and those which do not.

Unless the pattern of agriculture is changed, our cities of this region will stand as mute as those near the Great Wall of China, along the fertile crescent or the northern region of Egypt which once hosted grain fields that supplied the empire of ancient Rome.

If we are serious in our intention to negotiate with nature while there is still time for Americans to heal the split, are we not being forced to ask if nature will uncompromisingly require us to put vegetation back on the ground with a promise that we are not to plow except for the occasional replanting? If that is nature's answer from the corn belt to the Rockies, will it require that we develop an agriculture based on the polyculture of herbaceous perennials which will yield us seeds not too unlike our cereals or legumes? This category, so glaringly blank in our table, needs filling desperately; and yet to contemplate the research, breeding, establishment of the crops, the harvest and separation of seeds is mind boggling. All this effort must go hand in hand with the transportation, milling and ultimately, the eating of this "instant granola in the field."

Is it too much to expect plant scientists to come up with such perennials, either through some inter-generic crossing of our high-producing annuals with some perennial relatives, or by selecting some wild perennial relatives which show promise of a high yield of a product that is at once abundant and tasty? Any scenario surrounding such an agriculture does not seem to truly belong to a fantasy world. For mechanized agriculture it would mean either a minimum amount or a complete absence of plowing, disking, chiseling and mechanical power weeding. There would be only harvest, some fertilizing, pest control, genetic selection and the occasional replanting.

How about fruit or nut trees for saving our soils?

The virtues of orchards need little promotion. Trees have many advantages over their herbaceous relatives. Propagation by twig or bud through grafting allows the multiplication of any useful mutant by the millions. Because of their deep rootedness and woody nature, trees are better able to withstand fluctuations between drought and rainfall. Trees provide shade and fuel and are altogether handsome on the landscape. Because of their numerous attributes, I would encourage any lover of trees to commit all the acres he or she could to their culture.

In spite of all the gifts trees offer, the fact remains that year in and year out they do not compete with wheat, rice, corn and soybeans either in ease of production and harvest or yield. Even if we discount how long it takes for trees to bear fruit, any compelling substitute must lend itself to machine harvest and high production. Cultural tradition may be partly responsible here but even so there are few substitutes for grains.

Trees can compete in saving soil, however. There are a wide range of slopes, from the extreme of steep, rocky land all the way to the flat alluvial, with soils which can best be protected by orchard trees, if not returned to the wild. A land ethic stronger than a short-run production ethic will favor trees over high-yield annuals on sloping ground.

How feasible is the development of high-yielding, seed-producing herbaceous perennials for this century? The answer to this question hangs on settling a fundamental question of plant science, the question of whether perennialism and high-seed yield are mutually exclusive or not. Some highly reputable plant geneticists I have asked, who have worked and thought on the question, not only have discouraging comments but lean toward a categorical "no" when asked about the possibility of co-existence of perennialism and high yield. Others felt there were some possibilities. We began to explore this question at The Land Institute by going to the literature and later conducted direct investigations of our own. Smith reports that the Millwood variety of the honey locust tree will product 1,800 pounds of fruit / seed material on a per acre basis.[4] At The Land, smooth sumac, a shrub, with no human-directed selection will produce over 1,000 pounds of fruiting material per acre. Another shrub, sand plum from Dickinson County, Kansas, on a per acre basis, as determined by extrapolation from a 10.5-square-foot area, will yield 6,480 pounds of fruit / seed material. When the pit is removed, the dried flesh will yield 3,820 pounds! We can now be satisfied that perennialism and high yield are not mutually exclusive.

The next question is whether *herbaceous* perennialism and high yield are mutually exclusive. At The Land we have grown several such species in 5-meter-long rows and have extrapolated to a per acre basis, recognizing that such a method is likely to yield overly optimistic results. A three-year-old plot of *Ratibida pinnata,* a perennial member of the sunflower family, yielded 1,470 pounds of seed. This plant is important for it contains the two important fatty acids, linoleic acid and linolenic acid, which occur in oils and are essential in animal nutrition. Maximillian sunflower in the first year yielded 1,300 pounds but only 400 pounds on the 3-year plot. This latter response has been characteristic of perennial yields in other crops and may stand as a major barrier to crop development of many perennials. Nevertheless, these results from wild species in which little, if any, selection has taken place are encouraging. A critic might point out that these are all members of the sunflower family and that we cannot be considered serious until we look to the grasses and herbaceous legumes. But this is jumping ahead a bit for we have sought to answer several questions about perennialism and high-yield being mutually exclusive, one at a time.

As we have just seen, it required but minimum effort to show that they were not mutually exclusive when we consider woody species. Therefore, it is not a condition of *flowering plants.* Furthermore, our results with a few herbaceous members of the compositae or sunflower family suggest it is not mutually exclusive when we consider the *herbaceous* condition. At this point it is important to establish some minimum standard for what constitutes a high-yielding crop. Since 30 bushels per acre has long been regarded as a good wheat crop, at 60 pounds per bushel, an 1,800-pound yield for any herbaceous perennial would be a high-

yielding crop. As we have seen, at least a few members of the sunflower family approach this. Certainly grasses and legumes must have priority in new crop development and we are fortunate to find a few encouraging results in the literature. Perhaps most noteworthy is the work of Dr. Robert M. Ahring at Oklahoma State University. He has managed to produce yields in buffalo-grass of 1,727 pounds/acre/year under certain fertilizer treatments.[5] Over a four-year period his plots have averaged 1,304 pounds of seed burs per acre. Of course, much of the bur could not be considered edible. Nevertheless, it is fruit/seed material. The grass *Sporobolus cryptandrus,* with no selection, is reported to have yielded 900 pounds an acre. Essentially all 900 pounds are edible.[6]

Until now, most of the work on new crop development has involved the crossing of economically important annuals with some of their wild perennial relatives. As mentioned earlier, there is a tendency for older patches to decline in productivity. It is well known that perennials provide a fair to good stand the first year and often a pretty good stand the second, but by the third year, production is headed steeply down. Though this is certainly a problem, we can't say for sure that this will always be the case and that this need be a biological law any more than an average of 40-bushel-per-acre corn in the pre-hybrid days was immutable biological law. It may have been a biological reality, but was not a biological law.

There are numerous problems associated with the development of an agriculture based on perennials. Nevertheless, such a program would seem to have more promise that the effort to convert temperate grasses into legume-like, nitrogen-fixing cereals. At least the high-yield cereals we tested have numerous perennial close relatives, while the base line for any encouragement in the development of nitrogen-fixing cereals are the few wild tropical grasses in which minimum amounts of nitrogen are fixed.[7]

In spite of all the discouraging events certain to confront the plant science community, the development of only one new high-producing perennial crop could pay dividends for both developed and developing nations forever. Such a crop could go a long way toward preventing erosion and desertification, problems common to both types of nations.

The important point for our consideration here is that no new breakthroughs are necessary for us to begin a very large program now, involving scores, if not hundreds, of crosses and selection experiments in our universities and research organizations. Some incentive seed money is always needed to accompany policy change. But we need not wait for additional scientific and technological developments. These developments occurred earlier in our century as biologists sought to fuse Charles Darwin's ideas of evolution through natural selection with Gregor Mendel's principles of heredity, both of which had developed over thirty-five years before. This exciting period of history in biology, whose excitement we too readily forget with our contemporary mania over such gee-whiz genetics as cloning and genetic surgery, began early in the century with attempts to establish the chromosome theory of heredity and by and large culminated with the elucidation of the chemical structure of the hereditary material, the DNA, by Watson and Crick. During this period, techniques were developed to count chromosomes and follow them through the various stages of replication and division. Chromosomes were irradiated, broken and fused and some of their genes mapped. Sterility barriers between species came to be understood, and artificial hybrids, including some resulting from intergeneric crosses, were successfully made. We came to understand how species arose through chromosome numbers being doubled or reduced, and investigators learned to artificially induce these changes. Chromosome numbers have been successfully doubled through chemical agents to the point it has become a matter of routine. Numerous species have had their karyotypes or genetic fingerprints determined.

The work that linked the independent ideas of Darwin and Mendel is now a reservoir of practical knowledge. Interestingly enough, a relatively small amount of this information has been used in crop and livestock improvement. The plant scientist and the breeder did use some, but mostly they applied the tools from the newly-emerging field of statistics and made significant advances in crop production through improvement in experimental design and a better understanding of hybrid vigor. These assiduous experts were less interested in new crops than in their imaginative programs of "fine-tuning" the traditional crops. Thankfully, the same hardware (optical equipment, growth chambers, greenhouses etc.) and the basic research necessary for "fine-tuning" will be needed as we research the fundamental question of whether herbaceous perennialism and high yield are mutually exclusive or not. The supporting fields of plant physiology, plant pathology, entomology and biochemistry have the necessary working bibliographies, equipment and experts to work in concert with the geneticists to gain information which has an impact on our great national problem—soil loss.

This is a period in which we should encourage much wide-ranging imagination and speculation on new crop development. Numerous botanists and crop scientists will have plant candidates in mind. I have already mentioned several high-yielding wild perennial species, but only to shed light on the biological question as to whether herbaceous perennialism and high-yield are mutually exclusive or not. Species that currently have lower yields may be more important for development in the long run. At The Land Institute we are working on Eastern Gama Grass and the newly discovered perennial corn from Mexico. We have chosen Eastern Gama Grass, *Tripsacum dactyloides,* because it is a perennial relative of corn and a plant that

cattle relish. Its seed consists of 27 percent protein and it is nearly twice as high in the amino acid methionine as corn. This high protein percentage, three times higher than corn and twice as high as wheat, should allow the breeder to sacrifice considerable protein content in the push for higher yield. Right now the yield is around one bushel per acre, but there are several characteristics, which if put together might increase yield many fold right off. (1) It has already been extensively studied, particularly by those interested in the evolution of corn.[8] Therefore, important basic information already exists. (2) The species is already at home in our corn belt for it nearly rivals corn in the extent of its distribution, ranging from Florida to Texas and Mexico north to Massachu-

Figure 3
Planting Eastern Gamagrass. Similar to an arboretum, the Land Institute's Herbary, shown here, will contain as many perennial native and naturalized grasses and wild flowers of the prairie states as it is possible to grow and maintain. It will be used for education and research toward the development of an agriculture based on the cultivation of herbaceous perennials in polyculture.
(Photo by Phil Schermeister)

setts, New York, Michigan, Illinois, Iowa and Nebraska.[9] (3) Because this tall, stout perennial has thick rhizomes, any desirable races could be propagated vegetatively from clumps. (4) The part of the flower that sets seed is localized and separate from the part that produces pollen. Therefore, no tedious effort is necessary for the breeder to emasculate before making crosses. (5) The species contains two more or less true breeding chromosome races. The virtues of this species are indeed numerous.

Perhaps just as promising as the above mentioned corn relative are some of the relatives of our high-yielding, leguminous, nitrogen-fixing crop, soybean. *Glycine max* (L). Merr., as it is scientifically called, is an annual. Most species in this genus are perennial. The genus itself consists of three subgenera which include 10 species and 18 genetic entities; i.e. subspecies or varieties. Furthermore, there are three closely related genera comprising some 12 additional species.[10] The variation within *Glycine* alone is truly remarkable. However, the entire American soybean industry, which produces 75 percent of the world's supply, in the words of Professor Jack R. Harlan of the University of Illinois, "can be traced to six accessions introduced from the same part of Asia."[11] It would seem that something could be done to test our basic question concerning perennialism and high-yield with some of the other species of this genus or even the relatives of the closely related genera.

The third example involves a grass again, the Panicum complex, which includes broomcorn millet or Hog Millet, as it is sometimes called. Most species are perennials and the genus *Panicum* has a large range both in latitude and longitude, suggesting great genetic elasticity. A closely related genus *Setaria* includes the Common Millet as one of its species.

These are but three examples. The possibilities are there for other groups as well. All that is needed now is interest on the part of investigators and some seed money from foundations and the government for researchers to redirect their efforts.

Why have we not developed any new herbaceous perennial seed crops so far? One explanation might be that the development of a suitable crop is beyond us.

Another might be that we have lacked, in the right places, the kind of holistic thinking that would link the high-yield seed production of annuals with soil loss. Even if we have seen the problem, most of us must confine our breadwinning efforts to a narrowly-defined job description. In discussing the problem with colleagues, many, like myself, were aware that soil was probably being lost at an unacceptable rate, but were not aware until the release of the General Accounting Office's study that the problem was so acute and therefore we had not concentrated our minds on the need for an agricultural solution.

New crop development has had relatively little attention in the history of our species since eight to ten thousand years ago when several generations of the most important revolutionaries ever to live on earth gave us essentially all our crops and livestock. Of the thousands of seed-producing plant species known, fewer than one percent have been utilized by humans for food, clothing and shelter. By and large humans do the easy things first, and so our crop scientists have improved the plants that have already demonstrated their amenability to cultivation.

Of the hundreds of crops available in our inventory now, fewer than a dozen supply the huge bulk of food stuffs.

Because these plants have an economic history, there is a ready-made economic data base for evaluating market opportunities against cost for any breeding work to be done. After all, much of our culture is built around relationships involving the farmer, the processor and the consumer. There has always been plenty of work to do in crop improvement without looking for more.

Therefore, we have logically questioned the wisdom of adding more plants when we are not fully utilizing many of the proven plants which are already available.

There is probably another reason why we have not looked to herbaceous seed producers to save our soils and yield high-quality food. Imagine the psychological climate of the scientific community forty years ago. We were still in a depression, and the dust storms had already become legend. We have seen what a dramatic response the Roosevelt administration made to this problem. The high caliber people Bennett employed, the good reputation quickly gained, all of this allowed scholars and laymen alike to turn their attention to other matters, entirely confident that the effort to save the soil was in the best hands possible.[12] It would simply be a matter of time before this problem was solved. Since the procedures were both practical and scientific, everyone felt comfortable. There was little incentive to look elsewhere for solutions to the soil loss problem.

What environmental benefits (other than reduced soil loss) could we expect from an agriculture of herbaceous perennial seed-producers? Perennial culture could reduce energy consumption. The energy for traction in seed bed preparation and cultivation is significant; it comprises the major fuel bill for the farmer year in and year out.

Perennial culture could reduce pesticide dependency resulting in both energy savings and healthier soil and food. As mentioned earlier, the direct fossil fuel energy that goes into our pesticide program nation-wide is at least 80 percent of the one billion pounds sprayed on our fields each year.[13] This amounts to around two million barrels of oil. (Not included in these figures is the energy cost for making the chemicals, nor distribution to the farmer, nor his energy cost for application.) Because many of these new crops would presumably be the result of inter-specific and inter-generic crosses, they could represent a broad genetic base of disease resistance. The current "hard agricultural path" promotes a genetic narrowing and therefore increased vulnerability to pests overall.

Perennial culture would reduce our dependency on commercial fertilizer. I assume this because the application of fertilizer to perennial forage crops is, on the average, much less than to annual grain crops. The slow decay of plant materials from perennials releases nutrients at a rate that new growth can more efficiently assimilate. This saving would be significant, for not only is commercial nitrogen fertilizer energy-intensive, but it is toxic to children and farm animals.[14] It is not uncommon for water tables to have high high levels of nitrates and for aquatic ecosystems to be placed greatly out of balance. Besides, a real fertilizer crisis could develop. The feed stock for much of our commercial fertilizer is natural gas, and in 1976, 22 percent of the interruptible supply of natural gas was devoted to the manufacture of fertilizer.[15]

The development of new, high-yield perennial, seed-producing crops could reverse the current decline of our do-

*Plants for the herbary,
started in flats*
(Photo by Phil
Schermeister)

mestic genetic reservoir. Population increase and intensive agriculture have reduced the amount of "waste land" where teosinte, the wild relative of corn, once lived. For wheat and rice, too many of the old low-yielding but faithful varieties of various races and ethnic groups have been driven from the fields.[16] Many of these are low performers by modern standards, but have been the genetic bank which breeders would tap now and then to introduce new germplasm into crops made narrow by selection.

The cost for maintaining a very wide spectrum of genetic variation is prohibitive for most of the seed companies. The National Seed Storage Laboratory at Fort Collins, Colorado is charged with the expensive and difficult responsibility of keeping genes stored. The most efficient storage is in living organisms.

In summary, success in herbaceous perennial crop development would lead to a reduction in resource depletion for both fossil fuels and germplasm and would reduce pollution of our waters, soils and ultimately ourselves. Even if we are not successful in our attempts to develop high-yielding herbaceous perennial crops the low-yielding and otherwise useless new stocks may serve as a bridge for introducing new germplasm into our high-yielding annuals.

Perennial polyculture

The development of perennial seed producers to rival our annuals is not the most radical kind of agricultural research needed in the affluent countries. Traditional cropping systems have widely employed polycultures already. Eventually, the polyculture of perennials to meet a variety of human needs in the developed world will be necessary. Such a program may require 50 years or more before we see combines going through our fields harvesting seeds of three or more species, including legumes. These plants will have been selected to mature in synchrony and will accommodate themselves to machinery yet to be designed by agricultural engineers.

I have already discussed whether

perennialism and high yield are mutually exclusive. A second basic consideration has to do with the comparative yield of a perennial polyculture compared to a perennial monoculture in temperate regions of the globe. Numerous ensembles will have to be matched according to flowering and seed set time, to be taken into consideration along with root type and depth of penetration.

Our third and final major category of interest for the moment is related to the first two questions. We want to determine if several families of plants which are common to the native prairie could make yield-increasing contributions to our polycultures. For example, we know that legumes fix at least a minimal amount of nitrogen on the prairie, but what is the role of the sunflower family, or the rose family, the mint family, etc.? Perhaps they play no role in the overall health of the prairie ecosystem and are just there. In fact, even the value of the legume family might be brought into question because most of the nitrogen available to the prairie falls with the rain and snow.[17] Perhaps legumes are allowed not because of nitrogen fixation abilities which ultimately contribute to the entire plant community, but because they have niches somewhat independent of the other species.

Perennial polyculture and crumb structure

Continued soil fertility depends, to a large extent, on plant associations which form and preserve an appropriate crumb structure.[18] A crumb is a granular substance resulting from various chemical and physical factors at work in a field and is of prime importance in all highly productive land ecosystems. Without these crumbs some soils become powder, while others

consisting of clay change to a butter-stickiness when wet.

Crumb structure declines in year-in-year-out monoculture or where there is too much cultivation, too much fertilizer and too little humus. Knowledge of the conditions that promote this formation lends further support to the idea of perennial polyculture, in particular the perennial grasses. Associated with the grass roots are dead rhizosphere bacteria, which act as binding agents. But grasses have other virtues to assist crumb presence in the soil. Crumbs are less exposed in a grass field when it rains and grass roots exercise a wick effect, pulling water to lower levels. This downward allocation of water keeps the crumbs in the upper levels from slurrying off. A grass mat would also protect crumbs from the dessicating effects of frost and sunshine. The roots of annual grasses doubtlessly promote crumb formation, but strong roots, more likely to be found in perennials, produce more crumbs than grasses with smaller, more fibrous roots.[19]

Even when we are considering something as lowly as crumb formation, it seems inappropriate to simply swap annual monoculture for perennial monoculture. One reason is that clover in monocultures is less effective than grass in monoculture in producing crumbs. But when clover and grass are grown together the crumb-forming action increases.

After crumb structure has been drastically reduced in a field, redemption is not immediate. From four to thirteen years, depending on soils, is required before increase in crumbs can be detected.[20]

Why these humble, irregularly sized and shaped crumbs are such a strong factor in the soil environment begins to make sense when we contemplate how they affect soil texture. They create porosity, opening the soil so effectively that abundant water readily drains into the sub-soil. This granular soil allows the nutrients, oxygen, and carbon dioxide to readily diffuse in and around roots. Crumbs make it mechanically easy for roots to grow and worms to burrow. Crust formation or glazing is prevented and when dry weather does come the small soil particles are sufficiently held together to minimize blowing.[21]

In a successful herbaceous perennial polyculture, we would expect that soil erosion would cease to be a problem. Because of the chemical diversity of such an ecosystem, insects and plant diseases would also be less serious. In a natural prairie polyculture, weeds are managed by the shading system. Nutrient balance is also managed by the system with little human involvement. Water is held by the spongy mass and a deeply penetrating root system, as mentioned earlier, has a wick effect and "pulls" water down when the heavy rains occur. Once a balanced polyculture has been planted, soil preparation and preparation of seed and planting are all done by the system.

This is not to say that numerous problems do not await such an agriculture. Long before we get to the point of fine-tuning such a system our farmers will need to employ the entire array of sound soil conservation measures as a holding action.

It has always been hard to see where we stand in history as we are living it. Could it be that we have promoted monocultures of grains when possible because agriculture is back-breaking work? There have been advantages to concentrating our food energy as much as possible. Perhaps we can now think seriously of machine harvest of polycultures of grain on a massive scale. The paradox is that we can now live in

ecosystems more like the gathering-hunting ones in which we evolved because of high technology. We can almost "go home again," finally, because we have the technology which will allow us to live there.

A possible cultural barrier

Food is such an intricate part of cultures that perhaps we should not expect rapid adoption of many of these new crops into our diet. Humans have historically been rather conservative about food habits. There is one characteristic, however, that describes the human animal. We are grass-seed eaters and secondarily, legume-seed eaters. I would expect that any shift as far as texture and taste is concerned would be no more dramatic than the shift from rice to wheat or from wheat to rice with respect to both taste and texture. Nevertheless, there will be shifts which people may be reluctant to make. A major concern in all this is the importance of the sticky nitrogenous substance gluten, which allows bread dough to be stretched and restretched without breaking apart before making a beautiful loaf.

Different wheats have different flavors and other characteristics that determine the products that are made with them. The entire array of such characteristics which have already been adopted by humans may, in fact, capture much of the range of variation among species from wide crosses yet to be made. I see no reason why we should not approach the whole program with a sense of adventure—especially if we recognize the ecological benefits derived from growing the crops.

Overall, I am optimistic that there will be no meaningful cultural barrier to their adoption. If only a hundredth of the advertising is applied to the promotion of eating these healthful grains that is applied to the array of unwholesome junk food we ingest now, no cultural barrier can stand in the way of their whole-hearted adoption.

How does the proposal discussed here relate to the larger vision of the environmentalist?

Because sunshine is dispersed rather evenly over the earth; because nature's three-dimensional solar collectors, called green plants, are also dispersed; because these collectors are so critical to all other life forms, including humans; because the land for growing these collectors in the United States is eroding at the rate of nine tons per acre per year on the average: any who advocate a sunshine future or soft energy path must ultimately adopt a land ethic which embraces an energy ethic.

The soft energy path or sunshine future advocated by Amory Lovins, it would appear, would ultimately require a decentralized society. A major emphasis of Lovins' thesis is the thermodynamic match, i.e. energy source and energy end-use should be matched. Since both sunshine and plants are dispersed, should not nature's people be dispersed? It seems reasonable enough —but do we have enough information to say with any high degree of confidence what the distribution pattern should be? First off, *how* people live, in terms of consumption, is more important than *where* they live, in the first round of growing scarcity.

Let us assume for the moment that our systems analysts widely agree that eventual decentralization is absolutely necessary for a sustainable life on the planet. To build the infrastructure for decentralization may be both energy

and materials intensive. The romantic back-to-the-land movement, as minimal as it is thus far, is a signal of something desirable. But what happens when we all get there, after the first generation of back-to-the-land romantics have been buried organically in their gardens? Will their children maintain the back-breaking work most humans have sought to avoid over the centuries? Isn't this one of the components of the human condition? It has yet to sink in to our culture that we are still basically gatherers and hunters, and that the era of agriculture is but a thin veneer over an evolutionary past which tolerated a great deal of leisure. The appeal of the countryside is the appeal open space has always had for us gatherer-hunters. The appeal of the city is that it at least faintly suggests a mixture of leisure and stimulation most of us need. R. B. Lee has reported that only 65 percent of 31 !Kung bushmen in Botswana spent two to three days each week gathering food while "35 percent of the people did no work at all."[22]

Van Rensselaer Potter has pointed out that we all have a need for an optimum stressor level which varies for each of us.[23] On one side of this optimum is boredom, which can come from too long a period in the fields. At the other end is the problem of information overload which may come from being over-stimulated in the city. The only way I can see the decentralized culture joyfully surviving is for our technology to allow us both stimulation and time for leisure, so that we might play out the longings of that gathering-hunting body and brain.

But what do perennial seed-producers have to do with a Utopian vision—or with leisure and stimulation? In the Summer, 1949, issue of the now defunct *Land Quarterly* is an article entitled "Sweet Living at Yellow River" written by a Channing Cope. Mr. Cope describes a goal which he and his family had recently achieved on a farm in Georgia:

> At long last we have it. The result is far beyond our fondest dreams, for we never thought we would so utterly eliminate drudgery from farming through a combination of four basic plants working in natural unison to sustain life. These four plants are Kudzu, sericae lespedeza, Kentucky 31 fescue grass and ladino clover . . . Front porch farming calls for perennials to the greatest extent possible, and if these are not possible we court the annuals which have the habit of reseeding each year. Therefore, no plowing except to get the crop started.

Speaking of anyone who would have such a farm, he continued that such a person

> will pass it on to the next generation in better shape than he found it. He couldn't design a better monument than a weather-proof farm. It won't wash away. It won't wear out. It will furnish basic food. It gets better as the years move on. It makes a local, statewide and national contribution, and, to the extent of its influence, it helps prevent war.

Channing Cope's perennials, of course, are all plants devoted to the production of vegetative material. His personal dream could come true because he lived in a culture where the slack was taken up by the thousands of *seed-producing* farmers of our nation. Nevertheless, what he calls "front porch" farming as an appealing way of life brings to mind the need of the gatherer-hunter. It also illustrates that such leisure has provided Channing the opportunity to reflect on the old religious questions and critical values necessary for a sustainable culture and agriculture when he speaks of building a "weather-proof farm" as his "monument." He saw in his individual action a positive chain of events, perhaps as part of a web, but certainly as a local response to large problems which even included the prevention of war!

The scientific-technological revolution has surely already provided us with enough recyclable hardware to keep a decentralized society stimulated and in touch with one another at home through the telephone, television and perhaps even the home-based computer terminal.

But the human-nature split remains. As immodest as it may sound, I think we can at once provide leisure and begin to close the split if the Channing Copes can be provided with high-yield, seed-producing herbaceous perennials in polyculture.

The chemotherapy treatments to the land promote a temporary vigor more impressive than our fields have ever known. Though the physician may rejoice with his cancer patient that he is feeling better in response to the treatment, he is also careful to monitor the telltale systems of the body. Similarly, those interested in the long-term health of the land need only stand on the edge of a stream after a rain and watch a plasma boil and turn in the powerful current below and then realize that the vigorous production of our fields is, unfortunately, temporary. Since we initiated the split with nature some 10,000 years ago by embracing enterprise in food production, we have yet to develop an agriculture as sustainable as the nature we destroy.

References

1. J. Russell Smith, *Tree Crops* (New York: Devin-Adair Co., 1953).

2. Dr. Lloyd Hulbert, Plant Ecologist at the Kansas Agriculture Experi-

ment Station and Professor of Biology at Kansas State University, after observing the time in which woody vegetation encroaches when fire is not present, has supplied me with this number. In the eastern part of the prairie, it would be more frequent than ten years. In the western third of the grasslands, 15 years or more could lapse without fire. Grasses have probably evolved to invite fire.

3. In February, 1977, the General Accounting Office (GAO) released an analysis of the United States Department of Agriculture (USDA) soil conservation efforts. The GAO based its conclusions, in part, on visits to 283 farms in the corn belt, Great Plains, and the Pacific Northwest.

4. Smith, *Tree Crops.*

5. Robert M. Ahring, "The Management of Buffalograss for Seed Production in Oklahoma," Oklahoma State Experiment Station Technical Bulletin T-109 (May 1964).

6. H. Ray Brown, "Growth and Seed Yields of Native Prairie Plants in Various Habitats of the Mixed-Prairie," *Transactions Kansas Academy of Science,* 46 (1943): 87–99.

7. Joanna Döbereiner, "N Fixation Associated with Non-Leguminous Plants," *Genetic Engineering for Nitrogen Fixation,* Alexander Hollaender, ed. (New York: Plenum Press, 1977) p. 451.

8. See, for example, the paper by J. M. J. de Wet and J. R. Harlan delivered at the Symposium on Origin of Cultivated Plants at the XIII International Congress of Genetics. There are numerous literature citations which give one a sense of the history of studies on *Tripsacum.*

9. Julian A. Steyermark, *Flora of Missouri,* (Ames: Iowa State Univ., 1963), pp. 252–254.

10. J. M. Herman, "A Revision of the Genus *Glycine* and its Immediate Allies." U.S.D.A. Technical Bulletin no. 1268 (December 1962).

11. Jack R. Harlan, "Genetics of Disaster." *Journal of Environmental Quality* 1, no. 3 (1972).

12. Wellington Brink, "Big Hugh's New Science," *The Land* 10, no. 3 (1951).

13. Steven D. Jellinek, "Integrated Pest Management from Concept to Reality." U.S. Env. Protection Agency (December 1977).

14. Paul R. Ehrlich, Anne H. Ehrlich and John P. Holdren, *Ecoscience: Population, Resources, Environment,* (San Francisco. W. H. Freeman & Co., 1977), p. 558.

15. Guy H. Miles, "The Federal Role in Increasing the Productivity of the U.S. Food System." NSF—RAN-74-271, (November 1974), p. 20.

16. Garrison Wilkes, "The World's Crop Plant Germplasm—An Endangered Resource." *Bulletin of the Atomic Scientists* (1977). See also "Our Vanishing Genetic Resources" by J. R. Harlan, reprinted in *Food: Politics, Economics, Nutrition and Research.* AAAS P. H. Abelson ed., (1975).

17. Robert G. Woodmansee, "Additions and Losses of Nitrogen in Grassland Ecosystems" *BioScience* 28, no. 7 (July 1978), pp. 448–453.

18. N. Pilpel, "Crumb Formation," *Endeavour* 30:110 (May 1971).

19. Ibid.

20. Ibid.

21. Ibid.

22. R. B. Lee, "!Kung Bushman Subsistence: An input-output analysis." *Bull. Natl. Can.* 230 (1969), 73–94.

23. Van Rensselaer Potter, *Bioethics: Bridge to the Future,* N.J.: Prentice-Hall, (1971).

REFLECTION

The road of excess leads to the palace of wisdom

— William Blake

20 | Energy, Ecotechnocracy, and Ecology

Murray Bookchin

WITH THE LAUNCHING of the "energy crisis," a new mystique has developed around the phrase "alternate energy." In characteristic American fashion, this takes the form of ritualistic purification: guilt over the extravagant use of irreplaceable energy resources, fear in response to the apocalyptic consequences of "shortages," repentance over the afflictions resulting from waste, and the millenarian commitment to "new" techniques for achieving a stable energy system, i.e., "alternate energy." The operational term here is "technique." Whether one chooses to focus on Gerald Ford's plan to afflict America with some 200 nuclear reactors by 1980 or Professor Heronemus' plan to string the northern Atlantic with giant wind generators, the phrase "alternate energy" runs the grave risk of being debased and its radical content diffused of its serious social implications.

The trick is familiar enough. One intentionally confuses a mere variation of the status quo with fundamentally opposing concepts of life style, technology, and community. Just as the word "state" was cunningly identified with society, "hierarchy" with organization, "centralization" with planning—as though the latter couldn't exist without the former, indeed as though both words were synonymous—so projects that reflect a shrewd reworking of established techniques and outlooks are prefixed by the word "alternate." With this one magical word, they acquire the aura of the radically new, the different, the "revolutionary." The word "energy," in turn, becomes the solvent by which richly qualitative distinctions are reduced to the gray, undifferentiated substrate for a crude psychic, physical and "ecological" cybernetics—the ebb and flow, the blockage and release of quantified power. Accordingly, by dint of shrewd linguistic parasitism, the old in a seemingly "new" form becomes little more than an "alternative" to itself. Variety, qualitative difference and uniqueness, those precious traits of phenomena to which an authentic ecological sensibility must always be a response, are rarefied into a "cosmic" oneness, into a universal "night in which" (to borrow the mocking language of a great German thinker) "all cows are black."

The landscape of alternate technology is already marred by this regressive drift, especially by mega-projects to "harness" the sun and winds. By far the lion's share of federal funds for solar energy research is being funneled into projects that would occupy vast areas of desert land. These projects are a mockery of "alternate technology." By virtue of their scale, they are classically traditional in terms of their gigantism and in the extent to which they would exacerbate an already diseased, bureaucratically centralized, national division of labor—one which renders the American continent dependent upon and vulnerable to a few specialized areas of production. The oceans too have become industrial real estate, not merely as a result of proposals for floating reactors but also long strings of massive wind generators. And as if these mega-projects were not enough, Glaser's suggestions for mile-square space platforms to capture solar energy beyond the atmosphere and beam microwaves to earth-bound collectors would redecorate the sky with science-fiction industrial installations. Doubtless, many of these mega-project designers are well-intentioned and high-minded in their goals. But in terms of size, scale and ecological insight, their thinking is hardly different from that of James Watt. Their perspectives are the product of the traditional Industrial Revolution rather than a new ecological revolution, however sophisticated their designs may be.

Human beings, plants, animals, soil, and the inorganic substrate of an ecosystem form a community not merely because they share or manifest a oneness in "cosmic energy," but because they are qualitatively different and thereby complement each other in the wealth of their diversity. Without giving due and sensitive recognition to the differences in life-forms, the unity of an ecosystem would be one-dimensional, flattened out by its lack of variety and the complexity of the food web which gives it stability. The horrendous crime of the prevailing social order and its industry is that it is undoing the complexity of the biosphere. It is simplifying complex food webs by replacing the organic with the inorganic—turning soil into sand, forests into lumber, and land into concrete. In so simplifying the biosphere, this social order is working against the thrust of animal and plant evolution over the past billion years, a thrust which has been to colonize almost every niche on the planet with variegated life-forms, each uniquely, often exquisitely, adapted to fairly intractable material conditions for life. Not only is "small beautiful," to use E. F. Schumacher's expression, but so is diversity. Our planet finds its unity in the diversity of species and in the richness, stability and interdependence this diversity imparts to the totality of life, not in the black-painted-on-black energetics of mechanical spiritualism.

"Alternate energy" is ecological insofar as it promotes this diversity, partly by fostering an outlook that respects diversity, partly by using diverse sources of energy that make us dependent on variegated resources. The prevailing social order teaches us to think in terms of "magic bullets," whether they be chemotherapeutic "solutions" to all disease or the "one" source of energy that will satisfy all our needs for power. Accordingly, the industrial counterpart to antibiotics is nuclear energy, just as Paul Ehrlich's salvarsan, the "magic bullet" of the turn of the century, found its counterpart in petroleum. A "magic bullet" simplifies all our problems. It overlooks the differences between things by prescribing one solution for widely dissimilar problems. It fosters the view that there is a common denominator to the variegated world of phenomena—biological, social or psychological—that can be encompassed by a single formula or agent. A respect for diversity is thus undermined by a Promethean view of the world as so much "matter" and "energy" that can be "harnessed" to serve the maw of agribusiness and industry. Nature becomes "natural resources," cities become "urban resources," and eventually even people become "human resources"—all irreducible "substances" for exploitation and production. The language itself reveals the sinister transformation of the organic into the inorganic, the simplification of a richly diverse reality into uniform "matter" to feed a society based on production for the sake of production, growth for the sake of growth, and consumption for the sake of consumption.

To make solar energy alone, or wind power alone, or methane alone the exclusive "solution" to our energy problems would be as regressive as adopting nuclear energy. Let us grant that solar energy, for example, may prove to be environmentally far less harmful and more efficient than conventional forms. But to view it as the exclusive source of energy presupposes a mentality and sensibility that leaves untouched the industrial apparatus and the competitive, profit-oriented social relations that threaten the viability of the biosphere. In all other spheres of life, growth would still be pursued for its own sake, production for its own sake, and consumption for its own sake, followed eventually by the simplification of the planet to a point which would resemble a more remote geological age in the evolution of the

organic world. Conceptually, the beauty of "alternate energy" has been not merely its efficiency and its diminution of pollutants, but the ecological interaction of solar collectors, wind generators, and methane digesters with each other and with many other sources of energy including wood, water—and yes, coal and petroleum where necessary—to produce a new energy pattern, one that is artistically tailored to the ecosystem in which it is located. Variety would be recovered in the use of energy just as it would be in the cultivation of the soil, not only because variety obviates the need to use harmful "buffers," but because it promotes an ecological sensibility in all spheres of technology. Without variety and diversity in technology as a whole, solar energy would merely be a substitute for coal, oil, and uranium rather than function as a stepping stone to an entirely new way of dealing with the natural world and with each other as human beings.

What is no less important, "alternate energy"—if it is to form the basis for a new *ecotechnology*—would have to be scaled to human dimensions. Simply put, this means that corporate gigantism with its immense, incomprehensible industrial installations would have to be replaced by small units which people could comprehend and directly manage by themselves. No longer would they require the intervention of industrial bureaucrats, political technocrats, and a species of "environmentalists" who seek merely to engineer "natural resources" to suit the demands of an inherently irrational and anti-ecological society. No longer would people be separated from the means whereby they satisfy their material needs by a suprahuman technology with its attendant "experts" and "managers"; they would acquire a direct grasp of a comprehensible ecotechnology and regain the power over everyday life in all its aspects which they lost ages ago to ruling hierarchies in the political and economic sphere. Indeed, following from the attempt to achieve a variegated energy pattern and an ecotechnology scaled to human dimensions, people would be obligated to decentralize their cities as well as their industrial apparatus into new ecocommunities—communities that would be based on direct face-to-face relations and mutual aid.

One can well imagine what a new sense of humanness this variety and human scale would yield—a new sense of self, of individuality, and of community. Instruments of production would cease to be instruments of domination and social antagonism: they would be transformed into instruments of liberation and social harmonization. The means by which we acquire the most fundamental necessities of life would cease to be an awesome engineering mystery that invites legends of the unearthly to compensate for our lack of control over technology and society. They would be restored to the everyday world of the familiar, of the *oikos,* like the traditional tools of the craftsperson. Selfhood would be redefined in new dimensions of self-activity, self-management, and self-realization because the technical apparatus so essential to the perpetuation of life—and today, so instrumental in its destruction—would form a comprehensible arena in which people could directly manage society. The self would find a new material and existential expression in productive as well as social activity.

Finally, the sun, wind, waters and other presumably "inorganic" aspects of nature would enter our lives in new ways and possibly result in what I call a "new animism." They would cease to

be mere "resources," forces to be "harnessed" and "exploited," and would become manifestations of a larger natural totality, indeed, as respiritized nature, be it the musical whirring of wind-generator blades or the shimmer of light on solar-collector plates. Having heard these sounds and seen these images with my own ears and eyes at installations reared in Vermont at Goddard College and in Massachusetts at the research station of New Alchemy Institute—East, I have no compunction in using esthetic metaphors to describe what might ordinarily be dismissed as "noise" and "glare" in the vernacular of conventional technology. If we cherish the flapping of sails on a boat and the shimmer of sunlight on the sea, there is no reason why we cannot cherish the reflection of sunlight on a solar collector. Our minds have shut out these responses and denied them to our spirit because the conventional sounds and imagery of technology are the ear-splitting clatter of an assembly line and the eye-searing flames of a foundry. This is a form of self-denial with a vengeance. Having seen both technological worlds, I may perhaps claim a certain sensitivity to the difference and hope to transmit it to the reader.

If the current literature on alternate sources of energy is conceived merely as an unconventional version of the *Mechanical Engineering Handbook,* it will have failed completely to achieve its purpose. Mere gadgetry for its own sake, or in what philosophers call a "reified" form, exists everywhere and is to be desperately shunned. To be sure, one must know one's craft, no less so in ecotechnology than in conventional technology. This is the burden (if "burden" it be) of the sculptor as well as the mason, of the painter as well as the carpenter. But in ecotechnology one must deal with craftship in a special way. Overinflated into a swollen balloon, it may well carry us away from the ground on which we originally stood, from our sense of *oikos,* the ecological terrain which initially shaped our interests and concerns. I have seen this occur among my sisters and brothers in the ecological movement only too often. Indeed, having received a considerable training in electronics decades ago, I also know only too well how insanely obsessed one can become with the unending, even mindless, improvisation of circuit diagrams until one is as enamored by a drawing, say, of the electronic trigger for a nuclear bomb as for a television set. It is from people obsessed with reified technology and science that the AEC recruits its weapons' engineers, the FBI its wire-tappers, the CIA its "counterinsurgency" experts. Let us not deceive ourselves: "ecofreaks" are no more immune to "the man" from Honeywell and NASA than "electronic freaks" are to "the man" from General Electric and the AEC—that is, until they have become ecotechnologists, informed by a deeply spiritual and intellectual commitment to an ecological society.

This means, in my view, that they are committed not merely to an "efficient" alternate technology but to a deeply human alternate technology—human in scale, in its liberatory goals, in its community roots. This means, too, that they are committed to diversity; to a sense of qualitative distinction, to energy and technology as an artistically molded pattern, not as a "magic bullet." Finally, it means that they are ecologists, not "environmentalists," people who have an organic outlook, not an engineering outlook. They are motivated by a more sweeping drama than an appetite for mere gadgets and scientist "curiosities."

They can see the wound that opened up in society and in the human spirit when the archaic community began to divide internally into systems of hierarchy and domination—the elders constituting themselves into a privileged gerontocracy in order to dominate the young, the males forming privileged patriarchies in order to dominate the women, lastly male elites collecting into economic ruling classes in order to exploit their fellow men. From this drama of division, hierarchy, and domination emerged the Promethean mentality, the archetypal myth that man could dominate nature. Not only did it divide humanity from nature into a cruel dualism that split town from country, but it divided the human spirit itself, rearing thought above passion, mind above body, intellect above sensuousness. When finally every group tie—from clan to guild dissolved into the market place jungle of atomized buyers and sellers, each in mutual competition with the other; when finally the sacred gift became the avaricious bargain, the craze for domination became an end in itself. It brought us a formidable body of scientific knowledge and a stupendously powerful technology, one which, if properly reworked and rescaled, could finally eliminate scarcity, want, and denial, or one which could tear down the planet if used for profit, accumulation and mindless growth.

The authentic ecotechnologist knows that the wounds must be healed. Indeed, these wounds are part of her or his body. Ecotechnologies and ecocommunities are the mortar that will serve not only to unite age groups, sexes, and town and country with each other in a non-hierarchical society; they will also help to close the splits in the human spirit and between humanity and nature. Whether these splits were necessary or not to achieve the striking advances in technology of the past millennia; whether we had to lose the child-like innocence of tribal society, ripened by the painful wisdom of history—all of this is a matter of abstract interest. What should count when confronted by a technical work is that we are not beguiled from these immense themes—this sweeping drama in which we split from blind nature only to return again on a more advanced level as nature rendered self-conscious in the form of creative, intelligent, and spiritually renewed beings. To deal with alternate energy sources in a language that is alien to social ecology, to reify the literature on the subject as a compendium of gadgets—a mere encyclopedia of gimmicks—would be worse than an error. It would be a form of betrayal—not so much to those who have worked in this field as to oneself.

21 | Planning and the Paradox of Conscious Purpose

Gary J. Coates

SINCE THE DISCOVERY of fire, and in the past 7,000 to 10,000 years with the development of agriculture and the establishment of fixed settlements, human culture has been developing in a direction opposite that of organic evolution. Rather than moving toward greater complexity, diversity, symbiosis and stability, human-dominated ecosystems have moved progressively toward simplicity, homogeneity, competitive exploitation, and fragility. No other species has had the capacity to so drastically alter its environment to meet its own needs, and humanity has had neither the self control necessary to temper its demands nor the wisdom necessary to effectively regulate the environments it has had the power to create. So far, this unhealthy combination of intemperance and ignorance has proven disastrous for both nature and culture.

A civilization comes into existence through the development of new ideas, myths, and technologies and through the harnessing of energy for the exploitation of nature and the domination of other human groups. When the limit of that particular form of exploitation is reached, the civilization declines, often having consumed the material resources upon which it has come to depend, as well as its capacity for adaptive change in the face of new social, political and ecological realities. It is estimated that as many as 30 civilizations have followed this cycle of growth and decline through the loss of evolutionary potential, leaving behind a legacy of deforested hillsides, human-created deserts, and plains and river valleys denuded of topsoil where there was once fertile and abundant life.

Industrial civilization, through its use of fossil fuels and high energy technology, has managed to accelerate this anti-ecological and anti-evolutionary trend and has brought the entire planet within the orbit of its destructive influence. As a result, the whole earth is rapidly becoming a single ecosystem. This is an unprecedented development in evolutionary history and has serious implications. Life came into existence and has continued to evolve precisely because of the relative isolation and independence of ecosystems which comprise the thin layer of life known as the biosphere. Kenneth Boulding consid-

. . . And what you thought you came for Is only a shell, a husk of meaning From which the purpose breaks only when it is fulfilled If at all. Either you had no purpose Or the purpose is beyond the end you figured And is altered in fulfillment. . . .

T. S. Eliot, from "Little Gidding"

525

ers the recent emergence of a single interdependent global village to be a major threat to human survival.

> The world has not been a single ecosystem, but a mosaic of relatively isolated ecosystems with some possibilities of migration between them. Consequently, if a catastrophe wiped out one ecosystem, it did not wipe out all of them. Evolution was able to continue and eventually colonize the disaster area. The eruption of Krakatoa undoubtedly eliminated the total biological ecosystem of that island. Now after almost a hundred years it has been reestablished, perhaps not quite the same as it was before, but with innumerable species of all forms of life having colonized it from the undisturbed areas. Similarly, the Mayan civilization collapsed in about 900 A.D., quite irrecoverably, from the point of view of its own system. This did not affect either Europe or China, which knew nothing about it, and the catastrophe had very little impact on the general course of social evolution. On the other hand, if we have a single world eco-system, a single world society, then if anything goes wrong, everything goes wrong: if there is any positive probability of irretrievable catastrophe, then if we wait long enough it is almost certain to happen.[1]

As we have seen, this thin film of industrial culture that now envelops the earth, destroying indigenous cultures and disrupting the world's major ecosystems, is entirely dependent on nonrenewable resources that are certain to be effectively exhausted within the lifetime of someone born today.[2] The probability of "irretrievable catastrophe" for industrial civilization is rapidly approaching 100 percent, a fate which is now positively correlated with that of non-industrial cultures as well as the major living systems of the earth.

Thus, the crisis of industrialism raises serious questions about the ultimate viability of nature's experiment in human intelligence. Unless something is done to radically alter the present course of events we must ask whether or not *Homo sapiens* will prove to be "merely an evolutionary anomaly bound to be destroyed by its own contradictions, or the contradictions of its products?"[3]

At their root, then, the problems which confront us are far deeper than issues of resource availability or questions of technology. We must ask how the human species, which is itself a product of organic evolution, could have developed into such a threat to the very forces which have created it. Gregory Bateson suggests that the anti-ecological animus of human civilization is the result of the exercise of purposive consciousness in behavior which seeks to achieve narrowly defined human ends without concern or regard for the circular structure of cause and effect which characterizes the functioning of the rest of the living world. Since purposefulness is intrinsic to the functioning of consciousness, and since all human action is, to a certain extent, guided by the desire to achieve some future state through some present action, this diagnosis suggests a paradox central to the human condition. In order to survive we must act purposefully. Yet, to act purposefully leads us to disrupt the systems upon which we depend for survival. Moreover, since purpose is intrinsic to the nature of consciousness, it is not possible to renounce its use.

Thus, like the riddle of the Sphinx, or a Zen koan, the crisis of industrial civilization presents us with a paradox which must be resolved if we are to continue to exist. Unless we can find a way, both individually and collectively, to transcend the paradox of conscious purpose, we shall continue to win the battle for the domination of nature but lose the war of survival.

Before presenting some tentative suggestions for a way out of this dilemma, let us explore in more detail the nature of conscious purpose and its effects on the evolution of culture. We shall then be in a position to examine the systemic flaws in the organization of industrial civilization. By thus understanding the nature of the problem, perhaps we can come to an understanding of the nature of the solution. Whether or not any such theoretical formulations can, or will, be implemented, is something else again.

Conscious purpose

Bateson defines human consciousness as a relatively autonomous subsystem of the total mind / body of the individual organism. Because it is a part of a larger whole it is logically impossible for information about the whole system to be displayed on the "screen of consciousness." The information that does manage to become known to us is first selected from the total information available by the totally unconscious process of perception. We first transform the world into images through our senses and it is these images which become the basis for our necessarily limited consciousness of both internal and external reality.

Now, perception itself is shaped by purposes. We tend to see what we look for and what we look for is what is relevant to our purposes. This highly selective filtering process is a characteristic of all living systems from cells to ecosystems. If this were not the case, if the organism did not respond only to those stimuli that correspond to its own needs and capacities and remain blind or indifferent to everything else, it would not long survive.

So the structure of selective attention, characteristic of human perception and consciousness, is not unique to the human species. In fact, the *Umwelt*, or enclosing world, of the human organism is much wider and more diverse than that of any other species. Not only does it include the relevant portion of the immediately present world of nature, but it also includes broad expanses of time as well as the complex world of society and the equally complex inner world of personal feelings, needs and values.[4] Nevertheless, the world in which we live is not reality "as such," but is a culturally defined, personally constructed description of reality. However, because of the unconscious nature of the process of perception, it appears to us that we experience and inhabit an objectively real world that is accurately and faithfully reported to us by our sensory apparatus. We believe and act as if the map is the territory. This fundamental error in epistemology creates no end of problems, not the least of which is the failure to see the role played by purpose in shaping our image of nature, self and society. Thus, our conscious image of reality is a systematic distortion of its true nature, and action based on such reifications inevitably creates problems. As our power to act on the world increases, the problems that are created also increase. This is a uniquely human problem, since no other species is able to consciously reshape the world to correspond to its own perceptions and purposes to the extent that we can.

Purposive consciousness, then, can be described as a "short-cut device to enable you to get quickly at what you want; not to act with maximum wisdom in order to live, but to follow the shortest logical or causal path to get what you next want. . . ."[5] Thus, while it can produce a useful "bag of

Hui Tzu said to Chuang Tzu:
"All your teaching is centered on what has no use."

Chuang replied:
"If you have no appreciation for what has no use
you cannot begin to talk about what can be used.
The earth, for example, is broad and vast but of all this expanse a man only uses a few inches upon which he happens to be standing.
Now suppose you suddenly take away all that he is not actually using so that, all around his feet a gulf yawns, and he stands in the void,
with nowhere solid except right under each foot:
how long will he be able to use what he is using?"

Hui Tzu said:
"It would cease to serve any purpose."

Chuang Tzu concluded:
"This shows the absolute necessity of what has 'no use.'"

Chuang Tzu, from Thomas Merton, The Way of Chuang Tzu

tricks," such an instrumental rationality can never produce wisdom, which Bateson takes to be a knowledge of the interactive loop structure of complex systems of mind and nature. Consequently, "if you follow the 'common sense' dictates of consciousness, you become, effectively, greedy and unwise."[6]

It should come as no surprise, then, that industrial civilization, which has succeeded in implementing the narrowly conceived purposes of human consciousness with an unprecedentedly powerful technology, has become the most destructive, life-denying social system ever devised. But, as Bateson explains in the following story, the continued violation of the wisdom of a system is always disastrous to the violator:

Lack of systemic wisdom is always punished. We may say that the biological systems—the individual, the culture, and the ecology—are partly living sustainers of their component cells or organisms. But the systems are nonetheless punishing of any species unwise enough to quarrel with its ecology. Call the systemic forces "God," if you will.

Let me offer you a myth.

There was once a Garden. It contained many hundreds of species—probably in the subtropics—living in great fertility and balance, with plenty of humus, and so on. In that garden, there were two anthropoids who were more intelligent than the other animals.

On one of the trees there was a fruit, very high up, which the two apes were unable to reach. So they began to *think*. That was the mistake. They began to think purposively.

By and by, the he ape, whose name was Adam, went and got an empty box and put it under the tree and stepped on it, but he found he still couldn't reach this fruit. So he got another box and put it on top of the first. Then he climbed up

on the two boxes and finally he got that apple.

Adam and Eve then became almost drunk with excitement. *This* was the way to do things. Make a plan, ABC and you get D.

They then began to specialize in doing things the planned way. In effect, they cast out from the Garden the concept of their own total systemic nature and its total systemic nature.

After they had cast God out of the Garden, they really went to work on this purposive business, and pretty soon the topsoil disappeared. After that, several species of plants became "weeds" and some of the animals became "pests"; and Adam found that gardening was much harder work. He had to get his bread by the sweat of his brow and he said, "Its a vengeful God. I should have never eaten that apple."

Moreover, there occurred a qualitative change in the relationship between Adam and Eve, after they had discarded God from the Garden. Eve began to resent the business of sex and reproduction. Whenever these rather basic phenomena intruded upon her now purposive way of living, she was reminded of the larger life which had been kicked out of the Garden. So Eve began to resent sex and reproduction, and when it came to parturition she found this process very painful. She said this, too, was due to the vengeful nature of God. She even heard a Voice say "In pain shalt thou bring forth" and "Thy desire shall be unto thy husband, and he shall rule over thee."

The biblical version of this story, from which I have borrowed extensively, does not explain the extraordinary perversion of values, whereby the woman's capacity for love comes to seem a curse inflicted by the deity.

Be that as it may, Adam went on pursuing his purposes and finally invented the free-enterprise system. Eve was not, for a long time, allowed to participate in this, because she was a woman. But she joined a bridge club and there found an outlet for her hate.

In the next generation, they again had trouble with love. Cain, the inventor and innovator, was told by God that "His (Abel's) desire shall be unto thee and thou shalt rule over him." So he killed Abel.[7]

Now, Bateson's version of the Biblical myth of the fall of man (and woman, of course) from the Garden has been quoted in full because it not only contains an explanation of the epistemological and psychological implications of conscious purpose but it also demonstrates what happens when conscious purpose is allowed to dominate the process of social evolution, as it has since the rise of the first great hydraulic civilizations in the Middle East, Africa, and China. The myth of the Garden is human history miniaturized and accessible to conscious inspection. Let us take a closer look at it.

The story begins with the description of a condition of balance between nature, culture and consciousness. It is the mythical Golden Age in which the world is a harmony of opposites, a unity through diversity. But the potential for the loss of innocence and order is built into the very structure of the situation. Each complex system that is mentioned—the Garden as a whole, the two anthropoids, and each of the myriad species of plants and animals which comprise the Garden—is made up of a vast number of interrelated but relatively independent subsystems, each of which would go into exponential runaway if uncorrected by a vast number and variety of feedback loops and control circuits that maintain key system variables within the homeostatic ranges necessary for their adaptation and survival. These regulatory mechanisms ensure that no part is able to promote its own special purposes to the detriment of the whole. As long as this is the case, the Golden Age will continue and the Garden will remain a self-regulating, self-repairing, and self-organizing system.

However, this is not to be. There is one species which has the power to re-shape the Garden in its own image, and for its own ends. The two anthropoids, who presumably have already developed their capacity for language, are about to break with their evolutionary past and begin the long, sad process of cultural evolution, or history.

What sets this sequence in motion? Adam and Eve, no longer satisfied to accept the fruits of the Garden as a gift of God, make the decision to take what they desire. So they must have a fruit located beyond their human and biological dimensions. This is a subtle and profound shift in orientation to the world. An Arcadian life of biological adaptedness to nature is about to be replaced by a Promethean search for a humanized nature.[8]

Before this momentous decision, Adam and Eve had lived in God's "Grace," the state of being where it is understood "that everything gained and everything claimed follows upon something given, and comes after something gratuitous and unearned; that in the beginning there is always a gift."[9] By rejecting this idea that life is, in a fundamental sense, a gift of the larger systems of which they are a part, Adam and Eve are rejecting the sacredness of that which they cannot understand. As a result of this first step toward the desacralization of nature, Adam and Eve are stating, in a paraphrase of a famous modern corporate slogan, that "what is good for the anthropoid is good for the Garden."

Now what is the next step after this fall from "Grace"? It is the invention of technology. Adam does not ask God for the fruit. He improvises an instrument which allows him to reach it himself. He becomes, *Homo faber,* man the maker. Rather than changing himself to fit the environment, he invents a tool to reshape the environment to fit his own purposes. Since most of evolutionary history up till this point has involved change in the internal constitution of the organism to adapt to external change, this act constitutes a significant reversal in the relationship between the organism and the environment. And, it should be noted, it follows logically from the fall from Grace, which involved a shift from a contemplative orientation of wonder, thanks and celebration, to an active orientation that has rejected the gift of creation and has assumed total responsibility for remaking the world.

But their overwhelming success in achieving their purpose through planning and technology completely overshadows any sense of loss at this turn of events. Adam and Eve become intoxicated by their newly discovered power. This leads them to reflect on what has happened and they discover that they have invented "rational comprehensive planning." To get what you want you need a method. First, establish an explicit, objectively defined goal. Then state all possible alternate courses of action to achieve that goal and evaluate them in terms of their possibility of use and probability of success. Next, choose the best, most efficient course of action and, once implemented, evaluate the entire process to learn how to improve performance the next time around.

Note what this newly self-conscious model of purposive action implies. Activity is seen as a means to an end, rather than an end in itself. Any merely appreciative, contemplative and non-utilitarian encounter with the world comes to be seen as a waste of time, as useless. But what they have failed to grasp is that, if the world of leisure, play, and celebration has no value (i.e., serves no purpose), then life is reduced to a world of total work and constant struggle. The only reward is success in achieving goals, and this very success reinforces the purposive orientation to life. The result is to create a deep division within the self, a division that will replicate itself and reduce the world to an arena of conflict between irreconcilable opposites: work vs. play, male vs. female, nature vs. culture, the city vs. the wilderness, good vs. bad, and on and on.

Before the fall and the related ascendance of conscious purpose and instrumental rationality to a position of exclusive dominance, Adam and Eve had lived in a harmonious world. But now there is only fragmentation, division, and conflict. The divisions within Adam and Eve have been projected onto their environment. Whatever does not serve their own narrow purposes becomes an enemy, a "pest" or a "weed," or more generally, a "vengeful God." The world of *Homo faber,* the world of total work, becomes a world without grace, humor, security, or escape.

The tragic irony is that Adam and Eve fail to assume responsibility for these unintended "side effects" of their action. Everything that reminds them of their "sin," their rejection of their own systemic wholeness and the wholeness of the world, is seen as a curse. To escape the curse they redouble their efforts to solve the problems they have created. With the invention of the "free enterprise system" they manage to elevate selfishness, envy, and greed to the status of divine virtues, believing that the alchemy of the "invisible hand" will ultimately transmute base impulses into the universal harmony of a new Golden Age. Rather than recognizing their error and altering the course of their blind assault on nature, they believe that they can create a world where they are no longer reminded of their loss of wisdom.

Finally, the process of dividing self and world is consummated, as Cain, the planner, innovator, and technologist, kills the other half of his nature, Abel, who is the Arcadian shepherd willing to live within the bounds of what is given. The commitment to purpose is sealed in blood. There can be no turning back.

Bateson ends his version of the myth at this point but the Biblical prototype describes what happens next. After Cain slays Abel, he is summoned by God, and as was true in each earlier violation of systemic wisdom, the violator is cursed. As a result, Cain becomes a homeless fugitive, desperately searching for a world beyond the reach of this vengeful God. So Cain fathers a son, Enoch, and builds the first city and names it after his son. Thus, from its beginning, the city is an attempt to create a totally artificial environment efficiently planned to meet narrowly conceived human purposes. In the city, God and the Garden are both cast out and the anthropoids begin to expand their house of mirrors, disrupting ecosystems and exploiting rural peoples in a desperate and ill-fated search to reconnect themselves to the world.

The modern industrial city and the proposal to create totally artificial worlds in space[10] merely carry this theme to its logical conclusion. But it still won't work. As the story of the Garden illustrates, the lack of systemic wisdom is always punished.

Bateson's version of the Biblical story illustrates a number of important points not the least of which is the fact that it is far easier to intervene in the functioning of complex ecological systems than it is to understand or regulate them. Intervention requires only purpose plus technology (piling one box on another) whereas regulation, or stewardship, requires knowledge of the systemic wisdom of nature and self-constraint in human desires. Consequently, the crisis of industrial civilization can be seen as a failure in adaptive behavior related to our unwillingness and inability to assume responsibility for that which we have the ability to change.

That is why, in many cases, we continue to have the paradoxical situation of creating great evil even when we intend to do good. Take the case, for example, of the recent attempt of the World Health Organization (WHO) to control malaria in Borneo.

The standard method for eradicating malaria is to spray DDT in order to kill the mosquito that carries the disease. Because the inland Dayak people of Borneo live in long houses with as many as 500 or more people under a single roof, the program of spraying DDT proceeded in an efficient, orderly, planned manner. The short term effect was, as expected, a rapid and dramatic improvement in the health and vitality of the people. However, as in the story of the Garden, this intervention failed to take into account the systemic loop structure of ecological systems, a failure which led to some equally unfortunate "side effects."

Before spraying, the thatched huts of the villages provided a habitat for a small community of organisms, including cats, cockroaches, and small lizards. After spraying, the DDT was absorbed by the cockroaches. They were eaten by the lizards. The cats, in turn, ate the lizards. Because the DDT became more concentrated at each level of the food chain, the lizards contained enough DDT to cause the cats to die of DDT poisoning. When the cats died, the woodland rats invaded the villages bringing with them fleas, lice and other parasites. This new community of organisms, thus, presented a new threat to public health in the form of sylvatic plague. To prevent this disease from breaking out, the RAF parachuted living cats into the isolated Dayak villages to control the rats.

While the newly arrived cats were tending to the newly created problem of the rats, another side effect of the spraying program made its appearance. It seems that the DDT had killed the parasites and predators of a small caterpillar. While the previously controlled population of caterpillars typically caused only minor damage to the thatch roofs, the caterpillars became so numerous after the spraying that the roofs of the huts collapsed.[11]

This modern version of Bateson's story of Adam and Eve not only reinforces his point that lack of systemic wisdom is always punished, but it also illustrates the fact that, whereas modern civilization has greatly amplified its technology of purposive intervention, it has made very little progress in its understanding of the functioning of systems upon which it depends for survival.

The case of malarial control in Borneo is an example of a local intervention with relatively local effects. People in New York and Tokyo were not greatly affected one way or another. However, the activity of industrial peoples is no longer limited to single ecosystems. We are rapidly disrupting all the major ecosystems of the earth and may even be contributing to major changes in the planet's climatic system.[12] We are now caught in a vicious spiral where each intervention creates unintended "side effects," which become new problems demanding still further interventions, which create

more crises, and so on. The tragedy is that each new crisis leads to the adoption of more and more expedient "solutions" in a process that moves progressively further away from systemic wisdom. In another variant of Gresham's Law, crisis management based on purposive consciousness drives out wisdom, just as "Bad money drives out good."[13]

Conscious purpose and the evolution of culture

It was stated earlier that the greatest problem facing humankind today is that industrial civilization has created a single world ecosystem that is able to function only because of its continued exploitation of increasingly scarce and inherently limited natural resources. We have also seen, by both parable and anecdote, that when conscious purpose is the basis for interventions in complex ecosystems, the result is to drive God, or systemic wisdom, out of the Garden (and out of the self). It now remains to be demonstrated how cultural evolution results in a rapid loss of adaptive flexibility through overspecialization, which leads to a loss of diversity, and overcentralization, which leads to a loss of stability. These thoughts will lead us to a consideration of the kinds of corrective actions that must be taken to restore the evolutionary potential of human consciousness and human culture.

The vast number and diversity of interconnected life forms on this planet are the outcomes of an ongoing process of evolution. The individual organisms that are the result of this process are able to adapt to a wide variety of environmental conditions within the constraints set by their genetic inheritance.

The genetic diversity of a species is maintained by the constant recombination of the genetic material of individuals through reproduction, and the occasional adoption of relatively few random mutations which prove to have adaptive validity. The individual organisms which manage to survive pass on those traits which have thereby proven to be better adapted to prevailing environmental conditions. And, as new conditions arise, other types of individual organisms survive to pass on their traits to the species gene pool. In this way species remain adapted to their environments while maintaining a potential for future changes.

Since change in biological form results in a loss of flexibility and since all evolutionary change is irreversible, the process of species change must be very slow. In biological evolution this is assured by the existence of the barrier between somatic change ("bodily change brought about during the lifetime of the individual by environmental impact or by practice") and genetic change.[14] This barrier prevents overspecialization and the loss of evolutionary flexibility. According to Gregory Bateson, biological evolution, which proceeds by this Darwinian process of natural selection, is guided by a rule which says "that you should not make an irreversible change until a long time has elapsed so that it is reasonably certain that the irreversible change will pay and you won't regret the irreversibility."[15]

Unfortunately, cultural evolution proceeds by a process of Lamarckian rather than Darwinian evolution, (i.e. by the inheritance of acquired characteristics through the transmission of culture). Characteristics of technology, social practice and custom, education, economics, and so on, acquired by one generation are transferred to the next through learning and become "hard programmed" in the environment they create. There is no built-in equivalent to the barrier, which exists in biological evolution, between somatic and genetic change. Bateson explains what would happen if this barrier did not exist in the rest of nature.

> But let us suppose that in biological evolution there is a direct communicational bond between individual experience which will induce somatic change, as it is called, and the DNA injunctions to be passed on to the next generation. Let us imagine for the moment a Lamarckian universe, in which, if I tan myself in the sun, this will in some degree be passed on as increased brownness of the skin of my offspring. In such a system, my offspring will have *lost* a flexibility. They will no longer have my freedom. By hypothesis, I am flexible. I go brown in the sun, or I go bleach with no sun. But Lamarckian theory will in the end enforce an increasing rigidity, a loss of ability to adapt, and that won't do. Things are going to get too tight.[16]

This argument against the possible existence of Lamarckian evolution in nature also points up the inherent flaw of Lamarckian evolution in culture: adaptations to environmental conditions are passed on too quickly. Within a few generations of rapid innovation an entire culture can become highly specialized to the conditions which created it. Since all evolutionary specializations are irreversible, any future shift in prevailing conditions can not only make the immediate survival of the culture problematic, but can limit its ability to make further changes due to the loss of evolutionary potential.

This, of course, is a description of the dilemma facing the modern world. Philosopher Ty Cashman describes the history of industrial civilization as a case of Lamarckian evolution ending in maladaptation:

> When inheritance of acquired cultural

characteristics occurs in a society where a balance has been achieved between population size, the ecosystem which supports it, and the climate, a relatively steady state can occur. What gets passed on becomes 'tradition' which stabilizes social and economic patterns. But when changes in climate, resource availability, travel, and communication between cultures are joined with an inventive spirit in the people, one innovation leads to the next and an exponential curve of change develops, rising, as such curves do, first slowly and then faster and faster. When one generation invents the steam engine, the next generation is born with it, and can improve upon it. It can apply it to different uses: ships, textile mills, locomotives. The steam locomotive in turn allows the building of large cities, which can now be supplied from long distances. A next generation, from ideas derived from working with steam power, can invent the automobile, and then the airplane, and on and on.

Western culture today is the end result of the Lamarckian inheritance pattern stimulated by the scientific paradigms growing from the Renaissance, coupled with the discovery and exploitation of fossil fuels. The result of this major adaptation of human political economy to newly available cheap combustible energy is today's global, technological-industrial economy.

The Lamarckian evolution of the human economy seems now to be reaching the limits of its survival—for it is specialized not only within but as a whole. It is dependent at every point on readily available fossil fuels which are now reaching depletion. The system as a whole arose from this one energy source. It is also specialized in its goal, the maximum production of goods and services in the shortest amount of time, without regard for the long-term future. And it has up till now shown an ability to function well only in the very narrow range of circumstances which allow indefinite growth: virgin lands to exploit, ever increasing markets, and indefinite

supplies of metal ores, fibers, chemicals, water, and places to dump waste.

The very measure of success in achieving its goal has been the exhaustion of resources and the dislocation of the world-wide environmental support system.

There are no more virgin territories to explore and exploit; no more undeveloped regions to conquer and colonize. Even the vast seas, once teeming with fish and whales are becoming aqueous deserts. The Lamarckian technological economy has adapted so completely to the resources available 50 years ago that it has efficiently exhausted them.[17]

The idea of evolution has become so closely identified with the ideology of progress that this description of modern civilization as an evolutionary culde-sac seems to many people to be completely backwards. Haven't we evolved from a barbaric past where we lived in caves and gathered nuts and berries to a civilized present where we live in high-rise apartments in modern cities and eat food designed by science and grown and harvested by giant machines and a handful of farmers? Indeed, evolutionary theory has been evoked to give credibility to this popular myth. Just as nature began with a single cell and has evolved into a complex world-circling web of life, so human societies began as simple hunting and gathering tribes and have evolved into a single worldwide industrial civilization. Surely human civilization, like the rest of nature, has gone from the simple to the complex, the primitive to the modern. Elaborate analogies are even drawn between the specialization that has resulted from the subdivision of labor in human societies and the functional specialization of the myriad organisms that make up a climax ecosystem. Thus, rather than seeing cheap fossil fuels and energy-intensive technology as creating a mal-adaptive cultural form, cultural evolution itself is defined in terms of the progressive increase in per capita energy consumption. Anthropologist Leslie White has even stated "the basic law of cultural evolution" as follows:

> Other factors remaining constant, culture evolves as the amount of energy harnessed per capita per year is increased, or as the efficiency of the instrumental means of putting energy to work is increased."[18]

Here Professor White not only celebrates the consumption of energy as the key indicator of evolutionary advancement but also describes conscious purpose and its handmaiden technology as the driving forces behind progress. Since the United States consumes approximately 100 times as much energy per capita as a hunting and gathering society, one would deduce from the "law of cultural evolution" that we must be at least 100 times more highly evolved than our backward ancestors. In fact, this pernicious belief was acted out in our genocidal treatment of Native Americans and it continues to guide the actions of nations throughout the world as they attempt to bring the few remaining "stone age" groups into the 20th century as quickly as technology and government aid will allow. If, as has been suggested here, industrial civilization turns out to be an evolutionary dead end, we might hope that such arrogant and ill-advised efforts will at least afford us with knowledge of these remarkably well-adapted groups that is useful to our own future adaptation.

In any case, since Social Darwinism is so deeply engrained in the modern mind, it might be worth the time and effort to see why our complex interdépendent industrial civilization is inherently maladapted and may be headed for extinction due to its highly successful and rapid evolutionary specialization to conditions prevailing during the passing age of fossil fuels.

Hyper-coherence

Modern society is comprised of a vast and diverse number of highly interdependent organizations and systems of organizations. But interdependence does not necessarily imply community. The recent energy "crises" have made it clear that the decisions Americans make about where to vacation and how to get to work are directly tied to the internal politics of Iran or Saudi Arabia. The decision to grow wheat in Kansas is based as much on the weather in the Soviet Union or the production of phosphates in Morocco as it is on the health and fertility of the local topsoil. Even decisions affecting the future health of Colorado (which has 80 percent of U.S. oil shale deposits) are more directly tied to the escalating price and diminishing supply of crude oil in world markets than they are to the decisions made by the citizens of that state. The dependencies created within our current global village tend to foster conflictual relations among and within nations and to reduce the control any individual or group has over decisions crucial to their own survival. This mix makes the world system highly volatile and subject to almost inevitable disruption.

In the language of cybernetics and general systems theory the unhealthy inter-dependence of the world system can be described as a case of "hyper-coherence." Coherence is the extent to which a change in one system component produces changes in other components. In this sense any system must be considered to be somewhat coherent;

otherwise it would not be a system. In a fully coherent system, however, any change in one component would result in immediate and proportional changes in all other components.[19] Since such a level of integration would lead to the immediate spread of disruptions everywhere in the system, it would be impossible for a living system to be fully coherent.

While it is important that an organism be highly coherent, it is disastrous for higher levels of systems such as societies and ecosystems to exhibit the same level of integration. Diversity, redundancy, and systemic "incoherence," rather than strong centralized control, are essential to the stability, order, and survival of larger, more inclusive systems. The global village created by high-energy industrial technology is a clear example of "hypercoherence" and maladaptive organization.[20]

Over-segregation and over-centralization

The existence of a single world system creates a number of other problems. Because of long-distance transportation and cheap energy, it has been possible to achieve a level of regional specialization never before imagined. Entire states and even nations and regions have become monocultures for the production of single crops for world markets. Other areas have become company towns built around the extraction of raw materials needed to supply the voracious appetite of industry. The factory model of production has been applied to decisions affecting the character and long-term viability of entire landscapes. The result is widespread environmental degradation and the erosion of the diversity, richness, and stability of local cultures and ecosystems.

This reduction in the capacity for local self-regulation creates a situation where distant, large scale and complex organizations become increasingly involved in the management of local affairs. But this only makes matters worse, since it is impossible for higher level administrators to have information about local situations soon enough and accurate enough to make appropriate responses. And the attempt of distant authorities to regulate the details of everyday life only increases local resentment and further erodes local competencies. Such over-centralization of systems control violates W. Ross Ashby's "principle of requisite variety," which requires that the scale of authority be reduced as the complexity of action increases.[21] Thus, the loss of local regulatory ability can never be adequately compensated by the increase in centralized control. The loss of local ecological and social stability, therefore, increases the instability of the total world system.[22]

Thus, while it may appear on the surface that modern society has the diversity, interconnectedness and complexity characteristic of a mature and stable ecosystem, we find on closer inspection that the industrial ecosystem is a cruel caricature of natural systems. Just as Satan is a mimic of God, industrial society is an inversion of the basis for systemic health and wholeness.

And what is true of the whole is true of the part. Each individual in industrial society is a fragment, a specialized part of a maladaptive whole. Within the last generation most people in the industrial world have lost the knowledge and skill necessary to survive without the fragile and overextended network of life support systems built by cheap energy. We have lost the ability to feed, or clothe, or house or educate, or heal ourselves in direct proportion to our growing dependence on specialists of every kind. Most of us no longer know how our basic needs are provided. Living in decaying cities and sprawling suburbs we have even lost our sense of participation in the natural systems upon which we depend for survival. We are, indeed, "strangers in a strange land," completely dependent on forces we can neither control nor understand.

But, if a fragmented, overcentralized and overspecialized society creates individuals who are incapable of living in the world by their own knowledge and skill, it also creates the anxiety and fear necessary to ensure their continued allegiance to the very systems which render them incompetent. The service economy of postindustrial America grows fat off its failure to produce competent, whole, and self-reliant people. While centralized institutions and formal organizations become more and more complex and structured, everyday life becomes less and less orderly and sane.

By engendering such hyper-dependent and fractional individuals, industrial society becomes even more vulnerable and unstable. Should any of the complex, global systems upon which we depend for our everyday needs fail, as they must, there are no personal and local back-up systems to take their place. As Ty Cashman says, "We partake fully in the rigid Lamarckian specialization."[23]

This view of the present state of affairs leads to some sobering questions. If, as the conventional wisdom asserts, industrial civilization is the inevitable outcome of cultural evolution, and if the process of cultural evolution is the necessary expression of human conscious purpose, which is a concomitant of consciousness itself, then it may well be asked whether or not human intelligence is an evolutionary error. Perhaps given enough time, evolution in any form must lead to maladaptive overspecialization.

If we are to survive as a species we must learn how to restore the circular ecological structure of the world which our increasingly powerful technology has disrupted. This, in turn, requires the restoration of wholeness to our socio-politico-economic systems as well as to the structure of consciousness itself. Whether or not such profound changes in our thought and institutions can be accomplished in time to avoid the fate which usually accompanies the loss of evolutionary flexibility is the central question facing us today.

Unraveling the paradox

Let us summarize the argument up to this point. We have said that the crisis of industrial civilization can be traced to the operation of human conscious purpose. But we have also said that all living systems act on and respond to only that portion of the environment which corresponds to their own capacities for perception and meets their own needs for survival. Thus, how is it that human conscious purpose has become so maladaptive? The answer, in part, is that human intelligence allows the development of language, and this mode of symbolic communication makes possible patterns of behavior uncharacteristic of other living systems. By providing abstract representations of objects and relationships and by allowing the representation and recall of past experiences and events, it becomes possible to imagine alternative descriptions of reality and to foresee (within limits) the effects of action. This means that it is possible to plan and to shape the environment to meet humanly perceived needs.

Thus, the human species is able to

significantly alter its environment rather than simply being selected by it.[24] Moreover, it becomes possible, through culture, which is the product of language, to transmit to future generations changes in behavior that are acquired through experience. This new form of adaptation makes it possible to greatly accelerate the slow trial-and-error process of evolution which occurs through environmental selection and the differential reproduction of adaptive genetic potential.

However, even this radical innovation does not necessarily lead to maladaptation through overspecialization. For tens of thousands of years tribal bands of hunters and gatherers were able to develop patterns of belief and ways of living that were finely adapted to the ecosystems by which they were sustained. Even with the emergence of horticultural societies, which created special environments of domesticated plants and animals for meeting their needs, the potentially regenerative capacities created by conscious purpose, language and culture did not become a serious problem. As we shall see shortly, there are many examples, both historical and contemporary, of human cultures living in stable, balanced, and mutually beneficial relationships with their local environments.

What, then, has allowed civilization in general and industrial civilization in particular to develop in such an anti-ecological direction? The answer, as will be recalled from the story of the Garden, can be traced to the desacralization of nature: when life is no longer seen as a gift of the "Garden," narrow human purpose becomes the sole criterion of action. By no longer internalizing the interests of the non-human environment through an unshakeable belief in the sacredness of all creation, the regenerative potential of human

purpose, amplified by planning and technology and institutionalized in culturally prescribed behavior, is unleashed, resulting in a Lamarckian evolution toward overspecialization and maladaptation.

So, it would seem that human conscious purpose is not necessarily an evolutionary mistake, only a destructive potential which must be corrected and regulated by circuits of control which serve to direct human purposefulness towards goals and actions which coincide with the needs of the larger natural systems which sustain human life. The adaptive crisis of industrial civilization is the result of the loss of these regulatory processes.

The big question, then, is, "What are these control mechanisms and how can they be recreated and sustained?" It is to these questions that we must now turn.

Sanctity, purpose, and the recovery of wisdom

In a society in which, as Bob Dylan has noted, "Not much is really sacred," it is somewhat difficult to talk about the idea of the sacred, let alone understand the role of sanctity in constraining the regenerative potential of narrow human purpose. From our point of view it seems quite reasonable that the two anthropoids, Adam and Eve, would have developed a plan and invented a technology to get that apple. After all, if they were hungry, if the Garden has no more apples lower down to offer them as a "gift," wouldn't they have been wise to adopt a more effective strategy for survival? Indeed, for us, the appreciative, aesthetic, non-discursive and non-utilitarian attitude and the aggressive, technical, discursive, and instrumental approach to life are irreconcilable opposites. The best that can be hoped is to maintain both, but in tightly segregated compartments. One mode is suitable for church or poetic revery when one is in love, perhaps, but the other is what puts food on the table, what makes it possible for us to survive. So we kneel before God and pray in union with our neighbors in a fellowship of worship during a church service, only to run over each other in the parking lot to get home in time to catch the start of Sunday's televised presentation of ritualized conflict on the football field. It is no wonder, then, that we feel some sympathy for our poor ancestors in the Garden, who were, after all, only doing what was natural and necessary. It is God's vengeful behavior that appears a bit irrational and in need of some explanation. So, if the resolution of the paradox of conscious purpose means that we should go hungry while apples hang from the trees just beyond our reach, perhaps we should take our chances with nuclear power and space colonies and a priesthood of scientific-technological guardians.

But it is precisely this dualistic thinking, which creates such an either / or choice between aggressive intervention or contemplative appreciation, that gives rise to the paradox in the first place. To look at the problem in these terms is to fail to see the possibility of a dialectical synthesis of discipline and spontaneity, rigor and imagination, purpose and thanks. Perhaps an example would help us to see that such a harmony of opposites is at least possible. Toward that end, the poet Gary Snyder tells the following story about how a member of a modern "primitive" culture secures his venison:

Let me describe how a friend of mine from a Rio Grande pueblo hunts. He is

twenty-seven years old. The Pueblo Indians, and I think probably most of the other Indians of the Southwest, begin their hunt, first, by purifying themselves. They take emetics, a sweat bath, and perhaps avoid their wife for a few days. They also try not to think certain thoughts. They go out hunting in an attitude of humility. They make sure that they need to hunt, that they are not hunting without necessity. Then they improvise a song while they are in the mountains. They sing aloud or hum to themselves while they are walking along. It is a song to the deer, asking the deer to be willing to die for them. They usually still-hunt, taking a place alongside a trail. The feeling is that you are not hunting the deer, the deer is coming to you; you make yourself available for the deer that will present itself to you, that has given itself to you. Then you shoot it, you cut the head off and place the head facing east. You sprinkle corn meal in front of the mouth of the deer, and you pray to the deer, asking it to forgive you for having killed it, to understand that we all need to eat, and to please make a good report to the other deer spirits that he has been treated well. One finds this way of handling things and animals in all primitive cultures.[25]

This Native American method of hunting need only be compared to the practice of white buffalo hunters in the last century, who slaughtered millions of those great beasts and left them to rot in the sun after removing only their tongues for a quick profit, to understand the difference between a way of life that is based on a sense of the sacred and one based on a sense of the expedient. Clearly, the "primitive" deer hunter and the "civilized" buffalo hunter are both acting with conscious purpose and they are both engaging in behavior that is intrinsically violent. The important difference lies in the attitude behind the action. The Pueblo Indian is acting out of a pervasive awareness that nature is a community to which he belongs and upon which he depends. It is not a commodity to be used, not a resource to be exploited with maximum efficiency. While violence may be sometimes required in order to exist, it should be undertaken only if absolutely necessary and, even then, only with a deep sense of regret. This combination of respect, humility, and compassion for all sentient beings makes it possible to act upon the world passively, to obtain ends without use of means.

It is this way of acting that the Chinese sage Lao Tzu called *wu wei,* literally "not doing." This doctrine of inaction expresses the simple truth that force, or aggression, ultimately defeats itself.

> How does this pattern arise? It arises out of the inertia of existence, the tendency of every existing object or arrangement to continue to be what it is. Interfere with its existence and it resists, as a stone resists crushing. If it is a living thing it resists actively, as a wasp being crushed will sting. But the kind of resistance offered by living creatures is unique: it grows stronger as interference grows stronger up to the point that the creature's capacity for resistance is destroyed. Evolution might be thought of as a march towards ever more highly articulated and effective capacity for resistance. Humans and human societies are then highly responsive to challenge. So when anyone, ruler or subject, tries to *act* upon humans individually or collectively, *the ultimate result is the opposite of what he is aiming at.* He has invoked what we might call the Law of Aggression. (emphasis is mine)[26]

The deep wisdom of the Pueblo hunt is that the deer is considered to be a "person" with its own destiny and role in creation and it is understood that the relations between the human people and deer people are subject to this Law of Aggression. Thus, it becomes important to communicate to the spirit of the deer that the hunt is necessary, that it is not undertaken merely as a violent, bloodthirsty act. Whether or not there is a spirit of the deer to accept this explanation is, in one sense, not important. The attitude itself is sufficient to ensure that the carrying capacity of the land is not diminished by wanton destruction. By treating the deer as sacred, the Pueblo are able to control the regenerative potential of human greed and violence and to effectively regulate the complex ecosystems of which they are a part, while meeting their own legitimate needs for survival. The culture of the buffalo hunters, which has failed to similarly respect the sanctity of the world, is now playing out the Law of Aggression on a global scale. Unlike the Pueblo culture, we have yet to understand the paradoxical wisdom of the Tao Te Ching:

> Heaven is eternal, the Earth everlasting.
> How come they to be so? It is because
>   they do not foster their own lives.
> That is why they live so long.
> Therefore, the Sage
> Puts himself in the background; but is
>   always to the fore
> Remains outside; but is always there.
> Is it not just because he does not strive
>   for any personal ends
> That all personal ends are fulfilled?[27]

One can imagine Adam and Eve puzzling over such irrational and impractical advice. But, it will be remembered, it was they who cast out from the Garden the concept of their own systemic wisdom and its systemic wisdom and, in the act of doing so, created a world of mere things, a vengeful God, and a life of toil and suffering. Before moving on, let us take one more look at the Garden before the fall, before cultural evolution got caught up in the vicious cycles of the Law of Aggression.

Animism, the attribution of divine character, or "personhood," to natural objects and ecological systems, seems to be an important reason why traditional cultures are able to maintain a non-exploitative and stable relationship with their surroundings. Anthropologist Roy Rappaport, whose exhaustive field work and brilliant theoretical formulations have firmly established the causal relations between sanctity, ecology, purpose, and human adaptation, provides a summary of the conditions necessary for a symbiosis between nature and culture in the following analysis of forest horticulture among the Maring, an association of completely autonomous groups ranging in size from 150 to 900 people, who live in the mountains of Australian New Guinea:

We may reflect here on the general strategy of slash and burn forest horticulture. It is to establish temporary associations of plants directly useful to man on sites from which forest is removed and to encourage the return of forests to those sites after the plants have been harvested. The return of forest makes it possible, or at least much easier, to establish again an association of cultivated plants sometime in the future. The Maring recognize this, of course, and are almost as solicitous of the trees growing in their gardens as they are of cultivated plants. Their appreciation of the regenerating forest is clearly reflected in their term for it: *nduk mi,* which means "mother of the garden."

It is clear that the Maring nurture not only the garden species that provide them with food directly, but also those species upon which they indirectly, but nevertheless ultimately, depend: the forest species that make it possible for the garden species to flourish from time to time.

Effective ecological regulation, which

is to say the maintenance of the circular structure of ecosystems, depends in systems dominated by men on effective information feedback from the environment to those operating upon it (the flow of information through ecosystems, like the flow of materials through the same systems, must be circular). Information feedback from the environment is sensitive and rapid in small autonomous ecological systems in which everyone is a gardener. There are no special interest groups in the societies participating in such autonomous local systems. It is clear to *all* men living in such systems that their survival is contingent upon the *maintenance,* rather than the mere *exploitation* of the larger community of which they *know* themselves to be only parts. They comprehend more clearly than hunters and gatherers and more clearly than modern men the circular structure of their world, and they are likely to understand well that their own purposes or goals are limited by that structure and the need to maintain it.[28]

Ecocommunities: Toward a new synthesis of nature, self and society

We are now in a position to describe the necessary and sufficient means by which it is possible to transcend the paradox of conscious purpose and, by doing so, to create a society which, through its emulation of naturally occurring ecosystems and the evolutionary processes by which they are created, can ensure the maintenance of evolutionary flexibility and adaptive potential. This synthesis rests on two related ideas, sanctity and community. These two themes come together in the idea of ecocommunities, associations of plants, animals, microbes and people living together within the seasonal cycles of sun, wind, and water that provide the energy flows and nutrient recycling necessary to maintain life. Central to this concept of ecocommunities is the principle of symbiosis, the living together of diverse species in mutually beneficial relations. The ecocommunity, as symbol and strategy, is the basic building block for the creation of a new form of human culture that joins modern science and technology with the sacred worldview of archaic and mystical traditions in a new synthesis of nature, self and society.

Let us take a closer look at the part played by the themes of sanctity and community in this synthesis.

Sanctity

We have seen through Bateson's story of Adam and Eve that human conscious purpose becomes a problem as a result of the epistemological error of setting up an inaccurate distinction between self and environment. By no longer perceiving the mutually interdependent system of self-in-the-environment as a systemic whole, human purpose comes to be seen as separate from and in conflict with the needs of the larger system of which it is a part. A paradox is a seemingly contradictory statement that results from the unconscious existence of a false premise. Once such a premise is recognized as an error, the paradox dissolves in a higher synthesis. The paradox of conscious purpose is the result of the false dualism that it's "us" against the "environment." Once this is realized it becomes clear that true human purpose, even in a strictly narrow utilitarian sense, is identical with the needs of the larger systems of which we are a part. While it is not possible to avoid making distinctions in the phenomenal world, where everything is defined by its opposite, it is essential that the distinctions we make have adaptive value.

Clearly, the dualistic epistemology of Western technological culture fails by this criteria.

The crisis of industrial civilization leads to a paradox, i.e., in order to survive we must progressively deplete the non-renewable resources necessary for our survival. Thus, like a *Reductio ad Absurdum* proof in geometry, the assumption that self and environment are not one, leads to a logical absurdity. Bad epistemology has no survival value. We shall never escape the fate we have created for ourselves unless we radically change our root assumptions about the nature of reality.

Through the example of the Pueblo deer hunt and the Maring slash and burn forest horticulture we have seen that the conception of natural objects and systems as deified persons is one way of ensuring that human purpose coincides with the needs of more inclusive systems. It is suggested, therefore, that such an "animistic" worldview is a more accurate description of reality than our own rational, "scientific" worldview.

In dealing with complex systems which we can never, in principle, fully understand, it is essential that our action be based on a basic respect for the sanctity of those systems and an awareness of our own participation in and dependence on them. As Roy Rappaport has said, "Knowledge will never replace respect in man's dealings with ecological systems."[29] Because we now act on the assumption that we do adequately understand the complex interactive loop structure of natural systems, even our attempts to do good, as in the case of the malaria control program in Borneo, result in great harm to our environment and ourselves. But this paradox is the result of action which does not respect the Law of Aggression. By showing us how to act without acting, to obtain ends without means, the Pueblo Indian hunter and the Maring horticulturalist point us toward a mode of being in the world that is fundamentally non-violent and ultimately more effective. Unless we achieve a similar consciousness and embody it in our institutions and technologies, we shall continue to achieve the opposite of what we intend. At its root, an appropriate technology and culture must grow out of and express an appropriate epistemology. This, in turn, may well depend on the restoration of the sacred to our metaphysics.

Not only does sanctity ensure that a balance will be maintained between a human group and its environment, but it also prevents the vicious cycle of exponential runaway that we have referred to as Lamarckian evolution. It is the functional equivalent in cultural evolution of the Weissmanian barrier between somatic change and genetic change in organic evolution. Since genetic change in species form reduces long-term adaptive flexibility, and since all evolutionary change is irreversible, natural selection, to be successful, must be conservative. Through the ability to directly transmit patterns of behavior and environment from one generation to the next, cultural evolution, in the short run, is no longer bound by the selective mechanisms of the natural environment. In effect, we select the environments by which we are selected. Every cultural change creates the conditions which make further change in the same direction more probable. To ensure that the direction we are headed is the direction we want to go, we must make sure that the process is slow enough for us to see where we have been. For this to happen, innovation must be relatively infrequent and localized, and the criteria for the selection of changes to be introduced

must, at a minimum, be grounded in a concern for the long-term viability of the systems we intend to change. Our power to be greedy and unwise requires that we develop the wisdom necessary to control that power.

In planning it must be recognized that the outcome of our actions will never be completely or accurately predicted. Thus, sanctity, that "quality of unquestionable truthfulness imputed by the faithful to unverifiable propositions," must be a necessary part of any effective strategy for making adaptive evolutionary change.[30] It is as essential as the "necessary truth of logic and the empirical truth of experience" in the shaping of human behavior.[31] Sanctity regulates our relations with ecosystems in a way which ensures their (and our) long-term sustainability:

> In general terms, then, through sanctification the purposes of the higher order systems may be injected into lower order systems. As such, sanctification operates as a counterthrust to attempts on the part of subsystems which are also social groups to promote their own purposes to positions of dominance in higher level systems. In slightly different terms, sanctity helps to keep subsystems in their places.[32]

If sanctity is a necessary ingredient in any viable culture, community is the means by which sanctity is operationalized and transmitted to future generations. Each concept implies the other. Let us take a closer look at the idea of community and the nature of this relationship.

Community

Largely because of cheap fossil fuels and large-scale centralized technology, we no longer live within community. We live as individuals within a mass superficially connected to one another through interest groups, temporary coalitions and whatever shared consciousness is created by the banal fare of soap operas, sitcoms, newscasts, and sports circuses offered by the broadcast media.

This is a poor substitute for the deep and rich quality of human relationships fostered by small face-to-face communities of shared space, personal responsibility, and mutual obligation. We also no longer live within the limits of local ecosystems but, rather, depend upon the extraction of resources from every corner of the earth to meet our most basic needs. The idea of ecocommunities is to reintegrate these parts of our lives that have become so fragmented and dissociated in time and space.

The principle of sanctity leads to an attitude of respect for wildness, for the recognition of the fact that human life is totally dependent on the "useless" beings and processes that comprise the globally interdependent network of naturally occurring ecosystems. This respect for the sanctity of all creation must be embodied in the social, political, and technological systems by which we interact with the living world. This holistic vision of a climax ecosystem of culture-in-nature is expressed by Gary Snyder's notion of a democracy of all sentient beings and things:

> In Pueblo societies a kind of ultimate democracy is practiced. Plants and animals are also people, and, through certain rituals and dances, are given a place and a voice in the political discussions of the humans. They are "represented." "Power to all the people" must be the slogan.[33]

Without sanctity such a community could not exist but without the institutionalization of this worldview in the rituals and enactments of everyday life, the idea of the sacred could not exist.

Together, sanctity and community create a self-organizing, self-regulating and self-repairing system, a cybernetics of wholeness and balance through a harmony of opposites.

David Spangler, a leading spokesman for the idea of the new age and an active participant in the creation of new age communities, provides a definitive summary of the emerging synthesis of scientific perspectives in the fields of ecology, quantum physics, cybernetics, and communication arts, and the essentially mystical idea that humanity is entering a new era of spiritual growth, cultural transformation, and evolutionary advance:

> Like the idea of symbiosis, the essential image of the new age is of a state of wholeness, interrelationship and interdependency, all qualities that may also define community. In fact, in the new age vision, the universe itself may be perceived as a community, co-created by all the forms of life that inhabit it (remembering that even matter is considered to have a living, spiritual aspect and therefore is a participant in this co-creation). The proper way of relating to the world about us—to the forces of nature, to stones, plants, and animals, as well as to each other—is in terms of community: everything we see is a fellow member, a co-participant, in this community, with all of us being linked together by subtle bonds of spiritual communion and communication. The effect of this is to elevate the meaning of community from being simply a place for collective habitation and enterprise to being a reflection of our deepmost nature and the deepmost nature of creation. Community transcends its social aspects and becomes an educational enterprise, a "yoga of relationship" that can offer a path to union with the universal wholeness. It becomes a strategy for experiencing holistic consciousness at work and may even be defined in terms of that consciousness, becoming an inner state of being as much as an outer place of gathering.

Thus, community may come to mean not so much the act or result of living and working together but rather the state of consciousness which, reflecting the essential wholeness of life, can actively manifest wholeness in human and environmental relationships.

Furthermore, community may be defined as a multi-leveled or multi-stage activity. First, there is the community of my own being, my own internal wholeness which potentially exists between the parts of my body, my emotions, my thoughts and my spirit . . . and my objective is to nourish its emergence and find inner balance and harmony. . . .

The second level is the community of my fellow humans. Here I seek to establish wholeness and communication with loved ones, friends, co-workers, and others. Human society would not be possible without activity on this level. However, this level and the first one are symbiotically related: since I do not exist in a vacuum, my relationships help to define and inspire inner states, and my inner condition of wholeness and harmony reflects directly into my relationships and my ability to function in community with others. Both these levels of community influence each other. In the idea of the symbiotic or new age community, this mutual influence or exchange is beneficial; one level of community helps to co-create the other.

Third, there is the level of the ecology, the community of lives that make up the natural world and of which humanity is a part, though it often seems forgetful of that fact. The ecology of our world is a tightly knit community of interdependent and interbalancing relationships. Human community and human individuality need to act in harmony with these relationships, forming the greater community of life on earth. Our evolution is intimately tied into this community, and we, in turn, can affect, for better or for worse, the growth and development of the biosphere.

Fourth, there is the earth itself. For thousands of years, most of the great spiritual paths and teachings of our species have acknowledged our planet as a being, a living consciousness several magnitudes removed from our own. In analogy to ourselves, earth can be seen either as a great Individuality, participating in the larger community of the cosmos, or as a community itself, composed of all the parts (like ourselves) that make up its internal wholeness.

All these levels of community are seen, in the vision underlying the idea of a new age, as interactive and symbiotic, each contributing to the other, each demanding the creative participation of the other. . . .

It is through our successfully embodying the spirit of community in ourselves and in our relationships that we contribute to the on-going unfoldment of our world. Community, then, becomes a direct strategy in the process of the evolution of consciousness, a way of releasing from all levels of life and being new potentials of expression and vision.

This definition of community verges towards the mystical and makes the practice of living and working together a sacred act.[34]

This definition of community as a "yoga of relationships" by which the world is continually created is not only aesthetically pleasing and intuitively "right," but it is also remarkably similar to our emerging ecological understanding of the organization of the natural world. Unlike the global industrial ecosystem, which is structured along the lines of a machine in which each subunit is a fragment of the larger whole, completely unable to function alone, the living world is, like David Spangler's idea of community, composed of worlds within worlds in which each subunit is itself a whole system (or community). The health of the whole depends on the health of each part and the health of each part depends upon the health of the whole. "This way," notes biologist John Todd, opposite tendencies are fused by nature. For example, a cell is capable of carrying out all the functions normally attributed to life, and, as such, is a mirror image or reflection of higher levels of organization. It predicts the organism of which it is a component. And while the organism of which it is a part is dependent upon nutrients, energy and support from other organisms, it is at the same time capable of functioning as a complete entity. In nature a continuity exists in which the smallest living element is an image of each level of organization. A unicellular organism is structured and operates in much the same way as a complex organism such as a tree or a higher animal which, in turn, has much in common with the ecosystems that sustain organisms. The same kinds of process and principles of design extend from the organelle to the biosphere.[35]

So the idea of ecocommunities, rather than being a romanticized nostalgia for our preindustrial past, turns out to be an expression of the wisdom of organic evolution as well as a strategy for the recovery of the wholeness we have lost in our mad rush to industrialize the earth.

Ecocommunities and human ecology

The idea of ecocommunities is a symbol of wholeness, an ideal type, that, in principle, is capable of restoring to consciousness and culture a sense of the circular structure of the world. As a concept, it can apply at every scale of environment, from an individual household to the neighborhood, city, region, nation, or the entire planet. Just as the living world is composed of whole subunits joined by mutually beneficial associations into increasingly organized, complex, diverse and stable wholes in a co-creative, interdependent web of life, a human ecology based on

the concepts of sanctity and community would be characterized by wholeness (internal coherence) at every level of organization. This would tend to reduce the problems of hyper-coherence, overcentralization, and over-segregation characteristic of modern industrial civilization. By partially de-coupling local systems from the more inclusive global system, it would become possible to obtain a better match between lines of authority and levels of action. Like the Maring horticulturalists, feedback about the effects of interventions on ecosystems would be accessible to those making the interventions. In such an arrangement it would be much less likely that farmers in Kansas, for example, would be driven to deplete soils and ground water in order to make enough money to buy food and other essentials (e.g., fertilizers and pesticides) and to retire their debts on expensive farm machinery. Basic survival needs would be met from the non-monetary household economy of a healthy, diverse, and balanced farm. If long-term sustainability were to replace short-term expediency as a precondition for survival, ecologically derived practices would once again become common sense. The costs and benefits of interventions in ecosystems would be directly perceptible and the corrective actions necessary to restore order would tend to be direct, immediate, and effective.

Industrial societies, like individual organisms, achieve overall system control by the progressive centralization of regulatory functions in increasingly large and complex administrative bureaucracies. But, as we have seen, this means of ensuring coherence doesn't work. In a society organized according to the principles embodied in the idea of ecocommunities (i.e., locally self-reliant personal and socioeconomic wholes), it would still be necessary to ensure some level of overall system coherence. If, as has been suggested, human ecology should emulate in its functioning and evolution the principles which underly the operation of other living systems in nature, it would seem that social control should be similar to the basis of orderliness in ecosystems. Rather than relying on centralized regulation, a climax ecosystem achieves stability and adaptive resilience through diversity, redundancy, symbiosis, metabolic efficiency, nutrient and resource recycling, and the efficient utilization of the available flows of solar energy. A global federation of relatively small-scale, self-reliant ecocommunities, operating on the renewable energy flows of sun, wind, and water and integrated into ecologically and socially stable bioregional economies would make such a social ecology possible. While there would still be a great deal of interdependence, each community, city and region would be socially, culturally, and technologically distinct, reflecting a geographically and historically unique synthesis. Since local survival would be based on the maintenance of local flows of energy, matter, and money, economic relations between and among subunits would be based on choice, not necessity. By thus reducing the current unhealthy levels of compulsory dependence which characterize the present world system, the stability of the whole would increase—without the need for a strong, centralized world government. By thus increasing the coherence, or level of integration, of subsystems, it would become possible to decrease the coherence of more inclusive systems.

Moreover, the cultural and biological diversity generated by such an organization of human society would increase redundancy, and therefore stability, and would enlarge the "genetic" stock of social, political, technological and cultural forms. Thus, long-term as well as short-term adaptive flexibility of human culture would be maintained. Since the future behavior of the earth's more inclusive systems, such as the climate, is not predictable, the maintenance of such flexibility is sure to have importance in the continued evolution of consciousness and culture. And, as has been argued, the operation of the principles of sanctity and community in such a global system would tend to ensure that evolutionarily irreversible changes in human culture occur only when their immediate adaptive value has been proven.

In conclusion, a world organized according to the values and operating principles embodied in the idea of ecocommunities would, by making human conscious purpose coincide with the needs of more inclusive systems, restore to the process of cultural evolution the balance of innovation and conservation necessary for systemic health and orderly development.

Ecological scarcity and the transformation of industrial civilization

Having outlined the nature of the problem and the nature of the solution, the next obvious question is, "How can we get from here to there?" As might be expected, this presents us with another set of paradoxes. It has been argued that evolutionary change must be slow to guarantee that long-term adaptive flexibility is not lost through overspecialization. Yet, as has been documented in the introduction to this book, because of the Lamarckian overspecialization of industrial civilization to non-renewable resources which are rapidly being depleted, it has become vitally necessary to our short-term adaptation (and, perhaps, long-term survival) that the most change-resistant social form ever devised be transformed more rapidly than any other civilization in history. Moreover, to be successful, change at every level must be integrated and coordinated, since we no longer have the energy or capital necessary for ad hoc change and contradictory policy development. This would seem to require even more expedient, narrow and centralized planning to ensure that we do not run out of the time and resources necessary to reorder the entire global economy. But, if this is the case, the principle of local decision-making and control would seem to be a luxury we can no longer afford. Thus, when we move from idea to reality it would seem that the paradox of conscious purpose returns in an even more virulent form, since even its theoretical resolution appears quite impractical, if not impossible.

But if the arguments developed in this paper have been at all persuasive, it should be clear that the tendency to want to turn over global crisis management to a multidisciplinary scientific-technological elite must be resisted, not only because it is morally repugnant, but because, ultimately, it won't work. The solution to this dilemma, like the dilemma itself, must be paradoxical. Planning, which has created the problem, won't solve the problem, yet the problem can't be solved without more planning. The key to the resolution of this paradox lies in the issue of scale and in the recognition of the fact that, as stated in the Law of Aggression, every force organizes its own resistance. If industrial civilization has created a crisis of adaptation, it can be expected that it has also organized the counterforces necessary for its resolu-

tion. In fact, this law of opposites can be seen to be operating through the emergence of the phenomenon of ecological scarcity,[35] which is making it impossible for industrial civilization to long continue in its present form. Thus, the stage is set for a reversal of trends which have dominated the past five hundred years of cultural development.

Since, in all such dialectical processes of change, the synthesis is an emergent property of the total historically defined context, it is impossible to predict the ultimate outcome of this process. However, a major change in the direction of cultural evolution can be expected, and the spontaneously emerging corrective forces which will bring it about can be recognized and nurtured as they emerge. Thus, an understanding of the cybernetics of evolutionary change can lead to the development of a more appropriate and effective theory of action for social change. Rappaport explains:

> corrective, or potentially corrective forces emerge through unplanned evolutionary processes, and . . . theories of action should be predicated upon the existence and continued generation of such forces. Indeed, if such a theory is to avoid the dangers attendant upon meddling in the regulation of highly complex and poorly understood systems, it should focus upon spontaneously emerging corrective forces and upon their nurturance. No clear line can or need be drawn between planned intervention on the one hand and the nurturance of such spontaneous forces on the other, but emphasis in a theory of action should be on the latter. Such a theory of action should aim toward defining actions which encourage the development of regulatory mechanisms as a class, rather than attempting to specify the corrective actions to be undertaken in various circumstances.[36]

The concept of ecocommunities elaborated in this paper provides a set of criteria useful in assessing whether or not action is moving in the right direction. The many concrete examples of "spontaneously emerging corrective actions" documented in this book operationalize the concept of ecocommunities and provide evidence that industrial civilization does, indeed, contain the seeds of its own transformation. Since the global human ecology is too complex and poorly understood to allow its transformation to be planned from the top down by more inclusive systems, it must be changed through a process of planned interventions at the local level. As the kinds of spontaneously emerging grass-roots initiatives presented in this book are nurtured, more complete and integrated efforts will emerge, just as the idea of the self-reliant solar house has now led to a movement toward the creation of self-reliant neighborhoods, communities, new towns, neighborhoods, cities and regions. While such a grass-roots movement for personal, social, technical, political, and cultural change will involve far more planning than exists at present, the kind of society this process will create could never be planned.

The success of this revolution in consciousness and culture depends on nurturing its roots. Only if we are successful in creating a society of ecocommunities will we be able to discover how to maintain a viable world community. Like the development of an organism or an ecosystem the whole system must be an expression of the unfolding interaction of its parts and must be guided by an image of the whole toward which action is headed. The metaindustrial culture called for, and prefigured in, this book must be created by a process of evolutionary experimentation guided by an ecological and evolutionary ethic and informed by an abiding faith in the goodness of life and the sacredness of creation.

While it is not possible to forsee what will happen or to predict whether or not the actions of myriad numbers of small scale, local groups will be able to effect such a profound transformation of industrial civilization, one thing is certain—the future will not be boring. Nor will it be painless. And every day that passes without significant and widespread change increases the possibility that such "corrective action" will be too little and too late. I suspect that, during the last quarter of this century, we shall come to experience the true value of what we lost when we cast out from the Garden the concept of the systemic wholeness of nature, self, and society. In the words of William Blake we shall soon discover the price of wisdom:

> What is the price of experience do men
>   buy it for a song
> Or wisdom for a dance in the street? No
>   it is bought with the price
> Of all that a man hath his house his wife
>   his children
> Wisdom is sold in the desolate market
>   where none come to buy
> And in the witherd field where the
>   farmer plows for bread in vain.[37]

References

1. Kenneth Boulding, "Commons and Community: The Idea of a Public," in Garrett Hardin and John Baden, eds., *Managing the Commons,* (San Francisco: W. H. Freeman & Co., 1977) p. 289.

2. For documentation of emerging energy and resource scarcities, see Gary Coates, "General Introduction," in this volume.

3. Roy A. Rappaport, "Energy and

the Structure of Adaptation," *The Co-Evolution Quarterly*, no. 1, (Spring 1974): 27.

4. For a discussion of the concept of *Umwelt*, see Chapter II, "The 'I' and the 'Not-I' of the Outer World," in M. Esther Harding, *The I and the Not-I: A Study in the Development of Consciousness*, (Princeton, N.J.: Princeton Univ. Press, 1965) pp. 16–35.

5. Gregory Bateson, *Steps to an Ecology of Mind*, (New York: Ballantine Books, 1972) p. 433. Reprinted by permission of the publisher.

6. Ibid., p. 434.

7. Ibid., p. 434–436.

8. For a discussion of these two orientations to life, see Chapter 13, "Arcadian Life Versus Faustian Civilization," in Rene Dubos, *A God Within*, pp. 256–291.

9. Josef Pieper, *Leisure: The Basis for Culture*, (New York: Mentor Books / New American Library, 1952) p. 33.

10. For an analysis of the mythological, psychological, and historical roots of the space colony idea see Gary Coates, "Future Images, Present Possibilities: Revisioning Nature, Self, and Society," in this volume.

11. I am indebted to C. S. Holling and M. A. Goldberg for calling attention to this example of malaria control in Borneo. See their paper, "Ecology and Planning," in the *Journal of the American Institute of Planners*, 37, no. 4 (July 1971): 221–230.

12. See Coates, "General Introduction."

13. For a discussion of Gresham's Law and its implications for resource management, see Garrett Hardin, "The Rewards of Pejoristic Thinking," in Hardin and Baden, eds., *Managing the Commons*, pp. 126–134.

14. Gregory Bateson, *Mind and Nature: A Necessary Unity*, (New York: E. P. Dutton, 1979) p. 230.

15. Gregory Bateson, as quoted in Ty Cashman, "Evolution and the Symbiotic Community," unpublished manuscript, p. 2.

16. Gregory Bateson, "The Thing of It Is," in Michael Katz, William P. Marsh, Gail Gordon Thompson, eds., *Earth's Answer* (New York: Lindisfarne Books / Harper & Row, 1977), p. 153.

17. Ty Cashman, "Evolution and the Symbiotic Community," unpublished manuscript, pp. 4, 7.

18. Leslie White, as quoted in Rappaport, "Energy and the Structure of Adaptation," p. 20.

19. I am indebted to Roy A. Rappaport for this analysis of industrial society as an example of hyper-coherence, over-segregation and over-centralization. See Rappaport, "Energy and the Structure of Adaptation," p. 23.

20. Rappaport, "Energy and the Structure of Adaptation," p. 23.

21. W. Ross Ashby, *An Introduction to Cybernetics*, (New York: John Wiley & Sons, 1963) pp. 202–216.

22. Rappaport, "Energy and the Structure of Adaptation," pp. 24–26.

23. Cashman, "Evolution and the Symbiotic Community," p. 9.

24. All life forms act on their environment and, therefore, change it in a mutually causal circular process of action and reaction. The living world is a co-evolutionary process and the evolving unit is the organism-plus-environment. For a further discussion, see George T. L. Land, *Grow or Die: The Unifying Principle of Transformation* (New York: Dell Publishing Co., 1973). The view of evolution presented in this paper is mostly in agreement with Land's. However, we seem to disagree on the extent to which cultural evolution is reversible, and on the extent to which industrial civilization is a necessarily desirable outcome of the

process of evolutionary change by ectogenetic (cultural) means.

25. Gary Synder, *Turtle Island,* (New York: A New Directions Book, 1974) p. 109, 110. Reprinted by permission of the publisher.

26. Holmes Welch, *Taoism: The Parting of the Way,* (Boston: Beacon Press, 1965) p. 20.

27. Arthur Waley, *The Way and Its Power: A Study of the Tao Te Ching and Its Place in Chinese Thought,* (New York: Grove Press, 1958) p. 150.

28. Roy A. Rappaport, "Forests and the Purpose of Man," *The Co-Evolution Quarterly,* no. 12, (Winter 1976 / 77): 48–49. Reprinted by permission of the publisher.

29. Roy A. Rappaport, "Sanctity and Adaptation," *The Co-Evolution Quarterly,* no. 2, (Summer 1974): 59. My debt to Rappaport for the analysis

of the adaptive role of sanctity is obvious.

30. Ibid., p. 60.

31. Ibid., p. 60.

32. Ibid., p. 61.

33. Snyder, p. 104.

34. David Spangler, "The Idea of a New Age and the Meaning of Community," unpublished manuscript, 1976, pp. 7, 8, 9.

35. John Todd and Nancy Jack Todd, *Tomorrow Is Our Permanent Address,* (New York: Lindisfarne Books / Harper & Row, 1980), p. 45.

36. Rappaport, "Sanctity and Adaptation," p. 67.

37. William Blake, "The Four Zoas: Night the Second," in David A. Erdman, *The Poetry and Prose of William Blake,* (Garden City, N.Y.: Doubleday & Co., 1965) p. 318.

Contributors

DAVID BAINBRIDGE is the founder of the Passive Solar Institute. He has taught numerous classes and has authored many reports on energy, bicycling, and community design.

RICHARD BAKER-ROSHI has been Abbot of San Francisco Zen Center since 1970, succeeding his teacher, Shunryu Suzuki-roshi.

EARLE BARNHART, marine biologist, with the New Alchemy Institute since 1972, has published articles on topics ranging from the design of low-cost windmills and bioshelters to the cultivation of tree crops as a foundation for a permanent agriculture. Earle is also the Technical Editor for *New Roots,* a technical reviewer for the California Office of Appropriate Technology, and on the Board of Planners for the Coolidge Center for the Advancement of Agriculture in Topsfield, Massachusetts. Earle describes himself as a sculptor, beekeeper, tree planter, and toy maker.

TOM BENDER, former professor of architecture at the University of Minnesota, worked on the Governor's staff in Oregon researching energy sources. He is the author of *Environmental Design Primer,* a book of meditations on ecological consciousness, and author of many papers on appropriate technology. He is editor of *Rain: Journal of Appropriate Technology,* which provides information and discussion on the effort to create a more democratic, participatory, and environmentally benign society.

MURRAY BOOKCHIN has authored several books on the relationship between consciousness, technology, and the environment including *Post-Scarcity Anarchism, The Limits of the City* and *The Ecology of Freedom.* He teaches at the Center for New Studies at Ramapo College and is the Resident Director of the Institute for Social Ecology at Goddard College.

GEORGE BURRILL is Co-Director of the Center for Studies in Food Self-Sufficiency in Burlington, Vermont, and President of Associates in Rural Development Inc. He has written extensively on food and agriculture, appropriate technology, and renewable energy resources and served as an advisor and consultant on agriculture, energy, and rural and community development to state, national and international agencies. His long-term research effort involves energy, food, man and environment relationships.

PETER CALTHORPE, a San Francisco designer, is an advocate for Marin Solar Village as an ecological alternative to continued suburban development in the San Francisco Bay area. Peter was Project Designer of California's "Site One" office building in Sacramento and formerly Director of Solar Research and Design at the Farallones Institute. He also worked on passive solar research for the De-

552

partment of Energy and the Solar Energy Research Institute. He has designed nine passive solar homes, and won three HUD awards for passive solar residential design.

CHRIS CANFIELD is the founder and Director of the Town Forum, a non-profit educational corporation promoting the Cerro Gordo new town development and providing information about similar communities. Since 1971, he has been the Director of the Cerro Gordo project and the driving force behind the Cerro Gordo community.

GARY COATES, architect and environmental designer, is Associate Professor of Architecture at Kansas State University and Director of the Appropriate Technology Program at the University of Man (UFM) in Manhattan, Kansas, which provides design services, technical assistance, educational materials and workshops on energy conservation and solar energy use for home owners, small businesses and municipalities. He is also the editor of the book *Alternative Learning Environments* and has written and lectured extensively on participatory planning and community-based design, residential livability, community education, and appropriate technology.

MICHAEL FREEDBERG, Director of Housing Policy at the Conference on Alternative State and Local Policies in Washington, D.C., has been involved in housing and planning at the community level for the past ten years—in New Haven, Connecticut, California and New York City. He helped found the "sweat equity" program on the Lower East Side of New York, where he directed the 11th Street Movement. He is currently working with the Urban Homesteading Assistance Board in New York City, a national technical assistance project that involves the use of low-income housing coops in six cities. Mr. Freedberg also helped create and develop the newly-established National Consumer Cooperative Bank.

GARY GARBER is on the staff of the Wyoming State Energy Office. He is also Chairman of the Wyoming Solar Alliance and a member of the Board of Directors of the Solar Lobby. Gary directed the construction and operation of the Cheyenne Community Greenhouse from 1976 to 1977 and acted as Energy Programs Coordinator the following year. He served on the National Science Foundation Appropriate Technology Advisory Committee and represented Wyoming at the first "Solar Congress" in Washington, D.C. in 1978.

DANIEL GOLDRICH is Professor of Political Science at the University of Oregon. During 1978–79 he was a National Science Foundation Public Service Science Resident with the Whiteaker Community Council, doing education outreach on environmentally appropriate economic development.

MAUREEN GOOD, former Coordinator of the Urban Integrated Community Demonstration, (a project supported by a grant from the National Center for Appropriate Technology to the Whiteaker Community Council) has been an outreach worker for the Whiteaker neighborhood, where she currently resides.

SHIMON GOTTSCHALK is Associate Professor in the School of Social Work at Florida State University. He has been involved over a decade with New Communities, Inc. He is a former staff member of the International Independence Institute where he collaborated on *The Community Land Trust* (Center for Community Economic Development, Cambridge, Massachusetts). He is the author of *Communities and Alternatives: An Exploration of the Limits of Planning* and numerous papers on social planning, communal organizations, and rural development.

STEVE GREENWOOD works with the Whiteaker neighborhood as an Economic Development Specialist for the Department of Housing and Community Development, Lane County, Oregon.

DENNIS HOLLOWAY is currently a practicing architect in Boulder, Colorado. He has taught at the College of Environmental Design at the University of Colorado in Boulder and the College of Architecture at the University of Minnesota, where he was Director of Project Ouroboros. He and his students produced the books *Project Ouroboros* and *Winona: Towards an Energy Conserving Community*. Dennis has also presented papers at national and international forums on human settlements and appropriate technology.

MARSHALL HUNT is a micro–climatologist and solar expert who played a leading role in the development of the Davis energy conservation building code. He is editor of the *Energy Conservation Code Workbook* and co-author of *The Davis Energy Conservation Report* and *A Strategy for Energy Conservation*. He has been a member of Living Systems and a special consultant to the Solar Office of the California Energy Resources and Development Commission.

WES JACKSON and his wife DANA direct The Land Institute, a nonprofit, educational research organization in Salina, Kansas, which is devoted to the search for alternatives in energy,

shelter, agriculture and waste. Dr. Jackson is former Professor of Environmental Studies and Director of the Center for Environmental Studies at California State University in Sacramento. He has done research in plant genetics with emphasis on the flow of genes through populations and on the relationship between gene flow and morphological integration. He has written numerous articles on genetics, land use, and environmental ethics. Dr. Jackson is also editor of the popular college textbook, *Man and the Environment*. His latest book, *New Roots for Agriculture,* is published by Friends of the Earth.

AMORY BLOCH LOVINS is the author of numerous books including *Soft Energy Paths: Toward a Durable Peace, World Energy Strategies: Facts, Issues, and Options,* and *Non-Nuclear Futures: The Case for an Ethical Energy Strategy.* A consultant physicist since 1965, he now concentrates on energy and resource strategy. Lovins is active in international energy affairs, has testified before parliamentary and congressional committes, and has broadcast extensively. He is currently the British Representative of Friends of the Earth, Inc., a U.S. nonprofit conservation group.

JIM McCOY is the Director of the Whiteaker Neighborhood Economic Development Corporation, working on both cooperative housing and economic development. He has also served as President of the Whiteaker Community Council.

DAVID MORRIS is Co-Director of the Institute for Local Self-Reliance, in Washington, D.C. He is co-author of *Neighborhood Power: The New Localism* and has written a variety of papers on energy planning and self-reliant communities, including *Kilowatt Counter: Introduction to Concepts and Practices* and the *Dawning of Solar Cells*. David is also a consultant to community organizations and local and federal government on energy conservation, appropriate technology, local economic development, and community institution building. He is presently completing a book on the *New City States*.

JAMES R. NOLFI, biologist-ecologist, is Co-Director of the Center for Studies in Food Self-Sufficiency, Vice-President of Associates in Rural Development, and Dean of Goddard College, Vermont. He is a former faculty member of U.C., Berkeley, the University of Vermont, and the Vermont Institute of Community Involvement. Nolfi does research and writes on energy use in agriculture, decentralized planning, appropriate technology, minor breeds of livestock, philosophy of education, and aquaculture of crayfish. He and his wife operate a small diversified Vermont hill farm.

HELGA and WILLIAM OLKOWSKI focus their energies on developing environmentally sound methods of urban insect management and food production. They are founding members of the Farallones Institute and helped develop the Integral Urban House. They co-authored *The City People's Book of Raising Food*. Helga is also co-editor of *The Integral Urban House: Self-Reliant Living in the City* put together by the Farallones Institute. Presently they are Co-Directors of the Center for

the Integration of the Applied Sciences (CIAS) of the John Muir Institute for Environmental Studies.

DAVID POMERANTZ, Energy Project Director for the International City Management Association, Washington, D.C., specializes in urban and community planning. David has worked on environmental policy for the Vermont State Planning Office and was a newspaper editor and staff reporter on community and environmental issues as well as former staff environmentalist for the Massachusetts Public Interest Group. He was the Director of the Franklin County Energy Study and Co-Director of the Franklin County Energy Project to organize and educate citizen energy committees for local energy planning.

ELIZABETH RECHTSCHAFFEN is one of the founding members of the Abode of the Message. Together with her husband, Arif, the community's resident physician, she is active in all aspects of community life.

PETER VAN DRESSER, since the 1930s, has written on the pressing issues of our time—big business, the inhuman scale of modern energy-intensive technology, the need for decentralization and new technologies. Long before it became fashionable, Peter was using solar technologies (he built a sun-tempered adobe in Santa Fe in 1958). He is the author of *A Landscape for Humans* and *Homegrown Sundwellings*.

Credits